HUMAN ENGINEERING GUIDE TO EQUIPMENT DESIGN

HUMAN ENGINEERING GUIDE TO EQUIPMENT DESIGN

Sponsored by

JOINT ARMY-NAVY-AIR FORCE STEERING COMMITTEE

Editors

CLIFFORD T. MORGAN
University of California, Santa Barbara

JESSE S. COOK, III
McGraw-Hill Book Company

ALPHONSE CHAPANIS
The Johns Hopkins University

MAX W. LUND
Office of Naval Research

MC GRAW-HILL BOOK COMPANY, INC.   NEW YORK · TORONTO · LONDON

Human Engineering Guide
to Equipment Design

CONTRIBUTORS

CHARLES A. BAKER, Chief, Presentation and Processing of Information Branch, Behavioral Sciences Laboratory, Aeronautical Systems Division, Air Force Systems Command. *Chapter 2. Visual Presentation of Information, Chapter 7. Layout of Workplaces*

HUGH M. BOWEN, Ph.D., Senior Psychologist, Dunlap and Associates. *Chapter 5. Man-Machine Dynamics*

EDWARD P. BUCKLEY, Ph.D., Research Psychologist, Franklin Institute. *Chapter 1. The Man-Machine System*

ALPHONSE CHAPANIS, Ph.D., Professor of Psychology and Industrial Engineering, The Johns Hopkins University. *Chapter 5. Man-Machine Dynamics, Chapter 9. Design for Ease of Maintenance*

JESSE S. COOK III, Engineering Writer, Technical Writing Service, McGraw-Hill Book Company. *Chapter 9. Design for Ease of Maintenance*

BERNARD J. COVNER, Ph.D., Director, Man-Management Center. *Chapter 7. Layout of Workplaces, Chapter 8. Arrangement of Groups of Men and Machines*

ALBERT DAMON, Ph.D., M.D., Associate Professor of Epidemiology, School of Public Health, Harvard University. *Chapter 6. Design of Controls, Chapter 7. Layout of Workplaces, Chapter 10. Effects of Environment on Human Performance, Chapter 11. Anthropometry*

JEROME H. ELY, Ph.D., Vice President and Director, Human Factors Research Division, Dunlap and Associates. *Chapter 5. Man-Machine Dynamics, Chapter 6. Design of Controls, Chapter 7. Layout of Workplaces*

ROBERT S. GALES, Head, Psychophysics Branch, U. S. Navy Electronics Laboratory. *Chapter 3. Auditory Presentation of Information, Chapter 10. Effects of Environment on Human Performance*

WALTER F. GRETHER, Ph.D., Technical Director, Behavioral Sciences Laboratory, Aeronautical Systems Division, Air Force Systems Command. *Chapter 2. Visual Presentation of Information, Chapter 7. Layout of Workplaces*

v

MONES HAWLEY, Manager, Operations Planning, RCA Laboratories, Radio Corporation of America. *Chapter 4. Speech Communication*

HERBERT H. JACOBS, Ph.D., Vice President and Director, Management and Planning Research Division, Dunlap and Associates. *Chapter 7. Layout of Workplaces, Chapter 8. Arrangement of Groups of Men and Machines*

KARL D. KRYTER, Ph.D., Head, Psychoacoustics Department, Bolt Beranek and Newman. *Chapter 4. Speech Communication*

J. C. R. LICKLIDER, Ph.D., Vice President, Bolt Beranek and Newman. *Chapter 4. Speech Communication*

MAX W. LUND, Ph.D., Head, Engineering Psychology Branch, Office of Naval Research. *Chapter 1. The Man-Machine System*

ROSS A. McFARLAND, Ph.D., Professor of Environmental Health and Safety, and Director, Guggenheim Center for Aerospace Health and Safety, School of Public Health, Harvard University. *Chapter 10. Effects of Environment on Human Performance, Chapter 11. Anthropometry*

CLIFFORD T. MORGAN, Ph.D., Lecturer in Psychology, University of California, Santa Barbara. *Chapter 1. The Man-Machine System*

JESSE ORLANSKY, Ph.D., Research and Engineering Support Division, Institute for Defense Analyses. *Chapter 5. Man-Machine Dynamics, Chapter 6. Design of Controls, Chapter 7. Layout of Workplaces, Chapter 8. Arrangement of Groups of Men and Machines*

H. WALLACE SINAIKO, Ph.D., Defense Information Processing Systems, RCA Defense Electronic Products, Radio Corporation of America. *Chapter 1. The Man-Machine System*

HOWARD W. STOUDT, Ph.D., Research Associate, Guggenheim Center for Aerospace Health and Safety, School of Public Health, Harvard University. *Chapter 6. Design of Controls, Chapter 7. Layout of Workplaces, Chapter 10. Effects of Environment on Human Performance, Chapter 11. Anthropometry*

WARREN H. TEICHNER, Ph.D., Professor of Psychology, and Director, Institute of Environmental Psychophysiology, University of Massachusetts. *Chapter 10. Effects of Environment on Human Performance*

ROBERT M. THOMSON, Ph.D., Senior Psychologist, Dunlap and Associates. *Chapter 6. Design of Controls, Chapter 7. Layout of Workplaces, Chapter 8. Arrangement of Groups of Men and Machines*

JOHN C. WEBSTER, Ph.D., Research Psychologist, U. S. Navy Electronics Laboratory. *Chapter 4. Speech Communication*

PREFACE

IN MAY OF 1952, the Panel on Human Engineering, Committee on Human Resources, Research and Development Board, Department of Defense recommended that the three branches of the armed services jointly develop the "Human Engineering Guide to Equipment Design." A memorandum to the Secretaries of the Departments of the Army, Navy, and Air Force submitted by the Research and Development Board in October of the same year recommended that both design-engineering and human-engineering specialists be included in a Joint Services Steering Committee for the Guide.

The three services responded to this memorandum by appointing members to the steering committee and by providing the necessary funds. The Navy accepted responsibility for coordination among the services, and the Secretary of the Navy directed the Chief of Naval Research to assume this responsibility. The Chief of Naval Research, in turn, assigned responsibility for coordination to Dr. Henry A. Imus of the Office of Naval Research.

The first meeting of the Joint Services Steering Committee was held in February of 1953, and Dr. Arnold M. Small of the U. S. Navy Electronics Laboratory was elected chairman and authorized to appoint an executive council. On March 31 and April 1, 1953, the executive council, which consisted of Drs. Walter F. Grether (Air Force), Franklin V. Taylor (Navy), Lynn E. Baker (Army), Clifford P. Seitz (Navy), and Alphonse Chapanis (Air Force) in addition to Drs. Imus and Small, met to decide, among other things, the purposes to be served by the Guide.

In the words of the executive council, "The primary purpose . . . is to provide a guide in human engineering which the designer can use in the same manner as handbooks in other areas to assist in solving design problems as they arise . . . The primary emphasis in the Guide will be on recommended design principles and practices in relation to general design problems rather than on the compilation of research data. However, research data may, if necessary, be included as a means of supporting or clarifying the design recommendations."

By December of 1953, a detailed plan for the Guide had been drawn up, and, by March of 1954, work had begun on all but four of the proposed chapters. In August of 1955, a style manual to assist in preparing the Guide for publication was prepared by an editorial working group consisting of Drs. Small, Grether, and Chapanis and Wesley E. Woodson. Later, Drs. Imus and Small left the Navy, and Dr. Max W. Lund of the Office of Naval Research was assigned responsibility for chairing the group and coordinating its work. In June of 1956, Dr. Clifford T. Morgan joined the group as consultant and editor. In May of

1960, Jesse S. Cook III was assigned to work with the group in the actual preparation of the Guide for publication.

As is often the case when many individual people contribute to a book, preparation of the Guide was beset by many difficulties. Contributors were frequently late in submitting their drafts, and some submitted material not considered suitable for the stated purposes of the Guide; some chapters had to be put into new hands for preparation. Also time consuming was one important step through which most, if not all, the chapters have gone. This was a detailed review by several experts in each particular field to make certain that the material was complete and accurate and, also, a review by representative design engineers to obtain their comments about the applicability of the material to their design problems. Eventually, material meeting these requirements was completed. Then, it had to be carefully edited to avoid needless duplication, to get each topic in its proper place, to cross reference the various articles, sections, and chapters, and to achieve relative uniformity of style and format.

As far as possible, the editors have striven to fulfill the purposes given them by the original Joint Services Steering Committee. The committee was particularly emphatic in calling for simple, clear, and concise writing. The editors have worked hard at achieving this goal, often to the distress of some of the contributors. The editors, needless to say, are solely responsible for the final product.

A great many people were involved in the preparation of the Guide. The psychologists and engineers who gave us detailed reviews of chapters are too numerous to mention even though they contributed greatly to the accuracy and coverage of the Guide. Those who contributed material used in the Guide are listed on the contributors page and in footnotes at the beginning of the chapter, section, or article to which they contributed.

THE EDITORS

CONTENTS

Page

CHAPTER 1. THE MAN-MACHINE SYSTEM   **1**

1.1   System Considerations   1
1.2   System Analysis   3
    1.2.1   General methods of analysis   3
          FUNCTIONAL ANALYSIS   5
          DECISION ANALYSIS   6
          ACTIVITY ANALYSIS   8
          FLOW ANALYSIS   8
          JOB ANALYSIS   11
    1.2.2   The analysis of critical design requirements   12
    1.2.3   The analysis of equipment characteristics   13
          SYSTEM DISPLAYS   13
          OPERATOR CONTROLS   17
          WORKPLACES   18
          OTHER CHARACTERISTICS   18
1.3   The Man in System Design   20
    1.3.1   Variations among men   20
          GAUSSIAN DISTRIBUTIONS   20
          CUMULATIVE DISTRIBUTIONS   21
          THE MEASUREMENT OF ERRORS   22
    1.3.2   Man's sensory systems   23
          CHANNEL CAPACITIES   23
          SIGNAL DETECTION   26
          TACTILE INPUTS   26
          SENSORY INTERACTION   27
          MULTIPLE INPUTS   28
    1.3.3   Man's unique characteristics   28
          LEARNING   28
          MOTIVATION   29
    1.3.4   Man as a system component   32
    1.3.5   Man vs. machine   32
          AS SENSORS   34
          AS DATA PROCESSORS   35
          AS CONTROLLERS   36
          WORKING ENVIRONMENTS   36
          CONCLUSIONS   36

Page

1.3.6 The synthesis of man and machine   37
VERIFICATION BY DUPLICATION   37
MACHINES TO MONITOR MEN   37
MEN TO MONITOR MACHINES   37
MEN FOR FAULT LOCATION   39

1.4 System Evaluation and Testing   39
1.4.1 General methods of evaluation   40
THEORY AND "PAPER" ANALYSIS   40
SYSTEM SIMULATION   41
OPERATIONAL TESTING   41
1.4.2 Planning the evaluation   41
REPRESENTATIVE CONDITIONS   42
COMPARATIVE EVALUATION   42
COUNTERBALANCED DESIGN   42
SYSTEM VS. SUBSYSTEM   43
1.4.3 Selecting subjects   43
UNREPRESENTATIVE SUBJECTS   43
THE NUMBER OF SUBJECTS   44
1.4.4 Realism in evaluations   45
THE TRAINING OF SUBJECTS   45
THE NATURE OF THE TASKS   46
REALISTIC CONDITIONS   47
1.4.5 Measures of performance   48
OBJECTIVE MEASUREMENT   48
RELIABLE MEASUREMENT   49
VALID MEASUREMENT   49

CHAPTER 2. VISUAL PRESENTATION OF INFORMATION   **51**

2.1 General Display Principles   51
2.1.1 Conditions of use   52
2.1.2 Method of use   52
2.1.3 The purpose of the display   53
USING SYMBOLIC DISPLAYS   53
USING PICTORIAL DISPLAYS   53
2.1.4 The combination and integration of displays   54
COMBINING DISPLAYS   54
INTEGRATING DISPLAYS   56
2.2 Visual Detection, Identification, and Estimation   56
2.2.1 Visual acuity and factors affecting it   57
MEASURING VISUAL ACUITY   58
EFFECT OF ADAPTATION LEVEL   62
EFFECT OF COLORED LIGHTING   62
2.2.2 Searching for targets   63
2.2.3 The detection of colored targets   65
DETECTING SURFACE COLOR   66
DETECTING COLORED LIGHTS   66
2.2.4 Target detection against nonuniform backgrounds   66
2.2.5 Identifying targets in complex displays   67
TARGET SIZE   67

Page

DISPLAY CLUTTER   67
DISPLAY RESOLUTION   68

2.2.6   Magnification aids   68
DESIGN RECOMMENDATIONS   69

2.2.7   Estimating size, distance, and speed   69

2.3   Workplace Illumination   70

2.3.1   General workplace lighting   70
LIGHT DISTRIBUTION   70
SURFACE REFLECTANCE   72
SHADOW AND SURFACE COLOR   73
GENERAL ROOM LIGHTING   75

2.3.2   Radar-room lighting   75
CROSS-POLARIZATION SYSTEM   75
BROAD-BAND-BLUE SYSTEM   75
YELLOW-MINUS-YELLOW SYSTEM   76
MERCURY-MINUS-RED SYSTEM   76
COMPARING THE SYSTEMS   76

2.3.3   Indicator and panel lighting   76
DARK ADAPTATION   77
REFLECTION HAZARDS   78
BRIGHTNESS REQUIREMENTS   78
LIGHT DISTRIBUTION   78
SELECTING INDICATOR LIGHTING   78

2.4   Visual Coding   81

2.4.1   Visual-coding methods   81
COLOR CODING   81
SHAPE CODING   84
SIZE CODING   85
DOT CODING   86
LINE CODING   86
BRIGHTNESS CODING   86
FLASH-RATE CODING   87
STEREO-DEPTH CODING   87

2.4.2   Selecting a code   87
CODE COMPATIBILITY   88
SCALING QUANTITATIVE CODES   88
ASSOCIATION VALUE OF CODES   88
LOCATION TIME FOR CODES   88
DECODING ACCURACY   89
COMPOUND CODING   90

2.5   Warning and Signal Devices   90

2.5.1   Warning devices   90
GETTING ATTENTION   91
GROUPING SIGNALS   91
SELECTING SIGNALS   91
LIGHTS FOR WARNING SIGNALS   91

2.5.2   Caution and status signals   93

2.5.3   Mechanical "flag" signals   93

2.6   Mechanical Indicators   94

2.6.1   Selecting symbolic indicators   94

Page

BASIC TYPES OF INDICATORS   94
VARIATIONS OF BASIC TYPES   94
LONG-SCALE INDICATORS   96

2.6.2   The design of symbolic indicators   97
SCALE SELECTION   98
SCALE DESIGN   101
NUMERAL AND LETTER STYLE   102
SCALE LAYOUT   103
ZONE MARKING   104
POINTER DESIGN   104
MOTION OF MOVING ELEMENT   105
COUNTER DESIGN   107

2.6.3   The design of pictorial indicators   108
2.6.4   Indicator identification   108
LABELING   108
COLOR CODING   109
SHAPE CODING   109
POSITION CODING   109

2.7   Cathode-Ray Tubes   109
2.7.1   Cathode-ray-tube visibility   110
VISUAL FACTORS   110
DESIGN FACTORS   113

2.7.2   Cathode-ray-tube scope size   114
2.7.3   Indicating range on radar displays   116
RANGE MARKERS   116
OTHER METHODS   117
EVALUATING THE METHODS   118

2.7.4   Indicating bearing on radar displays   119
2.7.5   Three-coordinate displays   120

2.8   Printed Materials   121
2.8.1   Decals, check lists, and labels   121
DESIGN RECOMMENDATIONS   121
2.8.2   Graphs, tables, and scales   122
DESIGN RECOMMENDATIONS   122

CHAPTER 3.   AUDITORY PRESENTATION OF INFORMATION   **123**

3.1   The Use of Auditory Presentation   125
3.1.1   Signals suited to auditory presentation   125
3.1.2   Choosing the form of auditory presentation   126
3.1.3   Some common uses for auditory presentation   126
SONAR   127
ALARM AND WARNING DEVICES   129
3.1.4   Some new uses for auditory presentation   132
SPATIAL ORIENTATION   132
TARGET TRACKING   137
DETECTION OF RADAR SIGNALS   138
3.2   Perception of Sound Signals   138
3.2.1   Characteristics of sound signals   138

Page

	3.2.2	Methods of presenting sound signals to the ears	139
		SIMPLE BINAURAL PRESENTATION 139	
		DUPLEX BINAURAL PRESENTATION 140	
		BONE CONDUCTION 140	
	3.2.3	Absolute threshold of hearing	141
		PURE-TONE THRESHOLDS 141	
		BINAURAL VS. MONAURAL 141	
		EFFECT OF AGE ON HEARING 142	
	3.2.4	Loudness and pitch	142
		THE LOUDNESS-LEVEL SCALE 142	
		THE LOUDNESS SCALE 142	
		PITCH 143	
3.3		Signal Processing and Control	144
	3.3.1	Signal and noise relationships	144
	3.3.2	The masking of sound by noise	144
		MONAURAL MASKING 144	
		INTERAURAL MASKING 148	
	3.3.3	Filtering	148
		THE REDUCTION OF MASKING 148	
		THE REDUCTION OF LOUDNESS 149	
	3.3.4	Signal-level control	151
		MINIMUM SIGNAL LEVEL 151	
		MAXIMUM SIGNAL LEVEL 151	
		OPTIMUM SIGNAL LEVEL 151	
	3.3.5	Dynamic range and volume control	153
3.4		The Selection of Signals	155
	3.4.1	Single signals	155
		DETECTING FREQUENCY CHANGES 155	
		DETECTING INTENSITY CHANGES 156	
		SELECTING TONAL DURATION 157	
	3.4.2	Multiple signals	158
		USING MULTIPLE FREQUENCIES 158	
		SEQUENCING THE SIGNALS 159	
		IDENTIFYING THE SIGNALS 159	
CHAPTER 4.		**SPEECH COMMUNICATION**	**161**
4.1		Characteristics of Speech	162
	4.1.1	Speech production	162
	4.1.2	Representations of speech waves	162
		TIME REPRESENTATION 162	
		FREQUENCY REPRESENTATION 162	
	4.1.3	Time-varying characteristics	165
	4.1.4	RMS pressure of fundamental speech sounds	166
	4.1.5	Dynamic range	166
		DESIGN RECOMMENDATIONS 167	
	4.1.6	Estimating speech level	167
4.2		Intelligibility in Speech Communication	168
	4.2.1	Intelligibility testing	169
		SELECTING TEST MATERIAL 170	

Page

SCORING TESTS   170
INTERPRETING TEST RESULTS   172
4.2.2 Predicting intelligibility   173
COMMUNICATION SYSTEMS   174
FACE-TO-FACE COMMUNICATION   177
4.3 Noise in Speech Communication   180
4.3.1 The masking of speech by noise   181
NARROW-BAND NOISE   181
INTERMITTENT NOISE   185
4.3.2 Criteria for communication in noise   186
DAMAGE-RISK CRITERIA   186
INTELLIGIBILITY CRITERIA   186
NOISE CRITERIA   186
4.3.3 Ear-protective devices   188
EFFECT ON INTELLIGIBILITY   188
WHEN TO USE THEM   189
4.3.4 Microphone noise shields   190
DESIGN RECOMMENDATIONS   190
4.4 Component Selection and Application   191
4.4.1 Microphones   191
NOISE-CANCELLING MICROPHONES   191
CONTACT MICROPHONES   192
DESIGN RECOMMENDATIONS   192
4.4.2 Amplifiers, transmitters, and receivers   193
AUTOMATIC GAIN CONTROL   193
PEAK CLIPPING   195
4.4.3 Loudspeakers and headsets   200
LOUDSPEAKERS   200
HEADSETS   202
4.5 Special System Requirements   206
4.5.1 Multichannel listening   207
DESIGN RECOMMENDATIONS   207
4.5.2 Communication at high altitudes   208
DESIGN RECOMMENDATIONS   208
4.5.3 Underwater communication   209
LISTENING UNDERWATER   209
TALKING UNDERWATER   209
4.5.4 Communication through masks   209
4.6 Factors Affecting the Performance of Communication Systems   210
4.6.1 Personnel selection and training   210
4.6.2 Language factors   211
INFORMATION CONTENT OF WORDS   211
SENTENCE OR PHRASE STRUCTURE   211
THE SIZE OF THE MESSAGE SET   211
SITUATIONAL CONSTRAINTS   212
INTERACTION OF SPEECH SOUNDS   213
DESIGN RECOMMENDATIONS   215
4.6.3 Feedback to the talker   216

Page

CHAPTER 5.   MAN-MACHINE DYNAMICS   **217**

5.1   The Closed-Loop Manual-Tracking System   217
    5.1.1   Pursuit and compensatory tracking   218
        THE PURSUIT DISPLAY   218
        THE COMPENSATORY DISPLAY   218
        ANTICIPATION IN TRACKING   219
    5.1.2   Factors affecting display selection   219
        OUTPUT COMPLEXITY   219
        MACHINE DYNAMICS   219
        MOVABLE-ELEMENT RATE   220
        BACKGROUND CLARITY   220
        AIDED TRACKING   220
        DISPLAY SIZE   220
    5.1.3   Selecting the display   220
    5.1.4   Intermittency in the display of information   221
        CAUSES OF INTERMITTENCY   221
        THE EFFECT OF INTERMITTENCY   222
        DESIGN RECOMMENDATIONS   222
5.2   Human Dynamics   223
    5.2.1   Human transfer functions   223
    5.2.2   Human responses to various inputs   224
        STEP INPUTS   224
        RAMP INPUTS   225
        SINE-WAVE INPUTS   226
        COMPLEX INPUTS   226
    5.2.3   Human time lags   226
        ELEMENTS OF REACTION TIME   227
        VARIATION IN REACTION TIME   228
        FACTORS AFFECTING TIME LAGS   228
        DESIGN RECOMMENDATIONS   234
    5.2.4   Human time lags in watchkeeping   235
        FACTORS IN WATCHKEEPING   235
        DESIGN RECOMMENDATIONS   237
5.3   Machine Dynamics   237
    5.3.1   Machine transfer functions   237
    5.3.2   Aided tracking   239
        THE AIDING CONSTANT   240
        EFFECTIVENESS OF AIDED TRACKING   240
        ADDING HIGHER DERIVATIVES   241
        DESIGN RECOMMENDATIONS   241
    5.3.3   Quickening   241
        QUICKENED-DISPLAY DESIGN   242
        PARTIAL QUICKENING   243
        MAJOR ADVANTAGES   243
        MAJOR DISADVANTAGES   243
        AIDING VS. QUICKENING   244
        DESIGN RECOMMENDATIONS   244
    5.3.4   The effects of machine dynamics on operator performance   244
        THE EFFECTS OF LAG   245

CONTENTS

THE EFFECTS OF GAIN   245
THE EFFECTS OF INTEGRATION   245

CHAPTER 6.   DESIGN OF CONTROLS   **247**

6.1   Selecting the Best Control   247
6.2   Important Factors in the Design of Controls   250
    6.2.1   The control-display ratio   250
            OPTIMIZING THE C/D RATIO   250
            FACTORS AFFECTING C/D RATIO   251
    6.2.2   Control-display relationships   251
            GENERAL RULES   252
            SPECIFIC RECOMMENDATIONS   252
    6.2.3   Control resistance   256
            ELASTIC RESISTANCE   256
            FRICTIONAL RESISTANCE   257
            VISCOUS-DAMPING RESISTANCE   257
            INERTIAL RESISTANCE   257
    6.2.4   Control coding   257
            SHAPE CODING   259
            SIZE CODING   259
            MODE-OF-OPERATION CODING   259
            LABELING   260
            COLOR CODING   260
    6.2.5   Preventing accidental activation   260
6.3   Design Recommendations for Hand and Foot Controls   262
    6.3.1   General principles of control design   262
    6.3.2   Hand controls   262
            WHAT TYPE TO USE   263
            ONE VS. TWO HANDS   263
            DIRECTION OF MOVEMENT   263
            SPEED OF MOVEMENT   263
            RESISTANCE   264
            HANDGRIPS   264
    6.3.3   Foot controls   265
6.4   Design Recommendations for Specific Controls   265
    6.4.1   Pushbuttons   265
            HAND PUSHBUTTONS   267
            FOOT PUSHBUTTONS   268
    6.4.2   Switches   268
            TOGGLE SWITCHES   269
            ROTARY SWITCHES   270
    6.4.3   Knobs   271
            DESIGN RECOMMENDATIONS   272
    6.4.4   Cranks and levers   274
            CRANKS   275
            LEVERS   276
    6.4.5   Handwheels and pedals   276
            HANDWHEELS   278
            PEDALS   280

xvi

Page

CHAPTER 7.   LAYOUT OF WORKPLACES   **281**

7.1   General Rules   282
7.2   Workplace Dimensions   284
    7.2.1   Seated operators   284
        VISUAL AREAS   285
        MANUAL AREAS   287
        PEDAL AREAS   291
    7.2.2   Standing operators   294
        VISUAL AREAS   296
        MANUAL AREAS   296
        PEDAL AREAS   297
    7.2.3   Alternating between sitting and standing   297
        DESIGN RECOMMENDATIONS   297
7.3   Locating Controls and Displays   298
    7.3.1   Establishing priority positions   298
    7.3.2   Grouping controls and displays   299
    7.3.3   Control-display associations   300
7.4   Display Layout   303
    7.4.1   General layout considerations   303
    7.4.2   Layout for good visibility   304
        VIEWING ANGLE   304
        VIEWING DISTANCE   304
    7.4.3   Layout for identification   305
    7.4.4   Grouping displays   305
        GROUPING FOR CHECK READING   305
        GROUPING FOR FLOW DIAGRAMS   305
    7.4.5   Compatible space relationships   306
        DESIGN RECOMMENDATIONS   306
7.5   Control Layout   307
    7.5.1   The effects of body position and limb used   307
        HAND CONTROLS   307
        FOOT CONTROLS   308
    7.5.2   Locating controls   308
        HAND CONTROLS   309
        FOOT CONTROLS   310
    7.5.3   Spacing between controls   312
        DESIGN RECOMMENDATIONS   312
7.6   Seat and Panel Design   314
    7.6.1   Seat design   314
        THE SEAT PAN   314
        SEAT HARDNESS AND SHAPE   315
        THE BACKREST   315
        ARMRESTS AND FOOTRESTS   315
        ADJUSTABILITY   315
        CLEARANCES AROUND THE SEAT   316
    7.6.2   Panel design   316
        PANEL SHAPE   316
        PANEL CONTOUR   317
7.7   The Location of Shared Controls and Displays   318

			Page
7.7.1	Those shared by two operators		318
7.7.2	Those used by a stationary operator and a mobile observer		319

CHAPTER 8. ARRANGEMENT OF GROUPS OF MEN AND MACHINES — **321**

8.1	Link Analysis		321
8.2	Compartment Layout		324
	8.2.1	Factors affecting compartment size and shape	324
		HUMAN-BODY SIZE AND DYNAMICS 325	
		CREW SIZE AND MOBILITY 325	
		EQUIPMENT SIZE AND OPERATION 326	
		VISUAL REQUIREMENTS 327	
		COMMUNICATION REQUIREMENTS 328	
	8.2.2	The layout of traffic spaces	330
		AISLES AND CORRIDORS 330	
		CATWALKS AND TUNNELS 330	
		DOORWAYS AND HATCHES 334	
		LADDERS, STAIRS, AND RAMPS 339	
		ESCALATORS AND ELEVATORS 343	
		CEILINGS AND OVERHEADS 344	
	8.2.3	The layout of maintenance spaces	345
		WORKING SPACE AND CLEARANCE 345	
		AISLE SPACE 345	
		INTERACTION BETWEEN EQUIPMENTS 346	
	8.2.4	The layout of plotting spaces	348
		THE LIMITS OF REACH 348	
		STRUCTURAL AIDS 348	
		PLOTTING RATE AND DENSITY 350	
	8.2.5	Conference rooms and auditoriums	351
		CONFERENCE ROOMS 351	
		AUDITORIUMS 353	
8.3	Arrangement of Groups of Men		358
	8.3.1	The formation of groups	359
	8.3.2	The location of groups	359
		GENERAL PRINCIPLES 359	
		EXAMPLES OF ARRANGEMENTS 359	
	8.3.3	Rows and columns of operators	362
		ROWS OF OPERATORS 363	
		COLUMNS OF OPERATORS 364	

CHAPTER 9. DESIGN FOR EASE OF MAINTENANCE — **367**

9.1	Reliability and Maintainability		368
9.2	A Design Schedule for Maintainability		369
	9.2.1	Planning for maintainability	369
	9.2.2	Designing for maintainability	369
	9.2.3	Testing and revising the design	371
9.3	Planning for Maintainability		371

			Page
9.3.1	An overall plan for maintenance		371
9.3.2	Personnel capabilities and limitations		373
	PHYSICAL LIMITATIONS	373	
	MAINTENANCE SKILLS	374	
9.3.3	Maintenance conditions		375
9.4	Designing for Maintainability		375
9.4.1	Prime equipment		375
	UNIT DESIGN	376	
	UNIT COVERS AND CASES	380	
	CABLES AND CONNECTORS	382	
	EQUIPMENT ACCESSES	385	
	EQUIPMENT TEST POINTS	388	
	DISPLAYS FOR MAINTENANCE	391	
	CONTROLS FOR MAINTENANCE	393	
9.4.2	Installation in prime equipment		395
	EQUIPMENT SPACE	395	
	DESIGNING FOR ACCESSIBILITY	396	
9.4.3	Test equipment and bench mockups		397
	TEST EQUIPMENT	397	
	BENCH MOCKUPS	401	
9.4.4	Maintenance procedures		402
	GENERAL RECOMMENDATIONS	403	
	TROUBLE-SHOOTING PROCEDURES	403	
	USING THESE PROCEDURES	407	
9.4.5	Maintenance manuals		409
	THE FORM OF PRESENTATION	409	
	INSTRUCTIONAL CONTENT	409	
9.4.6	Maintenance tools		409
	DESIGN RECOMMENDATIONS	410	

			Page
CHAPTER 10. EFFECTS OF ENVIRONMENT ON HUMAN PERFORMANCE			**411**
10.1	External and Internal Environments		411
10.1.1	Special considerations for biophysical systems		412
	ADAPTATION	412	
	HABITUATION	412	
	PREPARATION	413	
	VARIATION	413	
	OPTIMIZATION	413	
10.1.2	Variation in the pattern of effects		413
10.2	The Atmospheric Environment		414
10.2.1	The physical characteristics of the atmosphere		414
10.2.2	The effects of altitude		419
	BODY FUNCTIONS	419	
	OXYGEN DEFICIENCY (HYPOXIA)	420	
	BAROMETRIC-PRESSURE PAIN	424	
	PROTECTION AGAINST ALTITUDE	424	
10.2.3	The effects of temperature and humidity		428

Page

BODY FUNCTIONS   428
HEAT STRESS   431
COLD STRESS   433

10.2.4   The effects of contaminants and toxicity   436
CARBON DIOXIDE   436
CARBON MONOXIDE   437
OTHER CONTAMINANTS   440
PROTECTION AGAINST TOXICITY   443

10.3   The Mechanical Environment   445
10.3.1   The effects of acceleration   445
LINEAR ACCELERATION   447
RADIAL ACCELERATION   455
ANGULAR ACCELERATION   458
PERFORMANCE IN ACCELERATION   459
SETTING TOLERANCE LIMITS   461
PROTECTION AGAINST G FORCES   462

10.3.2   The effects of vibration   466
BIOPHYSICAL RELATIONSHIPS   466
MAJOR EFFECTS OF VIBRATION   470
PROTECTION AGAINST VIBRATION   472

10.3.3   Effects of noise   473
HEARING LOSS   473
ANNOYANCE OR DISCOMFORT   474
REDUCED PERFORMANCE   474
PROTECTION AGAINST NOISE   475

CHAPTER 11. ANTHROPOMETRY   **485**

11.1   Physical Anthropology and Equipment Design   485
11.1.1   Goals for the design engineer   486
11.1.2   Factors affecting human-body measurements   486
HUMAN VARIATION   486
CLOTHING AND EQUIPMENT   487
11.1.3   The reliability and limitations of the data   491
SOURCES OF DATA   491
PERCENTILES   492
CORRELATION TABLES   495
11.1.4   What the designer should do   496
IN EVALUATING EQUIPMENT   497
IN DESIGNING NEW EQUIPMENT   499
11.2   Human-Body Dimensions   504
11.2.1   Factors affecting human-body measurements   504
AGE AND SEX   504
RACE AND OCCUPATION   504
POSTURE AND BODY POSITION   505
LONG-TERM CHANGES   506
11.2.2   Applying human-body dimensions   506
11.2.3   Static human-body dimensions   506
BODY HEIGHT (STANDING)   508

BODY HEIGHT (SITTING) 510
BODY WEIGHT 512
MAXIMUM BODY DEPTH 514
BODY BREADTH 514
HEAD LENGTH 516
MAXIMUM HEAD BREADTH 517
INTERPUPILLARY DISTANCE 518
EYE HEIGHT (STANDING) 518
EYE HEIGHT (SITTING) 518
SHOULDER HEIGHT (STANDING) 520
SHOULDER HEIGHT (SITTING) 520
SHOULDER-TO-ELBOW LENGTH 521
ARM REACH 521
SHOULDER-TO-SHOULDER BREADTH 524
CHEST DEPTH 524
CHEST BREADTH 524
WAIST DEPTH (STANDING) 525
ELBOW HEIGHT (STANDING) 525
ELBOW HEIGHT (SITTING) 528
FOREARM-HAND LENGTH 528
ELBOW-TO-ELBOW BREADTH 528
HIP BREADTH (STANDING) 531
HIP BREADTH (SITTING) 531
BUTTOCK-LEG LENGTH 531
BUTTOCK-KNEE LENGTH 532
BUTTOCK-POPLITEAL LENGTH 532
BUTTOCK DEPTH 534
THIGH HEIGHT (SITTING) 534
KNUCKLE HEIGHT (STANDING) 534
HAND THICKNESS 536
HAND LENGTH 536
HAND BREADTH AT THUMB 536
HAND BREADTH AT METACARPALE 538
KNEE HEIGHT (SITTING) 539
KNEE-TO-KNEE BREADTH 539
POPLITEAL HEIGHT (SITTING) 539
FOOT LENGTH 542
FOOT BREADTH 542
11.2.4 Dynamic human-body dimensions 543
WORKING POSITIONS 543
FUNCTIONAL ARM REACH 544
11.3 Range of Movement of Body Members 551
11.3.1 Joints and "links" 551
11.3.2 Factors affecting the range of joint movement 551
AGE AND SEX 552
BODY BUILD AND OCCUPATION 552
POSTURE AND BODY POSITION 552
11.3.3 Static range-of-movement measurements 552
11.3.4 Dynamic range-of-movement measurements 556
11.4 Muscle Strength 556

		Page
11.4.1	How the muscles do their job	557
11.4.2	Factors affecting muscle strength	557
	BIOLOGICAL FACTORS 557	
	ENVIRONMENTAL FACTORS 558	
	OCCUPATIONAL FACTORS 558	
11.4.3	The data	559

BIBLIOGRAPHY AND AUTHOR INDEX 571

SUBJECT INDEX 607

1

the man-machine system

THE SYSTEM CONCEPT of design and development is now widely accepted by the military establishment and its contractors, as well as by many industries. It is the concept of a group of components designed to serve a given set of purposes. In the U. S. Armed Forces, a set of purposes is called a mission, and, because this Guide is oriented toward military applications, that term will be employed here. In industry, the purpose might be the production of a commodity or the construction of a facility. In any case, system design is the design of a total system so that it serves its intended purposes or missions.

1.1 *System Considerations*

System design includes the traditional engineering of individual equipments but goes beyond it. The fact that the performance of any individual equipment is partly a function of the other equipments that are combined with it, and partly a function of the system's overall mission, requires a set of procedures for conceiving and developing a system as a whole in such a way that each component is fashioned to make its proper contribution to the ensemble.

System design is, or should be, an organized procedure. Though it inevitably involves a certain amount of traditional "cut and try," it can be a rational, orderly process of analyzing a system, more or less quantitatively, before it exists, then designing it, and, later, evaluating the system in its prototype or preproduction form.

This chapter, drafted by Clifford T. Morgan and Max W. Lund, is based, in part, on material prepared by H. W. Sinaiko and E. P. Buckley, formerly of the U. S. Naval Research Laboratory, and by R. M. Thomson, B. J. Covner, and H. H. Jacobs of Dunlap and Associates, Inc.

This system concept applies not only to equipments but, also, to the human beings who operate and maintain the equipments. True, equipments are being developed to take over many tasks human beings used to do, and man is a trivial component of some systems. Nevertheless, men are still integral parts of almost all systems. Men decide when and how to use machines; men feed inputs to and base their actions on outputs from machines. Machines work well only if the men operating and maintaining them can and do perform their jobs satisfactorily. The system concept, therefore, must be of a man-machine system.

A man-machine system is any group of men and machines that operates as a unit to carry out an assigned task or tasks. The group might be a large aggregate, such as a naval task force composed of many men and many ships, or it might consist of a single man and a single machine, such as a radio operator and his radio. The definition of a system is, therefore, arbitrary and depends on the purposes for which the system is designed and on the performances to be evaluated. One should keep in mind, however, that a small man-machine system is almost invariably a part of a larger man-machine system and that the performance of one depends on that of the other (see Fig. 1-1 above).

Designing and developing the various machine components of a system require the abilities of many different types of engineers. Just as one engineer is made solely responsible for power requirements, another for aerodynamic properties, etc., it is mandatory that a human engineer be made responsible for human factors. One consequence of not having someone responsible for human factors is that each of the others, in an effort to meet his requirements, will encroach upon the unrepresented territory of the human components in the system, with the result that serious operation and maintenance problems will almost inevitably be generated.

Such problems, generated in the absence of a human-factors representative on the design team, are usually discovered very late in the system development and are disproportionately expensive to solve by hardware redesign. If not solved in terms of hardware redesign, they might have to be solved even more expensively by a selection and training program devised to identify men who might be capable of fitting into the system after prolonged training. Thus, if a man-machine system is to perform at its best—for no better reason than that of economy—design must start with, and revolve around, the human components and their capabilities.

This man-machine-system concept governs the organization of this Guide. In this chapter, methods of analyzing a system to be designed, with emphasis on the human component of the system, are described (see section 1.2). Through system analysis, one determines, roughly, both what the system as a whole, and its various man-machine subsystems, can and must do. This chapter also gives a general survey of the human factors to be considered in the design of man-machine systems (see section 1.3), which factors subsequent chapters cover in detail. Finally, in section 1.4 of this chapter, methods of evaluating a man-machine system, once it has been tentatively designed, are described.

1.2 *System Analysis*

As the term is used here, system analysis is not the same thing as system evaluation. System analysis gives as accurate a picture as possible of the structure and functions of a system—of the way it is to be put together and of the processes that are to go on in it. A system evaluation, on the other hand, is a measure or set of measures of how well the system serves its mission. System analysis, in other words, tells one what a system is and what it does, whereas a system evaluation tells one what it accomplishes and how well it fulfills its mission.

A system analysis, when completed, is a detailed description of the components of a system and of the operating characteristics of those components, whether men or machines. It is a statement of the capabilities, limitations, and interdependencies of the components expressed in terms that are relevant to the overall mission of the system. As such, the system analysis serves the following purposes:

a. Scheduling development. In the development of new systems, system analysis is necessary to insure that all requirements are being met—and met on schedule. Analysis decreases the likelihood that serious problems will be overlooked, that the development of some parts of the system will lag behind others, and that human operators will be unable to obtain maximum performance from the system.

b. Identifying limiting factors. System analysis enables the designer to determine the factors that must limit the performance of a system. A system might have bottlenecks that seriously reduce the performance that would otherwise be possible. Through system analysis, it is possible to determine whether there are any bottlenecks and, if so, the nature of the problems to be solved to eliminate them.

c. Assignment of functions. System analysis enables the designer to make better decisions about the functions to assign to men and to machines. Without such an analysis,

the designer often needlessly assigns to a machine a function a man can do better, or assigns to men functions that machines could do better or that men are unable to perform well enough to satisfy the mission of the system. System analysis helps the designer make those changes, either in the design of the system or its components, that are necessary to achieve maximum performance.

d. Evaluation of systems. System analysis, finally, is a prerequisite to the evaluation and comparison of systems. Measures of performance of the system and its subsystems are needed to find out how a system can be expected to perform under actual operating conditions or whether one system can be expected to be better than another. These measures can be selected intelligently only from the information furnished in a system analysis.

Many different techniques are available for system analysis. Some of the general techniques covered in article 1.2.1 (below) give an overall picture of the system and its arrangement without analyzing in any detail the performance of its man and machine components. Other methods of analyzing a system are covered in articles 1.2.2, 1.2.3, and 1.2.4. Both articles list the advantages of the different methods for different systems.

Several, but usually not all, of the methods described can be used in analyzing any one system. The decision on which one to use depends on the kind of system involved. In any case, the analysis of a system proceeds in stages from the general ones described in article 1.2.1 to the specific ones treated in articles 1.2.2, 1.2.3, and 1.2.4.

1.2.1 *General methods of analysis*

The first step in analyzing a system is to construct an overall picture of the system,

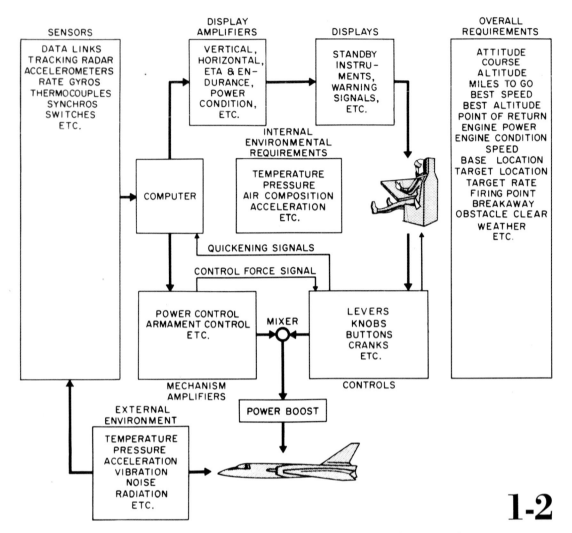

1-2

listing and depicting all its components, both man and machine, and the conditions under which they must operate. For this purpose, a system pictogram is recommended. To construct a system pictogram, arrange the following information on a diagram like that shown in Fig. 1-2:

1. The overall requirements of the system. Make them as specific as possible, and put them in terms such as the following:

a. The mission of the system—what it is supposed to accomplish. The mission description should include a profile under both normal and abnormal conditions; it should be stated not only in terms of minimum-performance requirements but, also, in terms of the

probable distribution of performances.

b. The conditions of use and the general environment in which it will operate, including weather, ambient illumination, temperature, etc.

c. The total time of its existence, including delivery and uncrating of the equipment, training operators, storing the components, and maintenance, abandonment, disposal, or conversion of the system, when necessary.

d. The design parameters or limits—any constraints on design such as size, weight, and mobility.

e. The provisions for emergency situations and other infrequent, but possible, uses of the system.

§ 1.2.1

f. The relation of this system to any other system.

2. Specify the external environments in which the system will operate in terms of the following:

a. The various signals and data that the sensing devices of the system (including human operators where they are used as direct sensors of the external environment) must detect and process.

b. The unwanted noises, hazards, and obstructions in the environment that will limit performance of the system.

3. Specify the internal environment of the system (the environment in which human beings and component equipments must operate), taking particular account of such factors affecting human performance as the following:

a. The lighting, noise, and atmospheric conditions under which personnel must work.

b. The amount of space available for equipment and personnel.

c. Conditions such as movement, shaking, buffeting, and acceleration.

4. List the sensing devices required to provide inputs to the system, including all detection, communication, and navigation devices.

5. List the equipments involved in the processing of data from sensors, including computers, display amplifiers or data-transforming devices, displays intended for human use, and other automatic devices linking the inputs and outputs of the system.

6. Specify the human-component requirements of the system in terms of the following:

a. The number of men to be used.

b. The kinds of jobs they are supposed to perform.

7. Specify the numbers and types of control devices required for system output, such as the following:

a. Control devices to be operated by human beings.

b. Devices that mix the outputs of human operators with those of other equipments.

c. Special devices such as quickening devices or control-signal devices.

Unless a large wall chart is made, all the information called for above cannot be fitted directly onto the pictogram. Moreover, the system analysis should include considerable detailed information. It is probably best, therefore, to compile this information in a looseleaf notebook and, by appropriate coding, merely list on the pictogram where the information can be found in the notebook.

FUNCTIONAL ANALYSIS

A pictogram shows the requirements of a system, some of its components and subsystems, and the general relation of inputs and outputs, but it is desirable to be more specific in setting down how each requirement of a system will be met. This is accomplished by writing up each requirement in more detail (see Table 1-1) and drawing a system diagram of the various functions to be performed in the system and the relationship between

Table 1-1 Functional Analysis of an Anti-aircraft-Defense System *

Requirement	Description
Mission	Protection of friendly area through destruction and/or disturbance of attacking enemy aircraft
Minimum performance	Ability to destroy 90% of attacking aircraft during medium-intensity raids (up to 50 planes per minute) at altitudes up to 50,000 ft, at distances of 50–100 mi from the protected area at aircraft speeds of 700 mph and with 5-g maneuverability
Condition of use	Raids will be conducted by enemy medium-bomber aircraft, type Baker, capable of electronic jamming. They will employ standard evasive tactics and are expected to launch their weapons no more than X miles from target. Bad weather conditions prevail 30% of the time
Constraints on design	Early-warning subsystem must be mobile. It must be capable of being fitted into two standard vans. It must be based on the employment of radar system type Y

* The table gives a brief statement of the overall requirements of a system and the means to be used in meeting these requirements (see also Fig. 1-3).

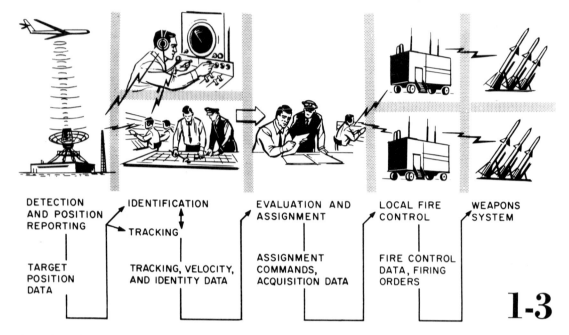

DETECTION AND POSITION REPORTING

IDENTIFICATION

TRACKING

EVALUATION AND ASSIGNMENT

LOCAL FIRE CONTROL

WEAPONS SYSTEM

TARGET POSITION DATA

TRACKING, VELOCITY, AND IDENTITY DATA

ASSIGNMENT COMMANDS, ACQUISITION DATA

FIRE CONTROL DATA, FIRING ORDERS

1-3

these functions (see lower half of Fig. 1-3). The designer should not be concerned here with particular items of equipment or of personnel; the important thing is to identify the different functions to be carried out.

DECISION ANALYSIS

A decision analysis is an analysis of decisions made on the basis of information transmitted and the resulting action that is taken. Decision analysis is most applicable to information-handling systems because such analysis can specify the information inputs required at each point, indicate the sequence of decision-making activities, and show the relationship between the elements of a system.

The first step in decision analysis is to determine all the functions to be performed by an operator. These functions then are translated into operator facilities by answering the following questions:

a. What *decisions* must the operator make to accomplish each function?

b. What *information* is required for each decision?

c. What *action* is required to execute the decision?

With these questions answered, it becomes obvious what indicators and controls are required, and then, from the resulting requirements, operator facilities can be specified.

To present the information thus arrived at in a systematic, easy-to-reference fashion, a chart can be made. This chart will depict the information-decision-action pattern for each function performed by the operator. An example of such a chart is shown in Fig. 1-4 (Coakley and Fucigna, 1955), which presents one section of a decision analysis of a radar-tracking system. All the operator functions are grouped into four phases of operation of the radar: pre-acquisition, acquisition, tracking, and release.

Figure 1-4 shows that part of the chart for the pre-acquisition phase. The specific functions performed during a phase are represented by three different symbols: a triangle for information, a circle for decision, and a square for action. The chart then shows, in exact sequence, the inputs (information), decisions, and outputs (actions) of the operator. Note that he receives information from the equipment, the target, and his learned operating procedures. He then makes a decision and performs two actions. These actions, in turn, bring him more information.

§ 1.2.1

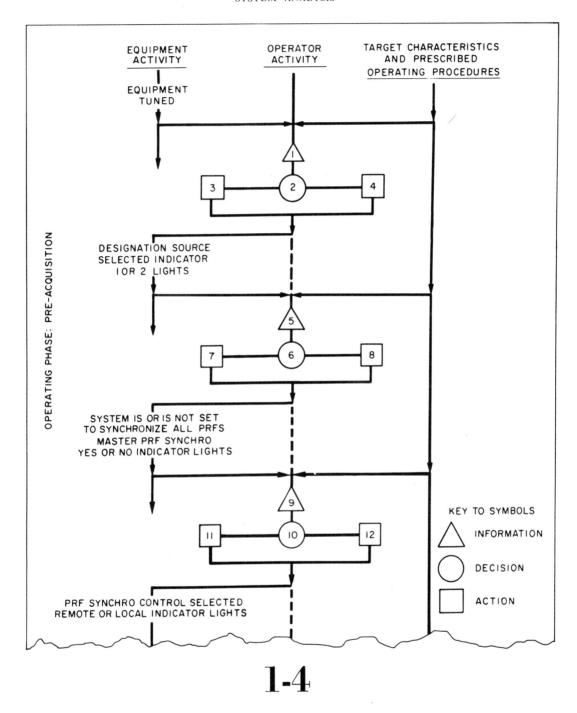

1-4

ACTIVITY ANALYSIS

Activity analysis is a study of the activities carried out by a man doing his assigned work in a man-machine system. It might consist of continuous data on activity throughout a long period or of time samples based on intermittent observation of the activity. Activity analysis is particularly useful for judging the relative importance of various operator activities and the demands they make on the operator's time and effort. Activity analysis can provide information for revamping operational procedures, redesigning equipments, unburdening operators, and redistributing duties and staff responsibilities. An example of an activ-

clerical operations, data-processing systems, information-handling systems, and many other kinds of activities. A flow analysis can be applied to large systems in their entirety, to small subsystems, or, even, to one-man operations. This method is useful for developing a picture of system operation; for indicating the functional relationships between system elements; for tracing the flow of materials, information, etc.; for showing the physical or sequential distribution of operations; or for identifying the inputs and outputs of particular subsystems.

Flow analysis can be made with or without time scales, depending on whether time is an important factor in the operation of the sys-

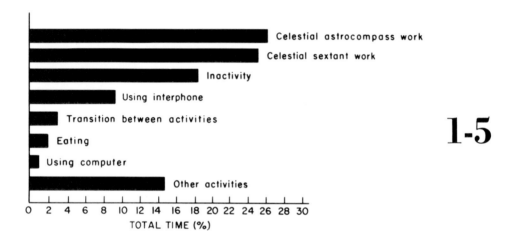

ity analysis is that of the second navigator's time on an arctic mission shown in Fig. 1-5 (Christensen, 1949).

The limitation of activity analysis is that it cannot direct attention to the fact that activities that occur only rarely might still occur simultaneously. A low percent of total time does not necessarily mean that conflicts could not occur.

FLOW ANALYSIS

A flow analysis depicts the sequence of events in a system. It can be employed to describe production processes and operations,

tem. An example of a flow analysis *without* a time scale is the diagram for information flow in an air-route traffic-control system shown in Fig. 1-6 (Fitts, 1951). The diagram depicts the flow of information without respect to time or to the particular persons processing the information. It is particularly helpful in "single-thread" analysis of information flow relative to a specific target, airplane, etc.

An example of a flow analysis *with* a time scale is the chart of activities in a Navy combat information center (CIC) shown in Fig. 1-7 (Systems Research Lab., 1945). The chart shows the timing and sequence of activities at five stations in the CIC. Each type of activity is coded. Reading from the left-hand

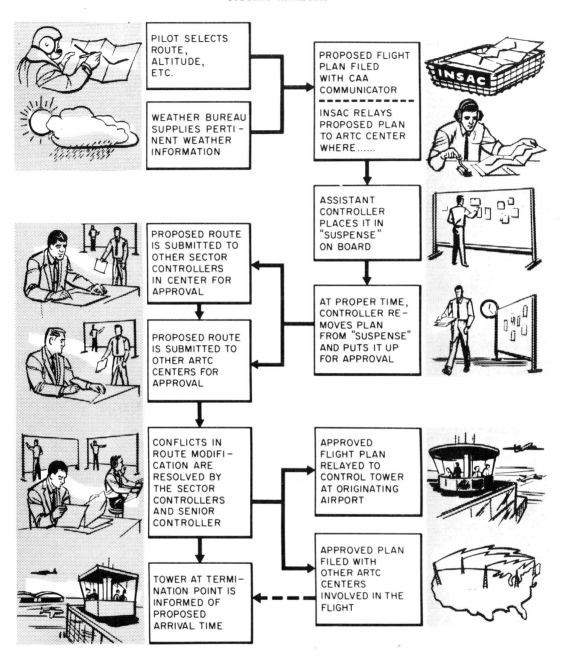

1-6

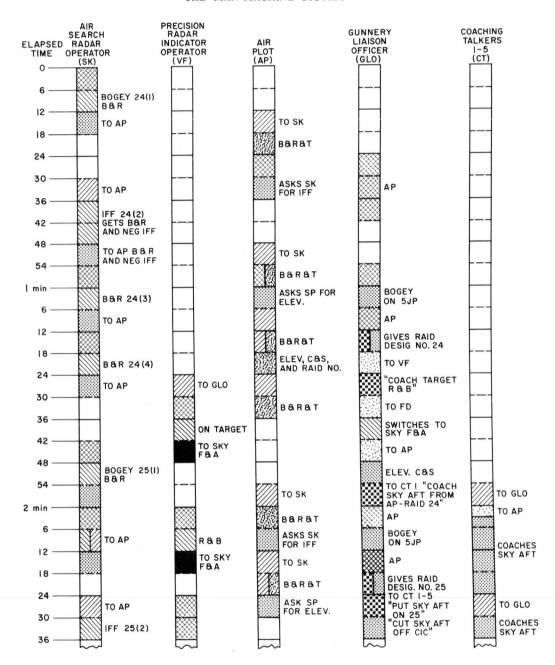

1-7

column, we see that SK is inspecting his scope during the first 6 sec. In the next 6 sec, he spots an unidentified aircraft (bogey), tentatively designates it as No. 24, and adjusts his scope to get the bogey's bearing and range (B&R). He then reports this information, via sound-powered phone, to AP.

AP listens to SK and then plots the bearing, range, and time (BR&T). After inspecting his plot, AP asks SK for identification, friend or foe (IFF); GLO, meanwhile, is watching AP's plot. SK triggers his IFF apparatus, gets another B&R, and a negative response to IFF. He then reports this information to AP. After listening to SK, AP plots the new B&R, inspects it, and asks the elevation-finding-radar operator (SP), who is not in CIC, for bogey's elevation.

Meanwhile, GLO, after watching AP plot the latest BR&T, is reporting the bogey on the 5JP circuit, and SK is watching his scope and getting another B&R, which he reports to AP, who, after listening to SK, SP, and GLO, plots the third BR&T, the elevation, the course and speed (C&S), and the raid number (which he got from GLO, who is near enough to him to tell him in person—everyone else getting it over the 5JP). After designating bogey as raid No. 24, GLO walks over to VF and tells him to coach the target at such and such a range and bearing (R&B).

VF listens to GLO, watches his scope, cranks onto the target, and mechanically reports the new R&B to the forward and aft antiaircraft guns (SKY F&A). GLO, meanwhile, walks over to the fire director (FD), switches it to SKY F&A, walks back to AP, and reports the elevation and C&S over 5JP. He then tells CT 1 to coach SKY AFT from AP. CT 1 listens to him, walks over to AP, and starts coaching. Meanwhile, SK reports another bogey—and so it goes.

The above illustrates the construction of a flow-analysis chart with a time scale showing what each man and equipment is doing in relation to others. To make such a flow analysis with a time scale, proceed through the following steps:

1. Make a chart with several columns, one column for each man-machine combination in the system.

2. Devise a suitable code for each type of man-machine activity.

3. Represent time on the vertical scale of the chart, and depict in each column the time elapsing for each activity.

Where data are available in previous studies of the same man-machine activities, use these data for constructing the chart. Where such data are not available, tentative estimates must be used, but at the earliest opportunity, check these estimates with actual measurements obtained from simulations of the tasks to be performed. (Refer to section 1.4 for guidance in conducting such simulated studies.)

When the flow-process chart is completed, study it for the following:

a. To determine points at which the man-machine system is overloaded or underloaded, paying particular attention to periods of "waiting time" during which one man-machine component is waiting for other activities in the system to be completed.

b. To get ideas for rearranging the system to distribute loads more evenly and to reduce waiting time.

JOB ANALYSIS

A job description is a statement of the duties performed by a man (or sometimes a group of men). The process of obtaining information for a job description is called job analysis. This type of analysis is usually based on detailed interviews with men skilled in a job, but it can (and should, where appropriate) include other, more objective, measures of the work done.

Job analysis is useful for recording the entire distribution of activities, operations, decision problems, and job demands of complex human tasks. It is particularly appropriate where human operators are called upon to meet a wide variety of situations created by external factors.

The following list describes the information that should be included, if possible, in a job analysis (see Table 1-2):

a. A general description of the duties of the operator.

Table 1-2   Partial Job Analysis for a Senior Control-Tower Operator *

Duty	General task	Specific task	Importance value
Controls traffic in flight and on ground using two-way radio and visual signals to keep flow to, from, and on airfield safe, orderly, and expeditious	Communicate with aircraft to transmit taxi, landing, and takeoff instructions by radio or visual signals	Report any hazards to pilots	10
		Receive requests and information from pilots	10
		Give weather information	10
		Select frequencies on which to transmit to aircraft	8
		Check aircraft visually before landing for wheels down position	10
	Control movement of all ground vehicles on airfield by radio contact or visual signals	Scan landing-area continuously for ground traffic requiring approval to cross runways	10
		Watch for unauthorized ground traffic on landing area	10
Maintains records concerning control-tower operations and activities by entering data on forms by hand or typewriter to maintain permanent record of airfield operations	Maintain all logs by making appropriate entries	Maintain Form 18 (Daily Control-Tower-Operations Log)	7
		Maintain Form 28 (Master Tower Log)	9
		Maintain Form 3-91 (Master Clock Log)	6
		Maintain Visitor's Log	9
		Maintain log giving information necessary for Navigation Aids Report	3
Supervises and instructs OJT tower operators by issuing verbal and/or written instructions and orders to maintain constant and efficient operation of control tower	Supervise tower operator in "B," "C," and "D" positions by issuing verbal and/or written instructions and orders	Make out work schedules	2
		Assure proper manning of all positions	7
		Correct any incorrect procedures that come to his attention	3
		See that "B" operator knows time aircraft take off	9

* Lenard and North, 1952.

b. A general description of the different tasks performed by the operator.

c. A specific description of all the tasks.

d. A quantitative statement of the relative importance of the different tasks. (In the example given in Table 1-2, the importance values are indicated by a descending scale starting with 10—most important.)

A complete job description should go on to state the following:

e. The speed and accuracy with which the operator should perform his task, and the highest workloads he can be required to carry.

f. Any special abilities, and the amount and kind of training, required to fulfill the requirements of the job.

All job descriptions should be checked against available data to determine whether operators can actually meet the requirements of the job description. If such data are not available, specific studies should be conducted to obtain them.

1.2.2 *The analysis of critical design requirements*

Some aspects of a system are "critical" and some are not. That is to say, there are some things the system must do to a certain level of performance or it is inadequate. Other aspects of the system are relatively unimportant,

§ 1.2.2

as far as performance is concerned, either because there is no question but that they will be satisfactory or because they have relatively little to do with the performance of the system.

Because the analysis of a system could go on indefinitely if decisions are not made about what it is important and unimportant to analyze, the system designer must do his best to identify those characteristics of a system that are critical. He cannot do this until he has much of the information derived from the analytical techniques described above. Once he has this information, however, he can put it to use in an analysis of the critical design requirements.

The purpose of such an analysis is to identify the choices to be made and to make these choices in such a way as to get optimum performance from a system. But the designer needs to be able to identify all such critical requirements of a system so that problems can be resolved to the advantage of the system.

To make such an identification, a preliminary analysis of the critical design requirements can be made as illustrated in Table 1-3, which lists the features of a radar-target-detection system, including the following:

a. The operations performed by the system.

b. A brief description of the activity or job required for each operation.

c. The outputs of the activity of each operation.

d. The critical operating variables in these activities.

e. The critical design requirements of the system that affect these variables.

Such an enumeration only identifies the critical design requirements; it does not, by itself, give the parameters to be used in the design. For example, in designing a target-detection system, the system designer might know that by using four operators rather than three he can increase, by a small percentage, the number of targets detected, but that at the same time, the additional weight, space, equipment, and maintenance requirements imposed by the fourth operator will reduce the overall system output. In all probability he will not know this, however, unless he has performed an analysis of the critical design requirements involved.

To make such an analysis, it is necessary to call up all information relevant to the design, and use this to evaluate possible alternate designs. To illustrate such an evaluation, Fig. 1-8 shows how specific solutions to two of the critical design requirements listed in Table 1-3—the number of search operators and the required ambient illumination—can be obtained. The evaluation proceeds by the following steps:

1. Select the critical design requirement.

2. Choose the critical operating variable relevant to that design requirement.

3. Determine the advantages and disadvantages of choosing different designs or parameters.

4. Weigh these advantages and disadvantages against each other, and arrive at the preferred design parameter.

1.2.3 *The analysis of equipment characteristics*

To carry out many of the analyses previously described, particularly that of the critical design requirements, the characteristics of the equipments that are to be used by human operators must be carefully analyzed. As the information in the next section (1.3) and in succeeding chapters of this Guide illustrates, such characteristics determine the performance that can be expected of operators and of the equipments they operate, i.e., the performance of the man-machine system.

SYSTEM DISPLAYS

In designing man-machine systems, the characteristics of the displays to be used by each operator should be analyzed, taking into account the following factors (for detailed information, see Chapters 2, 3, 5, 7, and 10):

a. The human sense or senses employed by the display. Consider whether any one sense

§ 1.2.3

Table 1-3 Preliminary Analysis of the Critical Design Requirements of a Radar Target-Detection System *

Operations	Activities	Outputs	Critical operating variables	Critical design requirements
Detection and position reporting	Search operator monitors scope to detect new targets, reports detections, periodically measures target position, and communicates data to plotter	Target position data	Probable distribution of detection ranges Probability of detecting targets Probable distribution of communication time Probable density of position errors Data-handling rate	Design and location of displays Number of search operators Required ambient illumination Design of communication system Location of operator with respect to plotter
Identification and tracking	Plotter receives periodic position reports, plots position data, develops track, estimates speed, and records identity	Target tracking, speed, and identity data	Probable distribution of plotting errors Data-handling rate	Design and location of displays Number of plotters Location of plotter with respect to evaluator
Evaluation and assignment	Evaluator observes position and track of targets, decides which interceptors should intercept which targets, and communicates assignments to controller	Assignment commands and aquisition data	Evaluation and assignment rate Evaluation effectiveness	Design and location of displays Number of evaluators Design of communication system Location of evaluator with respect to controller
Air control	Air controller receives assignments, develops intercept data, communicates data to interceptors, receives interceptor status reports, and communicates reports to evaluator	Intercept data and interceptor status reports	Probable distribution of vectoring errors Probable distribution of time to successive vectors Data-handling rate	Design and location of displays Number of air controllers Design of communication system

* Courtesy of Dunlap and Associates, Inc.

§ 1.2.3

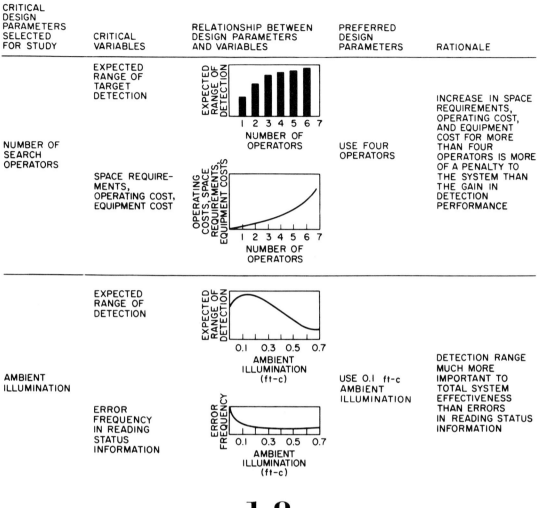

CRITICAL DESIGN PARAMETERS SELECTED FOR STUDY	CRITICAL VARIABLES	RELATIONSHIP BETWEEN DESIGN PARAMETERS AND VARIABLES	PREFERRED DESIGN PARAMETERS	RATIONALE
NUMBER OF SEARCH OPERATORS	EXPECTED RANGE OF TARGET DETECTION		USE FOUR OPERATORS	INCREASE IN SPACE REQUIREMENTS, OPERATING COST, AND EQUIPMENT COST FOR MORE THAN FOUR OPERATORS IS MORE OF A PENALTY TO THE SYSTEM THAN THE GAIN IN DETECTION PERFORMANCE
	SPACE REQUIRE-MENTS, OPERATING COST, EQUIPMENT COST			
AMBIENT ILLUMINATION	EXPECTED RANGE OF DETECTION		USE 0.1 ft-c AMBIENT ILLUMINATION	DETECTION RANGE MUCH MORE IMPORTANT TO TOTAL SYSTEM EFFECTIVENESS THAN ERRORS IN READING STATUS INFORMATION
	ERROR FREQUENCY IN READING STATUS INFORMATION			

1-8

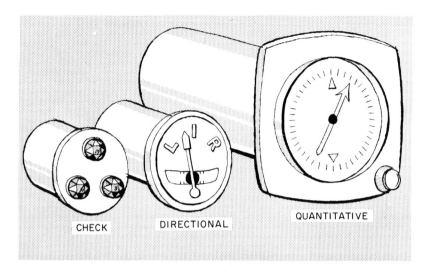

1-9

CHECK   DIRECTIONAL   QUANTITATIVE

1-10

THIS   NOT THIS

is likely to be overloaded while other senses are underloaded.

b. The form of the display. Consider whether the display in question is the best possible way of displaying information for human use. For instance, qualitative displays, such as those for check reading or for indicating direction of movement, should be designed differently from quantitative displays (see Fig. 1-9).

c. The accuracy, speed, and workload imposed by the display. Consider whether these requirements can be met by the operator.

d. Any adverse environmental factors. Consider whether adverse factors, such as acceleration, vibration, and noise, might impair the operator's ability to read the display.

OPERATOR CONTROLS

In designing man-machine systems, the characteristics of the controls to be used by each operator should be analyzed, taking into account the following factors (for detailed information, see Chapters 6 and 7):

a. The distribution of tasks among the various limbs. Consider whether any one limb is overloaded, and whether the same limb might be required to do two or more things at the same time (see Fig. 1-10).

b. The placement of controls. Consider whether all controls are within easy reach, are spaced far enough apart, and are placed according to their importance.

c. The type of control. Consider whether the proper type of control has been provided for each assigned task.

d. Any hazards. Consider whether controls can be accidentally actuated or if there are any other possibilities of operating controls incorrectly.

e. Overriding controls. Where control is automatic, consider whether the operator should be provided with a means of overriding the control in case of emergency.

f. Similarity to other controls. Consider whether an operator might have trouble learning the proper operation of controls, or make mistakes in their operation, because they require different movements than he has been trained previously to make (see Fig. 1-11).

§ 1.2.3

WORKPLACES

Human-body dimensions have been extensively measured (see Chapter 11) and must be considered in system design. When considering human-body measurements, data should be obtained for the same population of individuals that will operate and maintain the system to be designed. Why? Because, for instance, in World War II the physical dimensions of aerial gunners were significantly different from those of pilots (see Fig. 1-12). Thus, where weight is an important considera-

or almost the smallest, man in the population. If practicable, make the equipment adjustable in size or position so that it will accommodate men of different sizes (see Fig. 1-14).

c. In general, when designing seats, escape hatches, or anything involving the *size of a man,* design for the largest, or almost the largest, men in the population (see Fig. 1-15).

Sometimes these general rules are incompatible and compromises must be made. For example, the length and height of a seat should be designed for small men so that their knees are free of the seat and their legs can

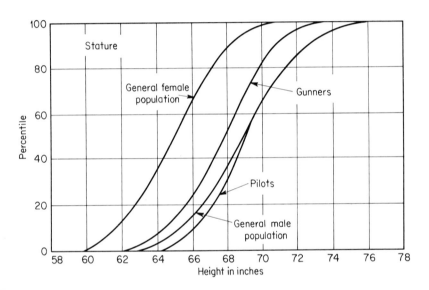

1-12 Cumulative distributions of heights of different populations. Civilian female and male populations consisted of about 4,000 adults selected at random in railroad stations. Gunners and pilots consisted of about 4,000 Army Air Corps personnel measured during World War II (Chapanis, et al., 1949)

tion, as in aircraft design, data should be used for the expected size and weight ranges of the population that will make up the crews.

Some further considerations are the following (for detailed information, see Chapters 7, 8, and 9):

a. Determine whether the man will be sitting, standing, or moving about, and choose appropriate human-body measurements (see Fig. 1-13).

b. In general, when designing for reach, strength, or anything involving the *utmost that a man can do,* design for the smallest,

reach the floor, but the width of the seat should be designed for large men so that all men can fit in the seat.

OTHER CHARACTERISTICS

In designing for human use, several other factors should be considered, including the following (for detailed information, see Chapters 8, 9, and 10):

a. Adequate space. Allow adequate space for operating and maintaining equipments,

§ 1.2.3

1-13

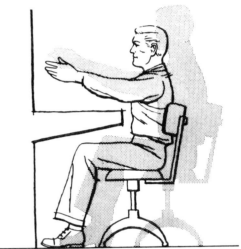

1-14

1-15

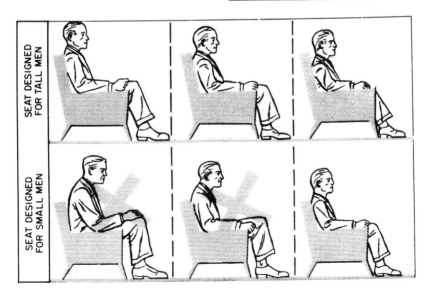

for standing and sitting, and for passageway.

b. Any hazards to safety. Avoid protruding objects, and provide safeguards against potential accidents.

c. The effects of the environment on human performance. Consider the effects of such environmental factors as temperature, humidity, glare, and g forces.

d. Personnel selection and training. Consider the selection and training of operators and maintenance men for the tasks they must perform.

1.3 *The Man in System Design*

This section of the chapter introduces some of the subjects that will be developed in more detail in later chapters—the human factors that are especially significant in the design of man-machine systems. These factors will be considered under the following headings: variations among men, man's sensory systems, man's unique characteristics, man as a system component, man vs. machine, and the synthesis of man and machine.

1.3.1 *Variations among men*

All measurements of human characteristics vary from measurement to measurement, and such variability must be taken into account in the design of man-machine systems. Measurements of human characteristics vary in the following ways:

a. Individual people differ in all measurable characteristics such as reaction time, strength of grip, and visual acuity.

b. Individual people vary from situation to situation and from one measurement to another. For example, people who are tall are not necessarily intelligent; those who are superior at one task might be inferior at another.

c. Individual people differ from time to time in the same characteristic. For instance, no two tests of visual acuity on the same person give exactly the same results—a rifleman

might come close to the bull's eye on one shot, hit it on the next few, and miss it completely on the last.

Such variation in the measurements of human characteristics or performance is of two general kinds, variable errors and constant errors. Variable errors are those that occur randomly from one measurement to the next. (Example: the case of the rifleman just cited.) Constant errors are those that tend consistently in a given direction. (Example: the rifleman whose shots tend to group to the right of the bull's eye even though they are grouped close together and exhibit little variable error, as shown in Fig. 1-16.)

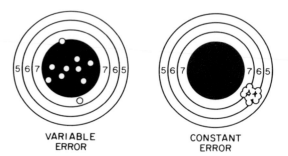

VARIABLE
ERROR

CONSTANT
ERROR

GAUSSIAN DISTRIBUTIONS

Many, if not most, measurements of human characteristics vary, approximately, according to Gaussian distribution. A curve of such measurements is called a normal, bell-shaped curve (see Fig. 1-17). In this distribution, the majority of the measurements lie near the center of the curve, and only a few are scattered out on the ends.

The best measure of the central tendency of the distribution is the arithmetic mean (M), which is $\Sigma X/N$, where X is each measurement, and N is the number of cases. The most precise measure of the variability of the distribution of measurements is the standard deviation σ, which is equal to $\sqrt{\Sigma x^2/N}$, where x is the deviation of each score from the

tribution of hip breadth), it is usually best to consult cumulative distributions. The cumulative distribution shows the number of people whose measurements fall at and below a given value, and curves plotted of cumulative distributions of human characteristics usually are shaped like the integral sign.

The cumulative distribution provides percentile values. A percentile value is the measurement indicating the percentage of people

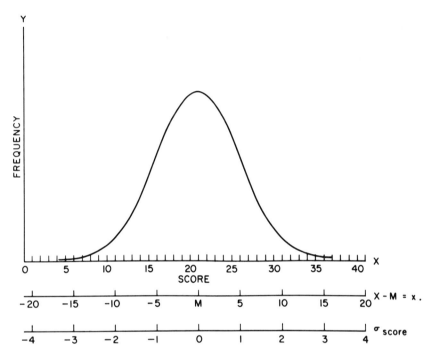

1-17 Normal bell-shaped distribution. Many sets of measurements of human characteristics approximate this distribution. Here X is measure of characteristic, and Y is relative frequency of individual people at different values of X

mean $(X - M)$. In other words, σ is the root-mean-square (rms) deviation from the mean. The range of values between $+1\sigma$ from the mean and -1σ from the mean includes 68% of the scores in the ideal bell-shaped distribution.

CUMULATIVE DISTRIBUTIONS

When distributions of measurements are used as norms for design purposes (e.g., dis-

talling at or below a particular value of measurement. For instance, in designing chairs, the proper width of the seat depends on the hip breadth of the individual people using the seat, and the cumulative distribution of such measurements (Fig. 1-18) shows that a hip breadth of 13 in. has a percentile value of 2, one of 14 in., a percentile value of 18, etc. These percentile values mean, respectively, that 2% of the population measured has a hip breadth of 13 in. or less, and 18% has a hip breadth of 14 in. or less. (The 50th per-

§ 1.3.1

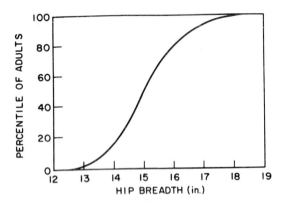

PERCENTILE OF ADULTS (y-axis)
HIP BREADTH (in.) (x-axis)

1-18 Cumulative distributions of hip breadth. Such distributions are progressive accumulations of frequencies of curve in Fig. 1-17. Percentile indicates percentage of people having certain hip breadth or less (Chapanis, et al., 1949)

centile, in this case, is about 15 in., and the 95th percentile is about 17½ in.)

THE MEASUREMENT OF ERRORS

Many, if not most, measurements of errors made by human operators approximate the normal, bell-shaped curve. When error is represented by such a distribution, the mean of the distribution is a constant error, and the standard deviation (σ) of the distribution is a variable error.

Human errors compound linearly just as those of machines frequently do; together they add up according to the squares of the standard deviations (see Fig. 1-19). Thus, the accumulation of two errors appears as:

$$\sigma_{1+2}^2 = \sigma_1^2 + \sigma_2^2, \qquad (1\text{-}1)$$

where σ_{1+2} is the error of the system, σ_1 is the first source of error, and σ_2 is the second source of error. It should be pointed out that Equation 1-1 applies to variable errors but not to constant errors, and it must be modified to include a correlational term when the components of system error are correlated, i.e., when the size of one error depends directly on the size of another.

In man-machine systems, when one source of error is moderately larger than another, and the two sources of error accumulate in the system, the smaller source of error can be neglected (see Fig. 1-20). On the other hand, the overall error of the man-machine system is greatly reduced by decreasing the size of the larger error. For example, if σ for the error of plotting range is 100 yd, and that for reading from the plot is 300 yd, a reduction of 50 yd in *plotting* error (the smaller source of error) will have a negligible effect on the error of the system. (Using Equation 1-1, $100^2 + 300^2 = 316^2$ and $50^2 + 300^2 = 304^2$, a difference of 12 yd.) In contrast, a reduction of 50 yd in *reading* error (the larger source of error) decreases system error by almost the full 50 yd. (Again using Equation 1-1, $100^2 + 250^2 = 269^2$, a difference of 47 yd.) Or, cutting the larger error in half (to 150) reduces system error to 180 yd, but cutting the smaller error in half only decreases system error to 304 yd.

In "go-no-go" situations, when errors are either all or none or are classified as tolerable

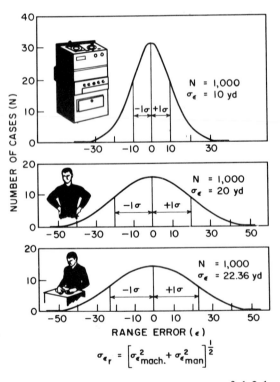

NUMBER OF CASES (N) (y-axis)
RANGE ERROR (ϵ) (x-axis)

N = 1,000
σ_ϵ = 10 yd

N = 1,000
σ_ϵ = 20 yd

N = 1,000
σ_ϵ = 22.36 yd

$$\sigma_{\epsilon_r} = \left[\sigma_{\epsilon mach.}^2 + \sigma_{\epsilon man}^2\right]^{\frac{1}{2}}$$

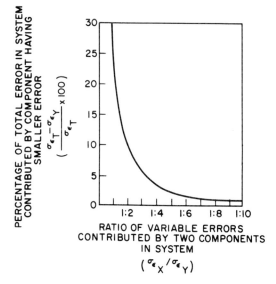

PERCENTAGE OF TOTAL ERROR IN SYSTEM CONTRIBUTED BY COMPONENT HAVING SMALLER ERROR $\left(\dfrac{\sigma_{e_T} - \sigma_{e_Y}}{\sigma_{e_T}} \times 100\right)$

RATIO OF VARIABLE ERRORS CONTRIBUTED BY TWO COMPONENTS IN SYSTEM $(\sigma_{e_X}/\sigma_{e_Y})$

1-20 Contribution of smaller of two sources of error to total man-machine-system error. Graph gives percentage of total error contributed by smaller of two errors for different ratios of two components when each error is expressed as standard deviation (Chapanis, 1951a)

or intolerable, the probabilities of error are compounded in a system by simple multiplication of probabilities of not making an error. In this case the formula is:

$$1 - P_{e_T} = (1 - P_{e_1})(1 - P_{e_2}), \qquad (1\text{-}2)$$

where P_{e_T} is the accumulated probability of error, P_{e_1} is the probability of error in one source (man or machine), and P_{e_2} is the probability of error in a second source. (The same formula can be expanded to represent several possible sources of error arranged in a series.)

1.3.2 *Man's sensory systems*

In many design applications, there is a tendency to overlook the fact that man is not limited to the two primary senses of vision and audition. In consequence, as complex systems have been developed that require increasing amounts of information about their functions, the eyes and ears have been given more and more to do until they are overloaded, in many cases. It often would be possible to lighten these loads by judicious use of other sensory channels. Much information can be conveyed to normal personnel by means of senses other than vision or audition with a minimum of training time.

By a direct comparison of the limits, the relative stimulus magnitudes that can be tolerated, and the sensitivity of the various senses, man can be put to better use in these increasingly complex systems. Table 1-4 presents a general survey of the senses, giving the sense organ, the kinds of physical energy that stimulate them, and the origin of the stimulation.

Any comparison of the sensory systems is handicapped, however, by the differences that exist between the end-organ receptors and the physical energies that they convey. Table 1-5 lists some of the ranges of values that are known for intensity of stimulation, and Table 1-6 shows examples of relative and absolute intensity discrimination. Some of the senses respond differentially to frequency changes as well as to intensity changes. Table 1-7 lists the frequency-detectability ranges for various sense stimulants and what is known about relative and absolute frequency discrimination.

CHANNEL CAPACITIES

Concepts derived from information theory have been applied to the eye and the ear to determine their basic channel capacities. It has been estimated that the ear is capable of transmitting 8,000 bit/sec, or 0.3 bit/sec per nerve fiber, whereas the eye is capable of transmitting at a rate about 430 times higher or about 5 bit/sec per nerve fiber. These numbers are of academic interest, however, and of little practical value. Depending on the method of encoding used, rates of about 2–25 bit/sec can be expected regardless of the sense channel employed (Mowbray and Gebhard, 1958). For a practical discussion of the operational uses of the eye and the ear, see Chapters 2, 3, and 4.

§ 1.3.2

Table 1-4 Survey of Man's Senses and the Physical Energies That Stimulate Them *

Sensation	Sense organ	Stimulation	Origin
Sight	Eye	Some electromagnetic waves	External
Hearing	Ear	Some amplitude and frequency variations of pressure in surrounding media	External
Rotation	Semicircular ear canals	Change of fluid pressures in inner ear	Internal
	Muscle receptors	Muscle stretching	Internal
Falling and rectilinear movement	Semicircular ear canals	Position changes of small, bony bodies in inner ear	Internal
Taste	Specialized cells in tongue and mouth	Chemical substances dissolvable in saliva	External on contact
Smell	Specialized cells in mucous membrane at top of nasal cavity	Vaporized chemical substances	External
Touch	Skin	Surface deformation	On contact
Pressure	Skin and underlying tissue	Surface deformation	On contact
Temperature	Skin and underlying tissue	Temperature changes of surrounding media or objects, friction, and some chemicals	External on contact
Pain	Unknown, but thought to be free nerve endings	Intense pressure, heat, cold, shock, and some chemicals	External on contact
Position and movement (kinesthesis)	Muscle nerve endings	Muscle stretching	Internal
	Tendon nerve endings	Muscle contraction	Internal
	Joints	Unknown	Internal
Mechanical vibration	No specific organ	Amplitude and frequency variations of pressure	External on contact

* Mowbray and Gebhard, 1961.

§ 1.3.2

Table 1-5 Comparison of the Stimulation-Intensity Ranges of the Senses *

Sensation	Range of stimulation intensity	
	Smallest detectable	Largest practical
Sight	$2.2-5.7 \times 10^{-10}$ ergs	$\sim 10^9 \times$ threshold intensity
Hearing	1×10^{-9} erg/cm^2	$\sim 10^{14} \times$ threshold intensity
Mechanical vibration	0.00025 mm average amplitude at fingertip	~ 40 db above threshold
Touch (pressure)	0.026 erg at ball of thumb	No data available
Smell	2×10^{-7} mg/m^3 of vanillin	No data available
Taste	4×10^{-7} molar concentration of quinine sulfate	No data available
Temperature	0.00015 gm-cal/cm^2/sec for 3-sec exposure of 200 cm^2 of skin	0.218 gm-cal/cm^2/sec for 3-sec exposure of 200 cm^2 of skin
Position and movement	0.2–0.7 deg at 10-deg/min for joint movements	No data available
Angular acceleration	0.12 deg/sec^2 for oculogyral illusion	Positive-g forces of 5–8g lasting 1 sec or more Negative-g forces of 3–4.5g
Linear acceleration	0.08g for deceleration	Same limitations as for angular acceleration for forces acting in direction of long axis of body

* Mowbray and Gebhard, 1961.

Table 1-6 Comparison of the Discrimination Abilities of Some of the Senses *

Sensation	Discrimination ability	
	Relative	Absolute
Sight	~ 570 discriminable intensity differences with white light	3–5 discriminable intensities in white light of 0.1–50 mL
Hearing	~ 325 discriminable intensity differences at 2,000 cps	$\sim 3-5$ discriminable intensities with pure tones
Mechanical vibration	15 discriminable amplitudes in chest region using broad contact vibrator with 0.05–0.5 mm amplitude limits	3–5 discriminable amplitudes

* Mowbray and Gebhard, 1961.

Table 1-7 Comparison of the Frequency-Detectability Range and Frequency-Discrimination Abilities of Some of the Senses *

Stimulant or sensation	Frequency-detectability range		Frequency-discrimination ability	
	Lowest	Highest	Relative	Absolute
Color (hue)	300 mμ	1,050 mμ at extremely high intensities	~128 discriminable hues at medium intensities	12 or 13 discriminable hues
Interrupted white light	One interruption	~50 interruptions/sec at moderate intensities and duty cycle of 0.5	375 discriminable interruption rates between 1–45 interruptions/sec at moderate intensities and duty cycle of 0.5	5 or 6 discriminable interruption rates
Pure tones	20 cps	20,000 cps	1,800 discriminable tone differences between 20 cps and 20,000 cps at 60 db loudness	4 or 5 discriminable tones
Interrupted white noise	One interruption	~2,000 interruptions/sec at moderate intensities and duty cycle of 0.5	460 discriminable interruption rates between 1–45 interruptions/sec at moderate intensities and duty cycle of 0.5	Unknown
Mechanical vibration	1 cps	10,000 cps at high intensities	180 discriminable frequency differences between 1 and 320 cps	Unknown

* Mowbray and Gebhard, 1961.

SIGNAL DETECTION

The detection of significant low-energy signals appearing against a background of random signals is a vital problem in many situations. For example, the typical search radar presents a polar-coordinate display of an immediate area, and superimposed on all land or sea returns are significant targets plus random returns that are both internal and external to the generating and receiving equipment. Although little systematic work has been done in comparing the ability of the eye and the ear to accomplish this particular task, in general, it appears easier to recognize a complex sound pattern against an altering sound background than it is to recognize an equivalent visual pattern against a visual background.

Work done in the use of combined visual and auditory inputs in sonar and radar indicates some improvement in detection. This relatively minor improvement, however, is a function of many parameters—such as time lag between the different inputs and compatibility of displays—and, under certain conditions, the combined visual and auditory inputs can lead to a serious reduction in detection.

TACTILE INPUTS

From Table 1-5, it can be seen that mechanical vibration of the skin shows a fairly wide range of sensitivity. In view of this, it is not surprising that the possibility of using this sense for communication has been explored (Geldard, 1960). In fact, a tactile-communication system was developed for laboratory exploration that used vibrators at different positions on the chest and modulated them in duration and amplitude of vibration. Five positions, three durations, and three amplitudes were used, and trained subjects were able to learn a tactile code for letters and numbers so that they could receive messages at the rate of about 38 words per minute (wpm). By way of comparison, Morse code can be received at a maximum of about 30 wpm (Geldard, 1957).

To test the feasibility of the system for communication under operational conditions, an additional study was made under simulated operational conditions (Slivinski, 1959). In this study, the subject was seated in a cockpit that was on a shake table and in a 110-db noise field. He was given a tracking task and a vigilance (watch-keeping) task (see Chapter 5) and was required to respond to messages coming in over headphones. His ability to respond to three-position, two-amplitude, three-duration tactile coding was measured, and, under conditions of vibration that would be expected in flight-deck operations (see Chapter 10), he responded with about 85% accuracy, although amplitude discrimination was lost at certain frequencies and amplitudes of the shake table. One of the conclusions from this study was that a simpler coding system, employing only position and duration, appears feasible.

The vibro-tactile sense has been put to another use, at least on an exploratory basis. It has been found to be possible to instrument an electro-mechanical tactile control system for use in aircraft (Ballard and Hessinger, 1954). In this system, tactile stimulators, placed on the thumb of the pilot, provide him with pitch and bank information. Although such a system would probably not be adequate for precise control over long periods of time, it could serve as an adjunct to more conventional systems.

SENSORY INTERACTION

For years an argument has continued about whether or not stimulation of one sense modality has any effect on the sensitivity of some other sense modality. The body of literature on this subject is vast and contradictory. There seems to be little doubt that cross-stimulation occurs, and, considering the numerous loci or converging sensory pathways in the nervous system, this fact should not be surprising. There seems to be as little doubt, however, that the effects of sensory cross-stimulation are so minute as to be of very little, if any, practical value at the present time.

Conflicting Inputs

Many tasks require attention to both visual and auditory flow of information at the same time. Generally, when a highly practiced motor skill is controlled by a sensory channel (hearing, for instance), the performance of that skill can be carried on adequately with simultaneous inputs to another sense channel. As an example one thinks of the experienced telegrapher who can receive or send messages, practically unhindered, while carrying on a conversation.

The problem differs, however, when conscious mental activity, rather than highly practiced motor skills, is involved. Evidence points to the fact that, when *different* information of a symbolic nature is being presented aurally and visually at the same time so that there is no chance of alternating the channels, then only one sensory input can be used at a time.

Visual and auditory conflict occurs also when one modality is being stimulated by meaningless inputs. For example, in visual tasks requiring continuous performance over long periods of time, the presence of an intense noise tends to increase the failures in attention to the task and cause general, overall deterioration of performance.

Improved Performance with Dual Inputs

Most studies have shown that comprehension of symbolic information is always improved when *identical* information is presented visually and aurally at the same time. For instance, studies have shown that the detection of sonar echoes is enhanced by the use of simultaneous visual and auditory displays, and research concerning simultaneous inputs in radar also demonstrates an enhancement of signal detection, especially in the case of heavy clutter or jamming.

MULTIPLE INPUTS

The senses are being bombarded constantly by multiple inputs. Usually, most of them are irrelevant to the task at hand and, unless consciously noted, are ignored. Of the two most important senses, vision and audition, vision is in the best position with respect to complex stimulation because *where* one looks and the objects *at which* one looks are under direct control. Many things might be, and usually are, going on in the peripheral field of vision without intruding upon the central task on which one is concentrating; to all intents and purposes they do not exist. On the other hand, if peripherally occuring events are important to the central task, they can be taken in quickly in successive fixations.

The auditory system is not so constituted and, because it is not, offers some special problems in the realm of multiple inputs. Because these problems have many important practical aspects, they have received considerable attention. Communication systems, for example, are susceptible to interference from overlapping messages, irrelevant atmospheric noise, and the like. These and other types of problems have been scrutinized from many angles, but multiple inputs to other sensory systems, by comparison, have been neglected.

1.3.3 Man's unique characteristics

Although some human abilities can be duplicated or surpassed by nonhuman devices, man has certain unique characteristics. These characteristics must be considered when designing devices and systems for human use.

LEARNING

Machines can store (remember) or record items of information fed into them, but human beings are far more capable than machines of changing their behavior (learning) on the basis of past experience. Man can learn in one or all of the following ways (see Fig. 1-21):

a. By practicing a skill over and over again until it becomes ingrained. (Example: learning to typewrite.)

b. By trial and error, in which the man attempts various solutions to a problem and adopts the one that succeeds. (Example: solving a difficult puzzle.)

c. By transfer of previous training. (Example: after a brief explanation, a person with training in radio can understand the principles of radar.)

The Transfer of Training

All learning, but particularly the learning of skills, is subject to the effects of transfer of training (effects of past learning on present learning). Equipment and tasks, therefore, should be designed to provide for as much positive transfer as possible and to avoid the possibility of negative transfer or habit interference.

When both the situation and the actions involved in present learning are similar to those of past learning, the rate of learning is accelerated. This effect is called positive transfer. For example, the use of a simulator, such as a Link Trainer, for training pilots assumes positive transfer; what the person learns in the trainer is supposed to carry over to the actual aircraft.

When the present situation is similar to that of past learning but the action required is different, and especially when it is the opposite of the actions required in past learning, the rate of learning is retarded. This effect is called negative transfer or habit interference. For example, in tracking down the causes of aircraft accidents some years ago, Air Force psychologists (Fitts and Jones, 1961) noted that a large number of accidents or near accidents occurred when pilots switched from one to another of the B-25, the C-47, and the C-82 aircraft. In particular, errors made by the pilots were often ones of operating the wrong control. The trouble, it turned out, was that different, but related, controls were ar-

THREE WAYS OF LEARNING

LEARNING A SKILL BY REPETITION

REACHING A SOLUTION THROUGH TRIAL AND ERROR

1-21

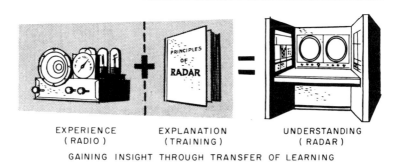

EXPERIENCE (RADIO)   EXPLANATION (TRAINING)   UNDERSTANDING (RADAR)

GAINING INSIGHT THROUGH TRANSFER OF LEARNING

ranged differently in these different aircraft, and, because of habit interference, pilots frequently operated controls in one aircraft as they had been accustomed to use them in other aircraft they had flown. Result: accidents, many of which would not have taken place if the controls in these different aircraft had been arranged similarly (see Fig. 1-11).

Learning Rate

The rate at which man learns is another factor to be considered in the design of equipment and systems. This rate is mainly dependent on three factors: simplicity, understanding, and feedback of results.

The simpler the task or problematical situation, generally speaking, the more rapid the learning, and the less training time required. The more a person is able to understand or acquire insight into a situation, rather than depend on repetitive practice or trial and error, the more rapidly he can learn. The more a person gets feedback of results (the more information he has and the quicker he gets it) about whether he is correct or incorrect, the faster he learns and the less likely he is to acquire bad habits. For example, to improve at gunnery, a person must be able to know whether each shot or burst of shots hits the target (see Fig. 1-22). If he has no feedback of information on how well he is hitting the target, he learns little or nothing and might even acquire habits that make him a poorer marksman.

MOTIVATION

Everything that has been said about man's capabilities assumes that he is motivated to perform as effectively as possible. Several factors can reduce human motivation, however,

§ 1.3.3

1-22

and thus indirectly impair human performance. Among these are fatigue and boredom and anxiety.

Fatigue and Boredom

Man gets fatigued or bored if he must do the same thing for a long time, and his performance deteriorates accordingly. The principal effect of fatigue and boredom is to reduce motivation—*willingness* to do one's best. Except where extreme exertion is involved, fatigue ordinarily does not impair the *ability* to perform. For example, men who have gone without sleep for days are able to do as well, when properly motivated, as they usually would do in a wide variety of physical and intellectual tasks when they are not fatigued. Ordinarily, however, lack of sleep greatly impairs performance because it lowers motivation (see Fig. 1-23).

With fatigue or boredom, a person's attention wanders, and the likelihood of making mistakes or having serious accidents increases. For example, radar operators on long watches will take their eyes off the screen and, as a result, the likelihood of their missing targets is increased. Also, people become more careless when tired and take chances they would not take when rested.

Some of the important conditions contributing to fatigue and boredom are as follows:

a. Periods of duty that are too long. The optimum cycle of work and rest depends on the kind of work, but, for tasks involving careful attention without much physical exertion, cycles of 40 or 50 min of work alternated with 8 or 10 min of rest are best. In general, total work periods should not be longer than 4 hr with 1 hr of rest.

b. Repetitive tasks. Simple tasks that must be done over and over again are boring. Where possible, provision should be made for some variation in the tasks to be performed.

c. Cramped and unchangeable positions. People become fatigued and bored when they must work in the same position for a long period. When possible, provision should be made for the person to sit or stand at his own option (see Chapter 7) or, in lieu of that, to shift into a variety of positions.

Anxiety

Men become anxious and upset under the following circumstances:

a. When they lose control of their own safety. They distrust automatic devices on which their lives, or sometimes simply their performance, depend. Therefore, where possible, operators ought to be provided with the opportunity to override automatic devices—unless the operator is thereby very likely to endanger the safety of himself and his equipment.

b. When they are deprived of adequate information about what is going on about them. Men want to see and hear as much as they can of the things that concern them. Consequently, even if it is not otherwise necessary, a man should be provided with all information relevant to his job. For example, submariners, who must spend many days submerged and are completely out of contact with the normal world, tend to be demoralized

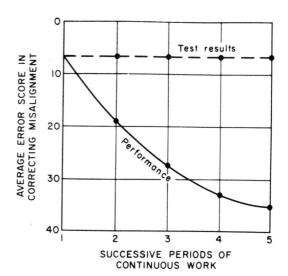

1-23 Difference between performance and capacity. In many kinds of human activity, performance deteriorates as work is continued even though it can be shown with tests that there has been no change in capacity. Difference is attributable to high motivation in tests but lowered motivation in actual work situations (Chapanis, et al., 1949)

§ 1.3.3

unless some of the conditions of normal existence are maintained. For this reason, it is necessary to create a schedule of activities and an environment simulating the normal world, e.g., a day-night cycle of lighting, news broadcast, evening entertainment, etc.

c. When they distrust or dislike their fellow crew members. Some groups, made up of individually competent members, have performed very badly as teams in communication centers, primarily because of personal dislikes and disgruntlement with other members of the team.

1.3.4 *Man as a system component*

A man-machine system is any system in which men and machines interact in performing a function. A man driving an automobile is a good example of this. The man reacts to inputs from the speedometer and other displays, inputs from the road and outside environment, noise from the engine, feedback to his muscles from the steering wheel, and other stimuli. From these inputs he makes decisions to perform certain control movements. These movements affect the machine, which in turn furnishes new and different inputs to the driver.

We consider such a man-machine interaction as a closed-loop system because it calls for continuous interaction between the man and machine (see Chapter 5). An open-loop system is one in which the interaction between man and machine is intermittent rather than continuous. For example, a communications system in which the talker gets no feedback as to whether the message has been received would be considered an open-loop system.

Human engineers have, for some time now, looked upon the man and the machine he operates as interacting components of the overall system. Figure 1-24 illustrates this concept. Thus, a man-machine system can be viewed as a pilot/aircraft control system, a diving-officer/submarine control system, a driver/armored-vehicle control system, etc.

In effect, this concept envisions the human operator as an organic sensor, data-processor, and controller component inserted between the displays and controls of a machine. An input of some kind is transformed by the machine into a signal, which appears on a display. The information so displayed is read by the operator, is processed mentally, and is transformed into control responses. The control signal, after transformation by the machine, becomes the systems output.

When the man and machine are considered in this fashion, it immediately becomes obvious that, to design the machine component properly, the capabilities and limitations of the man and his role in the system must be taken into full account. Such consideration of man's abilities is the only way of achieving insight into the best ways in which he can be used as a component.

1.3.5 *Man vs. machine*

Men and machines have different capabilities and limitations. Although they sometimes can do the same thing equally well, more often one is better than the other. Men can do some things much better than machines can, and machines can do things men cannot. Such differences in capability must be considered in detail when designing systems—they are important in deciding which jobs to assign to men and which to assign to machines. Differences in capability also often determine how a machine should be designed to be used most effectively by a human operator.

The statements made in this article are based on the known capabilities of machines, and thus are applicable to machines likely to be encountered in the next five to ten years. It is possible that, over a longer period of time, machines with more "human" capabilities will be perfected. Also, following the custom of laboratory workers who have obtained the measurements, the values of human sensitivity stated in this article are for a 50% probability of correct response. (As a rule of thumb, doubling the value giving 50% probability of success usually yields 99–100% success.)

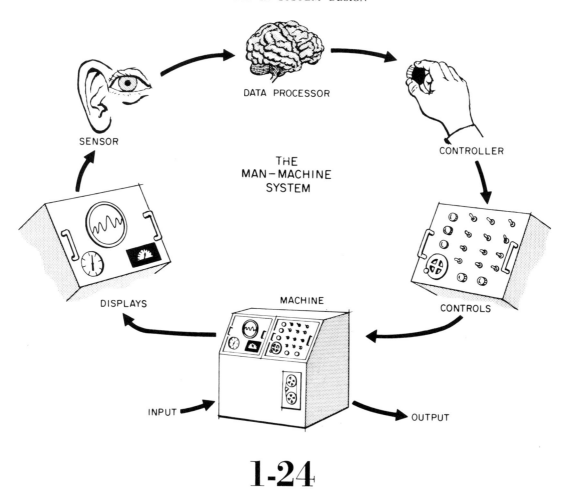

DATA PROCESSOR

SENSOR

CONTROLLER

THE
MAN—MACHINE
SYSTEM

DISPLAYS

MACHINE

CONTROLS

INPUT

OUTPUT

1-24

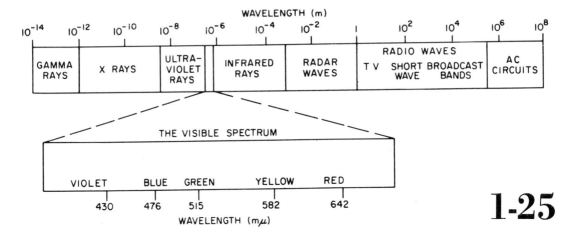

1-25

AS SENSORS

Human sensing is restricted to a relatively narrow range of physical energies. Man's visual sensing is limited roughly to the wavelengths between 300 and 1,050 mμ—an extremely small portion of the electromagnetic spectrum (see Fig. 1-25)—and his auditory sensing is limited roughly to the frequencies between 20 and 20,000 cps (in many people, the upper limit might be under 10,000 cps). But human sensitivity—in the sense of the minimum energy that man can detect—compares favorably with the sensitivity of machines. This can be seen from the following facts:

a. A man can detect the light of a match 50 mi away on a clear night—energy as little as 2–6 × 10^{-10} ergs (10^{-10} Lamberts).

b. He can detect a sound so weak that it is barely above the level of molecular noise of air—energy as little as 1 × 10^{-9} ergs/cm^2 (0.0002 dyne/cm^2).

c. A man's sensitivity to odors varies enormously with the chemical composition of the odor, but he can detect as little as 2 × 10^{-7} mg/m^3.

Human discrimination—the ability to detect differences in the intensity or quality of stimulation—also compares favorably with that of machines. Under ideal conditions, man can visually detect the following:

a. Differences in wavelength of 1 mμ (10 Å).

b. Differences in intensity of 1%.

c. Forms as small as 0.5 sec of arc.
And, under ideal conditions, man can audibly detect differences in frequency of 0.5% and differences in intensity of 7% (0.33 db).

In general, human discrimination becomes relatively better the higher the intensity of stimulation. But, because many instruments discriminate better at low or medium intensities, it is often necessary to design and operate equipments at levels that strike a compromise (and an optimum) between man and machine characteristics. For example, human discrimination of brightnesses, like those presented by PPI targets (see Chapter 2), is best at relatively high brightnesses, but the physical contrast of targets with their background is better at lower screen brightnesses. As a result, the best screen brightness is one that strikes an optimum compromise between the characteristics of the cathode-ray tube and those of the human eye.

Human beings are usually superior to machines in perceiving and interpreting sensory information, as is indicated by the following:

a. Human beings are good for tasks requiring discrimination of signals in noise (French, 1954). As examples, a radar operator can distinguish real echoes or targets in clutter, and an experienced radio operator can usually make sense out of words being heard through high-background static.

b. Man can identify similar patterns in different situations. This ability, which many

§ 1.3.5

situations require, is uniquely human. For example, man can be trained to recognize aircraft silhouettes when the aircraft are at different distances and in different positions (see Fig. 1-26).

c. Man can get information out of incomplete or sparse signals. For example: the telegram, "C-m- at ---- F-th-r dy-ng," can be interpreted easily by a man but not by a machine. (This ability to interpret partial information also has its drawbacks. Because of it, man often interprets incorrectly.)

d. Man is selective in his perceptions; he can shut out certain signals and respond to others. As examples, a teletype operator can respond to the clacking of the machine but ignore other noises in his environment, and an air traffic controller can listen to the radio channel that concerns him while ignoring messages coming in over other channels.

AS DATA PROCESSORS

Man has certain advantages and disadvantages as compared with computers. His access time (speed of recall) is slow compared to that of a computer, but he is able to recall generalized patterns of previous experience to solve immediate problems. As yet, no computer can do this. Man learns to do numerical computations, but in the main his time constants are such that he is a relatively poor numerical computer—especially under stress. He is, however, the only available computer that can solve problems by logical induction.

In general, man is superior to data-processing devices in the following respects:

a. For most tasks, he does not need extensive preprograming. Through further learning, he constantly develops and modifies his own programs. His previous education has already "programed" him.

b. He is more flexible; he can deal with unforeseen situations.

c. He can exercise judgment because he can selectively recall relevant facts and methods of solving problems.

d. He does not require special coding of messages; the information does not have to be transformed into digital form. He does, how-

1-26

ever, perform better when information is presented in certain forms than when it is presented in others.

On the other hand, data-processing devices are superior, in general, to human beings in the following respects:

a. They can store much more data accurately. A computer can store thousands of items of information that no human being could possibly remember.

b. They can compute answers with much greater speed and accuracy. A computer can do accurately, in a few seconds, computations that would otherwise require many man-months.

c. They can sort and screen data faster, rejecting all data that are not in a desired class and leaving the final judgment among the remaining alternatives to a human operator.

d. They are usually more reliable for routine decisions—decisions that are always made in the same way according to some rule.

e. They are less subject to fatigue, prejudice, and other transitory factors that distort man's judgments and decisions.

AS CONTROLLERS

In this role, man also has his capabilities and his limitations. He can push buttons and pedals, turn knobs, throw switches, and operate various other kinds of controls, provided such controls do not impose tasks that exceed his capabilities. Some of these can be listed as follows:

a. The forces that human operators can exert are limited (see Chapter 11).

b. Human operators are relatively slow in moving controls, as compared with machines. Also, compared with machines, human movements involve considerable time delay between the time the decision is made to move the control and the time the movement is initiated (see Chapter 5). Thus, when controls should be operated with little delay and with great speed, machines are superior to human beings.

c. Man is also limited in the kinds of movement he can make. He can reach in some directions and not in others, and he can reach

or extend his limbs only for limited distances (see Chapter 11).

d. The precision with which man can apply a given force to a control is also limited. If asked to maintain a certain pressure on a control, the actual pressure will oscillate around the desired pressure and will approximate the desired pressure with some average (or constant) error.

e. The time during which man can apply a force is limited.

f. Man, as a controller, is easily overloaded.

WORKING ENVIRONMENTS

Machines can be designed to operate within wide environmental extremes, but man requires a much more uniform environment to work at his best—indeed, to work at all. In general, human performance falls off when the oxygen pressure corresponds to an altitude of more than 12,000 ft. Human performance also deteriorates and men feel uncomfortable when the carbon-dioxide content of the air exceeds 1.5%. (This topic is treated in detail in Chapter 10.)

CONCLUSIONS

It should be stressed that man and machine need not be competitors, but, rather, the best design will use both the man and the machine to complement each other. With this in mind, the following conclusions seem warranted:

1. Use machines for routine tasks involving calculations and storage of large numbers of concrete facts or details.

2. Use machines when large forces need to be applied quickly and smoothly.

3. Use machines when large amounts of data need to be sorted and screened and all data not in a desired class rejected.

4. Use machines for making routine decisions, i.e., decisions that are always made in the same way according to specifiable rules.

5. Use machines where anticipated stresses have a high probability of producing failure in human performance.

6. Use machines where controls should be operated with very little delay and with great speed.

7. Use machines if the force to be applied to a control requires precision or where the force must be applied over a long period of time.

8. Use man for tasks requiring the discrimination of signals in noise.

9. Use man where the task requires pattern discrimination in a changing field.

10. Use man where discrimination must be made between multiple inputs.

11. Use man where his flexibility will be required in unforeseen situations.

12. Use man for tasks requiring problem solving.

13. Use man as a monitor, with override capabilities, in automatic and semiautomatic systems.

14. Use man where the sensing and reporting of incidental intelligence is expected in the course of a mission having other objectives.

15. Use man where alternate modes of operation are likely to be required.

1.3.6 *The synthesis of man and machine*

In addition to the human factors described thus far, there are some further principles to be followed in integrating human beings into man-machine systems. These are especially applicable to systems in which machines are largely automatic.

VERIFICATION BY DUPLICATION

Even when machines have been well designed for human use, operators make mistakes, usually on the order of 1–2%, depending on the task. To reduce such errors to negligible proportions the designer should do the following:

1. Arrange operators in parallel so as to have two operator-verifier teams in which members of each team perform identical operations but on different consoles.

2. Design special equipment to compare the output of the two teams and to accept for processing only those items that agree exactly.

3. Arrange the system so that all discrepancies are rejected and reprocessed by the operators until the results agree exactly.

These principles have been used in the RCA Bizmac electronic accounting system, which is said to be the largest commercial data-processing system so far constructed. By means of this system, illustrated in Fig. 1-27, errors have been reduced to a few parts per *billion*.

MACHINES TO MONITOR MEN

Where possible, equipment should be designed to stop, or to give a warning, whenever operators make mistakes. The following are some examples of such designs:

a. The "dead-man" switch on a railway locomotive automatically brings the train to a halt whenever the engineer, for any reason, takes his foot off of it, thereby indicating that he is no longer in control of the locomotive.

b. In a master distribution system for a television network, an operator at a control console is supposed to switch connections without error and at precisely the correct times. The task of the operator is to connect incoming programs (black buttons) with the proper outgoing lines (white buttons). To eliminate the possibility that two incoming programs might be switched to a single outgoing line, the console is so wired that, if two black buttons are depressed at the same time as a white one, no switching can occur, and the operator is warned, by a signal, that an error has been made (Collins and Hofmann, 1957).

MEN TO MONITOR MACHINES

Although many machines are made completely automatic, men often should be used to override the machine to meet emergencies

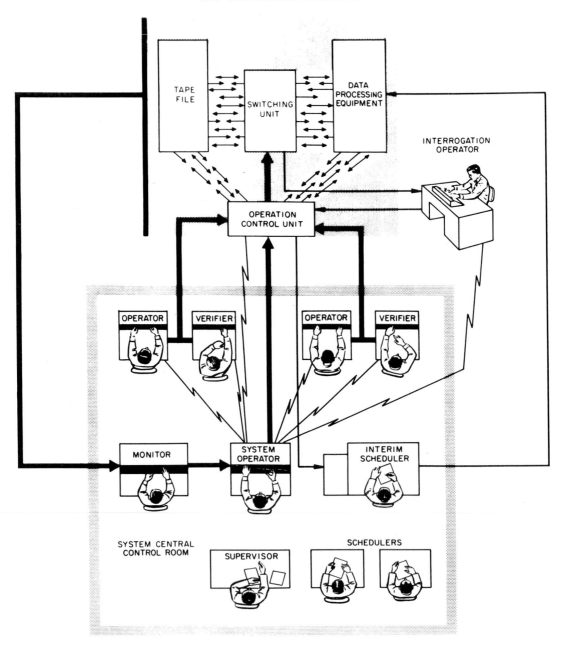

1-27 Bizmac system of verification. Diagram shows chain of command from central station in Bizmac system. Operation-control unit only accepts data from operator that agree with data from verifier (Owings, 1956)

or situations requiring judgments for which the machine has not been programed. For example, the decision was made to include a pilot in a new, and virtually automatic, interceptor aircraft. Although most aspects of the typical mission could be handled automatically, or from the ground, it was felt that a human pilot—riding as a passenger most of the time—could exercise judgment in selecting modes of operation for automatic elements in the system. Also, in the event of a failure or other emergency, the man could override the automatic controls (Seamans and Pickford, 1956).

MEN FOR FAULT LOCATION

Machines, no matter how reliable, break down, and men are required to find, and do something about, the cause of breakdown or malfunction. To assist men in doing this, equipment should be designed, whenever possible, so that human beings can interrogate it and determine the fault in it. For example, long-distance transmission of TV programs is accomplished by a system of 107 microwave relay towers spanning the United States. The major role of men in this system is to monitor and maintain the outputs of the relay towers. Because many of the towers are located in remote and inaccessible areas, and because breakdowns occur too infrequently to justify crews at each site, automatic trouble-indication equipment has been designed to enable engineers to interrogate remote towers and to diagnose breakdowns before dispatching repairmen. (See Chapter 9 for a detailed discussion of automatic trouble-indication equipment.)

1.4 System Evaluation and Testing

The data and recommendations given in the following chapters of this Guide should help engineers design man-machine systems that take into account the human factor. In some cases, however, the human-engineering information the designer needs might not be available, and he will have to conduct his own studies or tests to obtain it. In any case, there comes a time in the development of every system when it somehow must be evaluated to determine whether it will meet the requirements laid down for it or whether it will perform better than some other system. Hence, the designer should know how to conduct tests and evaluations of man-machine systems.

Evaluating man-machine systems differs from evaluating systems not involving men. The chief difference is that human beings, unlike machines, vary widely from one to another and from one time to another. This human variability requires precautions and procedures that are not required in ordinary engineering evaluation and testing. This section presents, briefly, the factors to consider in conducting man-machine evaluation and testing (see also Chapanis, 1959).

For convenience, the term "system" will be used throughout this section to refer to any man-machine system, large or small. Such a system might consist of one man and one machine or of many men and many machines that make up an operational system such as a bomber or a submarine. In practice, however, any evaluation that stresses the human factor is best done on relatively small systems or subsystems.

1.4.1 *General methods of evaluation*

There are three basic methods of evaluating a system: by theory and "paper" analysis, by simulating the system, or by "testing" the system in actual operation (see Fig. 1-28). Very frequently, it is necessary to combine certain features of all three methods, that is, to evaluate part of a system operationally, part by simulation, and part by theoretical analysis. Sometimes it is necessary to compare two or more systems by different methods: one by operational testing, one by simulation, and one by theory. We are in fact doing this, at least crudely, when we set out to develop a new system that is expected to be better than one we already have.

THEORY AND "PAPER" ANALYSIS

This form of evaluation ordinarily is performed in the early stages of the design and development process. Knowing, or at least assuming, the characteristics of individual equipments and operators, the evaluator works out on paper the probable performance of the system. The methods employed in this kind of evaluation are largely those described in section 1.2. In addition, more rigorous mathematical models and methods are some-

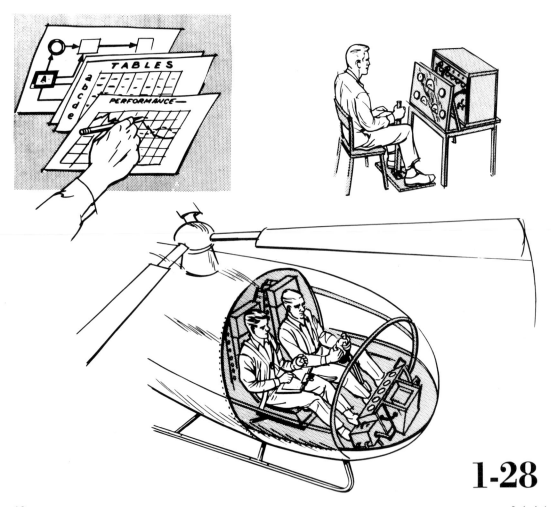

1-28

§ 1.4.1

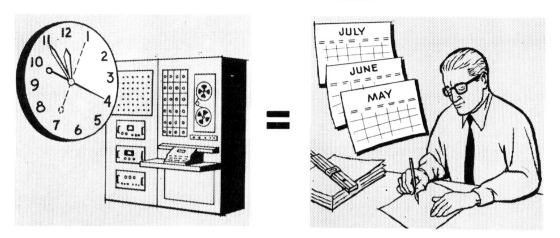

times useful in solving specific problems arising in such an evaluation. Because these are not uniquely concerned with the human factor, however, they will not be considered here.

SYSTEM SIMULATION

Before a system is completely designed, it can be evaluated by simulation. The simulation of a system can be performed either by a computer-type simulator, by a mockup, or by a combination of the two.

Computer Simulation

In computer-type simulation, a computer stores various transfer functions or anticipated response characteristics of various components and of their interactions with each other (see Chapter 5). The computer is then given data to determine what the expected output of the system would be with various inputs. This kind of simulation is akin to the theoretical analysis mentioned above, but it has the advantage of being more precise, more rapid (see Fig. 1-29), and sometimes less expensive than other methods of analysis.

Mockup Simulation

In a mockup, operators are given the equipments (or facsimiles thereof) that they would

have in operational use. Then, with the aid of some artificial inputs, they are asked to operate the system as they would under operational conditions.

Mockup simulation might appear to be a relatively simple and inexpensive way of doing an evaluation. If the system is not too complicated, it is. For complex man-machine systems, however, the time required to build an adequate mockup is often so long as to make this method unfeasible. Mockup simulation is best used when a whole family of related systems is to be evaluated.

OPERATIONAL TESTING

A third possible way of evaluating a system is to test it when it is sufficiently developed to be capable of operational use. As far as the human factor is concerned, however, this differs little from mockup simulation. The principal difference is that the evaluator of a system in operation usually does not have as much control over the various conditions of testing as he does when using a mockup.

1.4.2 *Planning the evaluation*

System evaluations must be planned with great care, for they involve so many possible sources of error that they can easily yield misleading results. For reasonably complex systems, the time and effort invested in planning the evaluation is by far the larger part of the cost of the evaluation. This article briefly considers some of the things that must be provided for in the planning stage. Later articles go into these in detail.

REPRESENTATIVE CONDITIONS

The evaluator should arrange the conditions of evaluation to represent fairly the conditions to be encountered by the system in actual use. In doing so, he should observe the following:

1. Require the system to carry out those missions, and only those missions, for which the system is intended or to which the system is likely to be assigned.

2. Make certain that the operator-subjects used in the evaluation represent those who will be operating the equipment in actual use, particularly with respect to such characteristics as age, general ability, experience, and training.

3. See to it that the tasks given to the operator-subjects are a fair sample of those to be performed when the system is in actual use.

4. Make the physical and environmental conditions duplicate those to be found in the future use of the system (see Chapter 10).

5. Motivate the operator-subjects to the same extent they are likely to be motivated in the future use of the system (see article 1.3.3).

COMPARATIVE EVALUATION

Even when every precaution is taken to use representative subjects and conditions for evaluation, it is seldom possible to duplicate, exactly, conditions in the field. This difficulty can be overcome, at least partially, by making evaluations comparative and relative. In general, if two systems are compared under similar conditions and one is found to be better than the other, this difference is likely to hold up in operational use even if operational conditions are not exactly duplicated in the evaluation.

The designer's choice for comparison usually is between two or more different systems, or between similar systems employing slightly different components or arrangements. Because his choice is relative, he should compare as directly as possible the systems under consideration, i.e., the two or more systems should be compared at the same time under comparable conditions, because it is difficult to duplicate subjects and conditions for evaluations conducted at different times. One exception to this principle, however, is that relatively simple systems with highly specific missions sometimes might be evaluated on a "yes" or "no" basis. In this case, the evaluation simply is to determine whether the system is capable of meeting the requirements of its intended mission.

COUNTERBALANCED DESIGN

Both machines and men, but particularly men, are likely to vary in their performance over a period of time. To minimize the influence of this variability on the outcome of an evaluation, that is, to prevent it from unfairly biasing the results, the conditions of testing should be counterbalanced in every way that might possibly bias the results. To do so, the evaluator should observe the following:

1. If possible, make a comparison of systems at exactly the same time. If this is not possible, then switch back and forth between systems in a predetermined counterbalanced order. In planning a counterbalanced order, avoid simple alternation because this might introduce a bias. Instead use an "ABBA" order, where "A" is one system and "B" is another.

2. Where possible, use the same men and the same machines in the evaluation of different systems. This minimizes the possibility that differences in outcome can be attributed to irrelevant differences among people and equipment. If systems are simultaneously compared, or if for some reason more than one crew is required, evaluations should be repeated, switching crew "A" to system "B."

3. Some systems, of course, are different because they are made up of different equipments that impose different tasks on operators. In this case, beware of habit interference (see article 1.3.3), which might be involved whenever two equipments or tasks require different habits or skills. If habit interference might be a factor, then it is better not to switch operators. Instead, operators of comparable skill in their respective tasks should be selected and kept on their respective equipments.

4. Counterbalance other factors and conditions that might affect performance. If, for example, different tasks varying in difficulty are performed, these should be counterbalanced for difficulty.

5. Where several factors are involved in an experiment, the statistical methods required to evaluate differences in performance due to these factors are rather complex and are likely to go beyond the statistical training of the engineer. In that case, the engineer should consult an experimental or statistical psychologist for advice. In any case, the statistical methods to be used in analyzing test data should be planned *in advance,* and the test should be designed so that the intended methods can be properly used. Otherwise, measurements might be so confounded that they cannot be analyzed properly by any statistical methods.

6. Because minor changes in design made between prototype and production models of equipment might seriously affect performance, production equipment rather than prototype equipment should be used in evaluations if possible. When prototypes are used for testing, repeat the evaluation when production equipment becomes available.

SYSTEM VS. SUBSYSTEM

In choosing measures of performance, a judicious balance must be struck between system performance and component or subsystem performance. In general, the evaluator should attempt to obtain critical measurements of overall system performance because it is risky to predict overall performance from the performance of components. Moreover, it can be quite wasteful to make a lot of measurements on component subsystems.

There are, on the other hand, cases in which measurements should be made on certain subsystems. Such measurements should be made, for example, where new or unusual components in the system might be crucial in system performance. It also is desirable to have a simple check on whether a subsystem is performing properly; otherwise, the performance of one man or machine might unduly influence an evaluation, yet go undetected. Measurements should be made also on those components that might be rearranged to revise or improve the system. In this way, the evaluator can learn how to maximize system performance.

1.4.3 *Selecting subjects*

The evaluation should employ subjects that are representative of those that will operate the system in the field. Representative subjects are those that are of the same general age, ability, and training and have the same experience with the equipment in the test as those that are expected to use the equipment after it has been in operational use for some time. Subjects that have been especially selected or have had unusually long experience (e.g., test pilots), are not representative—neither are designers of the equipment (see below). It is especially important to use representative subjects when a system contains new or radically different design features that might be less preferred by "old hands" or offer habit interference to such personnel.

UNREPRESENTATIVE SUBJECTS

The subjects used in tests can be unrepresentative in a number of ways—different sex or age, lack of training, "rustiness" at the tasks, motivated too much or too little—but there are two kinds of subjects commonly used that frequently distort seriously the results of an evaluation. These are subjects that are either biased or too experienced (expert).

Biased Subjects

Biased subjects are those that have some stake in the outcome of the evaluation. They include design engineers (even those who might have had nothing to do with the design of the particular equipment), office personnel, supervisors, and others concerned with the system. Such people usually are not typical, in training, experience, or other characteristics, of those who will operate the system.

Even if they were representative in such characteristics, they must be disqualified because of their "ego involvement" in the outcome. A person who wants one system to be better than another, or expects it to be, is prejudiced. No matter how much he tries to be fair, his prejudices influence his performance.

Also, those connected with the design of a system know too much about it. They probably know and understand it better than all but a few of the best trained operational personnel. As a result, they know how to compensate for its weaknesses and how to make it show up better than it actually will under field conditions.

Expert Subjects

Expert personnel are those who have had considerable experience with similar systems and equipment. Naturally, to obtain representative subjects, one needs subjects with a normal amount of experience, but there are two main reasons why unusually experienced personnel make bad subjects. These are as follows:

a. They tend to prefer the familiar and to distrust the new and different. Consequently, they might not give new equipments an unbiased evaluation or performance. This is especially the case where the operator is anxious about his own safety or about his ability to do his job well.

b. They usually suffer from habit interference. They have developed one set of habits with conventional systems, and these habits actually make it more difficult for them to use a new system effectively.

Sometimes it is necessary to use highly specialized, expert personnel. This is the case when a system is being developed on a "crash" basis as a stop-gap and there is no time to train new personnel. Or sometimes such personnel are required in acceptability testing to determine nonhuman performance factors. When it seems necessary or proper to use such personnel, it is also desirable, if possible, to run additional tests with more typical personnel, especially when there is any likelihood that the system, if adopted, will be in use long enough to be operated by newly trained personnel.

THE NUMBER OF SUBJECTS

Once representative subjects have been selected, an evaluation should employ a sufficiently large number of subjects to guard against random or sampling errors of selection —it takes more than one subject to be representative. From a statistical point of view, a sample of 30 or 40 people selected from a large population usually gives results that approximate the population. Although 30 or 40 subjects is an ideal sample size, in practice, however, that many subjects might not be available, or not enough equipments might be available to make use of that many, or that many subjects would generate more data than could be processed and evaluated, so a smaller number is very frequently all that can be employed.

In any event, the following should be observed:

1. With any number of subjects, but especially when it is possible to use only five or ten, care should be taken to insure that the group is neither all "average" nor all extremely good (or bad) but includes the range from poor to good (of the potential users of the equipment).

2. Where subjects are used in groups or teams, use several groups or combinations of groups (for example, eight groups of four, six groups of six, ten groups of three). The

1-30

MEN OFTEN WORK BETTER
WITH SOME MEN THAN WITH
OTHERS, ALTHOUGH THEY
MAY BE ALL EQUALLY
COMPETENT

same personnel sometimes perform quite differently when teamed with different groups of personnel (see Fig. 1-30).

3. Where possible, select subjects on the basis of tests or records known to be relevant to a particular task. For example, grades on an aptitude test, number of years of education, grades in special technical schools, or years of experience might be compiled on a large group of potential subjects. Out of these, a small group might be selected whose scores approximate the distributions of the larger group.

1.4.4 Realism in evaluations

A test or evaluation yields a prediction about the future performance of a system in operational use. The prediction will be good or bad in proportion to how well it simulates critical operational conditions. It follows that evaluations should be realistic in those respects that are critical.

How far to go with this realism is a matter of judgment and knowledge about the critical

factors in performance. If one knows well what these are, it is easy to decide what to make realistic and what to neglect. If the evaluator doesn't know, then he should "play it safe" and make a test realistic in all those ways he suspects might have something to do with performance.

There are three general ways in which it is particularly important to make evaluations realistic: in the level of training of subjects, in the choice of tasks used in the evaluation, and in the psychological conditions prevailing during the test.

THE TRAINING OF SUBJECTS

The following general rules for the training of subjects should be observed:

1. Give subjects adequate instruction in the tasks to be performed.

2. Provide an objective measure of training by scoring and recording their performance.

3. Continue training until further improvement is negligible, that is, until subjects have reached a plateau of performance on each system being compared.

4. When two systems are being compared, make certain that the personnel operating the

two systems have had comparable training in handling their respective tasks.

5. When two systems must be compared successively, rather than simultaneously, counterbalance the order of evaluation to equate training of subjects and improvement in the use of the systems.

6. If the same personnel are used in comparing two systems, avoid tasks that set up habit interference. Do not switch a man back and forth between equipments and tasks that require him to do similar things in different ways. For example, if controls or displays are mounted on the left in one system and on the right in the other, if controls must be pulled out in one system and pushed in in the other,

or if the several components of the system are arranged one way in one system and a different way in another system (see Fig. 1-31), select operators of comparable skill and experience in their respective tasks and keep them on their respective equipments.

THE NATURE OF THE TASKS

The evaluator should make the tasks to be carried out by subjects comparable in speed, number, and difficulty to those with which the system must cope in the future. To fulfill this requirement, the evaluator should do the following:

1-31

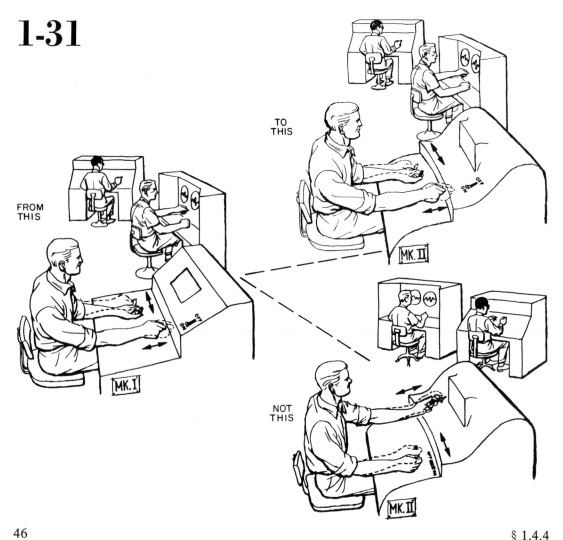

1-32

1. Require operators to work at realistic speeds. Demonstrations that permit operators to work at their own pace can make one system appear to be more accurate and to work more smoothly than it actually will work.

2. Give operators the same amount and kind of work to do that they will have in operational situations. Systems that perform very nicely at light or moderate loads can "break down" when higher loads are imposed.

3. Make other aspects of task difficulty realistic; the problems should not be too easy, nor should they be problems to which the operators already "know the answers."

4. Require operator-subjects to observe all the rules of realistic operation; even if some of these "rules" are not directly pertinent to the evaluation, they are necessary to duplicate the effects of the task on the performance of the system.

REALISTIC CONDITIONS

The conditions relevant to performance, as well as the training of subjects and the tasks given them, also should be realistic. What is relevant? The advice of persons familiar with operational conditions should be sought for a judgment. Their advice, however, should be taken "with a grain of salt." Such operational "experts" are seldom good scientists; they frequently advise that such realistic, but irrelevant, details be duplicated that good evaluation becomes impossible. They simply are not good at untangling critical from realistic variables. Somehow, out of the suggestions of operational personnel, design engineers, test engineers, and human-factors personnel, a decision should be made about the relevant realism to duplicate in the evaluation.

Some kinds of realism obviously are not relevant or critical to the performance of a system. For example, in air-traffic-control centers, there is usually a pot of coffee brewing while personnel are doing their assigned jobs. The pot of coffee, however, is not necessary for an evaluation of the system. In a realistic simulation of a submarine control room, on the other hand, the ship's motion must be simulated, and this obviously complicates the simulation (see Fig. 1-32).

§ 1.4.4

Motivation

Means should be devised for motivating operators in realistic fashion. If they feel they are just doing "exercises," they are likely to perform considerably below "par." On the other hand, very intense motivation, such as might be found in battle or in an emergency, often causes performance to deteriorate. If the system is likely to be used in such situations, this kind of motivation should somehow be duplicated, although it takes considerable ingenuity to accomplish it.

One, often essential, way of obtaining realistic motivation is to provide quick and correct knowledge of results to the operators. They should have the same kind of feedback, knowing that their performance is being scored, from their activities as they would have in operational situations. Sometimes it is necessary to build special devices in the simulated situation to provide this feedback.

Environment

The evaluator should reproduce environmental conditions that are likely to be important in performance (see Chapter 10). If extreme conditions of heat, cold, humidity, cramping of the body, long and fatiguing watches, etc., are to be encountered in operational use, these should be included in the conditions of the systems evaluation.

As a general word of caution, it should be stated that because things "look" realistic does not necessarily mean that they really are. More important than what they "look" like is whether they produce, for the operators, the same tasks, stresses, motivation, and knowledge of results that they will be subjected to under operating conditions.

1.4.5 *Measures of performance*

Perhaps the most basic problem in any evaluation of a system is the criterion problem. This is the problem of what to measure, and this is a matter of choosing critical parameters upon which the performance of the system will depend and then testing these, if at all possible. The evaluator is not interested in testing any and all performances that can be observed because, in many cases, these turn out to be trivial for purposes of system design and evaluation. There is no "pat" answer to the criterion problem; the designer and potential user must judge what aspects of performance are most likely to be critical in operational use.

OBJECTIVE MEASUREMENT

Objective measurements—measurements in which performances are recorded in quantitative terms—are strongly preferred to subjective opinions, comments, and ratings for the following reasons:

a. Opinions of observers are influenced by their own habits, experiences, and preferences. They might react unfavorably to some feature of a new system that once was found unsatisfactory even though it might be perfectly satisfactory or an improvement in a new and different system.

b. Observers who have had a great deal of operational experience tend to prefer the familiar rather than new things. This conservatism biases their evaluations of a system. There is, of course, a place for "user preference," but only after one has determined as objectively as possible the virtues of a system and found that one system is about as good as another.

c. In some situations, the ratings of observers are colored by what they think they ought to say—either what their own "command" would expect of them or what the designers hope they will say.

For these reasons, ratings and opinions often run counter to the actual, objective performance of a system. For example, the Naval Research Laboratory once evaluated three different tactical display systems, obtaining both objective and subjective measures. Objective measures included delays in target detection, accuracy in processing information, and related data. Subjective measures consisted of ratings made by experienced visitors from the fleet. According to the subjective ratings, system "A," which was a conventional tactical display, was the best; system "K," which was rather similar to a conventional display was next best; and the worst system was "M," an entirely unique display. The officers' familiarity with conventional displays apparently influenced their preferences because, by objective measurement of the target-handling capacities of the three systems, system "M" turned out to be the best by far.

RELIABLE MEASUREMENT

Reliability, as used with respect to measurements of human performance, refers to the consistency or repeatability of measurements. Measurements that appear to be reliable, even if they are objective measurements, often actually prove not to be. The only way to determine reliability is to make more than one measurement of the same kind to assess how well the two measurements agree; making only one measurement gives no indication of how reliable this kind of measurement is. Pairs (at least) of similar measurements should be made and compared.

If at all possible, the evaluator always should determine the reliability of his measurements of human or man-machine performances. He might frequently find that a given measurement proves unreliable. For example, in a study of an Air Force fighter-direction system, referees judged whether interceptor aircraft had successfully "shot down" target planes. Experimenters, however, found that, when two or three different referees judged the same situation, there often was little agreement among them. Thus, this method of scoring proved unreliable, and hence unacceptable, as a means of evaluating the system. (It should be noted that the rather general unreliability of subjective judgments is a principal argument for not using them, but, when objective methods are not available, subjective methods may be used when it is shown that different judges agree with each other and, hence, yield reliable measurements.)

There are several methods of determining the reliability of measurements, depending on the kind of data secured. In simple cases, reliability can be stated as the standard deviation (σ) of a mean (see article 1.3.1). In more complicated cases, reliability is expressed as a statistical correlation or as a percentage of agreement among measurements of the same thing (see Dixon and Massey, 1951; Mayne, 1957; McNemar, 1955; and Thorndike, 1949).

Reliability of measurements always should be stated in any report of a system evaluation so that one can tell whether differences between systems are significant. Small differences between systems might or might not be significant (even large ones might not be), depending on the reliability of the differences. The evaluator should not state that one system is so much better than another without also stating the error (reliability) of the measurements involved.

When differences between systems prove to be reliable, one still should be careful to distinguish between significant and practical differences. One system might be reliably better than another, as judged by statistical measures of significance, but the difference might be so small that it is not worth the cost in time and money to adopt the slightly better system (see Chapanis, 1959).

VALID MEASUREMENT

The term "validity," as used in the behavioral sciences, refers to the prediction of some criterion. In the case of system evaluation, valid measurements are those that truly reflect the later performance of a system when it is in actual use. This reflection of later performance is, of course, the whole purpose of a system evaluation; hence, validity is the crux of all evaluations. Thus, the following points concerning the validity of evaluations should be kept in mind:

1. Use only reliable measurements. Generally, measurements must be reliable to be valid. If different measures of the same thing do not agree with one another, the measures cannot validly predict operational perform-

ance. For example, in the study of the Air Force fighter-direction system mentioned previously, the fact that referees could not agree on when an interceptor was "shot down" makes the measurement invalid, even though it appears to be realistic and hence valid.

2. Try to choose those measurements that will reflect conditions that are critical to a system's success. Some measurements might be perfectly valid but not worth taking because they quite probably will have little to do with the success or failure of the system. Thus, the evaluator's task is to select those performances to measure that will be critical in later system success.

3. Consider all the possibilities for measurements being invalid. Such factors as the previous training of the subjects, the bias of experienced personnel or of design engineers, and the atypical performance of one man or equipment in the system can invalidate the entire measurement of systems performance.

For example, when experienced pilots fly a new aircraft in which many of the controls are different from the ones to which they are accustomed, any measure of performance might not be a valid one because it does not indicate what personnel without previous experience, but properly trained to fly the new aircraft, would be able to do with it.

4. Make certain that all measures used are relevant to the operational performance of the system. If the purpose of an evaluation is to determine the performance of a system when the men in it are healthy and the equipment is working, do not include measurements that are influenced by the breakdown of equipment or by the ill health of an operator. Of course, the evaluator must be very careful about discarding data. If the breakdown or the ill health of an operator are functions of the system, rather than irrelevant, random events, then the data should be included and not discarded.

2

visual presentation of information

IN THE CONTROL of most modern machines, the human operator needs information that his unaided senses cannot supply. To overcome this limitation, we use devices to gather the needed information and to translate it into inputs that the human beings can perceive. These devices are called displays.

It so happens that the eyes have unique properties (see section 2.2) that make them more suitable than the ears and other human sense organs for receiving most types of information the operator needs. Thus, we use compasses, radar scopes, warning lights, and other displays to present information to the operator visually. It is with the design of visual displays that this chapter is concerned. The presentation of auditory information is discussed in Chapters 3 and 4.

2.1 *General Display Principles*

There is much more to designing a good visual display than merely making it visible; the operator must also understand the presented information and, with minimum effort and delay, convert it into correct decisions and/or control actions. This means that the display must be designed to suit the particular conditions under which it will be used, the method of use, and the purposes it is to serve.

This chapter was drafted by Charles A. Baker and Walter F. Grether of the Air Force Systems Command.

2.1.1 *Conditions of use*

To provide the proper display, the designer should consider at least the following among the operator's working conditions:

a. Viewing distance. The maximum expected viewing distance should determine the size of the details shown on a display. The usual reading distance for printed materials is about 16 in., but many indicators are designed for reading at arm's length to permit the operator to reach switches or adjusting knobs on the indicator. This distance, generally set at 28 in., is used in determining the recommended dimensions for scale markings and numerals (see section 2.6). For other reading distances, these dimensions must be adjusted up or down in direct proportion to the distance.

b. Illumination. Most displays depend on reflected light to be visible, and the size of display details, therefore, should be suited to the lowest expected illumination level (see section 2.3). The color of the illumination also should be considered; occasionally red lights are used to preserve the operator's dark adaptation, but red light washes out any color coding (see section 2.4) on the display. Warning signal lights (see section 2.5) and cathode-ray tubes (see section 2.7) provide their own light and are usually hindered rather than helped by other lighting in the work station.

c. Angle of view. The preferred viewing angle (not to be confused with visual angle as defined in section 2.2) is usually normal (90 deg) to the plane of the display. On large display panels, or where more than one operator views the same display, there might be a considerable deviation from the 90-deg angle of view. This situation can give rise to excessive parallax, or cause parts of the display to be hidden, unless such offset viewing has been allowed for in the design. (For further details see sections 2.2 and 2.6.)

d. Presence of other displays. Usually, an operator divides his attention among a number of displays. Inconsistencies in the manner of presentation among the displays can confuse or slow up the operator and invite reading errors. But, if several different displays look too much alike, the operator might read the wrong one. Obviously, each display must be well identified. (For additional discussion see section 2.6.)

e. Compatibility with related controls. The design of a display is often affected by the location (see Chapter 7) and operating method (see Chapter 6) of associated controls. Ideally, displays and controls should be designed and located so that the operator, with little or no training, will select the correct control and operate it in the manner called for by the display. (Further discussion and specific recommendations will be found in section 2.6.)

2.1.2 *Method of use*

The way in which the operator will use the information presented to him is an important consideration in the design of displays. An analysis should be made, therefore, of the type of action the operator will be expected to take while or after he receives information from the display (see Chapter 1). Generally, displays are used in one or more of the following ways:

a. For quantitative reading. This is reading to an exact numerical value. Examples of this method of using a display include reading time from a clock, heading from a compass, and rpm from a tachometer.

b. For qualitative reading. This is judging the approximate value, trend, rate of change, or direction of deviation from a desired value. It differs from quantitative reading in that the operator does not read an exact numerical value. Examples of qualitative reading include noting that a ship has veered to the right of a desired course, or that engine temperature is going up.

c. For check reading. This is verifying that a normal or desired value is or is not being shown. If the reading has deviated from the desired value, the operator might want to look more carefully (make a qualitative reading) to decide in which direction the value deviates and whether the deviation is large enough to require corrective action.

d. For setting. This is adjusting a display to a desired position or value; it might merely consist of adjusting one display to match another display. Examples include setting target bearing and range into a fire-control computer or barometric pressure on an altimeter.

e. For tracking. This is intermittent or continuous adjustment of a display to maintain a normal or desired value (compensatory tracking) or to follow a moving target or reference marker (pursuit tracking). Holding a constant ship heading in rough sea is an example of compensatory tracking. Following a moving target with crosshairs on a radar scope is an example of pursuit tracking. (For a more detailed discussion, see Chapter 5.)

f. For spatial orientation. This is judging position and movement in one plane or in three-dimensions. The judgments might be made with respect to the operator's own vehicle, a target, or the relation between the two. They also might be made with respect to the location or movement of equipment components. Navigation and fire-control displays are usually of the spatial-orientation type.

Note that the first three of the above-listed ways of using displays (quantitative, qualitative, and check reading) refer only to the act of reading the display without considering the response to the readings. In the remaining three ways of using displays, the way in which the operator will respond to the displayed information is considered. It should be remembered, however, that any single display usually will be used in more than one of the ways described above.

2.1.3 *The purpose of the display*

The purpose it is to serve frequently determines the kind of display it should be. There are two basic kinds of displays: symbolic and pictorial. In symbolic displays, the information presented has no pictorial resemblance to the conditions represented. Words, abbreviations, letters, mathematical shorthand, numbers, and color coding are symbols rather than replicas of the conditions they represent.

Some displays do have a pictorial, geometric, or schematic resemblance to the things they represent, but there are many different degrees of pictorialism. Photographs and television are at one extreme. Maps and PPI radar scopes, which reproduce the geometry of the area they cover but not its true appearance, and schematic-wiring or flow diagrams, which show the functional interconnections but not the true geometry, also are considered pictorial. Many instruments, such as compasses and attitude indicators, which only show some of the spatial relationships of the situations they represent, are at the other extreme.

In general, whenever a display shows the geometrical or spatial relationship of the situation it represents, it is pictorial. Except for photographs and television, we rarely use a display that is purely pictorial. Usually, displays are much simplified pictures with symbolic representations added. Because quantitative values and identification details are usually hard to read from pictures, such information is represented by symbols. Thus, when we talk about pictorial displays, we usually mean combinations of pictorial and symbolic representations. When we talk of symbolic displays, we mean only those that have no pictorial or geometric resemblance to the conditions they represent.

USING SYMBOLIC DISPLAYS

There are many conditions that might need to be displayed that are essentially nonpictorial. Such parameters as temperature, pressure, and rpm, for instance, always are presented symbolically. Frequently, the use of symbolic displays saves panel space and permits a less complex display mechanism. In addition, as already mentioned, most pictorial displays are supplemented with symbolic representations.

USING PICTORIAL DISPLAYS

Pictorial displays are very helpful for showing relationships and orientation in space. For some uses, such as navigation, they are almost indispensable. In general, properly designed pictorial displays can be interpreted more easily and with less training than purely symbolic indicators for the same functions.

2.1.4 *The combination and integration of displays*

Frequently, more than one indication can be presented by a single display. The advantages in this are saving of panel space, economy of eye movements, and simplification of interpretation. Although these are real advantages, there are disadvantages that limit the number of indications that can profitably be combined. These disadvantages are the following:

a. The compression of several indications into a small area, particularly if they are superimposed, makes identification of the desired information more difficult.

b. Continued eye fixation on a single point or small area can produce an hypnotic effect and reduce the alertness of the operator.

c. Some techniques of instrument combination involving mirrors or optical projection greatly restrict the eye position of the operator and require artificial lighting—even in daylight.

d. Many kinds of combinations introduce penalties in reliability, maintenance, and cost.

COMBINING DISPLAYS

In spite of the above-listed disadvantages, there have been some desirable and apparently successful combinations. These are described in the paragraphs that follow as examples of what can be done by combining displays.

Combining Related Kinds of Information

In the indicator shown above (Fig. 2-1), two radio-compass needles are superimposed

over a magnetically slaved, rotating card. Magnetic heading to a station can be read directly under the radio-compass needle tuned to that station. From the angles formed by the two radio-compass needles, the pilot can estimate his ground position and course in relation to the two ground stations.

Combining First Derivatives

It is sometimes possible to use one pointer as a moving reference for the alignment of a second pointer. The indicator shown in Fig. 2-2 illustrates such an application. If the tip of the relative-heading pointer is kept aligned with the localizer line, the aircraft will approach the desired flight path in an asymptotic track. Matching these two indicators, in this case, is easier than integrating the two readings when they are presented on separate indicators.

This kind of combination is most applicable when one indication is the first derivative of the other. In this example, the localizer line shows aircraft position relative to a radio beam, and the relative-heading pointer defines the rate at which the aircraft approaches or leaves the flight path. Relative heading is the first derivative of position, as shown by the localizer line, and is more easily controlled by the pilot than is position. Thus, the goal of the pilot is proper aircraft position, and this is accomplished by controlling heading, which is under more direct control and responds with a much shorter time lag (see Chapter 5). The result is improved performance with less effort by the operator.

In combinations of this kind, the principle to observe is that the indicator being controlled directly by the operator should present the first derivative of the data indicated by the moving reference. In addition, the success of such a combination will depend on a proper movement ratio between the two values

is such a combination. In this indicator, the vertical line presents an electrical combination of position relative to the localizer path, relative heading (first derivative), and angle of bank (second derivative); and the horizontal line presents a combination of position relative to the glide path and aircraft pitch (first derivative).

By keeping the two lines of the Zero Reader centered (zeroed) the operator flies the air-

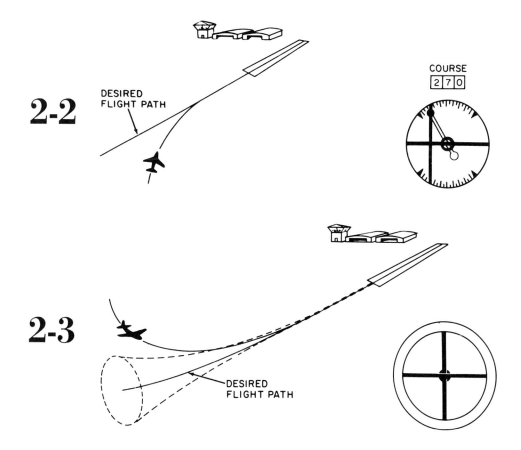

being indicated. This ratio must be determined for each application.

Combining Separate Values

In some cases, it is possible to present a single, computed indication that is an optimum combination of several separate values. The aircraft Zero Reader shown in Fig. 2-3

craft so as to make asymptotic approaches to the desired localizer and glide paths. The localizer line can be centered by controlling the angle of bank, and the glide-path line can be centered by controlling the pitch. Both of these are rather easily controlled, and involve minimum time lags (see Chapter 5). This, naturally, considerably simplifies the pilot's task when making an instrument landing and results in improved performance.

This kind of combination appears particularly suitable where the first and higher-order derivatives can be combined with the basic value that the operator is trying to reach or maintain. The number of derivatives to be combined, and the ratios to be used in the combination, must be determined for each application because different types of equipment, or different kinds of operations, might require different ratios.

A disadvantage of this kind of combination is that the individual values are lost to the operator unless they also are presented as separate indications. By keeping the lines zeroed, the operator will achieve the desired end result, but he is not shown the details of how this is accomplished. In the case of the Zero Reader, he does not know his exact flight path, which might be required for clearance of ground obstacles. Where necessary for safety reasons, the operator also can be provided with other indicators.

INTEGRATING DISPLAYS

The combining of indications in a single instrument can be carried one step farther by treating the entire panel as a single display. This is what usually is called integrating displays. Designing the entire panel as an integrated unit has definite advantages over the usual assembly of independently designed instruments: integration makes possible better use of the limited space on the panel, and, more important, it can result in improved operator efficiency. To design a properly integrated panel will require the application of much of what is covered in this chapter and in Chapter 7.

2.2 *Visual Detection, Identification, and Estimation*

This section provides data on the ability of human beings to detect and identify targets. (The term "target" will be used here to mean any object, pattern, or marking that operators have to see.) In many cases, the designer can do little or nothing about the visibility of targets, such as, for instance, the targets operators see in optical fire-control and bomb-sight systems. In these cases, data on our ability to see are important in telling us what we can expect of the human eye. In other cases, however, the designer can do something about the visibility of targets—because he designs them. This section will deal mainly, but not exclusively, with information for designing such targets.

In designing the most visible target, there are a number of points to keep in mind: How big is it? How far away is it? Is it colored? Is it stationary or moving? Will the operator know where it is or will he have to search for it? Article 2.2.1 presents data on visual acuity and the physical factors affecting acuity—illumination, brightness contrast, and brightness level. Article 2.2.1 also includes data on targets the operator will have to search for and discusses acuity with respect to colored targets. Article 2.2.2 covers targets seen against nonuniform backgrounds, article 2.2.3 discusses target identification in complex displays, and article 2.2.4 shows how vision can be aided by optical magnification—binoculars and telescopes—and gives some general recommendations about designing or selecting optical instruments for different uses. Finally, article 2.2.5 takes up the ability of the human being to estimate size, range, speed, and acceleration.

2.2.1 *Visual acuity and factors affecting it*

One of the most important kinds of data about the eye is visual acuity. The size of detail that the eye is capable of resolving is used as a measure of visual acuity. Visual acuity is measured by determining the smallest visual angle that can be resolved. It is usually specified as the reciprocal of the minimum visual

angle expressed in minutes of arc. The visual angle is the angle subtended by the viewed object (see Fig. 2-4) and is determined as follows:

$$\text{Visual angle} = 2 \arctan \frac{L}{2D}, \quad (2\text{-}1)$$

where L is the size of the object measured perpendicularly to the line of sight, and D is the distance from the eye to the object.

Visual acuity is usually measured in terms of a 50% threshold, i.e., a target of the size that has a 50% probability of being seen is a threshold target. In some cases, the designer might want higher probability values, such as, for example, 95 or 99% thresholds, so that targets are almost always detected. Unless stated otherwise, the data in this section are 50% thresholds. As a rule of thumb, to determine what size of target will be detected almost all the time, multiply these 50% thresholds by two.

The validity of the above rule is borne out by the curve in Fig. 2-5, which shows how the probability of detecting a target depends on its size when its location is known, target size being measured in terms of visual angle (as it will be throughout this section). Although it is a general curve, i.e., the abscissa scale can be shifted to the right or left by changing the amount of light on the target, its brightness contrast, its shape, or the amount of time the viewer has to look at it (all of these points

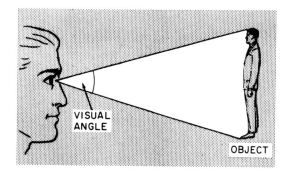

VISUAL ANGLE

OBJECT

2-4

2-5

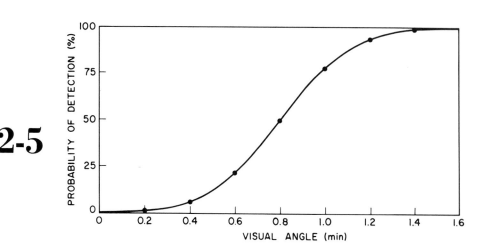

PROBABILITY OF DETECTION (%)

VISUAL ANGLE (min)

are discussed further later on), the importance of this curve is that it shows that doubling the size of a target for 50% probability of detection gives nearly 100% probability of detection.

MEASURING VISUAL ACUITY

There are several different kinds of visual-acuity measurements: minimum separable acuity, minimum perceptible acuity, stereoscopic acuity, and vernier acuity. Each of these will be discussed separately in the following paragraphs.

Minimum Separable Acuity

Also called gap resolution, this is the measurement of the smallest space the eye can detect between the parts of a target. Three

For most purposes, brightness is the most important measurement of the amount of light. Brightness is the amount of light reflected from, or emitted by, a surface. The brightness of a surface can be expressed by any one of the following (see also Table 2-1):

a. Lambert—a unit of brightness equal to the brightness of a perfectly diffusing and reflecting surface (see section 2.3) illuminated by one centimeter-candle (cm-c).

b. Millilambert—a unit of brightness equal to one thousandth of a lambert (L) and roughly equivalent to a foot-lambert (ft-L).

c. Foot-lambert—a unit of brightness equal to the brightness of a perfectly diffusing and reflecting surface illuminated by one foot-candle.

The curve in Fig. 2-8 (Moon and Spencer, 1944) shows the smallest Landolt-ring gap the eye can detect with different background brightnesses. This curve shows that, as the amount of light is increased, the eye can detect

ALTERNATING BLACK
AND WHITE LINES
EQUALLY SPACED

BLACK AND WHITE
CHECKERBOARD

LANDOLT RING
(GAP EQUAL TO
WIDTH OF RING)

2-6

kinds of targets commonly used for measuring gap resolution are shown in Fig. 2-6.

The effect of illumination. The acuity of the eye depends markedly on the amount of light—or illumination—on the target. Illumination is the areal density of the light falling on a surface. The most common unit of measurement of illumination is the foot-candle (ft-c). A foot-candle is the amount of light falling on the inner surface of a sphere of 1-ft radius when a point source of light with the intensity of one international candle is placed at the sphere's center. The following inverse square relationship applies to the foot-candle (see Fig. 2-7, right):

Illumination (ft-c)

$$= \frac{\text{Intensity of point source (c)}}{\text{Distance squared (ft}^2)}. \quad (2\text{-}2)$$

smaller and smaller gaps. This means that acuity increases as the amount of light increases. As a rule of thumb, it can be stated that the eye can detect a gap of about 1 min of visual angle at ordinary, indoor-light levels, but this rule works only for people who have normal eyesight and for targets that have high brightness contrast.

The acuity curve of Fig. 2-8 also is valid only for targets that are darker than their

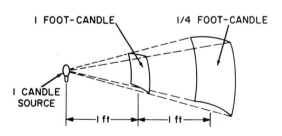

§ 2.2.1

Table 2-1   Conversion Factors for Brightness Units *

Units	Foot-Lamberts	Lamberts	Milli-lamberts	Candles per square inch (inch-candles)	Candles per square foot (foot-candles)	Candles per square centimeter (centimeter-candles)
ft-L	—	0.001076	1.076	0.00221	0.3183	0.0003426
L	929	—	1,000	2.054	295.7	0.3183
mL	0.929	0.001	—	0.002054	0.2957	0.0003183
c/in^2 (in.-c)	452.4	0.4869	486.9	—	144	0.155
c/ft^2 (ft-c)	3.142	0.00338	3.38	0.006944	—	0.001076
c/cm^2 (cm-c)	2,919	3.142	3,142	6.452	929	—

* Value in units in left-hand column times conversion factor equals value in units shown at top of column.

backgrounds. For white targets on black backgrounds or for letters and numbers cut out of a panel and lighted from behind, the curve looks different. As the brightness of white-on-black or cut-out targets increases, the acuity of the eye increases, at first, just as it does for black targets, but for brightnesses above about 10 mL, acuity for white-on-black targets drops off fast because the white parts blur. The technical visual term for this phenomenon is irradiation.

The effect of brightness contrast. Brightness contrast is a measure of how much target brightness (B_t) differs from the background brightness (B_b). The equation for obtaining brightness contrast is:

$$\text{Percent contrast} = \frac{B_b - B_t}{B_b} \times 100. \quad (2\text{-}3)$$

Contrasts can vary from 100% to zero for targets darker than their backgrounds and from zero to infinity for targets brighter than their backgrounds. With less contrast, there is lower acuity. For example, it is harder to see black on gray than it is to see black on white. This point is illustrated by the curves of Fig. 2-9 (Cobb and Moss, 1928), which show some measurements made with the

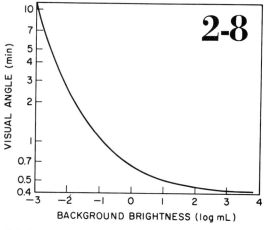

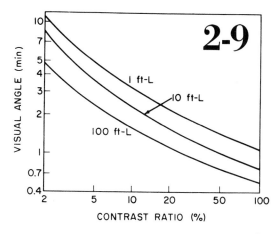

Landolt ring shown in Fig. 2-6 at three different background brightnesses.

Minimum Perceptible Acuity

Also called spot detection, this is the measurement of the eye's ability to detect the smallest possible target, and the spot can be lighter than its background or darker than its background. Spot detection depends both on brightness level and on brightness contrast, as is shown in Fig. 2-10. The curves labeled 1 to 100% in this illustration are for targets that are either brighter or darker than their

small. For example, against a bright sky, the normal human eye can see a wire 1 deg long 75% of the time, even if the wire is only 0.43 sec wide. Similarly, a dark square is visible against a bright sky 75% of the time even if the square subtends a visual angle of only 14 sec (Hecht, et al., 1947). For all practical purposes, these numbers represent the limits of minimum perceptible acuity.

Stereoscopic Acuity

The left and right eye are about 2.2 in. apart and, consequently, do not see things

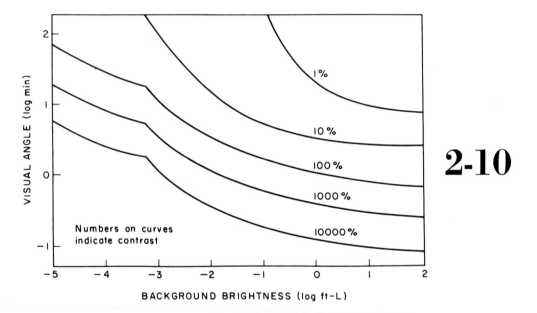

BACKGROUND BRIGHTNESS (log ft-L)

backgrounds. The curves for contrasts above 100% are for targets brighter than their backgrounds (this is the only way of getting contrasts above 100%). The thresholds in this graph are for a 99% probability of detection —that is, almost certain detection.

There is no lower detectable-size limit for spots that are brighter than their backgrounds. The eye can detect a bright spot, no matter how small it is, as long as it is bright enough. For instance, the star Mira can be seen even though it subtends an angle of only 0.056 sec.

Lines and squares are also visible against bright backgrounds even when they are very

exactly the same. The brain combines the slightly different images—or pictures—formed in the two eyes into a single image that has depth. The two pictures seen by the eyes differ most for objects near the eyes and least for far-away objects. To look at something close, the eyes converge until the lines of sight meet on the object. As the gaze is shifted to something farther away, the eyes diverge until, for very distant targets, the lines of sight are nearly parallel.

The threshold of stereoscopic acuity is the difference between the parallactic angles of two targets that are at just-noticeably-different distances from each other (see Fig. 2-11). The curve of Fig. 2-12 (Berry, et al., 1950) shows how stereoscopic acuity increases (visual angle decreases) as the amount of light increases. Figure 2-13 (Hirsch and Wey-mouth, 1947) shows how much better depth perception is with two eyes than with one at distances closer than 1,000 m (3,281 ft). Beyond about 2,500 ft, one eye does as well as two for perceiving depth.

Vernier Acuity

Vernier acuity is measured by using two lines, one of which is displaced laterally, as shown in Fig. 2-14. (The thickness of the lines makes little difference.) The threshold of vernier acuity is the smallest lateral displacement that can be detected. This kind of acuity is used in reading some instruments and in optical range finders in tanks and ships. The curve in Fig. 2-15 (Berry, et al., 1950) shows that vernier acuity is exceptionally good, and that it, too, increases with the amount of light.

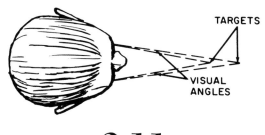

2-11

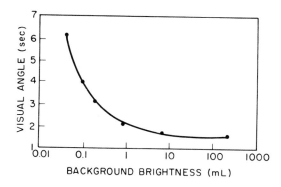

2-12

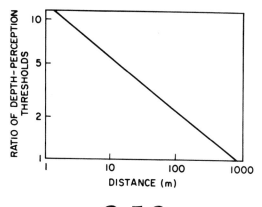

2-13

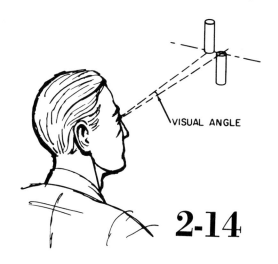

2-14

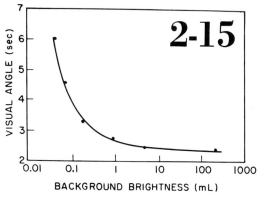

2-15

61

EFFECT OF ADAPTATION LEVEL

Visual acuity is best when the eyes have not been exposed to high levels of brightness. For example, if the captain of a ship has been out on the flying bridge scanning the brightly-lit ocean and then steps into the normally-lit pilot house, he is momentarily "blinded." If it is important for him to be able to see certain displays right away, the letters, numbers, or markings he has to see should be large enough or bright enough so that he can read them in this "blind" condition. Unfortunately, from what we now know, it is not possible to give a more specific design recommendation than the following: if visual displays have to be read by people who have just been exposed to high levels of brightness (the open sea, clouds, desert, or snow), the level of brightness of the displays should be higher than would normally be necessary—they should be at least 0.01 as bright as the pre-exposure field.

There is better information for the situation in which a person has to see a relatively dim object while being exposed to relatively high levels of brightness. The usual situation of this kind is that of the operator who has to see a target on a radar scope while being

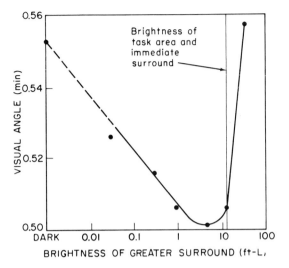

2-17

exposed to room illumination. Data and recommendations on this problem are given in article 2.3.2.

In general, visual acuity is at a maximum when the eyes are adapted to the brightness level of the target and immediately surrounding area (see article 2.3.3). But acuity is reduced when the target and immediate surround (see Fig. 2-16) are at a lower brightness than the greater surround or background. Acuity also is reduced if the background is considerably darker than the target, but this effect is very slight.

The curve in Fig. 2-17 (Lythgoe, 1932) shows the effect of surround brightness for backgrounds both darker and lighter than the target and the immediate surround. Note that acuity is best when the surround is a little darker than the target and that acuity is much poorer if the surround is brighter than the target. Thus, we can conclude that, for best acuity, targets should not be in a shadow or near a large area of much higher brightness.

EFFECT OF COLORED LIGHTING

Colored illumination can be obtained either by placing a filter in front of the light source

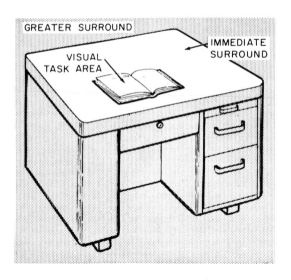

2-16

§ 2.2.1

or by placing a filter in front of the observer's eyes; both methods have the same effect. However, although there are some theoretical reasons why acuity should be better with colored illumination than with white, the only dependable finding from research studies so far is that blue illumination is not as good in improving acuity as other colored or white illumination. Actually, for acuity at its best, colored filters should not be used. A colored filter will always reduce brightness, or the total amount of light. This loss in brightness usually reduces acuity more than any effect the color might have in improving acuity.

Another good reason for not using colored illumination is that it distorts the colors of things that are looked at. For example, colors

equipment and cathode-ray tubes. (See article 2.3.2 for further discussion and recommendations.)

2.2.2 Searching for targets

For all data given so far in this section, the observer knew the location of the target and could look right at it. The necessity of searching for targets complicates the problem for the following two reasons:

1. Some parts of the eye are more sensitive than other parts.

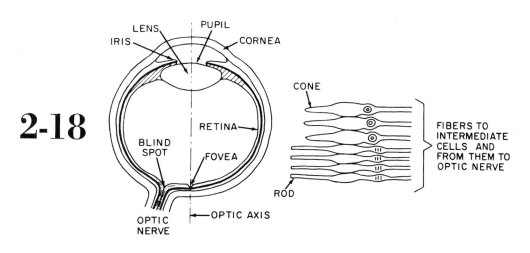

2-18

are changed or completely lost when looking through a deep-red or deep-green filter. In effect, a colored filter makes a person with normal vision color blind and, thus, reduces the total amount of information the eye can obtain.

There are exceptions to this rule, of course. Red lighting is recommended for people who have to keep their eyes in readiness for working in the dark. Examples of those who need such dark adaptation are pilots who fly at night, tank men who have to maneuver at night, x-ray technicians and photographers who have to work in darkrooms. In addition, selective-color lighting is recommended for rooms in which operators must watch radar

2. Success in searching depends on how the searcher moves his eyes.

Light reaching the eye is picked up by the retina, which is composed of two sets of light-sensitive cells, the rods and cones (see Fig. 2-18). The cones function best under daylight conditions; the rods function best under twilight or night conditions (see Fig. 2-19). All visual perception involves the cones and the rods; color discrimination involves the cones alone, and light-dark discrimination involves both the rods and the cones.

The eye sees differently from different angles as well as under different ambient light conditions because the fovea, a small area in the center of the retina, contains all cones

§ 2.2.2

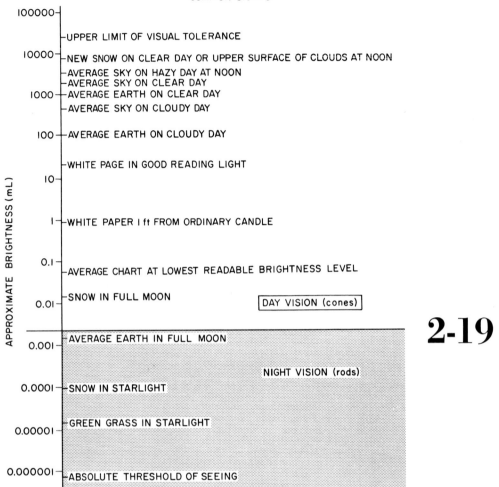

and no rods. Because the cones are insensitive to twilight or night conditions, foveal vision is not effective in seeking out dim targets after dark. But, as the angle of view from the fovea is increased, the concentration of rods becomes denser, and night vision is enhanced.

When you want to see something in ordinary daylight, you turn your eyes toward it—you point your fovea toward it—because this is the most sensitive part of the eyes in daylight. At night—when the illumination is below that of about full moonlight—this part of the eye is almost blind, and you cannot see faint targets at night by looking directly at them—you must look slightly away from them.

The curves of Fig. 2-20 (Mandelbaum and Sloan, 1947) show acuity of different parts of the eye at different levels of brightness. Zero on the abscissa scale corresponds to the fovea; the other numbers correspond to different angular positions toward the side away from the nose (temporal angles).

Note from Fig. 2-20 that, at high levels of brightness, the central part of the retina has the best acuity, and that acuity decreases as the temporal angle increases. When the brightness is a little less than 0.04 mL, acuity in the central part of the retina is not as good as acuity about 4 deg away from the fovea. Also, at lower levels of brightness—the equivalent of a dark, moonless night—acuity is

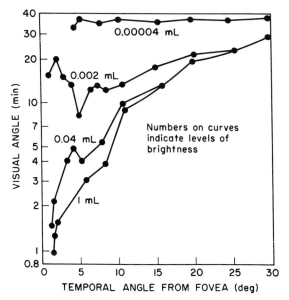

VISUAL ANGLE (min)

0.00004 mL

0.002 mL

0.04 mL

Numbers on curves
indicate levels of
brightness

1 mL

TEMPORAL ANGLE FROM FOVEA (deg)

the eye for this purpose is about 20 deg from the fovea (0 deg) on the temporal side. This series of curves shows the faintest light the eye can detect with different parts of the eye. (The solid curve is the average for 101 observers, and 95% of the observers are included between the dashed curves.)

Because light rays cross over in the hollow of the eye—just as they do in a camera—this means that, when light is picked up by the temporal side of the retina of the right eye, the object is off to the left, and, if it hits the temporal side of the retina of the left eye, it is off to the right.

By comparing Fig. 2-21 with Fig. 2-20, it can be seen that, if the observer merely wants to *detect* something at night, he should look about 20 deg to one side of where he expects it to be, and, if he wants to *identify* something at night, he should look 4–8 deg to one side of it.

poor in all parts of the eye. Thus, in searching the sky or sea in daylight, large targets can be missed easily unless systematic patterns of eye movements are used. To identify targets best under night conditions, the observer must look slightly away from them—about 4–8 deg off center.

In searching for something at night to detect it without identifying it, Fig. 2-21 (Sloan, 1947) shows that the most sensitive part of

2.2.3 *The detection of colored targets*

Most of the data given in the previous articles of this section are for achromatic— that is, white, gray, or black—targets on

2-21

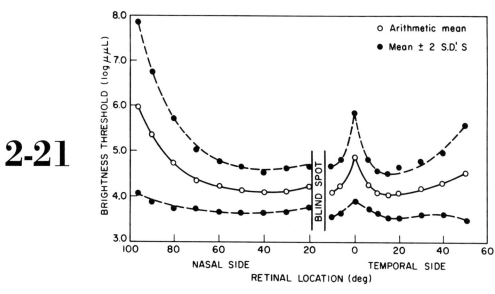

BRIGHTNESS THRESHOLD (log μμL)

○ Arithmetic mean
● Mean ± 2 S.D.' S

BLIND SPOT

RETINAL LOCATION (deg)

NASAL SIDE   TEMPORAL SIDE

achromatic backgrounds. When there is high brightness contrast between target and background, the addition of color contrast—making the target and background different colors—does not improve visual acuity very much. When the brightness contrast is low, however, color contrast can improve visual acuity appreciably, but acuity is increased much more by increasing brightness contrast than by increasing color contrast.

DETECTING SURFACE COLOR

Often an operator has to detect and identify targets by their colors. Detection is increased when the targets have both high brightness contrast and high color contrast with their backgrounds. Although no one color will be most visible against all types of terrain (desert, snow, sea, or jungle), International Orange is seen best at great distances against most backgrounds. Also, the detectability of fluorescent materials is usually much greater than that of nonfluorescent materials. The former are recommended for survival equipment, identification panels, and other targets that must be seen at great distances.

DETECTING COLORED LIGHTS

Color-coded lights are used on display panels, maintenance equipment, and navigational aids to air, submarine, and surface vessels. When the operator is close to the lights, there is usually no detection problem—the problem is mostly one of picking an efficient color code. (Color coding is covered in article 2.4.1.)

There is a detection problem, however, when lights are at great distances so that they become, for all practical purposes, point sources. The recognition of a signal color depends on the illumination at the eye from the light (this is proportional to the intensity of the light and inversely proportional to the square of the distance), the brightness of the background, and the color of the light.

The curves of Fig. 2-22 (Hill, 1947) show the intensity of point-source signal lights of various colors when viewed against neutral backgrounds of various brightnesses. (These are 90% thresholds, i.e., they will be correctly identified 90% of the time.) Other data not given here show that green and red lights are most accurately identified at a distance, white is next easiest to identify, and yellow is poorest because it is often confused with red. Blue is also a poor color for distant signaling because it is easily confused with green.

2.2.4 Target detection against nonuniform backgrounds

Detection is difficult when the target is displayed against a mottled or patterned background. This is especially true if the background has objects in it that resemble the target in size, color, or brightness. In such cases, targets should be much larger than one would predict from threshold-acuity data. The following rules will help make targets most visible against nonuniform backgrounds:

1. Choose a color that contrasts most with the colors in the background.

2. Choose a brightness that differs as much as possible from the background. Pick white or bright colors for targets on dark backgrounds, and vice versa.

3. Use a fluorescent color for targets against dark backgrounds.

4. Use as large an area of solid color as possible. Do not use stripes or checks; patterns like these are not visible at great distances—they only fuse and reduce the contrast of the target against its background.

5. If the target has to be seen against various kinds of backgrounds, have the target in two contrasting colors, dividing the target so as to make the two areas of solid color as big as possible; one or the other of the two colors will contrast with most backgrounds. Good pairs of colors for this purpose are the following: white and red, bright yellow and black, bright yellow and blue, and bright green and red.

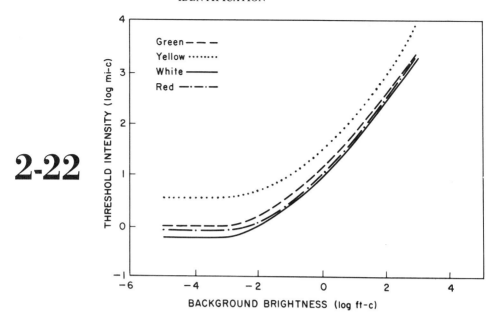

2-22

2.2.5 *Identifying targets in complex displays*

The visual task of personnel such as photo-reconnaissance interpreters, radar- or infra-red-display interpreters, or aircraft visual-reconnaissance pilots involves the identification of targets based on their unique form or pattern. These identification tasks assume the interpreter has a knowledge of the form or pattern of particular critical targets or reference landmarks such as airfields and missile-launching sites or cities, rivers, and lakes. Factors that affect the speed and accuracy of target identification include target size, amount of clutter or number of irrelevant targets in the display, and the resolution or distortion of the display system.

TARGET SIZE

The human eye is capable of identifying the letters of the alphabet if these letters subtend a visual angle of at least 5 min of arc. Indeed, the ability to perform visual identifi-

cations of arabic letters that subtend 5 min of arc defines 20-20 vision as measured by the Snellen eye chart. But the letters of the alphabet are highly discriminable and target patterns of the type involved in display interpretation generally are not. Figure 2-23 (Steedman and Baker, 1960) shows the relation of target size to accuracy and relative speed of identification of targets of this latter type. From the curve, it is evident that, when the visual angle subtended by the largest dimension of the target is smaller than 12 min, there is an increase in relative search-to-identification time and an increase in the number of errors in identification. These and other research data indicate that it probably is safe to assume that targets should subtend, as a minimum, 12 min of arc to insure reasonably accurate identification.

DISPLAY CLUTTER

The speed of target identification in complex displays is affected by the number of irrelevant targets (amount of clutter) in the display. It has been found that, as the number of irrelevant targets increases, there is a nearly proportional increase in the required search time (Boyton, et al., 1958 and Baker, et al.,

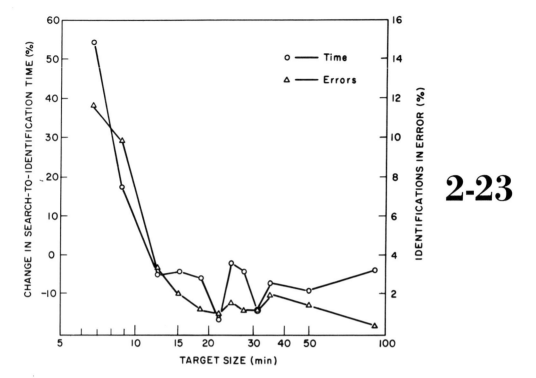

1960). Thus, if there is only a short search time available, the number of missed targets will increase proportionally with increases in clutter. Any means, therefore, that the designer can develop to filter out irrelevant targets should be used to avoid this possibility wherever the missing of targets is critical.

DISPLAY RESOLUTION

The accuracy of target identification is critically affected by the resolution integrity of the display system. For instance, a major difficulty encountered in interpreting cathode-ray-tube displays arises from the fact that they present an indistinct picture of targets (see article 2.7.2). This lack of distinctness, or definition, arises from a definite limitation in the resolving power of the radar because the amount of detail that will be displayed is roughly proportional to the resolving power of the radar system. The relationship of display resolution and target identification is a complex one, and it is only recently that studies have thrown some light on the problem

(see Williams, et al., 1960 and Baker, et al., 1960).

2.2.6 *Magnification aids*

Targets can be detected or spotted at greater distances than they can be identified. For instance, a ship at sea can be seen long before what kind of a ship it is can be determined. The reason for this is that, to recognize something, the observer has to be able to see details that are invisible at a distance.

Telescopes, binoculars, and magnifiers in general usually improve target detection and identification, although the degree of improvement is never equal to the magnification ratio —a 5-power telescope does not mean that one can see five times as far or five times as well. There are a number of reasons for this. For instance, magnification does the following:

a. Lowers the brightness of the target.

b. Lowers the contrast between the target and its background.

c. Makes the image of the target fuzzier.

§ 2.2.6

d. Increases the image movement of a moving target.

e. Makes the image of a steady target seem to move if there is any unsteadiness or vibration in the instrument.

f. Cuts down the field of view.

But, the size of these effects depends on the number of glass parts in the device, how accurately the lenses and prisms are aligned, the quality of the optical surfaces, whether the glass surfaces are coated, and so on.

The factors mentioned above are all related to the device itself. Other factors that make optical devices less effective than one might think are the quality of the air (haze, dust, etc.) and the fact that observers often do not use these devices in the proper way.

There are two general questions that are important in choosing a telescopic device: what are its design specifications, and in what way will it be used? In answer to the first question, magnification, exit-pupil size, diameter of the field, and light transmission are some of the most important parameters. These might be conflicting factors, however, and any optical device has to be a compromise. For example, a large exit-pupil size makes the device much easier to use, but exit-pupil size is inversely proportional to magnification. And, again, increasing the diameter of the field permits increasing the exit-pupil size; but this means increasing the size of the optical parts, which leads to a bigger and heavier device.

In answer to the second question (in what way will the device be used?) are such things as whether the device will be used in daylight, at night, or both; whether it will be used on a steady or moving platform; and so on. Good binoculars and telescopes are much more effective at night than one might think. The increase in magnification—or size of the image —more than makes up for the loss of light in the device. For daylight use, if the observer knows where the target is, or if he has to search a relatively small area, moderate-to-high magnification will be helpful; but, if he has to search a large area, if the target is moving fast, if he is moving, or if he has only a short time to look, magnification will be more hindrance than help. In most cases, an observer will do best by using his unaided eye

for initial scanning. Then, when he has spotted a target or located a suspicious area, magnification aids can help him to identify the target.

DESIGN RECOMMENDATIONS

1. Binocular devices are better than monocular ones, especially for night use. The advantage of binocular devices is small in daylight when brightness levels are high.

2. For binoculars in aircraft or moving ground vehicles, use hand-held or mounted binoculars of 3–4 power. Powers higher than this are not recommended because of the vehicle's motion and the small field of view.

3. For *daytime* use on a steady platform (the ground or a ship in normal seas), magnifications up to 6 power are recommended for hand-held binoculars, and magnifications up to 20 power are recommended for mounted binoculars.

4. For *night* use on a steady platform, magnifications up to 10 power are recommended for hand-held binoculars, and magnifications up to 20 power are recommended for mounted binoculars.

5. An exit-pupil size of 6 mm gives the best performance—other things being equal.

6. The lines of reticles should be thin enough so that they do not cut out targets but thick enough to see easily. In any event, their size should not exceed 2 min of angle.

7. In devices that will be used at night, reticles should be illuminated with deep-red light and should have an adjustable intensity control.

8. Rubber eye guards should be put around the eyepiece to help the observer get his eye in the right place and to hold his head steady.

2.2.7 *Estimating size, distance, and speed*

The human eye has extraordinary capacities for seeing very small details and faint amounts of light and for seeing small differences between things. It is very poor, however, at estimating absolute values. For example, the eye, under ideal conditions, can see a difference in the brightness of two areas if they differ by as little as 1%, but even experienced photographers have great difficulty estimating the amount of light in a room within 100% of the true value.

This characteristic of the eye shows up in the estimation of size, distance, speed, and acceleration in absolute or numerical terms. A further complication is that all these things are interrelated. Thus, the size of an unfamiliar target cannot be estimated accurately unless its distance is known, and anything that distorts a distance estimate will distort the corresponding size estimate.

Distances to targets are usually underestimated when they are seen across smooth water or snow because there are no other objects in the field of view to provide helpful cues. If the distance (or size) of some other object is known, the distance to an unfamiliar target usually can be estimated with fair accuracy. If there are no other objects in view—as when a target is high in the sky or across a large body of smooth water—estimates of distance are usually too short. It is almost impossible to estimate the distance of a target seen against a clear sky unless it is close or its size is known.

Estimates of the speed of moving objects —such as aircraft, birds, or automobiles— are poor. Estimates of speed are probably related to estimates of distance. If distance is underestimated, speed will be too. This might be why small objects (insects and birds) seem to move faster than big ones (aircraft). We know very little about human ability to estimate speed changes (acceleration) except that it is inaccurate and unreliable.

2.3 *Workplace Illumination*

Efficient use of vision in the operation of equipment dictates certain illumination requirements. These requirements vary from very low levels of illumination of a specified color, as on the bridge of a ship or in an aircraft cockpit, to the high levels of white illumination found in offices and machine shops. The purpose of this section is to provide background information on illumination principles as well as some specific lighting recommendations.

2.3.1 *General workplace lighting*

Adequate lighting is essential for efficient visual presentation of information. The most important considerations in workplace lighting can be listed as follows:

a. The distribution of light in work areas.

b. The brightness contrasts of the viewed objects and their details.

c. The quality and color of the illuminants and workplace surfaces.

d. The intensity of the illumination.

LIGHT DISTRIBUTION

The design engineer is concerned with two primary sources of light: natural light, which is that provided, either directly or indirectly, by the sun, and artificial light. The latter source of illumination may be thought of as falling into the following three categories, according to the method used to distribute the light over the task area (see Fig. 2-24):

a. Direct light. In this method, beams from the light source fall directly on the task area.

A light bulb with an opaque bowl inverted *over* it typifies this method.

b. Indirect light. In this method, most, if not all, of the beams from the light source are reflected from the walls and ceiling before they reach the task area. This can be achieved by placing an opaque bowl *under* the light.

c. Diffused light. In this method, the light source can be enclosed in a translucent bowl so that the light is scattered evenly.

There are, of course, many ways in which the methods listed above can be combined to produce different illuminating results. Which method, or combination of methods, it would be best to use can be determined once the visual task has been determined. The merits of each method vary somewhat, and each will be discussed briefly.

Direct lighting offers maximum light at the working plane when 90–100% of the output

with baffles, however, solve most of the glare problems for the diffusing enclosures.

Either direct or indirect light can be combined with diffuse lighting to provide modifications as needed. For example, a fluorescent desk lamp combines the downward-directed characteristics of direct lighting with the diffusing characteristics of fluorescent tubes.

Glare and How to Reduce It

When a relatively bright light source or its reflected image appears in the visual field, decreased visibility results because of the glare produced. Glare not only reduces visibility for objects in the field of view but also causes visual discomfort. *Direct* glare refers to the effect of a light *source* within the visual field, and *specular* glare refers to the effect of re-

LIGHT DISTRIBUTION METHODS

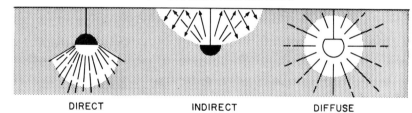

2-24

DIRECT INDIRECT DIFFUSE

of the luminaire (the entire lighting unit—socket, bulb, and directing or diffusing element) is directed downward toward the work area. Undesirable brightness contrasts, shadows, and glare (see below) are the most prominent faults of direct lighting.

Indirect lighting offers general, even lighting without shadows or glare when the source is shielded so that 90–100% of the light is directed upward, toward the ceiling and upper walls, from which it is reflected more or less evenly about the room. Although visual efficiency is lessened over prolonged periods of continuous reading, tests have shown that, over a 3-hr period, indirect lighting causes less fatigue and permits greater reading efficiency than direct lighting (Woodson, 1954).

Diffuse lighting requires less electrical power than indirect lighting but does cause some glare and shadows. Fluorescent units

flecting, bright *surfaces* within the visual field (see Fig. 2-25, next page).

Direct glare can be reduced by any of the following methods:

1. Avoiding bright light sources within 60 deg of the center of the visual field.

2. Using shields, hoods, and visors to keep direct light from the source out of the viewer's eyes.

3. Using indirect lighting.

4. Using several low-intensity sources rather than one high-intensity source.

Specular glare can be reduced by any one of the following methods:

1. Using diffuse light.

2. Using dull, mat surfaces (flat paints, desk blotters) rather than polished surfaces.

3. Arranging direct light sources so that the viewing angle to the work area is not equal to the angle of incidence from the source.

§ 2.3.1

Surround Brightness

The surround brightness should not be brighter than the visual task area, but, rather, the surround brightness should be at least 10% less than that of the visual task area. This recommendation implies that the sole source of illumination should not fall exclusively on the visual task area; there should be some illumination falling on the surrounding areas. It is more important, however, that the surround

an angle equal to the angle of incidence. Such reflection is specular.

c. Compound. Most surfaces actually encountered have both specular and diffuse reflectance characteristics. These surfaces are compound reflectors.

Selective Reflectance

The color of an object results from selec-

2-25 DIRECT GLARE SPECULAR GLARE

should be no brighter than the visual task area. The immediate-surround surfaces should have reflectance factors (see below) no higher than the targets in the central visual field when both areas are equally illuminated.

SURFACE REFLECTANCE

When light beams incident on a surface are redirected, we speak of reflectance. There are several kinds of reflectance, which may be listed as follows (see Fig. 2-26):

a. Diffuse. If the surface is composed of rough, irregular particles, the reflection of the incident light is diffuse.

b. Specular. Incident light on a polished surface, such as a mirror, will be reflected at

tive reflectance and selective absorption of particular wavelengths of incident light. A red object appears red because the longer wavelengths (red) are reflected, and the shorter ones (blue) are absorbed in the surface. Very high reflectors cannot be of a color other than white. Selective and spectral reflectance are specified by the percent reflected light at arbitrary wavelength steps.

Reflectance of Surround

The reflectance of ceilings, walls, floors, and furnishings or machinery contribute significantly to the general illumination level. For any specified level of illumination, a workplace with highly reflecting surfaces requires

§ 2.3.1

LIGHT REFLECTION FROM VARIOUS SURFACES

2-26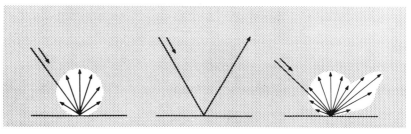

MAT SURFACE (DIFFUSE) POLISHED SURFACE (SPECULAR) SEMI-GLOSS SURFACE (COMPOUND)

a less intense light source than one with low reflecting surfaces. Figure 2-27 illustrates general recommendations concerning reflectances for surfaces in offices, study rooms, machine shops, power stations, etc. Large surfaces, such as walls and desk tops, should not have polished surfaces so as to reduce specular reflections. Smaller areas, such as door frames and moldings, can have polished surfaces to permit easy cleaning.

SHADOW AND SURFACE COLOR

Shadows can be avoided by using diffused light wherever possible and by using light colors on all surfaces where interreflections from these surfaces will increase the amount of light in obscured areas. Note from Table 2-2 that wood finishes generally have low reflectance factors. These and dark shades of gray, green, blue, red, and brown (see Table 2-3) should not be used on large surfaces, but pastels and light gray are recommended.

Table 2-2 Approximate Reflectance Factors for Various Wood Surface Finishes *

Surface finish	Amount of reflected light (%)	Surface finish	Amount of reflected light (%)
Maple	42	Walnut	16
Satinwood	34	Mahogany	12
English oak	17		

* Woodson, 1954.

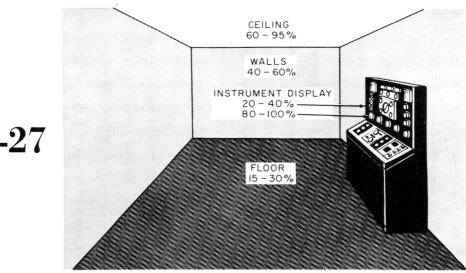

2-27

CEILING 60 - 95%

WALLS 40 - 60%

INSTRUMENT DISPLAY 20 - 40%
80 - 100%

FLOOR 15 - 30%

Table 2-3 Approximate Reflectance Factors for Various Surface Colors *

Color	Amount of reflected light (%)	Color	Amount of reflected light (%)
White	85	Green	
		Light	65
Yellow		Medium	52
Light	75	Dark	7
Medium	65		
		Blue	
Buff		Light	55
Light	70	Medium	35
Medium	63	Dark	8
Gray		Red	
Light	75	Dark	13
Medium	55		
Dark	30	Brown	
		Dark	10

* Woodson, 1954.

Table 2-4 General Illumination Levels and Types of Illumination for Different Task Conditions and Types of Tasks

Task condition	Type of task or area	Illumination level (ft-c)	Type of illumination
Small detail, low brightness contrast, prolonged periods, high speed, extreme accuracy	Sewing, inspecting dark materials, etc.	100	General plus supplementary, e.g., desk lamp
Small detail, fair contrast, speed not essential	Machining, detail drafting, watch repairing, inspecting medium materials, etc.	50–100	General plus supplementary
Normal detail, prolonged periods	Reading, parts assembly; general office and laboratory work	20–50	General, e.g., overhead ceiling fixture
Normal detail, no prolonged periods	Washrooms, power plants, waiting rooms, kitchens	10–20	General, e.g., random natural or artificial light
Good contrast, fairly large objects	Recreational facilities	5–10	General
Large objects	Restaurants, stairways, bulk-supply warehouses	2–5	General

§ 2.3.1

GENERAL ROOM LIGHTING

For general room lighting, the designer should strive for even distribution of illumination, avoiding shadows and glare. The levels required can be determined from Table 2-4.

Supplementary lighting is sometimes necessary to obtain the right amount of light for a specific task. This is a matter of providing specially mounted bench and desk lamps near the working area. Flexible-neck lamps are highly recommended because they can be adjusted to avoid glare and shadows.

2.3.2 *Radar-room lighting*

Radar operations traditionally have been performed in darkened rooms. Recently, however, several lighting systems have been developed that permit radar operators to see their scopes satisfactorily and yet provide enough illumination for the performance of other tasks, such as maintenance and chart reading, in the same area. Two basic considerations are incorporated in each system: ambient light is not allowed to reach the scope to prevent a reduction of target-to-background contrast, and indirect reflections from the scope face are not allowed to reach the operator's eyes.

CROSS-POLARIZATION SYSTEM

In this system, two polarized filters 90 deg out of phase are used—one over the scope and one over the room light. This arrangement prevents the room light from reaching the scope face. Proper placement and adequate shielding of the luminaires can prevent them from being primary glare sources and can also prevent specular reflections from the scope.

The advantages of this system are good target-to-background contrast, an adaptation level high enough to minimize fatigue, and unchanged object colors. Any phosphor color can be used with this system, and red ambient

light can be used in the area, when necessary, for dark adaptation of other personnel, without affecting the polarizing effects. In addition, either incandescent or fluorescent lamps can be used in the luminaire.

The disadvantage of this system is that luminaires must be mounted with care at each operating position. General overhead illumination cannot be used because such light tends to become depolarized on striking the walls, ceiling, and other objects in the area, thus reducing the effectiveness of the scope filter, and such general lighting would also illuminate the operator and thus create reflections on the scope face. In addition, the polaroid filter has a lower transmission factor than some scope filters used in other special-lighting systems.

BROAD-BAND-BLUE SYSTEM

In this system, a fluorescent light is covered with a blue filter (400–500 mμ), the scope face is covered with a yellow-orange filter, which absorbs wavelengths below 540 mμ, and scope operators wear goggles with the same yellow-orange filters. This arrangement permits a general increase in room illumination because the light is prevented from reaching the scope (because of its color), and specular reflections from the scope cover are eliminated by the operator's goggles. Special paint, however, is required on controls and indicator markings so that the scope operator wearing goggles can see them effectively (Kraft and Fitts, 1954).

The advantages of this system are good target/background contrast, high scope-filter transmission, and elimination of specular reflections from the scope face by the goggles regardless of room-light position. In addition, filtered blue light is effective in exciting fluorescing colors and permits personnel other than the operator to see very well for most tasks. The disadvantages are the following:

a. Color coding is limited by the range of the filters, although fluorescent paints can be used to improve this situation.

b. Monochromatic illumination might affect some people adversely, especially when combined with a moving platform (e.g., ship or aircraft) and other conditions such as poor ventilation.

c. Not all phosphors can be used with this system because the scope filter will not pass blue or green light.

YELLOW-MINUS-YELLOW SYSTEM

In the yellow-minus-yellow system, a sodium light can be used with a didymium filter over the scope because the narrow sodium-D line happens to fall at the same narrow cutoff point of this special filter (see Fig. 2-28). This coincidence prevents sodium light

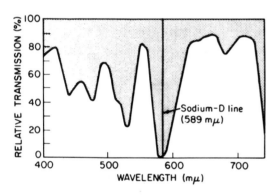

from reaching the scope face yet allows sufficient scope transmission. Didymium goggles can be worn by the operators to prevent reflections from the scope from reaching their eyes.

The advantages of this system are that all personnel can see to move about in the room, there is good target-to-background contrast, and specular reflection can be eliminated for all who wear goggles. The disadvantages are the loss of color and the fact that goggles are required. In addition, as with the broad-band-blue system, the phosphors that can be used are limited.

MERCURY-MINUS-RED SYSTEM

In the mercury-minus-red system, a mercury-vapor lamp can be used with two filters,

one (a Noviol filter) at the room light to remove ultraviolet and the other (red plexiglass 160) at the scope to prevent the shorter wavelengths from reaching the scope. Red goggles can be worn by the operators to prevent reflections from the scope from reaching their eyes.

The advantages of this system, like that of the sodium-vapor system, are that all personnel can see to move about in the room, there is good target-to-background contrast, and specular reflection can be eliminated for all who wear goggles. In addition, limited color perception is possible with this system. The disadvantages are the limited range of the color perception and the fact that goggles are required. In addition, as with the broad-band-blue and yellow-minus-yellow systems, the phosphors that can be used are limited.

COMPARING THE SYSTEMS

Thus, various combinations of filters and light sources can be used. Table 2-5 compares these various possible lighting systems. Note that one column in the table indicates the approximate scope-brightness loss resulting from the absorption of the filter in each system. These scope-brightness-loss values are for conditions in which the operators do not wear goggles with filters of the same type used over the display. If such goggles are worn, the scope-brightness loss will be greater than the values indicated.

2.3.3 Indicator and panel lighting

There are a number of specialized lighting problems in military and commercial installations, such as those found in aircraft or tank cockpit, combat information center, and air-traffic-control center. More specifically, the problems are ones in which very low levels of lighting are needed at the same time that high levels are required in the same area or when

Table 2-5 Comparison of Radar-Room Lighting Systems

| System | Light source | | | Scope | | Operator | Approximate brightness loss (%)* |
	Type	Filter	Emission	Filter	Absorption	Filter	
Yellow minus yellow	Sodium	none	5,900 Å	Didymium	5,900 Å	Didymium	60 63
Mercury minus red	Mercury	Noviol	Below 5,900 Å	Red	Below 6,000 Å	Red	90 77
Broad-band blue	Fluorescent	Blue	Below 5,400 Å	Orange	Below 5,400 Å	Orange	38 15
Cross polarization	Incandescent or fluorescent	Polaroid		Polaroid		none	65 65

*The upper value is for P-7 and the lower for P-19 phosphors. Other types might yield quite different values.

both extremes are needed at different times in the same area. Such combinations frequently introduce problems concerning dark adaptation and severe reflection hazards.

DARK ADAPTATION

The increase in sensitivity of the eye in the dark that results from prolonged prior periods in the dark is known as dark adaptation. Dark adaptation results in increased ability to see dimly illuminated objects. The time required for dark adaptation following exposure to white light of varying intensity and light of various colors is shown in Fig. 2-29 (Haig, 1941 and Peskin and Bjornstad, 1948).

These curves reveal two important facts: the time required to adapt to a given level of sensitivity is shorter when the pre-exposure brightness is less, and the time required to adapt to a given level of sensitivity is shorter when the pre-exposure light is composed of longer wavelengths (e.g., red). It also is known that loss of sensitivity to dim objects is a function of the duration of pre-exposure and of the size, in visual angle, of the area of pre-exposure light.

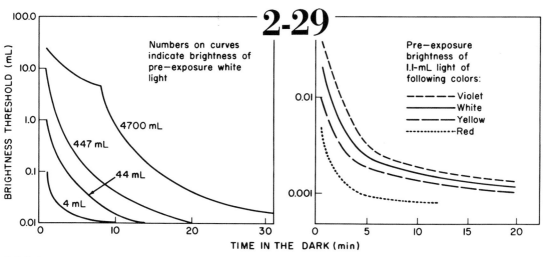

2-29

Because of these characteristics of the human eye, low-brightness red light is the most satisfactory for indicator lighting in situations where maximum dark adaptation is required for outside vision. Such red light is normally obtained by a filter with a cutoff of 6,000 Å. This cutoff point is rather arbitrary; a still higher cutoff would be slightly superior for dark adaptation but would waste an excessive proportion of the available light energy, and cutoff at a lower wavelength would entail some sacrifice in dark adaptation but would waste less light.

Red light, however, like any other highly colored light, has significant disadvantages; color discrimination is lost, and brightness relationships for colors are completely changed. This disadvantage handicaps the use of color coding for range markers on indicators, for color shading on maps, and for other, similar, purposes. This disadvantage does not handicap the use of colored warning lights; these contain their own light source and will be seen in very nearly their true colors.

REFLECTION HAZARDS

Any reflection from a windshield or window that reaches the operator's eyes reduces his ability to see out of the windshield or window and constitutes a hazard. This hazard can be reduced by observing the following:

1. Use glare shields placed in the light path so as to block any light that would otherwise be reflected from the windshield (see Fig. 2-30).

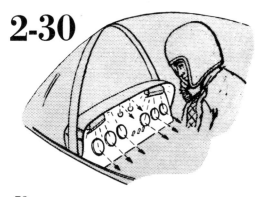

2. Place lights and lighted surfaces in such positions that reflections will not reach the eye.

3. Use dark, mat surfaces on those areas that might be reflected.

4. Use a minimum illumination level consistent with adequate visibility of the indicators.

BRIGHTNESS REQUIREMENTS

Both for maintaining dark adaptation and avoiding objectionable reflections, it is necessary to use the minimum illumination that will permit adequate indicator reading. The curves in Fig. 2-31 (Chalmers, et al., 1950) show the relationship between the brightness of indicator markings and the relative efficiency of indicator reading. Table 2-6 recommends various lighting systems, brightness levels, and adjustments for various conditions. For descriptions of the various lighting techniques, see below.

LIGHT DISTRIBUTION

The above recommendations assume a uniform distribution of light over all displays that must be read. In practice, uniform distribution is practically impossible to achieve with known lighting techniques (see below). Nevertheless, every possible effort should be made in the design and location of the lighting fixtures to provide for approximate equality of light distribution. Unless this is done, some details will not be legible while others are too bright. A ratio of 7:1 between the brightest and dimmest indicators or portions of indicators is considered the maximum range that is tolerable. In addition, direct or reflected light shining in the eyes of the operator must be avoided.

SELECTING INDICATOR LIGHTING

There are four basic techniques of instrument lighting: flood, indirect, edge, and rear lighting. These are illustrated in Fig. 2-32.

§ 2.3.3

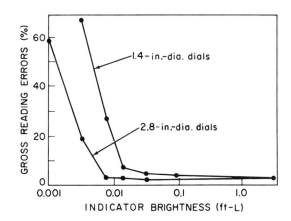

Table 2-6   Recommendations for Indicator, Panel, and Chart Lighting

Condition of use	Recommendations		
	Lighting technique	Brightness of markings (ft-L)	Brightness adjustment
Indicator reading, dark adaptation necessary	Red flood, indirect, or both, with operator choice	0.02–0.1	Continuous throughout range
Indicator reading, dark adaptation not necessary but desirable	Red or low-color-temperature white flood, indirect, or both, with operator choice	0.02–1.0	Continuous throughout range
Indicator reading, dark adaptation not necessary	White flood	1–20	Fixed or continuous
Panel monitoring, dark adaptation necessary	Red edge lighting, red or white flood, or both, with operator choice	0.02–1.0	Continuous throughout range
Panel monitoring, dark adaptation not necessary	White flood	10–20	Fixed or continuous
Either with possible exposure to bright flashes	White flood	10–20	Fixed
Either at very high altitude and restricted daylight	White flood	10–20	Fixed
Chart reading, dark adaptation necessary	Red or white flood with operator choice	0.1–1.0 (on white portions of chart)	Continuous throughout range
Chart reading, dark adaptation not necessary	White flood	5–20	Fixed or continuous

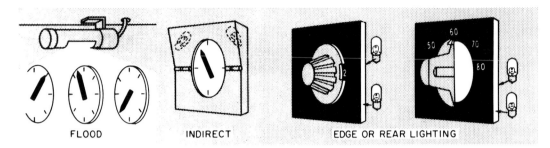

FLOOD   INDIRECT   EDGE OR REAR LIGHTING

Very often, two of these are used in combination.

Flood Lighting

With this technique, light is provided by a luminaire that is not integral with the indicator or panel. Because the light rays have a fairly large angle of incidence, the light source is usually located above the indicator so that all specularly reflected light will go downward rather than up into the windshield or the operator's eyes.

The advantages of this technique are the following:

a. Light distribution can be made fairly uniform.

b. Decals, knobs, and switches can be illuminated as well as the indicators.

c. The illumination of space between indicators aids distance perception.

d. A minimum number of luminaires is required, and they can be made easily accessible for replacement.

e. Luminaires do not obscure the edges of indicators as in indirect lighting.

The disadvantages of flood lighting are as follows:

a. Considerable light is scattered to other areas.

b. It is often difficult to position the luminaires without obstructing vision.

c. Shadows are cast by indicator bezels as the angle of incidence is reduced.

Indirect Lighting

With this technique, light is provided around the rim of the indicator by reflection from a light shield or by transmission through plastic. The light arrives at a very shallow angle of incidence. Shields can be tailored for individual indicators, or a single shield can cover an entire panel.

The advantages of this technique are the following:

a. Minimum light is scattered to other areas.

b. Light can be tailored for individual indicators.

c. Luminaires can be made integral with the indicator or panel.

The disadvantages of indirect lighting are as follows:

a. It is difficult to obtain uniform light distribution over a single indicator.

b. Shadows are formed in depressions (as on turn and bank and attitude indicators).

c. There is no light on decals, knobs, or switches between indicators.

d. It is difficult to avoid occluding the edges of indicators when oblique reading is necessary.

e. It is difficult to eliminate direct and specular glare.

f. Pointers are, generally, poorly illuminated.

g. Tailoring requires individual shields to fit each display.

Edge Lighting

With this technique, light is conducted from the edge of the display through transparent plastic and escapes through markings in the otherwise opaque covering over the plastic. This technique is not suitable for lighting conventional indicators, but it is excellent for printed instructions, labels, and control knobs on panels. Its advantages are that it scatters a minimum of light and that it can be made integral with the panel. Its disadvantages are the following:

a. It is not suitable for lighting moving parts, such as pointers and toggle switches, unless these can be made of plastic and large enough to trap and conduct light.

b. It is difficult to obtain uniform light distribution.

c. Luminaires must be tailored to fit each display.

Rear Lighting

With this technique, light is transmitted from the rear of the display through translucent markings in an otherwise opaque cov-

ering over transparent plastic. The effect is very similar to that obtained by edge lighting. The advantages of rear lighting are the following:

a. There is a minimum of scattered light to other areas.

b. It provides uniform distribution of the light.

c. It can be made integral with the panel.

The disadvantages of this technique are as follows:

a. It is difficult to illuminate moving parts (e.g., pointers and toggle switches) unless they are made of plastic and large enough to trap and conduct light.

b. Luminaires are generally inaccessible for replacement.

c. Unobstructed space is required behind the surface to be lighted.

2.4 Visual Coding

Spots of color, numbers, letters, lines, arrows, and other symbols are used to convey information all the time. Traffic lights, highway markers, route numbers, and color codes for wires and resistors are all examples of visual codes. Most of these codes are symbolic and must be learned, but, once learned, a good code is a simple and efficient way of getting information. Badly designed codes, on the other hand, can cause confusion and serious accidents.

This section deals only with visual coding. In many cases the designer should look at other kinds of codes—for example, codes that give information to the operator's sense of hearing or touch. This is a good idea, especially when the operator's eyes are overloaded. And, sometimes, auditory codes are better than visual ones; for example, someone can be warned with a horn even if he has his eyes closed because he can't close his ears. For a discussion and comparison of man's

sensory channels see Chapter 1. For a more detailed discussion of auditory presentation of information and speech communication, see Chapters 3 and 4.

2.4.1 Visual-coding methods

Information can be visually coded by color, number of dots, brightness, shape, orientation, flash rate, size, length of line, and stereo-depth. Table 2-7 compares and summarizes the advantages and disadvantages of these codes.

COLOR CODING

The number of colors that can be used for coding depends on whether colored lights or

Table 2-7 Comparison of Coding Methods

Code	Maximum number of items [*]	Evaluation	Comment
Color	11	Good	Little space required Location time short
Numerals and letters	Unlimited for combinations of symbols	Good	Little space required if contrast and resolution is good Location time longer than for color
Geometric shapes	~15	Good	Little space required if resolution is good
Size	5	Fair	Considerable space required Location time longer than for color or shapes
Number of dots	6	Fair	Considerable space required Easily confused with other coded items
Orientation of line	12	Fair	For special purposes
Length of line	4	Fair	Will clutter display with many signals
Brightness	4	Poor	Poor contrast effects will reduce visibility of weaker signals
Flash rate	4	Poor	Interacts poorly with other codes
Stereoscopic depth	Unknown	Fair	Requires complex electronic displays and special viewing equipment

[*] That generally will give overall accuracies of 95% or better.

§ 2.4.1

whether paints and reflected colors are used. In general, more saturated (i.e., more vivid) colors can be obtained with lights than with surface pigments or reflected colors, but there are more discriminable colors available for coding with surface pigments than there are for color coding with lights.

An important limitation of color coding is that it can be seriously distorted if it is used with certain kinds of illumination. For example, the color coding on maps and charts might be completely lost if the maps or charts are used in ready-rooms that are lighted with deep-red lights (see article 2.3.3). In general, however, colored lights are not so affected by the color of the general illumination as are surface colors.

Colored Lights for Coding

The number of spectral colors a normal person can easily identify depends on the brightness, the size (in visual angle), and the color of the light. The ten spectral colors in Fig. 2-33 can be identified correctly nearly 100% of the time after a relatively short training period when the light has a brightness of 1 mL or more and is bigger than 45 min of visual angle. These spectral colors are the purest that can be had with lights. It is difficult to get spectral colors in any practical situation, but one can come close by using high-purity, interference filters.

Surface Colors for Coding

Following is a summary of surface colors commonly used for coding physical hazards and equipment.

1. Red is the basic color for fire (alarm boxes, extinguishers, buckets, hose connections, sprinkler valves, hydrants, etc.), danger (cans with flammable contents, barricades and obstructions, signs, etc.), stop (bars on hazardous machinery, switches, signs, etc.), and for emergency (equipment shutdown switches, police lights, etc.).

2. Orange is another color for designating dangerous moving parts of machines; starting switches; levers of machinery with exposed hazards; inside of guards for gears, pulleys, chains, exposed gears, cutting edges, and pulleys; starting buttons; etc.

3. Yellow is the basic color for designating caution and for marking physical hazards that might cause a person to stumble, trip, fall, collide, etc. Yellow and black checks and stripes are usually recommended for mobile equipment, covering on guy wires, unguarded platforms, pillars and columns, etc.

4. Green is the basic color for designating safety and first aid equipment (safety bulletin boards, first-aid kits, stretchers, gas masks, etc.).

5. Blue is another color for designating caution generally limited to warning against starting or using equipment under repair (barrier flags or signs for elevators, ovens, boilers, etc., that are under repair).

6. Purple is the basic color for designating radiation hazards. Yellow should be used with purple for tags, labels, and signs for rooms and containers storing radioactive material or containers and areas contaminated with radioactivity.

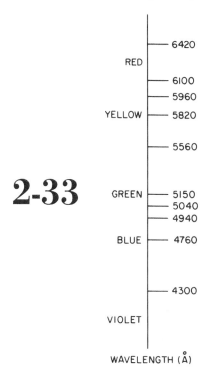

2-33

RED	— 6420
	— 6100
	— 5960
YELLOW	— 5820
	— 5560
GREEN	— 5150
	— 5040
	— 4940
BLUE	— 4760
	— 4300
VIOLET	

WAVELENGTH (Å)

Color Coding and Color Blindness

About 6% of healthy, adult males have markedly reduced sensitivity to colors. Most of these so-called color-blind people can correctly identify some colors—they merely do not see as many colors as color-sighted people do. Actually, only 0.003% of males are completely color blind, i.e., are unable to see any color except black or white.

If *colored lights* are to be used for coding, and if color-blind people will have to use the color code, there are only three colors that should be used. These three colors are aviation red, aviation green, and aviation blue as defined by the Army-Navy Aeronautical Specification AN-C-56.

The above colors, if used, must meet the requirements of the specifications exactly because there are many green, red, and blue hues that color-blind people cannot identify correctly. And even these colors can be used only at moderate distances; at great distances, the blue is often confused with the green. Also, white or yellow should not be added to the code because color-blind people confuse red with yellow and green with white.

The *surface colors* listed in Table 2-8 are ideal for coding because both color-sighted and color-blind people can recognize them relatively easily. The numbers refer to those in Federal Specification TT-C-595, except the one for blue (10B 7/6), which is a Munsell standard specification (Munsell, 1942).

SHAPE CODING

The number of different shapes a person can identify easily is quite large. For all practical purposes, the number is unlimited for combinations of letters and numbers. For geometric shapes, however, it is limited, as far as learning and retention are concerned, to some number around 15.

Numbers and Letters

The main restrictions in using letter and number codes are the space required and the

Table 2-8   Surface Colors for Color-Normal and Color-Blind People

Color	Spec. No.*	Color	Spec. No.*
Red	1110	Gray	1625
Orange	1210	Buff	1745
Yellow	1310	White	1755
Blue	10B 7/6	Black	1770
Purple	2715		

* From Fed. Spec. TT-C-595 except for Blue, which is from Munsell, 1942.

operator's ability to learn what the letters and numbers stand for. If letters and numbers have sharp outlines, high contrast, and are well lighted, they can be identified accurately if they are greater than 10 min of visual angle.

Although there are quite a number of letters and numbers that can be used for coding, some of them are easily confused with others because of their shapes. For example, 9's are often confused with 0's and 8's at great distances. It is possible, however, to design these numbers so that they are less often confused. Recommendations about the design of letters and numbers are given in article 2.6.2.

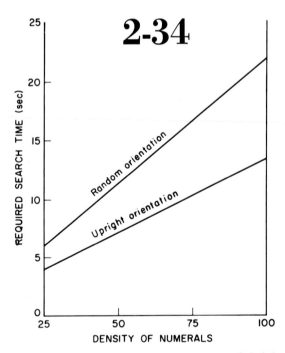

The graph of Fig. 2-34 (Green, et al., 1953) shows the search time required to locate a specific numeral as a function of the density of numerals on the display. Two numeral orientations were used; in one case, the numerals were upright with respect to the observer; in the other case, the numerals were randomly oriented. The visual angle subtended by the display was 20 deg (this is equivalent to a display 7 in. in diameter at a viewing distance of 20 in.). The visual angle subtended by the numerals was 14 min (this is equivalent to a $\frac{1}{12}$-in.-high letter at 20 in.).

From a study of Fig. 2-34, the following points can be noted:

a. Search time increases as the numeral density increases.

b. Search time is shorter when all of the numerals are upright with respect to the observer than it is when they are randomly oriented.

Geometric Shapes

If geometric shapes are needed for coding, as a primary criterion choose shapes that are compatible with and have association value with the coded objects, if possible (see article 2.4.2). As a secondary criterion, design the symbols to be highly discriminable. For example, the geometric shapes shown in Fig. 2-35 (Sleight, 1952) are easily identified and rarely confused. They are given in the order of the time required to identify each from a complex field of shapes. These forms can be identified correctly nearly 100% of the time if the maximum dimension is at least 12 min of visual angle, the outline of the shape is sharp, and the contrast is high.

SIZE CODING

Information can be coded by correlating symbol area with some actual characteristic of the target. The most obvious correlation is area of symbol with size of target, but the area of the symbol also could represent the range of the target, etc.

Figure 2-36 (below) shows how accurate a size code can be when the code has different numbers of symbols. The symbols in this experiment were isosceles triangles in which the base was $\frac{3}{5}$ of the altitude. The size of the smallest triangle was 10 min by 16 min, and the size of the largest triangle was 48 min by 80 min. The intermediate-size triangles were spaced logarithmically between these two extremes. It is evident that if more than five sizes are used, errors in identifying any particular size become excessive.

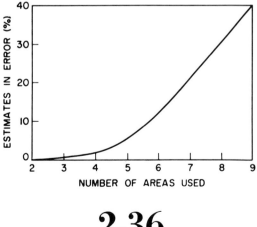

§ 2.4.1

85

DOT CODING

Targets can be coded by numbers of dots. For example, one dot on a map might represent one to five oil storage tanks, two dots six to ten tanks, three dots 11 to 15 tanks, and so on. Figure 2-37 (below) shows how accurately people can estimate the number of dots when the dots are exposed for only 0.1 sec. Note that accuracy is good for five dots or less, but is much poorer for six or more dots.

The data in Fig. 2-37 are for immediate identification of the number of dots. Accuracy improves as the time an operator can look at the dots increases (the slope of the curve will look more like that of the previous figure).

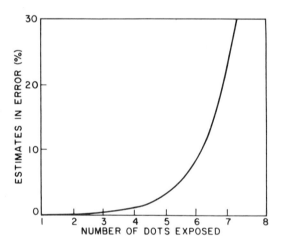

NUMBER OF DOTS EXPOSED

In addition, these data are for dots in random positions. Arranging the dots in familiar patterns or with uniform spacing improves accuracy even more. (Patterning dots, however, is actually a form of shape coding.)

LINE CODING

Figure 2-38 (above, right) shows how orientation and length of line might be used to code the course (direction of movement) and speed of a target. Studies of the accuracy of estimating target course by line orientation indicate that 50% of the course estimates will be in error by less than 6 deg, and 95% of

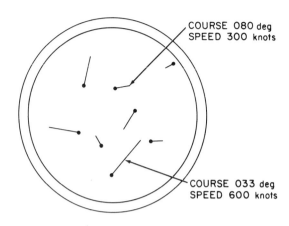

the course estimates will be in error by less than 15 deg (Baker and Grether, 1954). These values are valid for line lengths as short as 0.1 in. and for untrained observers viewing the display at 14 in.

Figure 2-39 (below) shows percentage of identification errors as a function of the number of line lengths used. In this case, the shortest line was 0.1 in., the longest was 1.0 in., and the intermediate lengths were equally spaced on a logarithmic scale, i.e., they progressed by equal ratios. The graph reveals that up to four line lengths can be identified without significant error when presented singly and that, when more than five line lengths are used, errors of identification increase rapidly.

BRIGHTNESS CODING

Under good viewing conditions, no more than four brightness steps can be used for

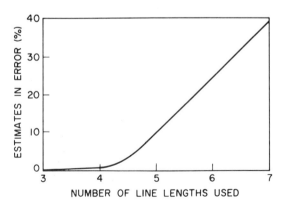

NUMBER OF LINE LENGTHS USED

coding. For most practical conditions only two steps—bright and dim or light and dark—can be used. Brightness coding is not very good because spots of different brightnesses are often distracting and tiring. In addition, the coded items often interfere with each other, e.g., dimmer targets are often obscured or masked by the brighter ones.

FLASH-RATE CODING

There are few data on this method of coding. The data we have seem to show that no more than four identifiable flash rates can be used even under ideal conditions. This kind

to the right of line four in the left-hand display. Thus, it will be seen in front of, or closer than, the background. If the positions of target B were reversed, it would appear to be behind, or farther than, the background.

To make stereo-depth coding work, there has to be some special equipment to produce the two different displays with the targets and coded information in their correct positions. In addition, further special equipment is needed to get each eye to see the proper display. There are several ways of doing this. One is to use a refinement of the stereoscope viewer that was popular years ago. More recently, motion pictures have used polarized light and polarized glasses to produce the

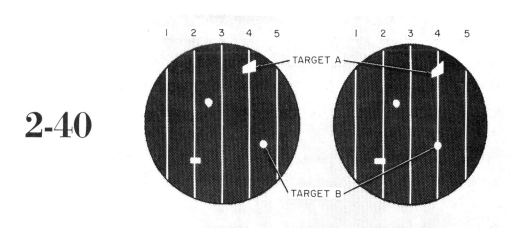

2-40

of coding should be limited to only one or two items on a display because a field of flickering lights is annoying to look at.

STEREO-DEPTH CODING

Stereoscopic depth is the result of the fusion of two slightly different pictures formed in the two eyes. Figure 2-40 shows a display that could be used for stereo-depth perception. The right-hand display must be looked at with the right eye and the left-hand display with the left eye. Target A is in the same place on both displays and so will appear to be in the same plane as the background. Target B, however, is on line four in the right-hand display and

same effect. Thus, the special equipment needed makes this kind of coding impractical for most purposes. Another limitation is that a sizeable proportion of healthy adults (perhaps 5%) do not have stereo-depth perception.

2.4.2 Selecting a code

In military and commercial navigational systems, range and bearing are two kinds of information that have to be coded. Recommendations about codes for these kinds of information will be given in section 2.7. Some other kinds of information that often are coded symbolically are the following:

a. The identification of the target (for example, friend or foe).

b. The type of target (for example, aircraft, ship, or vehicle).

c. The speed, course, and elevation of the target.

In selecting a code, the designer should consider the following:

a. The compatibility of the code with the kind of information that is to be coded.

b. The space required to use the code.

c. The association value of the code symbols.

d. How easily and accurately the operator can understand the code.

e. Whether the code will distract the operator or interfere with other codes.

f. The amount of information that needs to be coded and the amount of information that can be coded with each method.

CODE COMPATIBILITY

Information can be about different kinds of things (qualitative information) or about different amounts of things (quantitative information). Identification and type-of-target information are examples of qualitative information. Examples of quantitative information include such things as speed, course, and elevation. Codes also can be qualitative, quantitative, or both. Shape and color codes, for instance, can be either qualitative or quantitative; squares, rectangles, circles, and ellipses are frequently used for qualitative coding, but it is also possible to obtain continuous changes from a square to a rectangle or from a circle to an ellipse, which is quantitative coding. In general, however, codes are easier to use and understand if qualitative codes are used for qualitative information and quantitative codes are used for quantitative information.

SCALING QUANTITATIVE CODES

In making up a code, the first step is to pick the upper and lower limits of the scale.

Then decide how many steps there are to be. Finally, decide how to space or scale the steps to get the same amount of accuracy all along the scale.

For example, suppose that you have decided to use the size of a square on a map to code the size of fuel dumps, and, for practical reasons, you decide to use an area of 0.01 in.² to show the smallest fuel dump and an area of 1 in.² to show the largest one. Next, you decide that it is only worthwhile to show five different sizes—three in addition to the smallest and largest ones. The problem in scaling is this: what should be the sizes of the intermediate squares?

To solve this problem, apply the following rule: in scaling a code, the values should be equally spaced on a logarithmic scale rather than on a linear scale because they are less likely to be confused if they are on a logarithmic scale. Thus, the five sizes should be 0.01, 0.032, 0.10, 0.32, and 1.0 in.², with each area being 3.2 times the next smaller one. If you were to space the five areas on a linear scale, the sizes would be 0.01, 0.257, 0.505, 0.752, and 1.0 in.², with each area increasing by 0.2475 in.². As can be seen from Fig. 2-41, which is drawn to scale, the logarithmic progression is easier to recognize.

ASSOCIATION VALUE OF CODES

Because of our training and experience with them over many years, some kinds of codes have strong association value for almost everyone. For instance, there is nothing in the color green, by itself, that means "go," but all during our lives we have learned to associate green with "go." This is just one example; others could be cited. Thus, a good rule is: codes should take advantage of universal associations if there are such associations.

LOCATION TIME FOR CODES

As more and more coded information is put on display, the time needed to search the display to find the information increases. For crowded displays, visual codes should be picked to reduce the search, or location, time. Although tests have not been made comparing all of the common visual codes, there are good data on four kinds of codes. In general, location time increases for color, shape, brightness, and size codes in that order (color codes can be located fastest; size codes, slowest).

For example, in some air-defense centers, the positions of aircraft are plotted by moving blocks around on a large map. The officer in charge usually needs to detect quickly those aircraft that have not yet been identified. Therefore, because this is usually the most critical item of information, it should be color coded.

in a field of 25 red and 25 green numbers.

DECODING ACCURACY

In any code, accuracy decreases as the number of coded items increases. For example, accuracy is nearly perfect for a simple two-color code; it is still very high, but not so nearly perfect, for a five-color code; it decreases still more for a nine-color code; and it decreases much more for a 15-color code.

There is no simple formula for showing how the designer can trade off accuracy and number of items. But the results of a great

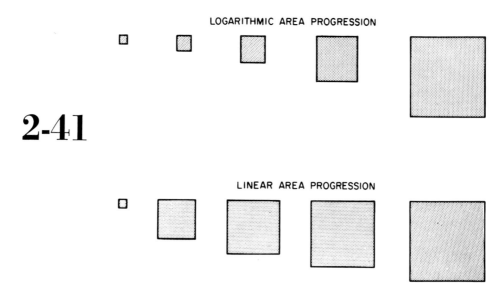

LOGARITHMIC AREA PROGRESSION

2-41

LINEAR AREA PROGRESSION

Color coding can also be used to reduce location time on a crowded display even though the color does not code a critical item of information. For example, if an operator has to search for a particular number on a display that contains many other numbers, location time will *decrease* if half the numbers are red and half green instead of all the same color and if the operator is told to locate "Red 342" or "Green 695." Conversely, if an operator is searching for a number of a particular color, say "Red 342," having numbers of another color will not *increase* the location time; it takes just about as long to find "Red 342" in a field of 25 red numbers as it does to find it

many experiments—some of which are given later in this section—have the general form shown in Fig. 2-42. Note that there are no numbers along either scale on this curve because the exact numbers depend on the kind of code—color, shape, size—and the conditions under which the code is used—the amount of time the observer has to look, the amount of light on the symbols, etc.

The important thing about the curve of Fig. 2-42 is its general shape. From the shape, it can be seen that, if there are only a *few* items in a code, one more item can be added without much penalty (in terms of errors). But, before long, adding one more item to a code

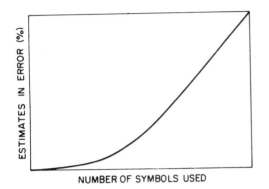

NUMBER OF SYMBOLS USED

the code. In spite of this, people still make errors in reading traffic signals because of momentary lapses in attention, fatigue, or other reasons. Fortunately, these errors are usually less than 1%.

COMPOUND CODING

A simple-coded target is one that is coded to convey only one kind of information. A compound-coded target is one that is coded to convey two or more kinds of information. Compound coding increases the amount of information that can be conveyed, but it also increases the difficulty of interpreting the code.

When considering compound coding, the following recommendations should be observed:

1. If only one kind of information is to be coded, it should be coded by only one coding method. Compound coding for only one kind of information usually is less satisfactory than simple coding if the single code used is the best available.

2. If two or more kinds of information are to be coded, the same number of coding methods should be used; do not use one coding method to code two or more kinds of information.

brings a big penalty in increased errors. The critical word here is "few," and there is no exact way to define it. Thus, the shape of the curve in Fig. 2-42 gives us the following coding rule: use only as many symbols in a code as are absolutely necessary because errors always increase as the number of symbols is increased.

There is another important point to remember about visual codes: there is no such thing as an absolutely foolproof code—operators will make errors with any code—the best one can hope to do is to keep errors down to tolerable levels. The traffic-light code is probably as nearly foolproof as any code; it is simple and clear, and the average city dweller has many hundreds of thousands of trials to learn

2.5 *Warning and Signal Devices*

Very often the operator needs only a warning of a dangerous condition or a signal that something is or is not operating. It is the presentation of such simple two-valued information that is covered in this section.

The most common devices for presenting simple two-valued information are signal lights, mechanical "flag" signals, and auditory signals. The latter devices are discussed in Chapter 3. Although the major emphasis is on warning devices, this section will also discuss the use of simple signals that indicate caution or operational status.

2.5.1 *Warning devices*

A good warning device should meet the following three requirements:

a. It should break through and get the attention of a busy or bored operator.

b. It should tell him what is wrong or what action to take.

c. It should not prevent his continued attention to other important duties if this is necessary.

GETTING ATTENTION

To break through and get the attention of a busy or bored operator will require a signal of high attention value. This is particularly true if such signals are rare and, therefore, unexpected. Attention value goes up as the size, brightness, loudness, or motion of a signal is increased, but the signal should not be so intense that the operator is blinded or startled.

GROUPING SIGNALS

The designer can help the operator to know what is wrong by grouping signal lights or mechanical "flags" in appropriate patterns. Such patterns also make a signal that differs from the others stand out so that detection is easier. A pictorial pattern, however, can be of even more help to the operator; by showing the positions of switches, valves, etc., as part of a pictorial diagram, the effects of their operation are easy to see.

Two examples of grouping signals that readily come to mind are the submarine "Christmas tree" and the railroad control-tower switchboard. The "Christmas tree" on a submarine shows the condition of all hatches, which must be closed before diving. For each hatch there are two lights: a red one for "open" (i.e., unsafe) and a green one for "closed" (i.e., safe). Before diving, all green lights must be on and all red lights off. The location of a red light in the pattern, plus an identification label, tells the operator which hatch is open.

In the control tower of many railroad switchyards is a "switchboard" that includes a diagram showing each switch in the yard. At each switch location are lights that indicate the position of the switch. The control-tower operator can tell at a glance if any given switch is in the proper position, and

a signal changing any switch position is easy to see.

SELECTING SIGNALS

In selecting a warning signal for a particular application the designer should consider the urgency of the information, the other duties of the operator, and other warning devices in the operator's station. If the operator is bothered with unimportant warnings, he might neglect the really critical ones, and too many warning devices of the same type will only serve to confuse him.

Auditory warnings are very attention-getting and are independent of where the operator is looking, but they are less suitable than visual signals for telling the operator what is wrong or what to do. Also, they can interfere with speech communication (see Chapter 4). Therefore, auditory signals should be used only for a few of the most urgent warnings. (For further information on auditory signals, see Chapter 3.)

Signal lights can be quite effective. By their location, labeling, color, or other coding, they can tell the operator what to do, but he must be looking in their general direction to notice them. Other visual signals, such as mechanical flags, have low attention value. They are good for giving "on-off" types of information rather than warnings.

Signals to other sensory channels (e.g., odor, vibration, electric shock) also can be used for warning and sometimes are. For data on these sensory channels, see Chapter 1.

LIGHTS FOR WARNING SIGNALS

By warning lights we mean those lights that signal a dangerous condition, a condition generally requiring prompt action by the operator. Such lights normally should be red because red means danger to most people. Any other signal lights in the operator's vicinity should be of other colors. In addition, the location, brightness, and attention value of lights for warnings should be considered. These subjects are discussed in the paragraphs that follow.

Location and Identification

Warning lights become less effective as they are moved out of the center of the field of vision. For urgent warnings, they should always be within 30 deg of the operator's normal line of sight (see Chapter 7).

Sometimes a large number of warning or caution signals must be used in a single operator station. This situation not only adds to the operator's identification problem, but it also creates the problem of finding panel space near the operator's normal line of sight.

A convenient solution to this problem is illustrated in Fig. 2-43; it consists of providing a master warning or caution light and a word panel. The master light can be located near the operator's line of sight on the instrument panel, and the word panel can be located where space is more readily available. Any time the master light comes on, the operator checks the word panel where the specific warning or caution also will be lit up. In the example shown, the master light is on, and the word panel warns of fire in engine No. 2.

Because warning lights call for fast and correct action by the operator, their identification must be simple and positive. They should be provided with labels that are always visible or that light up when they do. Ideally, each light also should have a unique location and be easily distinguishable from other lights. As a further aid, the warning light should be alongside of, or built into, the associated control device (see Fig. 2-44).

Brightness

Warning lights should be bright enough to stand out clearly against the panel on which they appear under all expected lighting conditions (see section 2.3), but they should not be so bright as to blind the operator. In work stations that are darkened at night, provision should be included for dimming the warning lights when other lights are dimmed. This can be accomplished by "tying in" warning lights with the same switch used to dim panel or general station lights. In this way, the proper level is provided automatically.

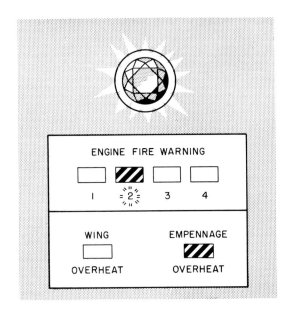

Attention Value

A flashing or interrupted light is somewhat more attention-getting than a steady one, but it also is more disturbing to the operator. Flashing lights should be used only for the most urgent warnings, and if used, a rate of about four flashes per second, with equal light and dark intervals, is recommended.

If the operator's head position is relatively fixed, the warning light can be beamed directly

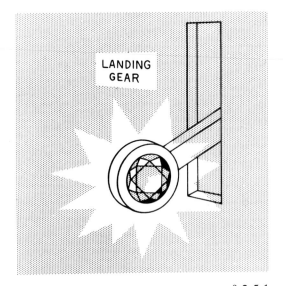

§ 2.5.1

at the operator rather than diffused, as is usually the case. Although this arrangement is almost certain to get his attention, the possible blinding effect rules it out unless the emergency is great and other methods of presentation are not adequate.

2.5.2 *Caution and status signals*

Signal lights also are used for many purposes that would not be considered as warnings, although it is not always easy to make a distinction. For instance, they are often used to signal minor failures that do not demand immediate action. Sometimes they merely signal the operational status of different system components. In all these uses for signal lights, getting the operator's attention is much less important than it is for warnings; the operator usually looks for the lights when he wants information.

The use of lights for status or caution signals is frequently overdone, however, with the result that large arrays of lights are provided that dazzle and confuse the operator. Some general rules for avoiding the excessive or improper use of such signal lights in a work station can be listed as follows:

1. Use red lights only for warnings (see article 2.4.1).

2. If the station must be operated at times in relative darkness (as in aircraft cockpits,

ship radar rooms, etc.) use signal lights only for intermittent and high-priority signals.

3. Avoid using signal lights for information the operator can get in other ways, such as by control position (see Chapter 6).

2.5.3 *Mechanical "flag" signals*

Small mechanical "flags," with word or pictorial labels, are often more suitable than signal lights for status or caution signals. The "flags" have low attention value, unless they are quite large and moving, so that the operator must be looking directly at the flag, or within a few degrees of it, to notice it. For this reason, flags should not be used for warnings, but only for status or "on-off" signals.

A common application of mechanical "flag" signals is that in which they are used for on-off indicators. In many instances, such indications are superfluous and should not be used. In some situations, however, it is desirable to indicate by a positive signal that some component of a system is or is not in operation. For example, inoperative or caged components can be clearly identified as such if mechanical or electrical detection of the component status is possible and practicable. In this case the operator can be alerted to such situations by a flag or shutter, such as that shown in Fig. 2-45, that moves into view whenever the component becomes inoperative for any reason.

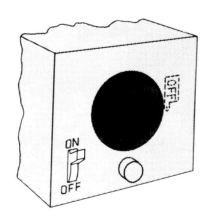
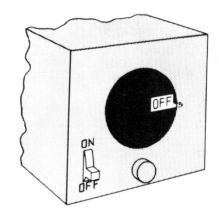

2.6 *Mechanical Indicators*

Mechanical indicators are those in which information is presented symbolically or pictorially by means of one or more moving elements. The moving element might be a pointer or pictorial reference marker (see Fig. 2-46), or it might be a fluid column such as in a thermometer. If the indicator has a scale, the scale might be the moving element, with the pointer or reference marker fixed, or in some cases, both the scale and pointer might move.

2.6.1 *Selecting symbolic indicators*

There are many different types of mechanical indicators. Which one will be best for a particular application depends on the conditions and method of use, which were discussed briefly in articles 2.1.1 and 2.1.2. This article describes the various types of symbolic indicators and gives their advantages and disadvantages. Pictorial indicators are discussed in article 2.6.3.

BASIC TYPES OF INDICATORS

There are three basic types of symbolic indicators (see Fig. 2-47): the direct-reading counter (A), the moving pointer with fixed scale (B), and the moving scale with fixed index (C). The selection of any one of these types of indicators depends on the particular use to which it is to be put.

Table 2-9 lists the relative advantages and disadvantages of the three basic indicator types with reference to the method of use. It is apparent from the table that, although the counter offers advantages in reading speed and minimum opportunity for error, for general purposes, the moving-pointer type of indicator offers the greatest number of advantages.

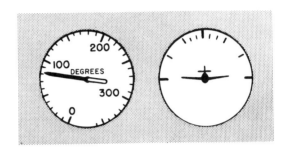

2-46

2-47

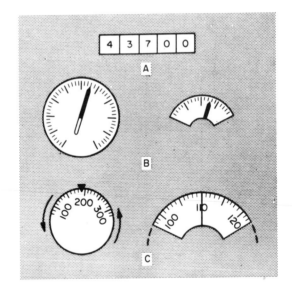

VARIATIONS OF BASIC TYPES

There are several possible variations of the last two basic types of symbolic indicators. These can be listed as follows:

a. Circular and curved scale with moving pointer. This design (A in Fig. 2-48) is gen-

§ 2.6.1

Table 2-9   Relative Evaluation of Basic Symbolic-Indicator Types

For . . .	Moving pointer is . . .	Moving scale is . . .	Counter is . . .
Quantitative reading	Fair	Fair	Good (Requires minimum reading time with minimum reading error)
Qualitative and check reading	Good (Location of pointer and change in position is easily detected)	Poor (Difficult to judge direction and magnitude of pointer deviation)	Poor (Position changes not easily detected)
Setting	Good (Has simple and direct relation between pointer motion and motion of setting knob, and pointer-position change aids monitoring)	Fair (Has somewhat ambiguous relation between pointer motion and motion of setting knob)	Good (Most accurate method of monitoring numerical settings, but relation between pointer motion and motion of setting knob is less direct)
Tracking	Good (Pointer position is readily monitored and controlled, provides simple relationship to manual-control motion, and provides some information about rate)	Fair (Not readily monitored and has somewhat ambiguous relationship to manual-control motion)	Poor (Not readily monitored, and has ambiguous relationship to manual-control motion)
General	Good (But requires greatest exposed and illuminated area on panel, and scale length is limited)	Fair (Offers saving in panel space because only small section of scale need be exposed and illuminated, and long scale is possible)	Fair (Most economical in use of space and illuminated area, scale length limited only by number of counter drums, but is difficult to illuminate properly)

§ 2.6.1

erally recommended. The circular scale permits a maximum of exposed scale length in a minimum of panel space, it permits a compact indicator case, and the long pointer and rotational movement aid in check and qualitative reading. The circular scale is preferred to the curved scale for most applications.

b. Vertical and horizontal straight scale with moving pointer. This design (B) is especially desirable for short-scale indicators. It permits a saving in front-panel space and provides a good means of pointer alignment and checking. The shorter pointer and lack of rotational movement, however, makes it more difficult for the eye to notice change in the position of the pointer.

c. Circular and curved scale with fixed index. A fully exposed scale usually is not necessary, and the partially exposed scale (C) can be generally recommended. This arrangement permits a large range of values in a limited panel space. Overlapping the covered scale portions also saves panel space. It should be noted, however, that the indicators used in tracking, such as magnetic heading indicators, should have the full scale exposed.

d. Vertical and horizontal straight scale with fixed pointer. In this design (D), a moving scale behind an open window is provided by a moving straight scale, drum, or tape. The moving tape is particularly suitable for presenting a large range of values that are to be read quantitatively.

LONG-SCALE INDICATORS

When a large range of values must be displayed on one indicator, the conventional methods of presentation are usually inadequate. For example, if we assume the need for an altimeter with a range of from zero to 70,000 ft, and if we also assume that the operator requires reading precision that necessitates graduated intervals corresponding to every 20 ft throughout the entire range, an indicator with a moving pointer and a fixed scale would require a scale length of about 245 in. to provide altitude information with this degree of precision. But an indicator with such a scale length is impractical.

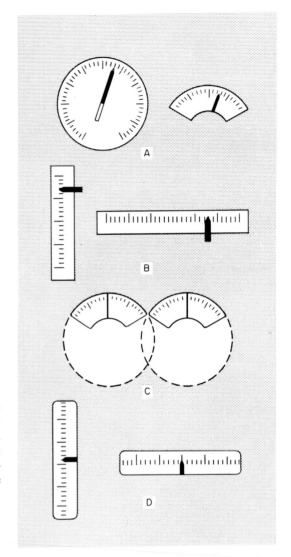

2-48

Several solutions to the problem of long-scale indication have been evaluated and can be listed as follows:

a. Multiple pointers. In this design (A in Fig. 2-49), there is one multirevolution pointer for fine readings and one or more other pointers for gross readings. With this design, the reader must mentally combine several separately indicated values, and the probability of gross reading errors is high (Grether, 1947).

b. Subdial. For certain applications it is possible to compress a long scale by means of a vernier subdial. With this design (B), the main dial provides gross values and the subdial permits more precise readings.

c. Direct-reading counter. This design (C) is an excellent means of presenting a large range of quantitative values, and it requires very little panel space. It is not satisfactory, however, for qualitative reading or tracking.

d. Moving-pointer-moving-scale combination. This design (D) is to be avoided because the error probability is high in combining these two types of indicators.

e. Moving-pointer-counter combination. This design (E) is a generally recommended solution for long-scale indicators for check and qualitative reading, but it is slightly inferior to counters alone for purely quantitative reading (Grether, 1947).

f. Moving-tape with fixed index. A straight scale with a moving tape (see Fig. 2-50) can be used for long-scale presentation. Although front-panel space is saved with this design, it takes up more area in back of the panel.

2.6.2 *The design of symbolic indicators*

A few of the terms to be used in this article and their definitions are as follows (see Fig. 2-51, top of next page):

a. Scale range. This is the numerical difference between the highest and lowest value on a scale.

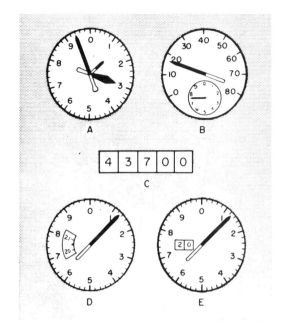

2-49

2-50

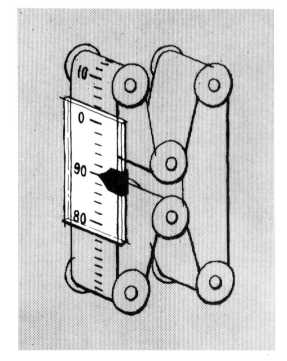

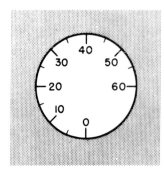

SCALE RANGE _60
NUMBERED INTERVAL VALUE _ _ _ _ _ _ _ _ _ _ _ 10
GRADUATION INTERVAL VALUE _ _ _ _ _ _ _ _ _ _ 5

b. Numbered-interval value. This is the numerical difference between adjacent numbers on a scale.

c. Graduation-interval value. This is the numerical difference represented by adjacent graduation marks.

operator should not be required to make mental conversions of the indicated values to be able to use them. An example of transformed scale values can be found in jet-aircraft-engine tachometers that have been calibrated in percent rpm rather than actual rpm. For the pilot, this has several advantages. Maximum rpm differs for different engine models and types. Transforming the scale values into percent rpm relieves the pilot of the necessity of remembering operating rpm values for different engines. In addition, the range from 0 to 100% is more easily interpreted than a range of true values, such as 0–8,000 rpm, and the smaller numbers on the dial make a more readable scale. These advantages can be seen in the two tachometers illustrated in Fig. 2-53 (bottom of page). The dial on the left can be read more precisely than the one on the right, and it is less cluttered.

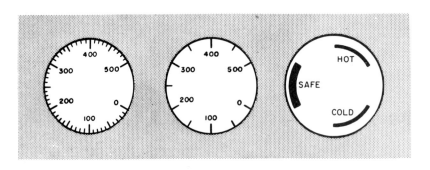

2-52

SCALE SELECTION

Before a designer selects a scale for a mechanical indicator he should decide on the appropriate scale range and should estimate the reading precision required. The scale should be designed to be read as precisely as the operator needs to perform his task but no more precisely.

More information should not be present on a scale than the operator needs. Figure 2-52 gives examples of different levels of scale complexity. The designer should select the least complex scale that fulfills the needs of the operator.

All displays, if possible, should provide information in an immediately usable form; the

Interval Values

Some combinations of graduation-interval values and scale-numbering systems are more satisfactory than others. The following recommendations will assist the designer in select-

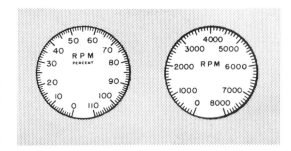

GRADUATION INTERVAL VALUE	RECOMMENDED SCALES	NUMBERED INTERVAL VALUE	GRADUATION MARKS		
			MAJOR	INTERMEDIATE	MINOR
0.1, 1, 10	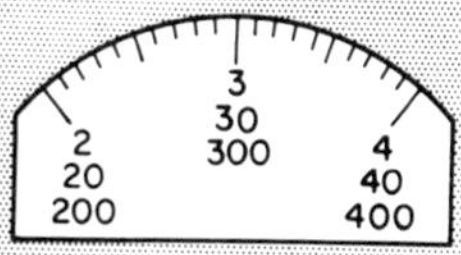	1, 10, 100	X	X	X
	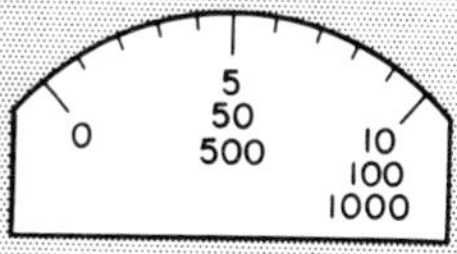	5, 50, 500	X		X
	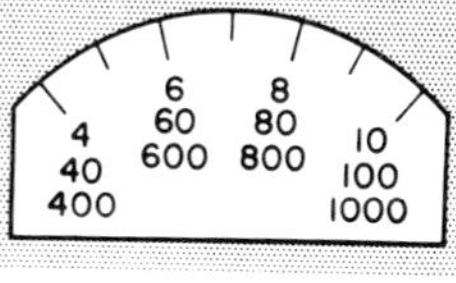	2, 20, 200	X	X	
0.2, 2, 20	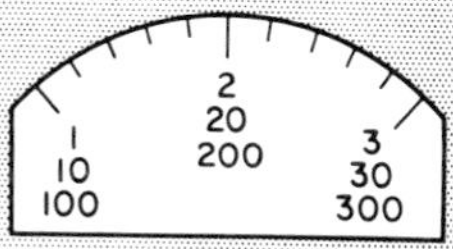	1, 10, 100	X		X
	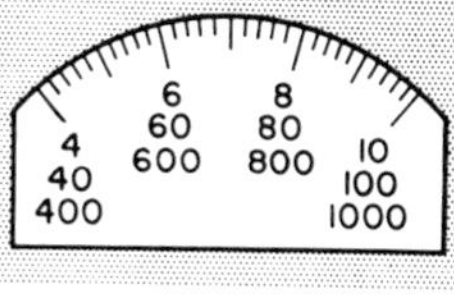	2, 20, 200	X	X	X
0.5, 5, 50	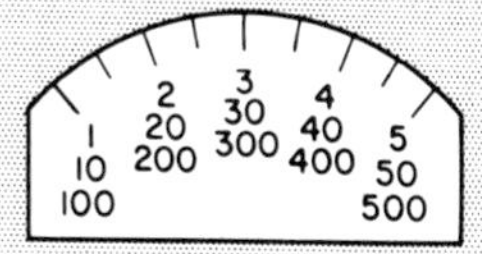	1, 10, 100	X	X	
	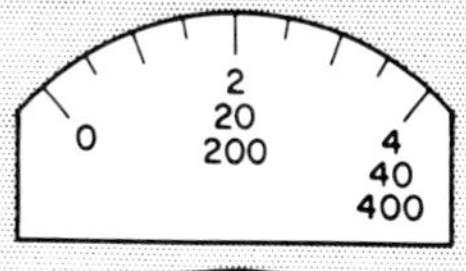	2, 20, 200	X	X	X
	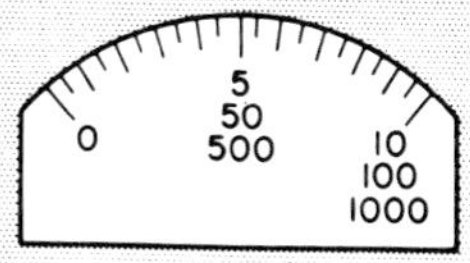	5, 50, 500	X	X	X

2-54

§ 2.6.2

99

Table 2-10   Examples of Good, Fair, and Poor Progressions for Scale Numbers

Good					Fair					Poor				
0.1	0.2	0.3	0.4	0.5	0.2	0.4	0.6	0.8	1.0	0.25	0.5	0.75	1.0	
1	2	3	4	5	2	4	6	8	10	2.5	5	7.5	10	
10	20	30	40	50	20	40	60	80	100	25	50	75	100	
100	200	300	400	500	200	400	600	800	1000	250	500	750	1000	
0.5	1.0	1.5	2.0	2.5						0.4	0.8	1.2	1.6	1.8
5	10	15	20	25						4	8	12	16	18
50	100	150	200	250						40	80	120	160	180

ing the most readable scale (see Fig. 2-54):

1. The graduation-interval values should be one, two, five, or decimal multiples thereof. Graduation-interval values of two are somewhat less desirable than values of one or five. Table 2-10 gives examples of good, fair, and poor numerical progressions.

2. The number of graduation marks between numbered graduation marks should not exceed nine, i.e., there should be no more than ten graduation intervals.

3. Normally, scales numbered by intervals of 1, 10, 100, etc., and subdivided by ten graduation intervals, are superior to other acceptable scales.

4. It is generally recommended that scales be designed so that interpolation between graduation marks is not necessary, but when space is limited, it is better to require interpolated readings than to clutter the dial with crowded graduation marks.

With this information in mind, the designer can select from Fig. 2-54 the most suitable scale. (For special cases, such as nonlinear and long-range scales, see below.) Assuming sufficient space, a scale that is to be read to the nearest 1, 10, or 100, etc. should be selected from those scales in Fig. 2-54 with graduation-interval values of 1, 10, or 100. If accuracy to the nearest 0.5, 5, or 50 units is required, scales with 0.5, 5, or 50 graduation-interval values should be selected, and so on.

Scale Interpolation

In general, scales that are to be read quantitatively should be designed so that interpolation between graduation marks is not necessary; scales should be designed to be read to the nearest graduation mark. For instance, if we assume a scale range of 50 and a scale that is to be read to the nearest unit, the preferred scale would be numbered by tens with a graduation mark for each unit as shown in Fig. 2-55(A). If the space available for this scale were restricted to 2 in., the same scale would appear as in Fig. 2-55(B), but the

A

B

2-55

C

graduation marks on this scale are too crowded to be read accurately and rapidly under low illumination; the midpoints are only 0.04 in. apart, and this is 0.03 in. less than the recommended minimum. In situations such as this, it is better to design a scale in which interpolation is necessary as, for example, Fig. 2-55(C). This scale has a graduation-mark spacing of 0.08 in., which is acceptable for low illumination. Also, this scale requires only a simple interpolation of one unit between graduation marks. When space is greatly limited, it might be necessary to interpolate in fifths or even tenths, but such interpolation will increase reading errors.

Special Scales

Certain applications of scales require unique design features, and, in such cases, compromises with the recommendations listed above must be made. Examples of these special cases include multirevolution and non-linear scales.

Multirevolution scales. The heading indicator in Fig. 2-56(A) violates the scale-numbering recommendations because it uses the numerical progression of 30, 60, 90, etc. This, however, represents a compromise between good numbering progression and manageable dial size. On the heading indicator, the cardinal points of the compass (north, east, south, and west) serve as anchoring points in the interpretation of the indication, and progression by 30's appears to be a good solution when the dial is relatively small. When the dial can be made large enough, however, the numbered graduation intervals should progress by 10's.

Nonlinear scales. Nonlinear scales condense a large range into a relatively small space but in such a way as to permit sensitive readings at certain critical ranges of the scale. In situations where error tolerances are a constant percentage of the indication, logarithmic scales are very suitable if they contain sufficient numbered graduation marks to minimize errors as a result of the linear-scale reading habits of operators. Figure 2-56(B) illustrates such a scale.

§ 2.6.2

SCALE DESIGN

To have clarity in scale design, sufficient separation must be maintained between scale indices. In addition, cues should be provided for determining differences between major and minor graduation marks. More specific recommendations for scale dimensions depend on the illumination level at the dial face.

For Normal Illumination

The following recommendations apply to indicators that are reasonably well illuminated, and low levels of illumination for dark adaptation are not required. Assuming high contrast

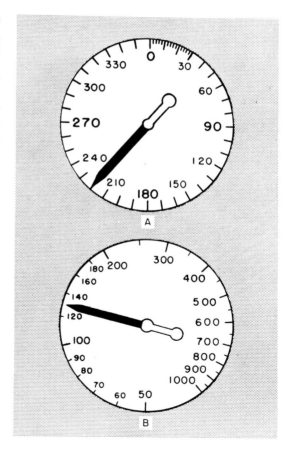

2-56

between the graduation marks and the dial face, illumination levels on the dial face above 1 ft-c, and reading distances of 13–28 in., the following recommendations should be observed (see Fig. 2-57, right):

1. The minimum width of a major graduation mark should be 0.0125 in.

2. Although graduation marks may be spaced as close as 0.035 in., the distance should never be less than twice the stroke width for white marks on black dial faces or less than one stroke width for black marks on white dial faces.

3. The minimum distance between major graduation marks should be 0.5 in.

4. The height of major, intermediate, and minor graduation marks should not be less than 0.22, 0.16, and 0.09 in. respectively.

For Low Illumination

When indicator scales must be read in other than normal illumination, as for example, in a dimly lighted aircraft cockpit or ship bridge at night, special care must be taken to gain maximum readability for the scale design. Under these conditions, the additional aid of varying the stroke width of major and minor graduation marks becomes important.

The recommended minimum dimensions shown in Fig. 2-58 are applicable to scale design for low-illumination levels and should be followed whenever possible. These dimensions, however, should not be considered as fixed values in the sense that other factors, such as scale size, number of graduation marks, and importance of indication, are not given equal consideration. Instead, these recommended dimensions should be used as models for relative dimensions. For instance, a reading distance of 28 in. is assumed for the dimensions in Fig. 2-58; for other reading distances, increase or decrease the recommended scale dimensions proportionately.

NUMERAL AND LETTER STYLE

Numerals and letters on indicator dials (and on panels and consoles for that matter)

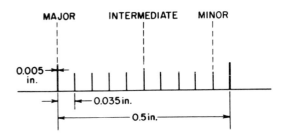

should be designed for maximum legibility for all conditions of use, but space restrictions and the range of illumination levels must be considered. The recommendations in the following paragraphs apply to general flood-, indirect-, and edge-lighted numerals and to back-lighted letters (see article 2.3.3).

The numeral style used in all the illustrations in this Guide is preferred, although other numerals of the same simple style also are acceptable (see Atkinson, et al., 1952). The width of all numerals should be $\frac{3}{5}$ of the height (see Table 2-11), except for the "4," which should be one stroke-width wider than the others, and the "1," which should be one stroke width. In addition, the stroke width should be from $\frac{1}{6}$ to $\frac{1}{8}$ of the numeral height.

Capital letters are visible at greater distances than lower-case letters, and therefore single-word labels or short identification sentences on all indicators should be in "all caps" instead of "initial caps and lower case." The letter style used in all of the illustrations in this Guide is preferred, but commercial types also may be used if they are of the same simple style (see Brown, 1953). The width of all letters should be $\frac{3}{5}$ of the height (see Table 2-11), except for the "I," which should be one stroke width, and the "m" and "w," which should be about $\frac{1}{5}$ wider than the other letters. Again, the stroke width should be from $\frac{1}{6}$ to $\frac{1}{8}$ of the letter height.

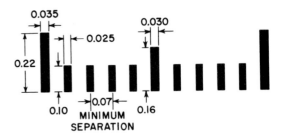

Table 2-11 Recommended Numeral and Letter Heights

	Height (in.) [1]	
Nature of Markings	Low brightness [2]	High brightness [3]
Critical markings, position variable (numerals on counters and settable or moving scales)	0.20–0.30	0.12–0.20
Critical markings, position fixed (numerals on fixed scales, control and switch markings, emergency instructions)	0.15–0.30	0.10–0.20
Noncritical markings (identification labels, routine instructions, any markings required only for familiarization)	0.05–0.20	0.05–0.20

[1] For 28-in. viewing distance. For other viewing distances, increase or decrease values proportionately.

[2] Between 0.03 and 1.0 ft-L.

[3] Above 1.0 ft-L.

SCALE LAYOUT

On circular and curved scales, the numbers should increase in a clockwise direction, on vertical straight scales from bottom to top, and on horizontal straight scales from left to right (see A in Fig. 2-59). Except on multi-revolution indicators, such as clocks, there should be a scale break between the two ends of a circular scale (Kappauf, 1951). When the scale has a break in it, the zero or starting value should be located at the bottom of the scale (B), except when pointer alignment is desired for check reading. In this case, the zero or starting value should be positioned so that the desired value is located at the "nine o'clock" position (C). The zero or starting value on multirevolution indicators should be at the top of the scale (D), which is where the operator will expect it to be because of his experience in reading clocks, heading indicators, etc.

In general, it is better to place numerals inside of the graduation marks on circular scales to avoid constricting the scale. If ample space exists, however, the numbers should be placed outside of the marks to avoid their being covered by the pointer (E). On vertical and horizontal straight scales, the numbers should be located on the side of the gradua-

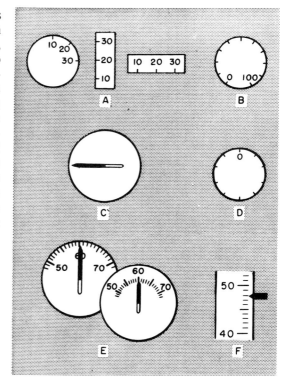

2-59

§ 2.6.2

tion marks opposite the pointer, and the graduation marks should be aligned on the side nearest the pointer and "stepped" on the side nearest the numbers (F). It is further recommended that the pointer be to the right of vertical scales and underneath horizontal scales.

ZONE MARKING

On many indicators, zone markings are used to indicate various operating conditions. These markings, because of the frequent need for relocation, are usually placed on the indicator's window in preference to placing them on the dial face. Such zone markings can be coded to convey information such as the desirable operating range, danger or lower limit, danger or upper limit, caution, desirable, inefficient, etc. Two methods of coding these zone markings have proven useful: color coding and shape coding.

Color Coding

Figure 2-60 shows recommended colors to be associated with various operating conditions and also indicates how color-coded zone markings can be used. Again, the designer is cautioned not to use color coding if the indicator is illuminated with colored light, particularly red, because colors are not readily distinguishable when illuminated by colored light sources.

Shape Coding

The shape of zone markings also can indicate various operating conditions. The shapes in Fig. 2-61 (Sabeh, et al., 1958) are recommended because they are easy to learn, are distinguishable under low illumination, and are distinguishable under any color light.

POINTER DESIGN

The basic principle to be followed in pointer design is that of simplicity; all unnecessary

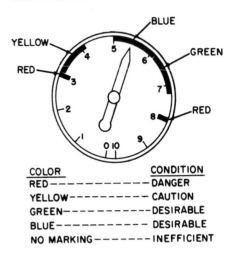

COLOR	CONDITION
RED — — — — — — — — —	DANGER
YELLOW — — — — — — —	CAUTION
GREEN — — — — — — — —	DESIRABLE
BLUE — — — — — — — —	DESIRABLE
NO MARKING — — — — —	INEFFICIENT

"frills" should be avoided. Other recommendations for pointer design are listed as follows (see Fig. 2-62, next page):

1. Pointers should extend to, but not overlap, the minor scale markings (A).

2. The pointer should be as close to the dial face as possible to minimize parallax (B).

3. For most applications, the section of the pointer from the center of rotation to the tip should be the same color as the dial markings. The remaining portion of the pointer should be the same color as the dial face (C).

4. For indicators designed for horizontal pointer alignment, the tail end of the pointer should extend beyond the center of rotation by an amount equal to about one half of the head of the pointer (D).

5. In cases where it is necessary to read the position of the tail of the pointer as well

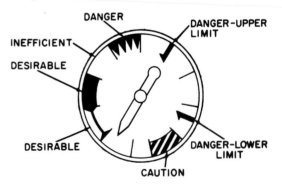

2-61

as the head (e.g., heading indicators), the tail should extend beyond the center of rotation by an amount equal to about three fourths of the head, but the tail should be blunt rather than pointed to avoid confusion with the head (E).

6. The recommended pointer angle is as illustrated in Fig. 2-62(F).

MOTION OF MOVING ELEMENT

Several other considerations enter into the proper design of mechanical indicators. These considerations concern the direction of motion of the moving element in relation to the following:

a. The numerical value being indicated.

b. The direction of motion of the associated control (see also Chapter 6).

c. The direction of motion of the vehicle or component to which the indicator refers.

Moving-Pointer, Fixed-Scale Indicators

Circular scales. Clockwise movement of a pointer should increase the magnitude of the reading (see A in Fig. 2-63). Where positive and negative values around zero are being displayed, the zero should be located at the "nine" or the "twelve o'clock" position (B). This arrangement provides for pointer increase up or to the right, which is the way the operator will expect it to move. Thus, the positive values will increase with clockwise movement of the pointer and the negative values will increase with counterclockwise movement. In addition, clockwise movement of a pointer should result from clockwise movement of the associated knob or crank; movement forward, upward, or to the right of an associated lever; or movement upward or to the right of the associated vehicle or component (C).

Straight scales. The pointer should move up or to the right to indicate an increase in magnitude (see Fig. 2-64). In addition, movement of the pointer upward or to the right should result from clockwise rotation of the associated knob or crank; movement forward,

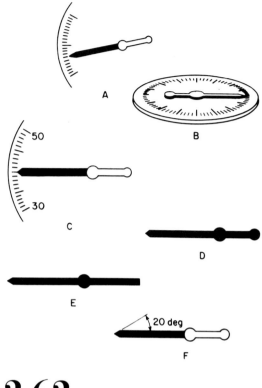

2-62

2-63

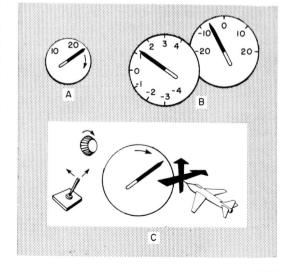

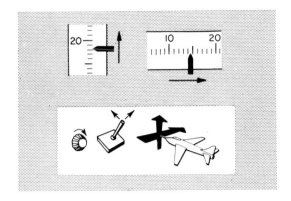

upward, or to the right of a lever; or movement upward or to the right of the associated vehicle or component.

Moving-Scale, Fixed-Pointer Indicators

Circular scales. Certain ambiguities exist between moving circular scales and associated control movements. This can be seen from the following three recommended practices, one of which must be violated in the design of circular moving scales:

1. Scale numbers should increase in a clockwise direction around the dial. Thus, values on moving circular scales will increase with counterclockwise movement of the dial face.

2. The direction of movement of the associated control should be compatible with the direction of movement of the dial. Thus, clockwise movement of the control should result in clockwise movement of the dial.

3. Clockwise movement of a control should result in an increase in function.

If the first recommended practice is compromised (i.e., numbers on the scale increase in a counterclockwise direction), operators tend to make final setting errors. If the second practice is compromised (i.e., clockwise movement of the control results in counterclockwise movement of the dial), operators are likely to err in the initial direction of turn (Bradley, 1954). If the third practice is compromised, a standardized control-movement-system-movement relationship (see Chapter 6) is violated.

Because of these ambiguities, it is recommended that moving-pointer indicators be used in preference to moving-scale indicators wherever possible. If, however, a moving-scale indicator must be used, the following recommended practices in the design and use of circular moving scales will minimize the effects of these ambiguities:

1. The numbers should progress in magnitude in a clockwise direction around the dial face so that counterclockwise movement of the dial face increases the readings (see A in Fig. 2-65, below).

2. If the associated control (B) has no direct effect on the behavior of the vehicle

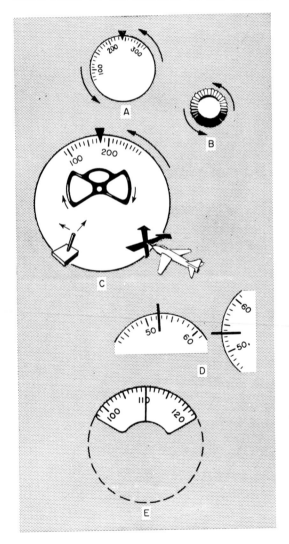

(e.g., tuning in radio stations, monitoring electronic equipment, etc.), the scale should rotate counterclockwise (increase) with counterclockwise movement of the associated knob or crank.

3. If the associated control does have a direct effect on the behavior of the vehicle (e.g., increases or decreases speed, direction, etc.), the scale should rotate counterclockwise (increase) with clockwise movement of the associated knob, wheel, or crank; with movement forward, upward, or to the right of a lever; or with movement forward, upward, or to the right of the associated vehicle or component.

4. The fixed pointer, index, or lubber line should be at the "twelve o'clock" position for right-left directional information, and at the "nine o'clock" position for up-down information (D). For purely quantitative information, either position may be used.

5. If an indicator is used for setting, such as for tuning in a desired wavelength, it is usually advisable to cover the unused portion of the dial face (E). In such cases, the open window should be large enough to permit at least one numbered graduation to appear at each side of any setting. If the display is used in tracking, as in the case of heading indicators, the whole dial face should be exposed.

Straight scales. The same direction-of-motion ambiguities exist in these as in circular moving scales, and the same recommendation about using moving-pointer indicators applies. If, however, a moving-scale indicator must be used, the numbers should increase from bottom to top or from left to right (see Fig. 2-66), and the scale should move down or to the left (increase) in these situations:

a. When the associated knob or crank is moved clockwise.

b. When the associated lever is moved forward, upward, or to the right.

c. When the associated vehicle or component moves up or to the right.

COUNTER DESIGN

The following design practices are recommended for counter indicators:

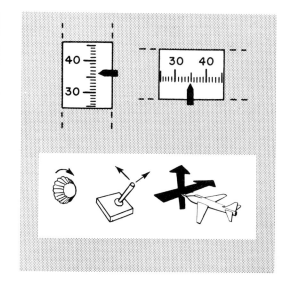

1. The numbers should change by snap action in preference to continuous movement.

2. Clockwise rotation of a knob or crank should increase the counter indication, and counter numbers should move upward for increase to be most compatible with the motion of the setting knob or crank (see A in Fig. 2-67, below).

3. Do not space numbers too far apart or crowd them too close together (B).

4. Avoid windows that limit the viewing angle and increase the space between numbers (C).

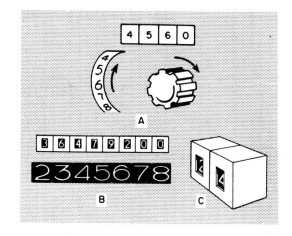

2-67

2.6.3 *The design of pictorial indicators*

The pictorial aspects of an indicator can vary considerably in degree of realism. In determining the degree of realism, the designer should keep the following factors in mind:

a. The display should be as easy to identify as the object represented in the display.

b. The pictorial representation chosen should be simple enough so as not to confuse the operator.

c. The relationship of the stationary and moving parts of the display to the things they represent should be clear and unambiguous.

If used properly, pictorial displays offer a great deal in terms of clarifying and speeding up the interpretation of information, but Fig. 2-68 demonstrates how realism can be detrimental to the precision of reading, for example, the angle of aircraft bank. The horizontal stabilizer of the first design gives the impression that the aircraft is diving. This ambiguous cue is the result of overenthusiasm for realism. The tapered wings and round fuselage of the second design do not amplify the attitudinal planes that are needed for precise interpretation. The simple straight lines of the third design make it easier to determine the bank angle and yet provide sufficient identification cues to remind the operator that the pictorial represention is the aircraft.

Pictorial representations can be used effectively as pointers, but caution should be exercised to see that the exact position of the pointer is clear. Figure 2-69 illustrates how a pictorial pointer required clarification.

Position, or changes in position, of equipment components should be represented with the indicator as the fixed frame of reference. In addition, the location and movement of the pictorial part of the indicator should have the same orientation as the equipment component itself. This is illustrated in Fig. 2-70, which shows two aircraft-flap-position indicators. The one on the left shows the flaps oriented in the same plane as the actual flaps on the aircraft.

2.6.4 *Indicator identification*

It is important that the operator have as many cues as possible to identify indicators. Identification can be assisted by labels and by indicator position, shape, and color. Although size and unique configuration assist identification, these cues result from other design considerations.

LABELING

Indicators should be labeled in the most simple and direct manner possible. The following design practices are recommended for indicator labeling:

1. It is usually best to label indicators in terms of what is being measured and not by

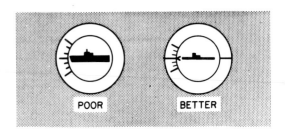

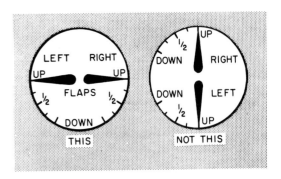

the name of the device, as illustrated in the following: use ALTITUDE, not Altimeter; use RPM, not Tachometer; use ACCELERATION, not Accelerometer; use SPEED, not Speedometer.

2. Labels should be as brief as possible, but should not be made up of abbreviated words unless the abbreviated form is familiar to all expected operators. Words may be omitted or initials may be used, however, as in some of the following: use CLIMB, not Rate of Climb; use RPM, not Revolutions per minute; use MAN. PRESS., not MP; use RANGE, not Rng; use BEARING, not Brng.

3. The label should be positioned so that the numerical designations or graduation marks are not crowded or obstructed. In a circular, moving-pointer, fixed-scale display, the center of the dial face is usually the most appropriate location for the label.

4. Company names or trade names should not appear on the visible portions of the display.

COLOR CODING

Different color schemes for different indicators can be used to assist in identification. In general, the recommendations for color coding in article 2.4.1 should be followed. The designer is cautioned, however, that if indicators have to be read at any time under any illuminant other than white light, color coding should not be used.

SHAPE CODING

Shape coding for indicators has not been thoroughly investigated, but some suggestions can be made from design experience. Differences between rectangular, square, triangular, or round indicators have proven useful for identification purposes. For example, the shapes in Fig. 2-71 are suggested by the instrument movement.

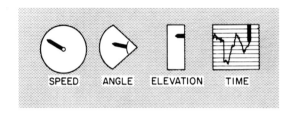

SPEED   ANGLE   ELEVATION   TIME

POSITION CODING

One of the best means of assisting indicator identification is to maintain a consistent instrument position among various models of the vehicle or component. This subject was discussed in Chapter 1 for controls, and the same principles apply to indicators.

2.7 Cathode-Ray Tubes

Cathode-ray tubes (CRT) provide a convenient means of presenting many kinds of information visually. The most common applications are in various types of radar displays used for air-traffic control, navigation, and air defense. Another common use is in electronic-test and -monitoring equipment. This section is concerned, primarily, with the use of CRT's for displaying radar data.

More of academic than of practical interest is the use of CRT's as digital readouts. There are a few systems (such as shaped-beam CRT's and character generators that can write decimal information on any conventional CRT) that can present alphanumeric information positioned on detailed maps and the like (Proctor, 1960), but these systems will not be discussed.

2.7.1 *Cathode-ray-tube visibility*

Although the term visibility has a more general meaning, we will restrict its meaning in this section to refer to the detection of a target on the CRT scope. We will not include under the problems of CRT visibility such things as identification and classification of targets; visibility problems are here restricted to a few particular uses of radar systems, i.e., to those situations in which large areas are scanned to detect the presence of relatively small targets, such as those in air-search and sea-search radar. Problems of visibility are not prominent when radar systems are used for bombing and navigation. In such uses, large land areas usually are scanned, and the problem is chiefly one of scope resolution (see articles 2.2.3 and 2.7.2).

VISUAL FACTORS

The visibility, or probability of detection, of CRT targets depends on the following:

   a. The size, in visual angle, of the target.
   b. The brightness of the background.
   c. The brightness of the target.

   d. The length of time the target is present on the scope.
   e. The operator's visual-adaptation level.

As applied to CRT displays, background refers to that portion of the scope that includes noise and clutter but no actual target. Noise refers to those lighted areas on the tube face that do not represent reflecting objects. Noise is usually random and usually appears as bright spots that change position from sweep to sweep. Clutter refers to signal returns from objects other than targets; these might be clouds, the sea, etc.

Target Size and Brightness

The curves in Fig. 2-72 (Blackwell, 1946) show the target-to-background contrast required for 99% probability of detection for targets of various sizes (in visual angle) and for various background brightnesses. These data apply to the following situations:

   a. The operator is visually adapted to the brightness level of the task.
   b. The target is either brighter or darker than the background.
   c. The background brightness (noise) is distributed evenly.
   d. The operator has several seconds to detect the target and is alerted to the task.

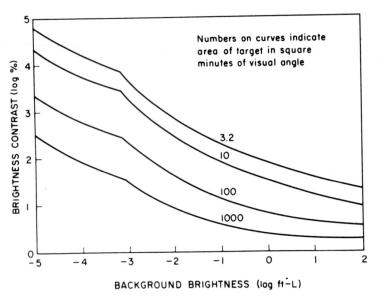

2-72

The curves in Fig. 2-72 reveal that, with large targets on bright backgrounds, the brightness contrast can be low and still provide 99% probability of detection. The absolute brightness increment (or decrement), however, must be greater with high background brightnesses.

Signal Duration

The visibility of dim targets is partially a function of the length of time that they are exposed. The relationship between the duration of a flash of light and the relative intensity of the flash required to be seen is shown in Fig. 2-73 (Blondel and Rey, 1911). It can be seen from the curve that the eye apparently summates energy fairly well up to about 0.2 sec and that further exposure has little effect on visibility.

Operator Adaptation Level

The dark-adaptation curves of Fig. 2-29 show that, immediately after the eye has been exposed to high brightnesses, its sensitivity to dim visual stimuli is reduced. After a period of time in relative darkness, this sensitivity is regained. The curves in Fig. 2-74 (Hanes and Williams, 1948) show the time lost in the detection of a target on a CRT scope as a function of the pre-exposure brightness for various scope brightnesses. The signal, which subtended a visual angle of 20 min of arc at the eye, has a 99% probability of detection for an operator whose eyes were adapted to the brightness level of the task. In this experiment, a detection time of 5 sec is equivalent to immediate detection because it took that long for the subjects to move from the adaptation screen to the CRT scope.

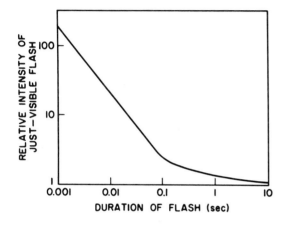

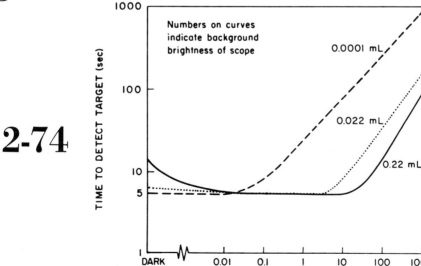

The curves in Fig. 2-74 reveal the following:

a. For very dim scopes (0.0001-mL background brightness) the operator can be pre-exposed to brightnesses as high as 0.01 mL without impairing target visibility.

b. For dim scopes (0.022-mL background brightness) the operator can be pre-exposed to brightnesses as high as 2 mL without impairing target visibility.

c. For moderately bright scopes (0.22-mL background brightness) the operator can be pre-exposed to brightnesses as high as 20 mL without impairing target visibility.

d. A completely dark-adapted operator will suffer a slight loss in detecting threshold targets on scopes with background brightnesses of about 0.02 mL and above.

With the above revelations in mind, the following general recommendations can be made:

1. The visibility of threshold targets is best when the operator is visually adapted to the level of the scope brightness.

2. If the operator must do other visual tasks at higher brightness levels than those required for the above, visibility will not be seriously affected if the higher brightnesses are not more than 100 times as bright as the average brightness of the radar scope. In other words, if the operator must scan daylight skies (about 2,000 mL), the average scope brightness should be set up to 20 mL or more to maximize visibility under these circumstances.

Signal strength. We have seen how high pre-exposure brightnesses have affected the visibility of targets that were seen nearly 100% of the time by operators visually adapted to the level of the task. It was noted that, with higher scope brightness, the intensity of pre-exposure can be greater without affecting detectability but that it might be impossible to get maximum target-to-background contrast if the operator is pre-exposed to a brightness 100 times that of the scope. This is particularly true if the pre-exposure brightness is 100 mL or more, in which case it is of interest to know what the signal strength must be so that a target is immediately visible to an operator who has been pre-exposed to high brightnesses.

The curves in Fig. 2-75 (Hanes and Williams, 1948) show the time required for a target to be detected as a function of the pre-exposure brightness for targets of various intensities. In every case, the scope background brightness is 0.022 mL, and the target subtends a visual angle of 20 min of arc. As before, the detection time of 5 sec represents immediate detection. The lowest contrast (13%) is for a target having about 99% probability of detection for operators adapted to the brightness level of the task. The other targets are above this threshold level.

It is evident that, with stronger signals (higher contrasts) the range of tolerable adapting brightnesses is much greater. Indeed, for this background brightness (0.022 mL), a

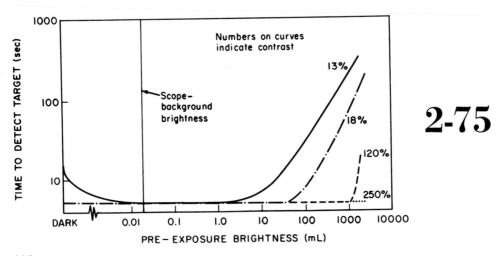

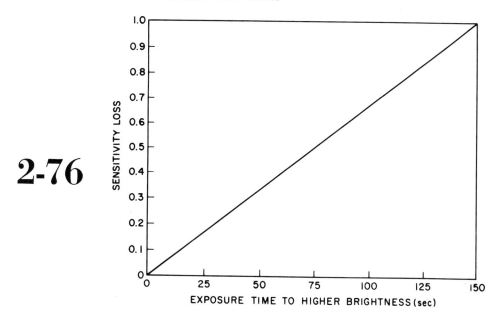

2-76

target that is 2½ times as bright as the background can be seen immediately after the operator has adapted to 2,000 mL. Thus, if a given radar operation does not require the detection of weak signals, greater tolerances in the operator's brightness adaptation are permissible.

Duration of pre-exposure brightness. We have seen that the eye is less sensitive to dim visual stimuli for some period after having been exposed to relatively high brightnesses. The data given above and in article 2.3.3 show the effect on visual sensitivity of adapting the eye to high brightnesses for 5 min or more. After the eye has been exposed to relatively high brightnesses for about 2.5 min, it reaches, for all practical purposes, a "steady state" of adaptation. This means that longer periods of pre-exposure have little further effect on the immediate sensitivity of the eye. If shorter periods of pre-exposure are used, however, the sensitivity is affected proportionately less. This relationship is shown in Fig. 2-76 (Mote and Riopelle, 1953), which shows sensitivity loss vs. exposure time.

In Fig. 2-76, for any given exposure duration, the value on the ordinate is used as a multiplier of the exposure brightness to give the steady-state-adaptation level of the eye.

This relationship means that, if the eye is exposed to 2,000 mL (daylight brightness) for 15 sec, the eye has a sensitivity loss equivalent to that of being exposed to 200 mL ($^{15}/_{150} \times$ 2,000 mL) for 150 sec or more. These adjusted values then can be used with the data above and in article 2.3.3.

DESIGN FACTORS

The ideal way of specifying the design factors that affect CRT visibility would be to give a series of curves showing how each of the physical variables affects human performance. It is possible to do this with, for example, machine controls, for which we can specify human performance in terms of gear ratios, etc. In the case of radar systems, however, it is impossible to get this kind of quantitative data for the following reasons:

a. The number of variables is too large. It has been estimated that there are at least fourteen electronic variables that affect radar detection. To these must be added a number of other physical variables, such as, for example, those concerned with phosphor, and we still do not have adequate data on the ways in which these variables act singly, much less how they act in combination.

§ 2.7.1

b. No one has yet figured out how to translate the electrical variables into visually significant ones, e.g., what is the equation to get from "volts" to "millilamberts"?

c. There is an enormous amount of variation from one radar to another, from one CRT to another, and in one radar from time to time. A translation from "volts bias" to "millilamberts" might hold for a particular radar for a limited time, but it almost certainly would not apply as soon as the tube was replaced.

These considerations limit greatly what we can say about design factors in radar systems. It also accounts for the rather unusual recommendation given in item 3 below—that a signal generator be built into the radar system. It is believed that the human, on-the-spot, calibration of radar systems is the only feasible way of dealing with the complexities of the situation.

The design factors that affect visibility can be enumerated as follows:

1. Target size. The size of the target can be increased by increasing such electronic variables as beam width and pulse length. Increases in size, however, proportionately degrade scope resolution, and, in this way, limit the use of the display.

2. Scope brightness. Because the eye is most sensitive to brightness contrasts at higher brightnesses (above 1 mL), a well constructed CRT should have characteristics such that maximum target-to-background contrast is obtained when the background brightness is about 1 mL or above.

3. Scope-brightness adjustment. The optimum CRT-bias setting for any piece of equipment depends on video gain, antenna-rotation rate, pulse-repetition frequency, and random-noise levels. It is recommended that a signal generator be provided with the equipment so that the operator can conduct visibility tests during CRT operation. Then, for any given set of operating conditions, the operator can adjust the CRT bias and other electronic variables so that the settings permit the detection of the weakest target that is simulated. This procedure would be particularly helpful in air-search radar, in which targets might not be available for such adjustments.

4. Contrast direction. The targets can be made to appear as bright spots on a dark background or as dark spots on a bright background. The CRT visibility data above apply to both contrast directions.

5. Scope-brightness distribution. The scope brightness should be as uniform as possible over the entire scope face. In conventional radar, the center of the scope usually gives a much brighter target and background than the surrounding portions of the scope. This situation impairs target detection and makes scope photography difficult.

6. Viewing angle. Whenever possible, the scope face should be in a plane that is perpendicular to the operator's normal line of sight (see Chapter 7). If space for the equipment, personnel, and special lighting conditions necessitate viewing the scope obliquely (see Chapter 8), there will be a loss in visibility for threshold targets because oblique viewing reduces the visual angle of the signal. It has been found, however, that the scope can be tilted 30 deg from a position normal to the line of sight without noticeably affecting the detection of weak targets (Williams, 1949).

7. Viewing distance. Because it is generally agreed that 16 in. is a minimum viewing distance for the prevention of visual fatigue, it is recommended that this viewing distance be used whenever possible. Shorter viewing distances increase the visual angle subtended by targets, however, and visibility can be improved by close viewing. Therefore, if periods of scope observation are short, and it is important that dim signals be detected, the recommended 16-in. viewing distance can be reduced to 10 or 12 in. (see Bartlett and Williams, 1947; Craik and McPherson, 1945; and McFarland, et al., 1942).

2.7.2 Cathode-ray-tube scope size

The solutions to the problem of finding the optimum scope size depend on many complex factors. Some of the more important considerations deal with such things as what is being displayed, what the observer must "see" in the display, the viewing distance, etc. Many of the factors involved in determining the solution to the problem of scope size are not fully understood. Nevertheless, the following general statements can be made concerning the effect of scope size on visibility, resolution, and target identification:

a. Visibility. If, when increasing scope size, the resolving power of the radar system is essentially unchanged, signal detectability will be improved if the target size increases. The extent of improved detection can be determined from the curves in Fig. 2-72. (Optical magnification of the CRT scope would result in about the same improvement.) If target size does not increase with scope size, visibility will be unaffected.

b. Resolution. If the major electronic variables are held constant, increases in scope size do little to enhance radar-system resolution. The displayed detail will be larger, however, and therefore more discernible to the eye. (Scope magnification would have about the same effect.) If resolution and scope size are each increased, the interpretation of complex target areas might be considerably enhanced. Generally speaking, as scope resolution is increased, scope size will have to be increased (actually or optically) so that fine detail can be seen by the operator.

c. Target identification. In section 2.2.3, data were presented indicating that a target, in general, should subtend no less than 12 min of arc to insure reasonably accurate target identification. Assuming a viewing distance of 12 in., a target would have to have a linear dimension on a display of no less than 0.042 in. to meet the minimum angular subtense of 12 min. Thus, given the scale factor of an analog display, such as a radar-navigation display, one can compute the actual dimension of ground targets required for acceptable visual recognition on the analog display.

Figure 2-77 shows the required display size plotted against target size for various ground ranges. Individual values were calculated as follows:

$$\text{Display size} = \frac{\text{Range}}{\text{Target size}} \times 0.042. \quad (2\text{-}4)$$

It can be seen in Fig. 2-77 that, if the smallest target one needs to recognize is 1,000 ft in its greatest dimension, for example, and the system displays an analog of a strip of ground 40 mi wide, the display must have one dimension of not less than 10.2 in. On the other hand, if a critical target has a length of 50 ft, and the display size is fixed at 10 in., the ground range displayed cannot exceed 2.1 mi (Steedman and Baker, 1960).

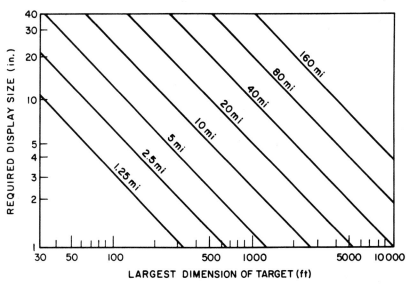

2.7.3 *Indicating range on radar displays*

The various methods for indicating range can be evaluated in terms of the accuracy of the estimates and the speed in making the estimates. In the evaluation of the range-indicating methods, we will consider the optimum design within a method and also make comparisons among the various methods.

RANGE MARKERS

Figure 2-78 illustrates the arrangement of range markers on polar-coordinate and rec-

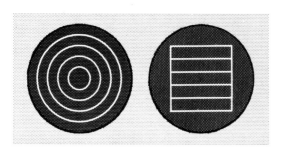

tangular-coordinate displays. The recommendations in the following paragraphs apply, primarily, to range markers on polar-coordinate displays, but the more general of them will apply to rectangular-coordinate displays as well.

Range-Mark-Interval Values

The range-mark-interval scale should be represented as part of a scale that starts at zero with the numbers progressing by one's, two's, or five's and with the appropriate number of zeros following after each digit. Examples of good numbering systems are shown in Fig. 2-79. No other range-mark-numbering systems are acceptable. In general, progression by one's (1, 2, 3, or 10, 20, 30, etc.) is superior to progression by two's or five's (Chapanis and Leyzorek, 1950 and Barber and Garner, 1951).

Range-Mark Separation

Two tasks are involved in the estimation of range: the identification of the nearest inner range-mark value and the interpolation of target position between range marks. For a given scope size, the number of range marks used affects range-mark spacing. If the scope size is fixed, a change in the number of range marks affects the numbering system of the range marks. The effect of range-mark spacing on speed and accuracy is dependent on interpolation accuracy, range-mark identification, and range-mark coding. These are discussed in the paragraphs that follow.

For interpolation accuracy. An operator is able to interpolate the position of a target between two range marks with the following accuracy:

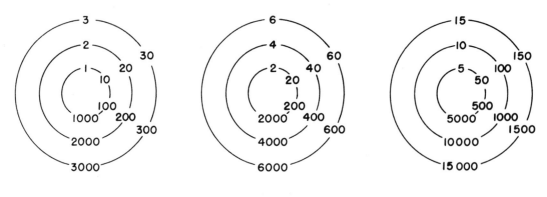

2-79

a. About 50% of the range estimates will be in error by less than 4% of the distance between range marks.

b. About 95% of the range estimates will be in error by less than 14% of the distance between range marks.

c. Operators tend to overestimate the target range by 2% of the interval distance, i.e., there is a positive constant error of 2% of the interval.

The above values apply in the following situations:

a. The distance between range marks subtends a visual angle greater than 22 min.

b. The target is a relatively small, well defined spot.

c. The operator proceeds as rapidly as possible and attempts to read to the nearest 1% of the interval.

For identification. Errors occur in the identification of the range marks adjacent to the target. Such errors are gross errors and are multiples of the range-mark-interval value. For example, if the range marks represent intervals of 1,000 yd, the gross errors would be of this value or multiples of this value. The frequency with which gross errors occur depends on the number of range marks used on a display.

The curves in Fig. 2-80 (Baker and Vanderplas, 1956) show the percent of readings in error as a function of the number of range marks used. These data apply to operators that are reading ranges as rapidly and as accurately as possible. The range marks were scaled so that every fifth ring was discriminably different (thicker) than the others (see below). The time required to determine the range of each signal is also included on the graph.

Thus, we can conclude that, if more than five range marks appear on a radar display, every fifth mark should be brighter than the others (see Fig. 2-81). This arrangement will assist the operator in the identification of any particular mark (see also Garner, et al., 1949).

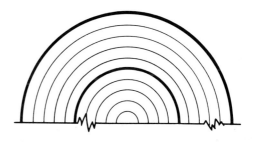

OTHER METHODS

The electronic range cursor provides a movable range marker. The marker or cursor moves with the antenna sweep and leaves a decaying trace as illustrated in Fig. 2-82(A). The operator moves the position of the cursor radially by means of a crank or knob. When

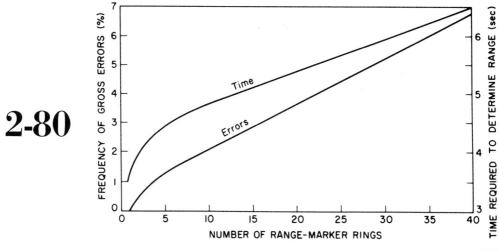

2-80

FREQUENCY OF GROSS ERRORS (%)

TIME REQUIRED TO DETERMINE RANGE (sec)

Time

Errors

NUMBER OF RANGE-MARKER RINGS

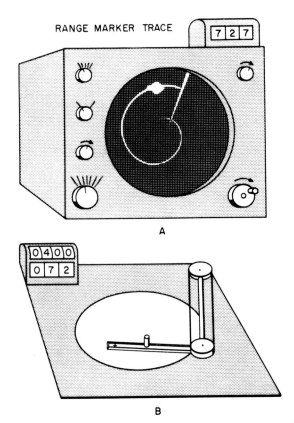

RANGE MARKER TRACE

A

B

case, was estimated without using a cursor, and reports were made orally.

The accuracy of determining range with a range cursor or pantograph is dependent on the operator's ability to bisect a target or to center a point on a target. For a target 0.26 in. in diameter, 50% of the readings will err by less than 0.002 in. (less than 1% of the diameter) and 95% will err by less than 0.006 in. (Ford, et al., 1950). These accuracies are possible with the pantograph even if only 2 sec is allowed; the range-cursor method requires about 15 sec to acquire this level of accuracy. When the operator proceeds more rapidly (one target every 7 sec), range-cursor errors become ten times greater (Chapanis, 1949; Gebhard, 1948; and Gebhard and Bilodeau, 1947).

From the above, it can be concluded that, when accuracy alone is essential (speed is not important), the range rings are inferior to the other methods. When both speed and accuracy are important, however, the range marks are superior in both speed and accuracy to the range-cursor method, but the pantographic method is superior to both of the other two methods in speed and accuracy.

the target is bisected, the range value is read from a counter. The operator should be able to control the cursor brightness so that the cursor trace does not completely decay in the time required to make one revolution.

In the pantographic method of indicating range, the operator positions the point or crosshair cursor over the target on the scope and reads the coordinate information from counters geared to the pantograph arm's movement. Figure 2-82(B) illustrates the pantographic device (Ford, et al., 1950).

EVALUATING THE METHODS

The chart in Fig. 2-83 shows the amount of time required for operators to determine the range and bearing of one target for various range-indicating methods. The operators were instructed to proceed as accurately and as rapidly as possible. The bearing, in each

118

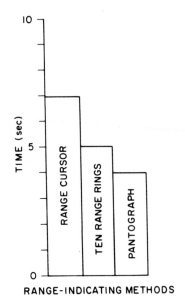

RANGE-INDICATING METHODS

2-83

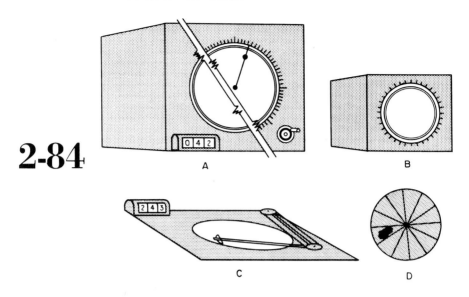

2-84

A

B

C

D

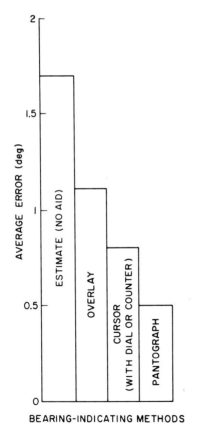

AVERAGE ERROR (deg)

ESTIMATE (NO AID)

OVERLAY

CURSOR (WITH DIAL OR COUNTER)

PANTOGRAPH

BEARING-INDICATING METHODS

2-85

2.7.4 Indicating bearing on radar displays

The various methods for indicating bearing also can be evaluated in terms of the speed and accuracy with which the operator is able to read or relay the information. Bearing can be indicated by the following methods:

a. Cursor and bearing dial or counter (see A in Fig. 2-84). A mechanical or electronic cursor is moved by a crank or knob until the signal is bisected. The bearing value is read from a bearing dial that is around the scope or it can be read from a counter.

b. Bearing dial alone (B). The operator sights along the target to the bearing dial and estimates the value; no cursor is used.

c. Pantograph (C). The operator manually places a crosshair over the target, and the bearing then is read from a counter.

d. Overlay of radial lines (D). A transparent overlay is placed over the scope face. The radial lines assist in estimating the bearing.

The graph in Fig. 2-85 shows the approximate accuracy of the various methods. These data apply when the operator is proceeding as rapidly as possible. It also has been found that there is a time saving of about 1 sec in

119

estimating bearing with no aids or with the use of overlays over the cursor and bearing method. The pantograph, however, is superior in both speed and accuracy to all the other methods considered.

2.7.5 *Three-coordinate displays*

To determine the position of an aircraft in space, it is necessary to display three coordinates to the operator, usually bearing, range, and altitude. A conventional method for displaying three coordinates on two scopes is shown in Fig. 2-86. Attempts also have been made to display three coordinates of information (e.g., range, bearing, and altitude) in a single integrated display (see article 2.1.4). It is believed that, if this is properly done, interpretation will be easier.

One proposed method of displaying three coordinates on a single display is shown in Fig. 2-87. Two targets appear for a single object. The range is displayed in the inner circle and the altitude is displayed in the outer circle. When the bearing is estimated, and range rings are used, the bearing, range, and altitude can be orally reported in 8.8 sec per target (Gebhard and Bilodeau, 1947). This method requires $\frac{1}{3}$ less time than the two-scope presentation. It should be noted, however, that, although this display results in rapid reading of the space coordinates in quantitative terms (yards and degrees), it does not result in an accurate "perception," i.e., the spatial positions are not easily visualized.

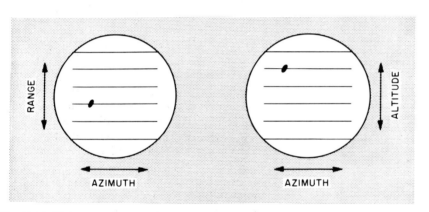

2-86

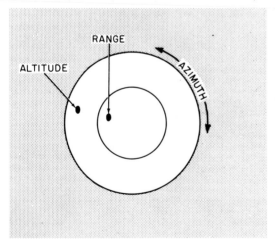

2-87

2.8 *Printed Materials*

This section will cover the practices to be employed in the design of printed materials. The recommendations apply to decals, check lists, and labels for operating instructions to be attached to equipment or display panels and to graphs, tables, and scales for numerical operational data.

2.8.1 *Decals, check lists, and labels*

The legibility of instruction decals, check lists, and labels becomes a critical consideration when the operator is pressed for time in emergencies and especially when, under these circumstances, he must operate infrequently used equipment.

DESIGN RECOMMENDATIONS

The following recommendations apply to operating instructions attached to the equipment or display panel:

1. Style of print. Capital letters ("all caps") are recommended for general use, but "initial caps" and lower case letters are permissible. The use of letters of the style used in the illustrations in this Guide, or any similar commercial form, is satisfactory (see article 2.6.2). The stroke-width-to-height ratio should be from 1/6 to 1/8. The letter width-to-height ratio should be 3:5 wherever possible. When space will not permit this optimum ratio, the width-to-height ratio may be reduced, but this might require a narrower stroke width to maintain the clarity of the identifying features of the letters.

2. Size of print. The recommended letter size depends on the viewing distance and illuminating conditions. Assuming a viewing distance of 28 in. or less and a wide range of illuminating conditions (including illuminances below 1 ft-c), the letter height should be at least 0.20 in. For less critical functions, or when the illumination is always above 1 ft-c, letter height may be reduced to 0.10 in.

3. Brevity. Emergency instructions and check lists should be made as concise as possible without distorting the intended information. This saves reading time and panel space. Figure 2-88 shows examples of good and poor emergency instructions.

4. Word selection. Words and sentences are more immediately recognized according to the degree of familiarity the reader has with them (Howes and Solomon, 1951). Decals, check lists, and labels, therefore, should be composed of words that are relatively common to the reader but only if the common words will say exactly what is intended. For common words of the general population see Thorndike and Lorge, 1944. For particular populations, such as military pilots, common technical terms may be used even though these words occur infrequently for other populations.

	THIS	NOT THIS
2-88	TO EJECT JETTISON CANOPY FEET IN STIRRUPS RAISE ARM RESTS SIT ERECT SQUEEZE TRIGGER	FOR EMERGENCY EJECTION IN FLIGHT JETTISON CANOPY BY PULLING THE CANOPY JETTISON HANDLE. HOOK HEELS IN FOOT REST. RAISE BOTH ARM RESTS TO HORIZONTAL POSITION. ASSUME ERECT POSTURE ACTUATE EJECTION TRIGGER FOR SEAT EJECTION.

5. Contrast. In a task in which dark adaptation is required, the letters should be white on a dark background. In tasks where dark adaptation is not essential, the print should be black on a white matte background.

2.8.2 *Graphs, tables, and scales*

Flight and other personnel are frequently required to use mathematical data for such operations as cruise control, navigation, and bombing. The general techniques for presenting such information are by the use of tables, graphs, and scales (see Fig. 2-89).

DESIGN RECOMMENDATIONS

For recommendations concerning scales, see article 2.6.2. The following general rec-ommendations apply, mainly, to graphs and tables (Carter, 1946 and Connell, 1947):

1. If the general shape of the function is important in making decisions, a graph is superior to tables or scales. Also, if interpolation is necessary, graphs and scales are superior to tables.

2. Graphs should be constructed so that numbered grids are bolder than unnumbered grids, and if ten-grid intervals are used, the fifth intermediate grid should be less bold than the numbered grids but bolder than the unnumbered grids.

3. Reduce tables to the simplest form consistent with the degree of sensitivity necessary to permit reading without interpolation. For example, if altitude steps of 5,000 ft (as shown in Fig. 2-89) are not sufficiently sensitive for the accuracy required, more altitude steps should be included so that the operator is not required to interpolate values.

4. When table columns are long, separate numbers into groups by providing a space between groups of five.

5. Provide at least 0.166 in. between columns that are not separated by vertical rules.

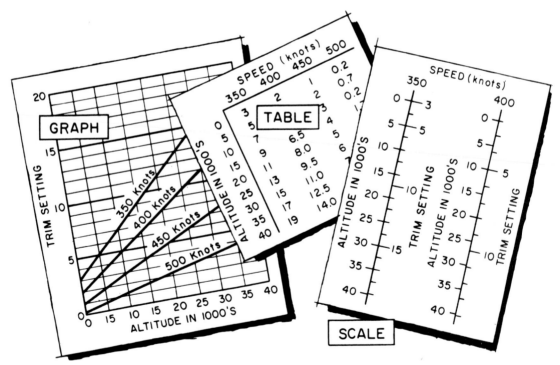

§ 2.8.2

3

auditory presentation of information

MAN'S AUDITORY SYSTEM is a good deal more versatile and sensitive than most of us realize. For instance, these are some of the things it can do:

a. It can detect and identify sounds over a wide range of intensities and frequencies— from the tick of a wrist watch to the roar of jet aircraft (see Chapter 1).

b. It can be alert at all times and in all directions.

c. It can localize, with fair accuracy, the source of a sound.

d. It can analyze, within limits, the components of a sound and pick out the wanted sound (signal) from the unwanted sound (background noise).

e. It can listen to sounds from many sources and attend to one at a time.

The auditory system consists of the ear, the auditory nerve, and a complex set of pathways and centers in the brain. Included in the

term "ear" is the outer ear, which acts as a sound collector; the middle ear, which matches impedance between the eardrum and the fluid-filled inner ear; and the inner ear, which transduces mechanical vibrations into electrical energy and sets up nervous impulses in the auditory nerve and higher regions of the brain. The anatomical configuration of the ear (magnified many times) is shown in Fig. 3-1 (next page), together with a schema illustrating how it operates.

Some characteristics of man's auditory system can be determined by presenting a physically defined acoustic stimulus to a human subject and systematically observing his responses. Many different methods, called psychophysical methods, have been devised for this purpose. Data obtained by these methods, and design recommendations based on them, are given in this chapter.

Before we get into the more technical aspects of this subject, however, we will present a discussion of the use of auditory presentation, including what signals are suited to, and how to choose the form of, presentation.

This chapter was drafted by Robert S. Gales of the U. S. Navy Electronics Laboratory.

123

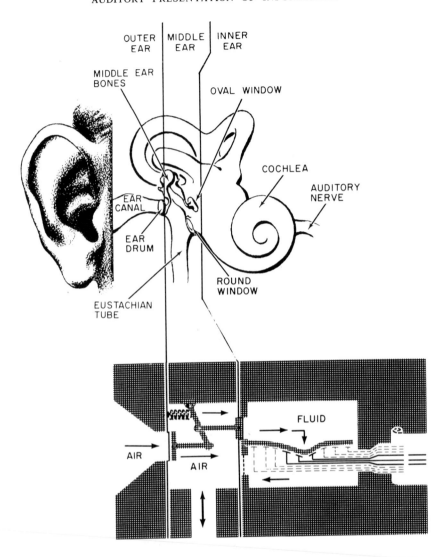

3-1 Functional diagram of ear. Sound waves impinge on outer ear and cause ear drum to vibrate. Vibrations are conducted via lever action of middle-ear bones to oval window, which actuates fluid-filled inner ear. Portions of nerve endings in cochlea are selectively excited, and their outputs terminate in brain

3.1 *The Use of Auditory Presentation*

Some signals are better suited for auditory than for visual presentation (see Chapter 2) and vice versa. The choice of the form of presentation depends on the nature of the signal, the conditions under which it must be received, and the characteristics of the person involved. Table 3-1 summarizes, and the following paragraphs discuss, the situations in which one form of presentation is preferred over the other.

Table 3-1   When to Use the Auditory or the Visual Form of Presentation

Use auditory presentation if:	*Use visual presentation if:*
1. The message is simple	1. The message is complex
2. The message is short	2. The message is long
3. The message will not be referred to later	3. The message will be referred to later
4. The message deals with events in time	4. The message deals with location in space
5. The message calls for immediate action	5. The message does not call for immediate action
6. The visual system of the person is overburdened	6. The auditory system of the person is overburdened
7. The receiving location is too bright or dark-adaptation integrity is necessary	7. The receiving location is too noisy
8. The person's job requires him to move about continually	8. The person's job allows him to remain in one position

3.1.1 *Signals suited to auditory presentation*

Auditory presentation is recommended for the following:

§ 3.1.1

a. For signals of acoustic origin. For example, even though many ingenious visual displays for speech have been devised, none is likely to supplant the ear except when deafness, intense noise, or other conditions render hearing useless. (See Chapter 4 for a complete discussion of speech communication.)

b. For warning signals. To see a warning signal, a person must have his eyes open and be looking in the general direction of the signal. When these conditions are not met, a visual warning signal does not "warn." Hearing, however, has no such limitation. It is omnidirectional and cannot be involuntarily shut off (our eyes can shut involuntarily but not our ears). Thus, auditory warning signals are best for calling attention to imminent danger or potentially dangerous situations.

c. To supplement overloaded vision. Many complex tasks, such as piloting an airplane, require so much attention to visual indicators that additional displays are undesirable. In such cases, auditory presentation can be used to supplement the overloaded visual system.

d. When information must be presented independently of the orientation of the head. When a person's duties require him to move about or to turn his head and body in different directions, visual presentation is undesirable because of the possibility that he might miss some important information or be so confined in his movements that he can perform the task only inefficiently.

e. When vision is limited or impossible. When a man's duties require him to work in the dark, the best way of getting information to him is through auditory channels. For example, the night lookout on a ship, or the night lookout at a forward command post, has to keep his eyes at maximum sensitivity (see Chapter 2). The best way to communicate with him is to use an auditory signal.

f. When a person must work under conditions of anoxia because of high altitudes or high positive g forces. Auditory sensitivity is much more resistant to anoxia than is visual sensitivity. For this reason, a man suffering from oxygen deficiency can still hear signals when his vision is seriously impaired (see Chapter 10).

g. When signals must be distinguished from noise. The ear acts as a frequency analyzer, making it an effective detector of periodic signals in noise. If the signal is a sinusoid (pure tone) or a combination of sinusoids (complex tones), the ear can detect the signal even when it is considerably weaker than the background noise. The ear also efficiently detects periodic modulation in the very-low-frequency range and responds to variations in intensity or frequency.

3.1.2 *Choosing the form of auditory presentation*

Use tonal or noise signals, rather than speech, under the following conditions:

a. The message is extremely simple.

b. The listener has had special training in the meaning of coded signals.

c. The signal designates a point in time that has no absolute value.

d. The message calls for immediate action.

e. Speech signals are overburdening the listener.

f. Conditions are unfavorable for receiving speech messages. (Tonal signals can be heard in noise that makes speech unintelligible.)

g. Security of the message is important. (Speech can be readily understood by unintended listeners whereas coded tonal or noise signals can be devised that cannot be understood unintentionally.)

h. Speech communication channels are overloaded.

i. Speech will mask other speech or annoy other listeners for whom the message is not intended.

Use speech, on the other hand, rather than tonal or noise signals, under the following conditions:

a. Flexibility of communication is necessary.

b. It is necessary to be able to identify the source of the message.

c. The listener has had no special training in the meaning of coded signals.

d. Rapid two-way exchanges of information are necessary.

e. The message deals with a future time requiring some preparation. (Example: The countdown preparatory to firing a missile—tonal signals could be miscounted.)

f. Situations of stress might cause the listener to "forget" the meaning of the code.

3.1.3 *Some common uses for auditory presentation*

Speech is the primary communication method for urgent signals, and the maximum dependable rate of transmission is 250 words per minute (wpm). Morse code, on the other hand, is readable under signal-to-noise ratios too low for reliable speech reception, but the maximum dependable rate of transmission is only 30 wpm.

Tonal or noise signals are prevalent for navigation at sea and in the air. As examples, diaphones located in lighthouses are pulsed in Morse code to indicate their positions and are audible for long distances, whistling and bell buoys locate channels and shoals, radio-range signals and fan-marker radio beacons mark the airways.

Auditory presentation is used in virtually all sonar systems, both for detection and for echo ranging, and warning and alarm signals are commonly auditory. Examples of warning signals are the air-raid warning siren; the klaxon horn in aircraft, which warns the pilot of "wheels up" on landing approaches; the klaxon horn in a submarine, which serves as a diving alarm; the high-pitched boatswain's whistle aboard ship, which alerts listeners to a voice message to follow; and the crew-emergency alarm bell in aircraft.

SONAR

Sonar devices pick up sounds transmitted through the water from objects in the water. *Passive* sonar systems detect the natural sounds made by the objects themselves; *active* sonar systems send out signals and detect the echoes of these signals when they are reflected from the objects (see Fig. 3-2). Auditory presentation of sonar information is used in both systems.

sonnel should be carefully selected and given considerable training (see Webster, 1953).

Signal detection. To detect a signal, the operator must recognize that a change has taken place in the sound output of his listening device. With the omnidirectional hydrophone, the operator has to listen for some time to the normal background noise, to establish his reference, and then be able to recognize a departure from this reference as a signal. This signal might take the form of a definite change in sound quality, such as the onset of a tonal component, or it might merely sound like a gradual rise in noise level. The latter case is hard to detect if it occurs very slowly because the operator has no ready reference.

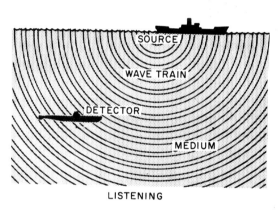

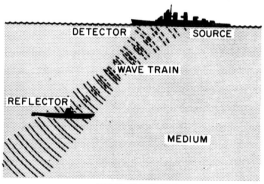

LISTENING

ECHO-RANGING

3-2 Listening (passive) and echo-ranging (active) sonar systems. At left, submarine equipped with listening hydrophone detects noise of freighter's screws. At right, destroyer equipped with echo-ranging sonar detects echo reflected by submarine caught in sound beam radiated by destroyer's sonar projector

Passive (Listening) Sonar

Passive sonar, which is mainly found on submarines and harbor-defense installations, picks up sounds emitted by other objects such as ships, submarines, and torpedoes. The sounds are transduced by a hydrophone, amplified, filtered, sometimes translated in frequency, and finally presented to the operator. The display usually is auditory because the human ear is so well suited both to detecting weak signals in noise and to identifying the source of a complex noise. To be proficient in using such displays, however, per-

With the directional hydrophone, on the other hand, the operator conducts a search by slowly sweeping the sensitive lobe of the hydrophone in bearing until he hears a change in sound quality that repeatedly occurs at a given bearing. The ability to train the hydrophone on and off the suspected target bearing and observe the correlated sound-quality change is a great aid to the operator in confirming a contact. By training off the target, the operator has ready reference to the background-noise condition and does not need to rely on long-time memory as he does with the omnidirectional hydrophone.

§ 3.1.3

Signal level. The gain of the sonar amplifying system must be turned high enough to override all ambient noise in the listener's environment by at least 15 db and to make the water background noise clearly audible at the frequency of the expected signal. Failure to hear water noise is a sign that the gain is too low for the optimum detection of weak signals. Where the frequency of the signal to be detected is not known precisely, water background noise should be audible at all expected signal frequencies.

Frequency response. A fairly wideband amplifier, usually covering the entire audio-frequency range, can be used to insure the optimum detection of all signals. The amplifier can be supplemented by filters and equalizers operated by the listener. The filters can be used to eliminate noise from frequencies known not to contain a detectable signal, and, for the detection of noise-like signals, wideband filters can be used (see article 3.5.1). The equalizers can be used effectively to maintain background noise at equally audible levels for all frequencies where signals are expected.

Frequency translation. Where signals above 5,000 cps are to be detected, the signals should be translated downward to frequencies between 200 and 5,000 cps because the ear can discriminate much better at these lower frequencies than it can at the higher ones. Frequency translation can be accomplished with a heterodyne oscillator, a mixer, and appropriate filters.

Bearing information. Once a target is detected, passive sonar can provide accurate bearing information about the target if the sonar system is designed and properly employed for this purpose. The following methods can be used:

1. One method is to rotate a directional hydrophone until the signal sounds loudest to the listener. This way, the listener must make an intensity discrimination, but his task is made easier, and his accuracy is improved, if the hydrophone has a narrow lobe of maximum response to give it very directional properties. Once the listener determines the direction of the loudest signal, the bearing of the target is read from a bearing pointer synchronized with the hydrophone.

2. Another method, which increases bearing accuracy, makes use of a binaural display (Horton, 1957). Two hydrophones are each connected to a different ear and are mounted so that a slight deviation from the on-target bearing introduces a time delay in the arrival of signals at the two ears. Such a difference in time of arrival is readily interpreted by the hearer as a directional shift, even when the difference is as little as 10 μsec. Bearing is obtained by mechanically rotating the hydrophones to reduce the time difference to zero, and, thereby, center the sound image.

3. A variation of the second method, used with fixed hydrophones, employs a set of variable delay lines, sometimes called "compensators," to adjust the interaural time delay to zero. The compensator dial is calibrated in degrees.

All of the above methods of presenting bearing information are often supplemented by visual indicators. A Bearing Deviation Indicator (BDI) is useful to indicate the direction to train the hydrophone to get back on target as the operator trains his beam across the target bearing. Mental correlation of the deflection on the BDI with the audible sounds helps the operator make and confirm his detection. But, although the BDI is useful to confirm and supplement auditory information, the operator continues to rely mainly on his auditory system for detection because his ears, unless signal processing with very high gain is used, can usually discriminate signal from noise better than his eyes can.

Bearing-search rate. Bearing search can be accomplished by coupling the hydrophone to a hand wheel or motor drive. With either method, the angular sweep speed must be designed so that the target will be in the beam long enough to be clearly heard, yet not so long that the audible contrast with the noise is lost. Thus, a narrow beam must be swept slowly and a wide beam more rapidly. The optimum beam width is such that the signal lies in the beam for about 0.2 to 1.0 sec. With a hydrophone beam 30 deg wide, for example, the maximum sweep speed should be 30 deg in 0.2 sec or 150 deg/sec or 2.4 sec/rev, and the minimum speed should be about 30 deg/sec or about 12 sec/rev.

Active (Echo-Ranging) Sonar

Echo-ranging sonar differs from passive sonar in that it sends out a high-intensity sound that is reflected back from the target and is picked up as an echo by the sonar. In this case, the sonar operator listens for the echo rather than for signals originating at the target.

Active sonar possesses the following four important advantages over passive sonar:

a. It can detect silent targets (such as a motionless submarine).

b. It can provide information on the range of the target. This information is derived from the time taken by the sound signal to travel out to the target and back again.

c. It can provide information about the motion of the target. This information is derived from the physical phenomenon known as the doppler shift. (A sound reflected from an approaching object increases in frequency; one reflected from a retreating object decreases in frequency.) To make use of this cue, however, the operator must have good pitch discrimination.

d. Because the frequency of the signal is known, the designer can provide filters and signal-processing equipment that minimize noise outside the region of the signal and maintain the sound level close to that required for optimum detection.

The signal processing just mentioned enables the designer to provide visual displays for some of the information supplied by an echo-ranging system. Hence, visual displays, such as the following, are commonly used in echo-ranging sonar:

a. The Bearing Deviation Indicator (BDI) previously discussed.

b. The Tactical Range Recorder, which provides a permanent record on sensitized paper of target range as a function of time.

c. The Plan Position Indicator (PPI), which displays, on an intensity-modulated oscilloscope of long persistence, a plan view of target position in polar coordinates with the echo-ranging ship at the center.

As with passive sonar, unless the signal processing used provides very high processing gain, the ear can out-perform most visual displays in the detection of signals. Therefore, auditory presentation, combined with visual displays, is nearly universal in existing sonars. Auditory presentation is particularly effective for the following:

a. Detecting echoes in noise, especially echoes longer than 30 msec in duration.

b. Detecting dopplered echoes against a background of sea reverberation (see Fig. 3-3, next page).

c. Identifying the source of echoes on the basis of such cues as doppler shift and quality of the echo.

The frequency of sonar signal that is best for auditory detection of doppler effects is 500–1,000 cps. Although the doppler frequency shift is detected slightly better at 500 cps, the better sensitivity of the human ear at 1,000 cps and above makes an 800-cps signal a good compromise for listening.

ALARM AND WARNING DEVICES

Auditory signals are often used as alarms and warning devices to call attention to an urgent situation that might require instant action. Many warning devices are used in everyday situations; others have been developed for special purposes. Table 3-2 summarizes, and the following paragraphs discuss, the principal characteristics and special features of different types of auditory alarm and warning devices. (See Chapter 2 for a discussion of alarm and warning devices in general and visual ones in particular.)

Diaphones (foghorns) have high power and low frequency for long-range transmission and operate intermittently. Other horns have high power, are generally directional, can be efficient radiators of low-frequency energy, and are easily made to operate intermittently. Whistles usually have high power, can be made directional, are usually high in frequency, and can be operated intermittently.

Sirens have high power for long-range transmission, and their high pitch is clearly differentiated from normal environmental noises. The characteristic rise and fall in pitch of sirens is attention-getting and penetrates the masking spectrum of environmental noise.

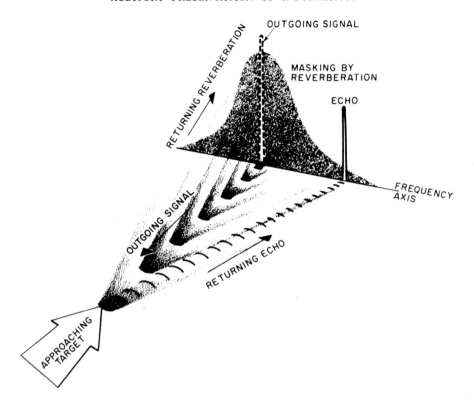

3-3 Detection of dopplered echo in presence of reverberation. Powerful outgoing signal emitted by echo-ranging sonar strikes small inhomogeneities, such as bubbles and fish, in water, which results in relatively continuous return of "reverberation" that lies mainly at frequency of outgoing signal. When outgoing signal strikes moving target, doppler effect results in echo with frequency removed from that of reverberation. Resultant pitch difference makes it easily detected by trained ear

In addition, sirens can be made intermittent by rotating a directional beam or by turning them on and off.

Bells ordinarily have low power, but their abrupt onset is excellent for demanding attention, and their high-frequency components are audible through low-frequency noise. In addition, human reaction to the bell sound is usually quicker than to other sounds. Buzzers are also generally low in power, but have a wide frequency spectrum, and are good attention-getters. If provided with manual shutoff, like an alarm clock, they sound a continuous alarm until action is taken. This last is true also, of course, of bells and some other alarm and warning devices.

Chimes and gongs are generally low in power and are less attention-getting than other types of signals. They are best suited to indicate action that is not urgent and for situations in which a warning signal would interfere with other activities that are not affected.

Oscillators generate tones electrically and can present them over an electrical communication (intercom) system. Set at a frequency of 1,000–2,500 cps, they are audible even in aircraft noise (Houston and Walker, 1949).

Design Recommendations

For the selection and design of signals for alarm and warning, the following principles should be observed (see also Table 3-3):

1. Use sounds having frequencies between 200 and 5,000 cps, and, if possible, between

§ 3.1.3

Table 3-2 Types of Alarms, Their Characteristics and Special Features

Alarm	Intensity	Frequency	Attention-getting ability	Noise-penetration ability	Special features
Diaphone (foghorn)	Very high	Very low	Good	Poor in low-frequency noise Good in high-frequency noise	
Horn	High	Low to high	Good	Good	Can be designed to beam sound directionally Can be rotated to get wide coverage
Whistle	High	Low to high	Good if intermittent	Good if frequency is properly chosen	Can be made directional by reflectors
Siren	High	Low to high	Very good if pitch rises and falls	Very good with rising and falling frequency	Can be coupled to horn for directional transmission
Bell	Medium	Medium to high	Good	Good in low-frequency noise	Can be provided with manual shutoff to insure alarm until action is taken
Buzzer	Low to medium	Low to medium	Good	Fair if spectrum is suited to background noise	Can be provided with manual shutoff to insure alarm until action is taken
Chimes and gong	Low to medium	Low to medium	Fair	Fair if spectrum is suited to background noise	
Oscillator	Low to high	Medium to high	Good if intermittent	Good if frequency is properly chosen	Can be presented over intercom system

Table 3-3 Summary of Design Recommendations for Auditory Alarm and Warning Devices

Conditions	Design recommendations
1. If distance to listener is great	1. Use high intensities and avoid high frequencies
2. If sound must bend around obstacles and pass through partitions	2. Use low frequencies
3. If background noise is present	3. Select alarm frequency in region where noise masking is minimal
4. To demand attention	4. Modulate signal to give intermittent "beeps" or modulate frequency to make pitch rise and fall at rate of about 1–3 cps
5. To acknowledge warning	5. Provide signal with manual shutoff so that it sounds continuously until action is taken

§ 3.1.3

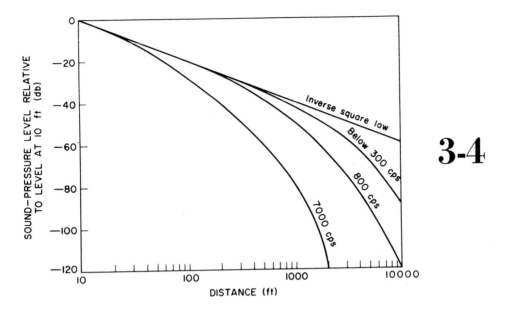

500 and 3,000 cps, because the human ear is most sensitive to this middle range.

2. Use sounds having frequencies below 1,000 cps when signals must travel long distances (over 1,000 ft) because high frequencies are absorbed in their passage through the air and hence cannot travel as far. Figure 3-4 shows attenuation of sounds of various frequencies in calm air for distances from 10–10,000 ft under conditions free from the effects of reflecting surfaces and obstacles.

3. Use frequencies below 500 cps when signals must bend around obstacles or pass through partitions. High frequencies cannot pass around or through solid objects as well as can low ones (see Fig. 3-5).

4. In a noisy environment, use signal frequencies as different as possible from the most intense frequencies of the noise. In this way, the masking of the signal by the noise is reduced to a minimum.

5. To demand attention, use a modulated signal, such as intermittent beeps repeated at rates of one to eight beeps per second, or warbling sounds that rise and fall in pitch. Such signals are seldom encountered in a normal environment and are different·enough to get immediate attention. If important speech communications are likely to be necessary during the alarm, use an intermittent, pure-tone signal of relatively high frequency.

6. Use complex tones rather than pure sinusoidal waves, if possible, because relatively few pure tones can be positively identified, whereas there are a very large number of complex sounds that can be identified because each such sound is noticeably different from the other sounds.

3.1.4 Some new uses for auditory presentation

A number of studies have been conducted to determine new uses for auditory presentation of information. A few of the more promising uses indicated by these studies include the auditory presentation of information for spatial-orientation, for tracking, and for detection and identification of radar signals. These new uses for auditory presentation are discussed in the following paragraphs.

SPATIAL ORIENTATION

The eye is much better adapted for the perception of spatial information than is the

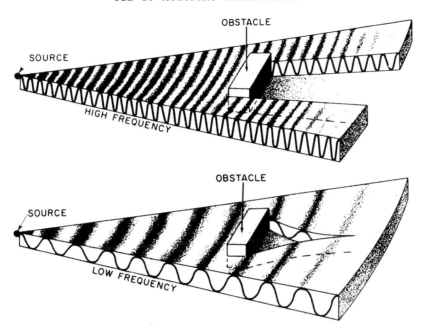

3-5 Sound shadows cast by obstacles. High-frequency sounds (wavelength shorter than width of obstacle) are greatly attenuated in shadow zone. Barriers based on this principle are sometimes used for control of high-frequency noise

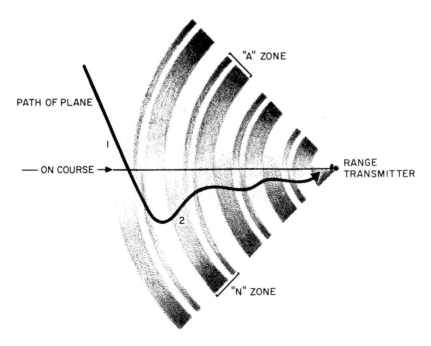

3-6 Four-course radio range. Pilot in upper sector ("A" zone) at position 1 hears succession of dit-dahs. In lower sector ("N" zone) at position 2, he hears series of dah-dits. When exactly on course he hears the two merge into steady tone

ear. Auditory displays of spatial information, however, can be designed and used satisfactorily (when they are needed to prevent overloading the visual system) if the limitations of the ear are taken into account.

Up to the present time, relatively few auditory displays have been devised for the presentation of spatial information. Even fewer have been put into operational use. Thus, experience with such displays is limited, and we can only summarize here the systems for displaying spatial information in auditory form that have so far proved satisfactory either in laboratory tests or in operational use. This summary classifies existing systems according to whether they represent one, two, or more dimensions of information.

One-Dimensional Displays

The most efficient auditory displays of spatial information are those representing one dimension of information.

Course. In the LF/MF four-course radio range, long used in U. S. aviation, intensity differences are used to represent deviation from course (see Fig. 3-6). Two directional radio signals, one carrying a Morse code "A" signal and the other an "N" signal are so arranged that a pilot flying on course hears a steady tone of 1,020 cps. If he gets off course on one side, the "A" signal (which interleaves with the "N" signal to form the continuous tone when he is exactly on course) becomes louder. If he gets off course on the other side, the "N" signal becomes louder. Because this system only requires the pilot to discriminate the difference in intensity between the "dit dah" or "dah dit" and a continuous tone, which is a very easy discrimination, it has long served well as the standard guidance system for U. S. airways.

Airspeed. A British system for representing airspeed to a pilot landing on an aircraft carrier has proved quite satisfactory in experimental trials (Ellis, et al., 1953). The system, shown schematically in Fig. 3-7 (right), can be described as follows:

a. At 90 knots, the pilot hears a steady, continuous pure tone of 2,300 cps.

b. If his speed exceeds 90 knots, the 2,300-cps tone pulses at rates starting with two pulses per second (pps) and increasing, with higher speeds, to 6 pps.

c. If his airspeed drops to 87.5 knots, a pulsed, 170-cps square wave is heard superimposed on the 2,300-cps tone.

d. If airspeed drops to 85 knots, the 2,300-cps tone disappears, leaving only the low-frequency square wave.

e. If airspeed drops below 85 knots, the interruption rate of the 170-cps square wave increases and thus serves as a warning of danger.

Altitude. In another experimental system, called the Automatic Annunciator (Miller, et al., 1946), altitude is presented automatically to the pilot in words such as "four-thousand two-hundred feet." These word messages are stored on magnetic loops in such a way that any combination of words is selected merely by picking up the word signals on the appropriate one of 24 loops in the desired sequence. The appropriate sequencing is carried out by a relay system coupled to the altimeter. Five seconds are required to present to the pilot an altimeter reading in thousands and hundreds of feet, and the mechanical rhythm of the annunciator distinguishes it from radio speech communications also being heard by the pilot over his earphones.

Two-Dimensional Displays

Two systems have been devised on an experimental basis for presenting the two dimensions of aircraft course and elevation in the

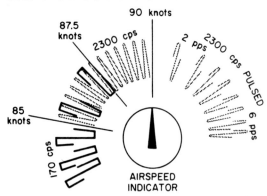

form of an auditory display (Humphrey, 1952). Both systems use frequency for elevation information and interaural intensity for course guidance.

In the first system, elevation above or below a desired one is indicated by the frequency of a tone. The reference tone is 2,000 cps, representing the correct elevation. For a small deviation above the correct elevation, the tone switches to 5,000 cps; for a large deviation, the tone switches to 8,000 cps. Similarly, for a small deviation below the correct elevation, the tone drops to 800 cps; and for a large deviation below, to 100 cps.

Left-right deviations from the correct course in this system are represented both by ear stimulation and by interruption rate. When on the correct course, the operator hears a steady tone of equal intensity in both ears. With any deviation to the right or left, the tone appears in only the right or left ear, as the case may be. With a small deviation in either direction, the tone is interrupted at 1 pps; with a moderate deviation, the interruption rate becomes 1.12 pps; and with a large deviation, it becomes 2 pps.

This system requires that the operator learn to identify correctly any one of 35 combinations of frequency, binaural intensity difference, and interruption rate. Obviously, special training is required, but it has been found that, in the course of such training, the number of mistakes drops rapidly to a satisfactory level. After training, operators most frequently make errors in identifying frequency and interruption rate. This is to be expected because the absolute identification of these parameters is known to be difficult. It is possible, however, that the identification of different interruption rates could have been improved by using a wider range of rates.

The second system is a proposed auditory landing system presenting information on deviation from the glide path in elevation and course (Cornell, 1948). When the pilot is above the glide path, he hears two high-pitched notes followed by a single reference standard. When below the path, he hears two low-pitched notes followed by the standard. When on the path, the three notes match in pitch. Course information is presented binau-

rally. A strong signal in the left earphone indicates deviation to the left of the proper course. A strong signal in the right earphone means that he is to the right of the proper course. Equal signals in both ears denotes "on course."

Multidimensional Displays

One satisfactory multidimensional display of information in auditory form has been developed to date. It is an experimental system and has not actually been put into practice but has been "flown" successfully by experienced pilots in extensive tests in link trainers. This system is known as Flybar (Flying By Auditory Reference).

The Flybar system employs a signal that can be varied in pitch, intensity, and interruption rate, and the changes in pitch can be superimposed on an interaural difference in intensity. Turn is indicated over binaural earphones by a repetitive, sweeping motion of the signal from the left ear to the right ear, or vice versa, depending on the direction of turn (see Fig. 3-8). Bank is indicated by a decrease in the pitch of the signal as it "sweeps" from one ear to the other. Airspeed is presented by the repetition rate of a "put-put" signal, which is most informative near stalling speeds; at such speeds, the very slow "put-put" gives the impression of falling through the air. All three aspects of the auditory signal combine to create in the observer very compelling illusions of turn, bank, and speed.

When to Use Auditory Displays

Consider the following points when deciding whether or not to use an auditory display for spatial information:

1. Use auditory displays to relieve the eyes. Although the eye is a better space-discriminating device than the ear, it can look in only one direction at a time. In general, auditory spatial displays should be used only when the eyes are fully engaged and it is essential to present additional spatial information. For

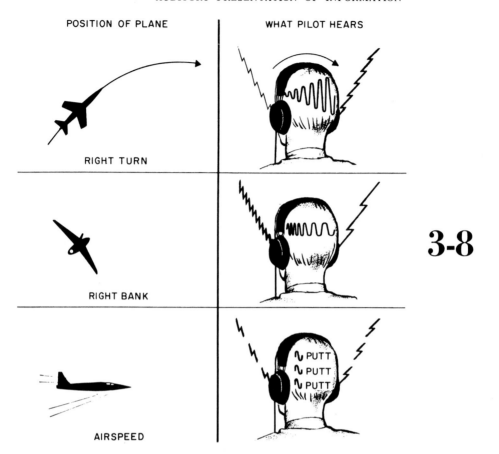

POSITION OF PLANE | WHAT PILOT HEARS

RIGHT TURN

RIGHT BANK

3-8

AIRSPEED

example, a pilot making a carrier landing must watch the deck of the carrier. At the same time, he needs continuous information about his airspeed. He cannot watch the deck and his airspeed indicator at the same time. Hence an auditory display of airspeed is very helpful.

2. Use auditory displays (other than speech) to present rather restricted information. Such displays are incapable of presenting many different kinds of information, but they can be quite suitable for a few kinds, such as the following:

a. "Yes-No" information and indications of the amount or degree of something. They can represent easily the error or deviation from a course, speed, attitude, or any other "normal" condition.

b. Continuous Information. For example, radio-range signals present practically continuous information about one kind of event

—the course the plane is flying.

c. Automatic Information. This might be presented as recorded word signals as in the Automatic Annunciator.

3. Use auditory displays of tonal or noise signals when speech channels are already fully employed. Most of the auditory displays that utilize tonal signals can be heard through speech, and, conversely, speech can be understood while hearing the tonal signals over the same receiving system.

Radio-range signals are a good example of all of the above points. They relieve the pilot's eyes, they present one restricted kind of information (course), they do this continuously while giving both "yes-no" and amount of error in course, they present the information automatically, and they avoid overburdening the speech channel while making it possible for the pilot to hear both speech communications and the range signals.

Design Recommendations

When designing auditory display for spatial orientation, keep the following recommendations in mind:

1. Confine auditory displays, if possible, to the representation of a single dimension. Good one-dimensional auditory displays compare favorably with visual displays. Multidimensional auditory displays are generally less effective than their visual counterparts.

2. Always provide a standard stimulus to represent the "normal" or desirable state of affairs. Then, if possible, make abrupt changes in this stimulus to indicate departures from the normal. Human observers are quite sensitive to changes (of frequency or intensity) but are poor at identifying a unique signal.

3. Use changes in intensity rather than frequency as a spatial cue if possible. Some people have poor pitch discrimination, but almost everyone with fairly normal hearing can detect changes in intensity. Moreover, it is usually easier to control intensity changes than it is to control frequency changes.

4. Use intermittent or repeated changes in a signal rather than a single change followed by a continuous signal. The ear is much more likely to detect the change if it occurs every second or two rather than at longer intervals.

5. Limit the number of signal categories to three or four if absolute identification of signals is required; listeners cannot correctly identify more than a few different intensities, pitches, or interruption rates.

6. Use "natural" relationships between auditory signals and the dimensions they represent. The following are some relationships that are quickly learned or, even, are perceived with no training at all:

a. Binaural differences in intensity can represent left-right information. Intensity differences between the ears normally serve to localize (in bearing) the direction of a sound. Such differences, therefore, are "natural" auditory displays and are readily perceived by people with fairly normal hearing.

b. Pitch differences naturally represent up and down. People speak, for example, of "high pitch" and "low pitch." Hence, if one wants to indicate climb or pointing upward,

raising the pitch is a good way to do it. This idea, combined with binaural changes in pitch from one ear to the other, can be used to represent, for instance, "left wing high."

c. Interruption rate, especially if it is fairly slow, is a natural indication of speed—an increase or decrease in interruption rate is immediately perceived as a change in the speed (or rate) of interruption.

TARGET TRACKING

Tracking is accomplished by an operator controlling an instrument to maintain a normal or desired value (compensatory tracking) or to follow a moving reference marker or target (pursuit tracking). Compensatory tracking requires a display of the tracking error only, preferably in both direction and magnitude. Although visual displays are normally used for tracking tasks, such as sighting a gun, auditory signals have proved satisfactory in laboratory studies, particularly for compensatory tracking.

Two different systems have been studied. In one system, displaying error direction only, the auditory presentation consisted of a 400-cps tone switched to one ear or the other when the operator veered off target (Humphrey and Thompson, 1952). When he centered his joy-stick control "on target," he heard nothing in either ear. This method of auditory presentation was compared with visual tracking in which one of two lights signaled "off target" to the left or right. The two kinds of presentation were equally good for both simple courses (two-cycle-per-minute sinusoid) and complex courses (combinations of 2-, 6-, and 15-cpm sinusoids).

In another, more complex, system, displaying both direction and magnitude of error, tracking performance with an auditory presentation was not as good as with a visual presentation (Humphrey and Thompson, 1953). The auditory presentation was a continuous tone in both ears for "on target," shifted to the left or right when "off target" and, at the same time, was interrupted at a rate proportional to the error in displacement from the on-target position.

When compared with a corresponding visual presentation in the form of a spot on an oscilloscope, the auditory presentation of this system was inferior. But, the operator was permitted to expand the visual presentation by adjusting a gain control. Had a similar adjustment of the auditory presentation been provided, the results probably would have been more favorable to the auditory method.

DETECTION OF RADAR SIGNALS

The important role of auditory presentation of information in the detection and identification of sonar signals has been described in article 3.1.3. The importance that radio operators place on the ability of their ears to detect and identify radio signals is well known. This auditory capability can be generalized to include other types of radio-frequency sources such as radars.

Although visual displays are preferred for presenting most radar information, auditory presentation has advantages for certain rather special purposes. Auditory presentation is useful for the following:

a. To detect the presence of radar signals. The pulse-repetition frequency often is in the audible-frequency range. When it is, the train of radar impulses is audible at the detector.

b. To identify particular radars. With training, a listener can identify such characteristics of a radar signal as repetition rate.

c. To detect a target through nonelectronic jamming.

3.2 *Perception of Sound Signals*

3.2.1 *Characteristics of sound signals*

Important characteristics of sound are amplitude, frequency and waveform, and duration. The amplitude usually is measured by sound pressure—the alternating pressure superimposed on the normal atmospheric pressure. A unit of this alternating pressure is the dyne per square centimeter (dyne/cm²) or its equivalent, the microbar (μbar). The root-mean-square (rms) pressure is usually used to describe the magnitude of the sound.

Because man can hear sounds over an extremely wide range of sound pressures (from about 0.0001 to 1,000 μbar), instead of using the value of sound pressure directly, it is customary to deal with sound-pressure level (SPL) defined by

$$L = 20 \log (p_1/p_0) = 10 \log (p_1/p_0)^2, \quad (3\text{-}1)$$

where L is the sound-pressure level of sound pressure p_1, and p_0 is a reference pressure.

The unit of sound-pressure level is the decibel (db). The db is a relative unit; it refers to a ratio of sound pressures (e.g., p_1 and p_2). Thus, the difference between two sound-pressure levels, L_1 and L_2, is

$$L_2 - L_1 = 20 \log (p_2/p_0) - 20 \log (p_1/p_0)$$
$$= 20 \log (p_2/p_1). \quad (3\text{-}2)$$

Note that the reference pressure (p_0) does not affect the difference, provided that the same reference pressure is used in both expressions for the two levels.

The pressure $p_0 = 0.0002$ μbar has been adopted as a standard reference pressure, and it is understood, ordinarily, when a sound-pressure level is stated. Practically all commercially available sound-measuring equipments are calibrated to read in sound-pressure level based on this reference pressure.

The standard reference pressure of 0.0002

μbar was adopted because it is very close to the lowest level (absolute threshold) the human observer can hear when the signal is a 1,000-cps pure tone (man happens to be about as sensitive to this frequency as to any other). Figure 3-9 shows typical SPL's for some common sounds. Also shown are the corresponding rms sound pressures and intensities for sound waves in air.

Waveform is most conveniently specified in terms of the various frequency components that comprise the sound. Thus, sounds having a precisely periodic waveform are composed of a series of single-frequency components located at discrete frequencies and integrally related. Aperiodic sounds similarly might consist of discrete components, or they might be composed of a continuum of frequency components distributed over a broad band; the former are said to have a line spectrum, the latter a continuous spectrum.

3.2.2 *Methods of presenting sound signals to the ears*

The fact that man has *two* ears can be put to good use in designing auditory-presentation systems. Sometimes, in monitoring situations, the two ears can be used relatively independently of each other. In other cases, by adjusting the interaural phase and amplitude of signals, the two ears can use directional information effectively (Licklider, 1951). These are examples of the use of binaural presentation. Monaural presentation is used where it is desirable to leave one ear uncovered for hearing ambient sounds.

SIMPLE BINAURAL PRESENTATION

The simplest form of binaural presentation is presenting the exact same sound to both ears but from two different sources, e.g., a

headset with two earphones. This form of binaural presentation has the following advantages over monaural presentation:

a. Under very quiet conditions, the absolute threshold of hearing is about 3 db better for simple binaural than for monaural presentation.

b. The loudness of the sound heard from the two sources is about twice that of the same sound heard from one source.

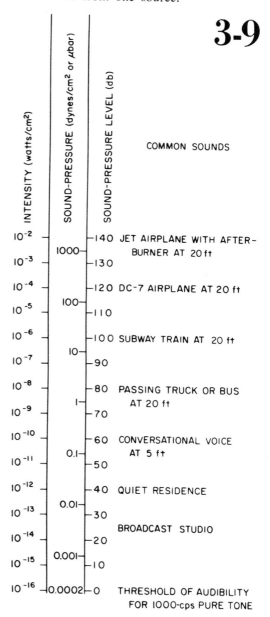

3-9

§ 3.2.2

Increasing Detectability

In the presence of masking noise (see article 3.3.2), such as radio static or sonar water noise, the gain in detectability by binaural rather than monaural presentation is negligible. If it is possible to invert the interaural phase of the signal with respect to the noise, however, a gain in detectability of about 10–12 db can be realized at frequencies between 200 and 500 cps with binaural presentation (Hirsh, 1948). It is almost never possible to do this, however, because signal and noise are seldom under separate control. A possible exception is the case in which signals presented through earphones must be heard in strong, local, low-frequency, acoustic noise such as that found in aircraft. Here, reversing the connection to one earphone to invert the signal phase is recommended.

Providing Auditory Perspective

Two methods can be used to preserve the azimuth directional property of a sound picked up by microphones. In one method, the outputs of a pair of microphones separated by about the distance between the human ears (or, better yet, mounted in the ears of a dummy head) are fed through separate channels to their respective earphones. This method provides the aural illusion that the listener is located at the position of the microphones. A second method, known as stereophonic presentation, accomplishes a somewhat analogous result by using multiple microphones and speakers to reproduce an approximate replica of the original sound field (Snow, 1953).

Artificial directional effects can be obtained by controlling intensity and time delay at the earphones or multiple loudspeakers. An interaural time delay of only 10 μsec will produce barely perceptible shifts in localization (Klumpp and Eady, 1956), and a time delay of the order of 0.6 msec will completely lateralize a sound when it first arrives. The sound will continue to remain lateralized for time differences up to about 2 msec, beyond which it will tend to be heard separately in the two

ears. Beyond 20 msec, lateralization disappears rapidly (Blodgett, et al., 1956). In general, complex sounds, such as speech, clicks, or broadband noise, are localized much better than pure tones.

DUPLEX BINAURAL PRESENTATION

In duplex binaural presentation, different sounds are presented to the ears from two different sources. Because interaural masking (see article 3.3.2) is low, the listener can easily detect and identify the different signals, but his attention can only be directed to one signal at a time. Hence, duplex presentation is best suited to monitoring tasks in which signals are only occasionally heard and then only when the two signals are very seldom heard at the same time.

BONE CONDUCTION

In some situations, it is convenient to bypass the normal pathway of the external ear canal and introduce sound into the inner ear through the bones of the skull. Bone-conduction vibrators are available for this purpose. The vibrator is ordinarily held in contact with the mastoid or forehead with a force of the order of 500 gm, but bone conduction can be obtained satisfactorily from nearly any other position on the head with but a slight reduction in sensitivity. In fact, vibratory energy can be conducted to the inner ear from sources applied to more remote locations on the body but with greater transmission loss.

Bone conduction can be used to advantage in underwater hearing. When using underwater earphones or loudspeakers, the poor match between the low acoustic impedance of the eardrum and the high impedance of the water results in a lowered sensitivity (about 50 db) of the ear to sound (Hamilton, 1957). When the head is immersed in water, sound signals can be presented through bone-conduction vibrators because it appears that underwater sound is conducted to the inner ear about as readily by bone conduction as by the normal eardrum-middle-ear path.

3.2.3 *Absolute threshold of hearing*

The absolute threshold of hearing is the minimum sound-pressure level of a specified sound that is required to elicit the sensation of hearing in a specified fraction of trials (ordinarily, 50%, unless otherwise stated) with no masking noise present. The value of the absolute threshold depends on the type of sound (frequency, duration, repetition rate, etc.), method of presentation (loudspeaker or headset, binaural or monaural, etc.), and the listener (age, past exposure to noise, listening experience, history of ear trouble, etc.).

PURE-TONE THRESHOLDS

There are three generally accepted absolute thresholds for pure tones: the Minimum Audible Field (MAF), the Minimum Audible Pressure (MAP), and the Normal Threshold of Audibility (NTA). These are all shown as a function of frequency in Fig. 3-10.

Minimum Audible Field

This is the sound-pressure level at the absolute threshold of a young, but trained, listener who has no history of ear trouble. The listener is facing the source in a free-sound field, such as out in the open air or in an anechoic room, and SPL is measured at the point where the center of the head would be.

Minimum Audible Pressure

This also is the sound-pressure level at the absolute threshold of a young, but trained, listener who has no history of ear trouble. Here, however, the sound is presented by an earphone, the listener is in a quiet room, and the SPL is measured at the eardrum, under the earphone. The slight elevation of this threshold over the MAF is caused by the elimination of the effects of acoustic diffrac-

tion around the head and by the physiological noise generated in the ear cavity when it is enclosed by an earphone.

Normal Threshold of Audibility

This is the accepted American standard for the calibration of audiometers. It is the modal value of the minimum sound-pressure level at the entrance to the ear canal that can be heard by a large sample of young (18–30 yr) and *unpracticed* listeners wearing earphones in a quiet room. Because young, *practiced* listeners can hear much better than this threshold, there is a strong movement to accept the British normal threshold, which is much closer to the MAP.

BINAURAL VS. MONAURAL

The binaural threshold for ears of equal sensitivity is about 2–3 db below the monaural threshold. If ears of unequal sensitivity differ by more than about 6 db in their monaural thresholds, the binaural threshold is essentially that of the better ear. On the average, the better ear differs from the mean of the two ears by about 2 db at frequencies below 1,000 cps and up to 6 db at 10,000 cps (Fletcher, 1953).

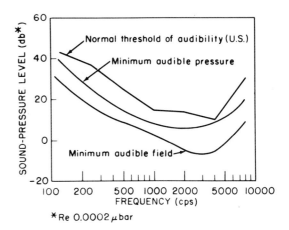

*Re 0.0002 μ bar

3-10

EFFECT OF AGE ON HEARING

Hearing sensitivity at high frequencies tends to decrease with age, particularly for men. Figure 3-11 (American Standards Assoc., 1954) shows the average hearing loss for pure tones at different frequencies for men and women of different ages. Individual people might vary markedly from these curves; some lose their hearing early and others reach old age with no appreciable hearing loss.

3.2.4 *Loudness and pitch*

Loudness is the magnitude of the auditory sensation elicited by a sound stimulus. It is a subjective response to a sound and depends, primarily, on the sound pressure and, secondarily, on the frequency, duration, and spectrum of the sound. Although a subjective response, loudness can be quantitatively evaluated, as shown in the following paragraphs.

THE LOUDNESS-LEVEL SCALE

Two sounds can be equated in loudness by alternately listening to one and then the other and adjusting the level of one until the two seem equally loud. This technique of loudness balancing has been used to construct a loudness-level scale for quantitatively evaluating the loudness of sounds. The unit of this scale is the phon. The loudness level of a sound in phons is defined as the sound-pressure level of a 1,000-cps pure tone that sounds equally loud. Equating the loudness of pure tones of various frequencies and levels yields the equal-loudness contours shown in Fig. 3-12.

THE LOUDNESS SCALE

The equal-loudness contours of Fig. 3-12 provide data on equally loud tones, but they do not tell us how much one tone is louder than another when their loudnesses are unequal. For this purpose, a loudness scale is used, the unit of which is the sone. Unit loudness on this scale is the loudness of a 1,000-cps tone 40 db above absolute threshold. Sounds are then scaled in terms of their loudnesses judged as multiples or fractions of this reference sound. Thus, a sound ten times as loud as the reference sound has a loudness of 10 sones.

Loudness judgments are very difficult to make and are subject to many influences. Nevertheless, the relation between loudness (in sones) and loudness level (in phons) can be shown reasonably well by the line in Fig. 3-13. This shows that loudness doubles for each 10-phon increase in loudness level (Stevens, 1955b).

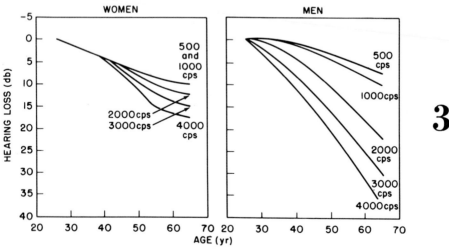

142

PITCH

Pitch, like loudness, is also a subjective attribute of sound. It is determined primarily by frequency, although it is affected somewhat by loudness, spectrum, etc. A scale for the quantitative rating of the magnitude of pitch

in a manner similar to that described above for loudness has been established. The unit of this scale is the mel, which is defined as the pitch of a 1,000-cps pure tone at a level 40 db above absolute threshold.

Figure 3-14 (Stevens and Volkmann, 1940) shows the dependence of pitch on frequency.

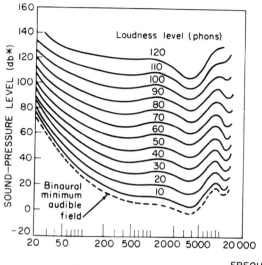

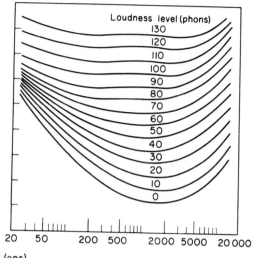

3-12 Equal-loudness contours for pure tones. For left data, listener is in free field facing source; sound pressure is measured at point where center of head of listener would be (Robinson and Dadson, 1957). For right data, listener is wearing earphones; sound pressure is measured under earphones (Fletcher and Munson, 1933)

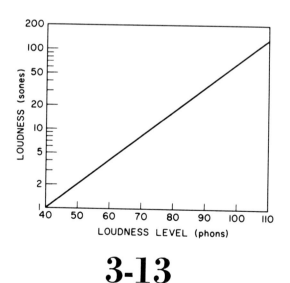

3-13

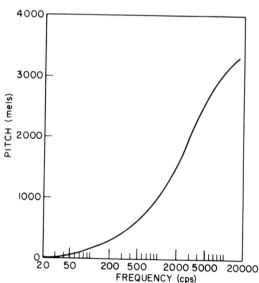

The data in this figure can be used, for example, to select the frequencies of a set of pure tones so that the intervals between them are equal in pitch.

3.3 *Signal Processing and Control*

In designing an auditory presentation, the designer must consider the following:

a. The signals and the unwanted noises that might be picked up by the system.

b. The choice of ways in which the system can process the signals and noise.

c. The method by which the processed information can be presented to the listener.

3.3.1 *Signal and noise relationships*

Because few environments are free of noise, noise is usually a limiting factor in a signal-processing system. The designer should, therefore, consider whether it is possible to design a signal-processing system that will separate signal and noise. In attempting to do this, he will find signal and noise related to one another in the following ways:

a. Sometimes the noise is fixed by the environment, but the designer can select the signal to be used. For example, in sending radio-range signals to a pilot, the noise of the aircraft is relatively fixed, but the designer can choose the frequency to be used for presenting the desired information.

b. In other instances, both the signal and the background noise are determined by the listening environment and not by the designer. For example, in passive sonar, the exact nature of sounds emitted by ships of unknown identity is indeterminate. Here, data on the background noise and the probable nature of the signals must be used to determine how the signal should be processed. Often, adjustable controls should be provided so that the experienced operator can set the combination of signal and noise most favorable for signal detection and identification.

c. In still other cases, the signal is fixed but the noise can be controlled either by reducing its overall level or by appropriate networks that reduce the noise level in regions of the spectrum away from the signal. For example, earmuffs can be used to prevent environmental noise from masking signals heard over earphones (see Chapter 4), electrical filters (see article 3.3.3) can be employed to reduce the interference of static and radio noise with Morse code signals, and peak clippers (see article 3.3.5) can be used to reduce the high peak amplitudes of impulse noise such as that from automotive ignition systems.

3.3.2 *The masking of sound by noise*

Noise mixed with a signal tends to raise the threshold for hearing that signal above the threshold in quiet, or absolute threshold. This phenomenon is called masking, and the elevated threshold is known as the masked threshold.

MONAURAL MASKING

The masking effects of a pure tone, or of a noise with a strong component in one part

§ 3.3.1

of the spectrum, are different from those of a narrow- or wide-band noise. Thus, masking by each of these will be discussed separately in the paragraphs that follow.

Masking by Pure Tones

The masking effect of a pure tone, or of a noise with a strong tonal component, is greatest near the frequency of the tonal component but also extends to signals on both sides of the masking tone (see Fig. 3-15). By the same token, the masked threshold of the signal is raised more by frequencies in the vicinity of a signal than by those located farther away in the spectrum and is raised more by frequencies below that of the signal than by those above the frequency of the signal. At relatively high intensities, however, the masked threshold of signals that are some integral multiple of the masking tone is raised more than those having no harmonic relationship to the masking tone.

Curves of masking versus frequency for masking by pure tones of various frequencies and levels are shown in Fig. 3-16. The presence of audible beats at frequencies very near the masking tone and its harmonics increase the audibility of the tone and, therefore, sharply reduce the effective masking at these frequencies. Note that masking tends to be confined to the vicinity of the masking tone for tones of low level (20–40 db), whereas, at high levels, considerable masking occurs, extending particularly to frequencies above the masking tone.

Masking by Narrow-Band Noise

Curves of masking versus frequency for masking by a narrow band of noise are shown in Fig. 3-17 (Egan and Hake, 1950). These are somewhat similar to the curves for masking by pure tones except that the sharp dips caused by beats are absent.

Masking by Wide-Band Noise

The masking effects of a wide-band noise extend over and somewhat beyond the entire spectrum of the noise. The frequency analysis performed by the ear is much like that of a band-pass filter (see article 3.3.3). Such a

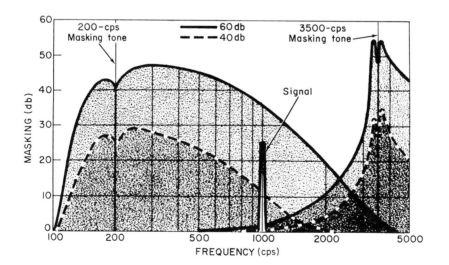

3-15 Masking produced by pure tones. Masking produced by 200-cps pure tone at 60 db and 40 db is shown by solid and dashed curves at left. Signal, shown in middle, is masked by 60-db tone but is audible above 40-db tone. Solid and dashed curves at right are for 3,500-cps pure tone at 60 and 40 db. Because masking does not tend to spread downward in frequency, 1,000-cps signal remains unmasked by 3,500-cps tone

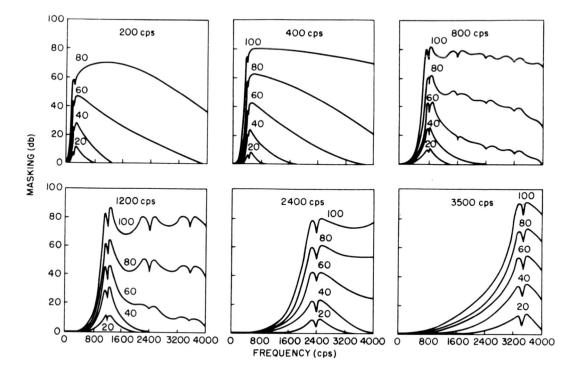

3-16 Masking as function of frequency for masking by pure tones of various frequencies and levels. Number at top of each graph is frequency of masking tone. Number on each curve is level above threshold of masking tone (Wegel and Lane, 1924)

filter, with its limits set to include the frequency of the signal, rejects noise outside of these limits, thereby increasing the signal-to-noise (S/N) ratio and making the signal more audible. The ear, in effect, does the same thing. The width of its "filter," called the critical bandwidth, varies from about 50 to over 200 cps, depending on the frequencies con-

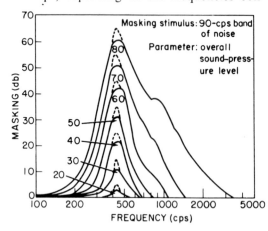

cerned (Fletcher, 1953). At a frequency of 800 cps, the critical bandwidth is ~50 cps.

Figure 3-18 (Hawkins and Stevens, 1950) shows masked thresholds of pure tones when masked by a wide-band noise of uniform spectrum (white noise). The linear increase of masking with sound-pressure level of the masking noise is apparent from the regular spacing of the contours.

Predicting the masked threshold. The masked threshold of a pure tone masked by wide-band noise can be predicted if the spectrum level of the noise is known at the frequency of the tone. In making such a prediction, it may be assumed that the masking is caused by noise components, the frequencies of which lie in a band near that of the tone and, in fact, lie within the same critical band as the tone. When used to predict masking, the critical bandwidth is so defined that the SPL of the noise in the critical band is just equal to the SPL of the tone at its masked threshold. Figure 3-19 shows the generally

§ 3.3.2

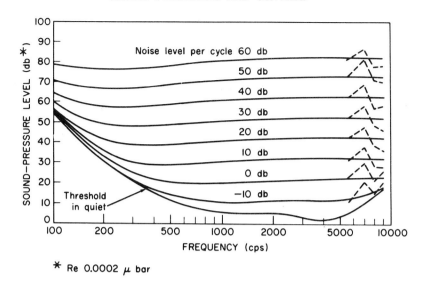

3-18

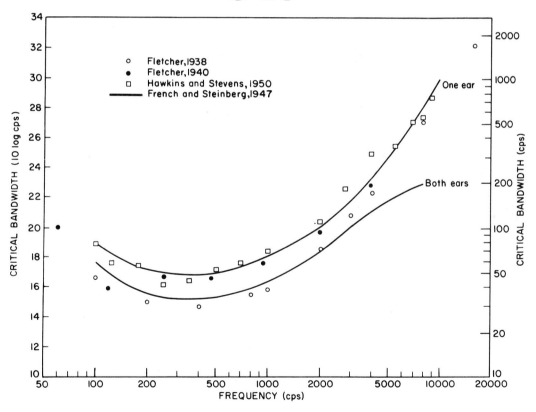

3-19

accepted values of critical bandwidth as a function of frequency.

To predict masked threshold at a frequency f by this method, proceed as follows:

1. Measure the spectrum level of the wideband masking noise at f.

2. Correct this measured level to the level in the critical band at f by adding the 10 log of the critical bandwidth. This correction can be read directly from the left-hand ordinate of Fig. 3-19.

3. This corrected value is the masked threshold at f if the value is more than 20 db above the absolute threshold at f. If it is less than 20 db, a correction must be made for nonlinearity in the masking-vs.-noise-level function near the absolute threshold.

Correcting for nonlinearity. Masking at any particular frequency is a linear function of the level of noise in the critical band at the frequency, except for the toe of the function, which, at very low noise levels, flattens out and becomes asymptotic to zero. The level of noise in a critical band above the absolute threshold of a pure tone at the center frequency of this band is known as the effective level (Z) of the noise at the center frequency.

If masking (M) is plotted as a function of Z for a number of different frequencies, the plotted points tend to lie on the single curve shown in Fig. 3-20. Note that, when M is greater than about 20 db, $M = Z$, and that, when M is less than 20 db, $M > Z$. The magnitude of the correction that must be added to the level of the noise in a critical band to predict the masked threshold is the value of the difference $M - Z$, which can be obtained from Fig. 3-20 (right).

INTERAURAL MASKING

The statements made above apply to monaural masking—when signal and noise together reach the ear or ears from the same source. In interaural masking, when the signal is fed into one ear and the noise into the other, rather different rules apply. No masking of the signal occurs when the SPL of the noise is relatively low, say below 40 or 50 db, because the listener is able to distinguish clearly sounds heard separately by the two

ears. Masking occurs only when the SPL of the noise is sufficiently high for the sound to be conducted through the bone of the skull to the opposite ear (Fletcher, 1953), which might be at SPL's of 50 db or higher. Such masking, however, reduces to a case of monaural masking with the head serving as an attenuator. Thus, interaural masking becomes a problem only when earphones are used, and then only when the sound in one greatly exceeds that in the other; the effective level of the masking noise in one ear must be about 50 db or more above the signal in the other ear to produce interaural masking.

3.3.3 *Filtering*

Filters are often useful for enhancing the audibility of signals in the presence of noise. Filtering in the frequency domain is the selective passing of certain wanted frequencies and the exclusion of unwanted ones. This process can be accomplished by electrical, mechanical, or acoustical elements.

THE REDUCTION OF MASKING

Filters can be used to reduce the masking effect of a noise on a signal, thereby making the signal audible. Two types of masking can be reduced by filtering: the masking produced by components within a critical bandwidth centered at the signal frequency (called

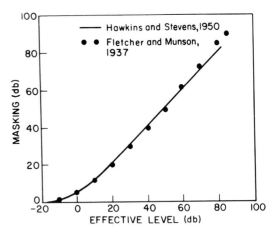

direct or centered masking) and the masking effect of pure tones or tonal noises on signals lying outside the critical band (called remote or displaced masking). These are discussed in the following paragraphs.

The Reduction of Direct Masking

Very narrow band-pass filters that reject noise within the critical band can be used to reduce the masking of a wide-band noise on a tone that lies at a frequency within the noise spectrum. For such a band-pass filter to be of value, however, it must be narrower than the critical band. Otherwise, it only rejects noise that has no masking effect anyway. Up to a certain point, the narrower the filter, the greater the reduction of masking noise (Schafer, et al., 1950).

On the other hand, the band-pass filter should not be made too narrow because the noise passing through a very narrow filter takes on a tonal quality that is difficult to distinguish from the signal itself. Furthermore, if the pass band is narrower than the reciprocal of the signal duration, it begins to reduce signal strength (see article 3.4.1). But, because the band-pass filter must be quite narrow to effect any improvement in audibility, it can be used only with signals that are very stable in frequency.

The Reduction of Remote Masking

Filters that reject noise in the spectrum outside the signal and its critical band can be used to some advantage whenever the masking noise is of such high amplitude that it causes remote masking at the signal frequency. The removal of such noise by a filter reduces the remote masking the noise produces and increases signal detectability. Because remote masking is greater when the masking noise has a lower frequency than the signal, the greatest benefit of a filter is realized when it is used to reject noises at frequencies below that of the signal.

To reduce remote masking, a filter should be designed to reject the components of noise causing the remote masking without appre-

ciably reducing the amplitude of the signal. Thus, in Fig. 3-15, a 500-cps high-pass filter could remove the 60-db, 200-cps noise component, with its remote masking, so that the 1,000-cps signal would become audible. Figure 3-21 illustrates a similar effect as achieved by a band-pass filter centered on the frequency of the signal.

THE REDUCTION OF LOUDNESS

Under certain circumstances, filters can be used to improve signal detection by lowering the overall noise level and permitting the operator to increase the gain so that the signal is at the optimum level for detection (see article 3.2.4). The circumstances are as follows:

a. When the noise is greatest in bands not containing the signal, filters can be used to reduce it separately from the signal.

b. When the noise is distributed over a wide band of frequencies, and the signal can occur at any frequency in the band, an equal-

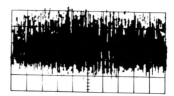

UNFILTERED

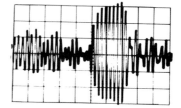

FILTERED

3-21 Oscillograms of signal consisting of 10-msec pulse of 800-cps tone buried in wide-band white noise. Effective filter action makes signal clearly visible on oscilloscope after filtering signal and noise by 200-cps band-pass filter

izer can be used to shape the noise spectrum so that its masking is about the same at all frequencies.

Wide-band noises that are loud enough to raise the masked threshold more than 20 db at all frequencies are likely to be uncomfortably loud. The resulting discomfort causes the operator to turn his gain down, thereby reducing the signal level to an intensity less than 20 db above his absolute threshold. This is particularly probable when the signal is relatively low in frequency, and the noise con-tains much high-frequency energy.

Thus, the overall noise level can be reduced by inserting filters or equalizers in the signal processing system. By reducing the noise level, such filtering or equalizing networks permit the operator to increase his gain without making the noise uncomfortably loud. The increased gain brings the signal level into the optimum-detection zone of 20–80 db above absolute threshold. As a result, his ability to detect the signal is improved. This fact is illustrated in Fig. 3-22.

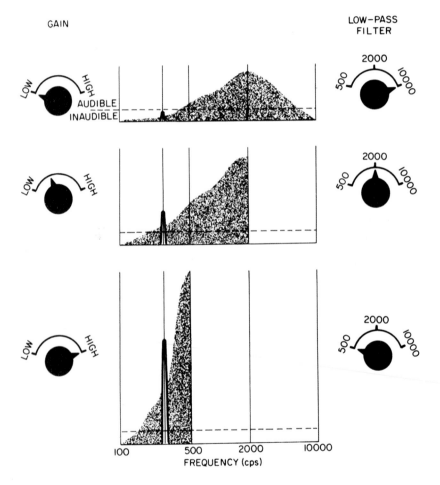

3-22 Use of filters to reduce loudness of background noise. Spectrum at top shows signal in presence of wide-band, high-frequency noise, which, though not masking the signal, is so loud (unfiltered) that operator has reduced his gain control to point where signal is below absolute threshold and, hence, inaudible. In center case, 2,000-cps low-pass filter has allowed operator to increase his gain control to point where noise is as loud as previously (equal grey area), but signal is now raised above absolute threshold and becomes audible. Lower spectrum has 500-cps low-pass filter to further increase gain and signal audibility

§ 3.3.3

3.3.4 *Signal-level control*

Any signal used in an auditory display must exceed the absolute auditory threshold or it will not be heard, even under the ideal circumstance of an attentive listener and quiet surroundings. In actual practice, requirements are more stringent because the listener generally must make critical discriminations between characteristics of sounds, and he is likely to be in a noisy environment.

MINIMUM SIGNAL LEVEL

It ordinarily is necessary to present sounds at levels well above the absolute threshold. Discrimination of small changes in signal intensity and pitch is performed best at levels more than 60 db above the absolute threshold (see article 3.4.1). In the presence of noise, the signal must exceed its masked threshold, preferably by at least 15 db for good discrimination (see article 3.3.2).

MAXIMUM SIGNAL LEVEL

High SPL's can impair hearing or be uncomfortable and painful (see Chapter 10). Individual people differ considerably in the levels they will tolerate, but enough data are available to establish the following satisfactory working rules:

1. To avoid feelings of discomfort, do not use SPL's above 120 db. These are uncomfortable and cannot be tolerated for very long periods of time.

2. To avoid feelings of pain, do not use levels above 135 db. These are so painful for most people that they cannot be tolerated for even brief periods.

3. Make exposures to intense sounds as brief as possible. The human ear can stand extremely intense sounds for a few seconds (e.g., 130 db for 10 sec) without lasting effects, but prolonged exposure to intensities of 85–95 db or above can cause damage to the ear and an accompanying hearing loss. Figures 3-23 and 3-24 show recommended upper limits for noise exposure.

4. Avoid using high-frequency sounds as much as possible. With low-frequency sounds (500 cps and below), there is much less risk of damage to hearing than with higher ones.

OPTIMUM SIGNAL LEVEL

A typical auditory task is to detect small changes in intensity or frequency (see article 3.4.1). This can be done best at comfortable, but fairly loud, listening levels. The optimum level, however, depends on whether the individual is listening in quiet or in noise. For listening in quiet, do the following:

1. If the task is to detect changes in intensity, set the signal level 60 db or more above the absolute threshold (Riesz, 1928). Because threshold varies with frequency, this will re-

3-23 Damage-risk criteria for maximum exposure (8-hr work day) of the unprotected ear to noise. Data are for octave-band levels of continuous wide-band noise. For pure tones, lower curve is recommended. For daily exposures less than 8 hr, add appropriate correction from lower curve of Fig. 3-24 (Rosenblith and Stevens, 1953)

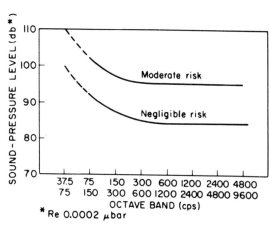

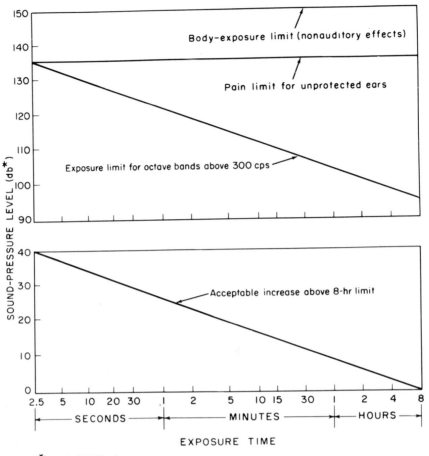

*Re 0.0002 μbar

3-24 Damage-risk criteria for exposures of less than 8 hr per day. Basic 8-hr-day criteria of Fig. 3-23 are increased by amount determined from lower curve. Upper curve shows damage-risk criteria for octave bands of noise between 300 and 9,600 cps. Pain limit for unprotected ears is shown at 135 db. When ear protectors are used, sound-pressure level in sound field can exceed these criteria by amount of attenuation provided by protector (see Chapter 10). Body-exposure limit at 150 db is point at which potentially dangerous nonauditory effects occur. This level should not be exceeded in any case (Eldred, et al., 1955)

3-25 Comfortable listening levels for pure tones. Dashed curve shows mean level judged most comfortable by 33 observers while listening binaurally to pure tone. Upper solid curves show maximum and minimum levels that were still considered comfortable by these listeners. Lower solid curve, reading right-hand ordinate, shows range between upper and lower limits for comfort (Pollack, 1952)

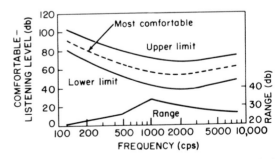

§ 3.3.4

sult in a higher SPL at low and high frequencies than at medium frequencies between 1,000 and 4,000 cps.

2. If the task is to detect changes in frequency, set the signal at least 30 db above absolute threshold (Shower and Biddulph, 1931).

3. For the most comfortable listening level, set the signal about 40–50 db above the absolute threshold (Pollack, 1952). Because comfortable listening, like ability to detect intensity or frequency changes, depends on acoustic frequency, consult Fig. 3-25 for more precise specifications.

4. For listening in noise, a convenient rule of thumb for specifying the optimum signal level is to select one midway between the masked threshold and 110 db.

3.3.5 *Dynamic range and volume control*

Signal level at the ear can vary considerably and still transmit information effectively. (In this respect, the ear is far superior to the eye.) Signal level can, in fact, vary between the absolute or masked threshold as a lower limit and the threshold of discomfort as the upper limit. This range of acceptable signal levels is called the useful dynamic range, which de-

pends on the frequency of the signal and on the background noise (see Figs. 3-25 and 3-26). To be detected and identified effectively, auditory signals must be kept within the useful dynamic range. This can be done in the following ways:

a. A signal can be controlled at its source by using suitable metering equipment. For example, in radio broadcasting, an announcer regulates his voice signal by watching a VU meter. This meter is designed to have temporal response characteristics somewhat like the human ear, and it indicates the signal level of the voice in decibels. By controlling his voice so that the needle of the VU meter regularly hits a constant value as he talks, the announcer can keep his voice signal within the dynamic range of his listeners (and also that of the radio carrier wave).

b. The signal level can be set by the listener. If the signal is reasonably constant in level, the listener can be provided with a volume control that he can set to a desired listening level. Such volume controls can be continuous, as they are in phonograph, radio, and television sets, or they can be stepped, as they frequently are in electrical attenuators. (It should be noted that volume control in successive steps of 1 db or less sounds virtually continuous, 2 db steps are slightly noticeable, and steps greater than 5 db are used only in special circumstances.) This manual method of setting the volume control is satisfactory when the available dynamic range is fairly large (40 db or more), in which case

EFFECT OF MASKING NOISE IN REDUCING DYNAMIC RANGE

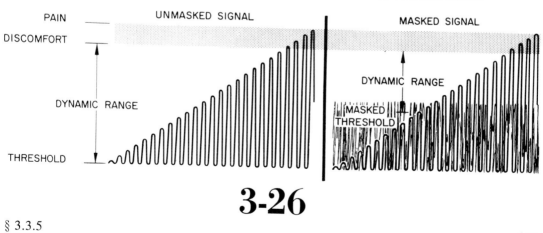

3-26

deviations of 10 db or more from the optimum listening level can be tolerated.

c. Signal level can be brought within the dynamic range by a compressor (see Fig. 3-27). This device is particularly suitable for cases in which the signal unavoidably varies in strength more than the acceptable dynamic range. The compressor, by reducing the amplitude of the larger signals while leaving weaker signals nearly unaltered, reduces the range of signal variation. When the average level of the signal varies widely, it might be necessary to supplement a compressor with either an AVC (see below) or a manual volume control. A well designed compressor does not distort the wave form of the signal. For this reason they are used extensively in recording and broadcasting of speech and music. To avoid distortion, the attack and release times of the compressor action must be compatible with the dynamic properties of the source material. For speech and music, a fast attack time of about 10 msec combined with a slow release time of the order of 1 sec has been found to be satisfactory (Hathaway, 1950). The rapid attack time enables the circuit to adjust immediately to the sudden onset of a new signal, and the slow release time tends to stabilize the gain during reception of sounds inherently intermittent in nature such as speech and music.

d. The signal level can be set by an automatic volume control (AVC), also called automatic gain control (AGC), in the signal processing system (see Fig. 3-27). Some sort of automatic control becomes critical when high ambient-noise levels reduce the usable dynamic range to 20 or 30 db or less. Most radio receivers have AVC circuits that maintain a relatively constant volume by controlling the amplification of the radio carrier wave. (See Chapter 4 for a more detailed discussion of AGC.)

e. For some purposes, a peak clipper (see Fig. 3-27) can be used in place of a compressor to bring signals within the usable dynamic range. As mentioned in article 3.3.1, peak clippers sometimes are useful for reducing the peaks of electric impulse noise. In addition, a peak clipper can be used with speech to keep the peaks of speech waves from exceeding the threshold of discomfort (see Chapter 4). Because little intelligibility is contained in the peaks that are clipped off, the signal is about as effective as before clipping, provided that clipping is no more than 20 db. Because peak clipping markedly distorts a signal, however, its use should be limited to cases where distortion is acceptable. For example, it is extensively used in military speech-communication systems but not in systems that are used for entertainment.

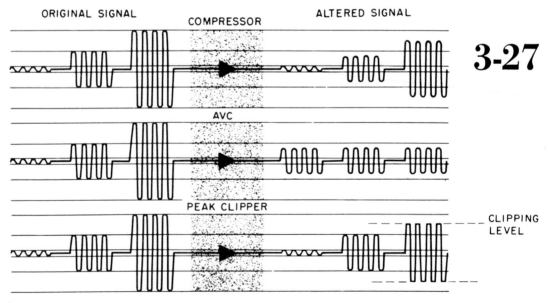

ORIGINAL SIGNAL   COMPRESSOR   ALTERED SIGNAL

3-27

AVC

PEAK CLIPPER

CLIPPING LEVEL

§ 3.3.5

3.4 *The Selection of Signals*

3.4.1 *Single signals*

In many systems of auditory presentation, the operator can select the kind of signal he uses. For example, a sonar operator can adjust the frequency or duration of his signal by adjusting controls at his disposal, or a Morse-code operator can adjust the beat-frequency oscillator on his receiver to select his listening frequency. The selection of signal parameters depends on the nature of the change the operator must detect. The change either in frequency or in intensity (usually stated as sound-pressure level) that is just perceptible (or just noticeably different) depends on the sound-pressure level, frequency, duration, and method of presenting the differences.

DETECTING FREQUENCY CHANGES

Figure 3-28 (Shower and Biddulph, 1931) shows just-noticeable differences (JND) in frequency for pure tones at various levels above threshold. Note that the smallest JND is about 2 or 3 cps and is found at frequencies below 1,000 cps, whereas, above 1,000 cps,

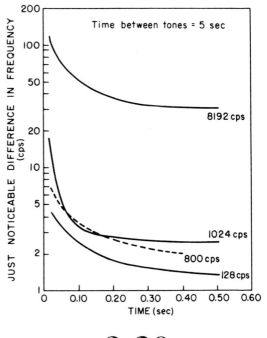

3-29

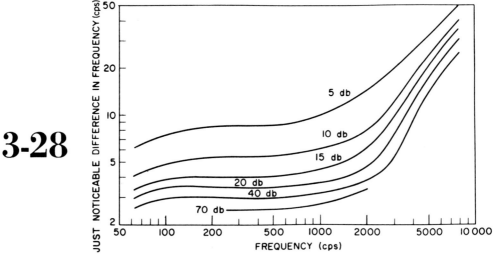

3-28

155

the JND is about 0.3% of the frequency.

Small changes in pitch are heard best at comfortably loud levels (30 db or more above threshold) and at durations in excess of 0.1 sec. The dependence on duration of the JND in frequency is shown in Fig. 3-29; the JND is smaller for a change repeated cyclically than for a single occurrence. A repetition rate of 2–3 cps is optimum.

If the operator is to detect a change in frequency, a compromise often must be made between the frequency at which changes are most easily detected and the masking effects of ambient noise. The smallest changes in frequency can be detected at low frequencies, but ambient noise is usually greatest at low frequencies (Beranek, 1957b). Thus, the best compromise is between 500 and 1,000 cps.

DETECTING INTENSITY CHANGES

Figure 3-30 (Riesz, 1928 and Miller, 1947a) shows JND in sound-pressure level for pure tones of various frequencies and for wide-band noise. Note that the smallest changes are detectable at the higher intensity levels (about 60 db or more above threshold). If the changes in sound-pressure level occur cyclically, the JND is smallest at a rate of 2 or 3 cps. In addition, Fig. 3-31 shows that the JND in sound-pressure level for bands of noise is dependent on bandwidth as well as on frequency. Note that smaller differences can be perceived for wider bands.

Changes in the intensity of a pure tone are most easily detected at frequencies between 1,000 and 4,000 cps. If the signal has a wide, continuous spectrum, such as random noise, and the operator must detect changes in intensity, it is best to choose a wide rather than a narrow band of the noise because a listener can more easily detect changes in the wide band (see Fig. 3-31). The reason for this phenomenon, in all probability, is that the

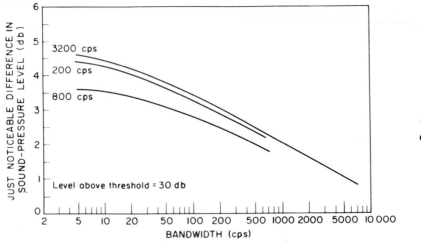

3-30

3-31

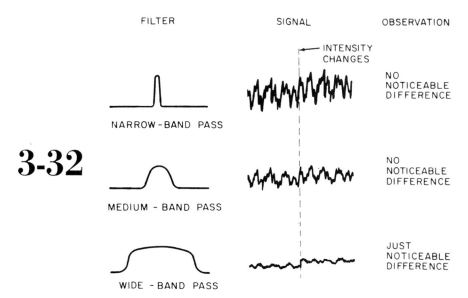

3-32

FILTER   SIGNAL   OBSERVATION

INTENSITY CHANGES

NARROW-BAND PASS   NO NOTICEABLE DIFFERENCE

MEDIUM - BAND PASS   NO NOTICEABLE DIFFERENCE

WIDE - BAND PASS   JUST NOTICEABLE DIFFERENCE

listener hears more random fluctuation in the intensity of the narrow band than he does in that of the wide band; hence, he is less able to detect a small shift in the intensity of the narrow band. This fluctuational effect is illustrated in Fig. 3-32.

SELECTING TONAL DURATION

The audibility of a sound depends on its duration because the response of the ear is not instantaneous. Rather, in the case of pure tones, it takes 200–300 msec to build up (Munson, 1947) and approximately 140 msec to decay (Stevens and Davis, 1938), although wide-band noises build up and decay somewhat faster. As a consequence of this

property of the ear, sounds of less than 200–500 msec in duration do not sound so loud and are not so audible in noisy backgrounds as are sounds of longer duration.

A slight gain in detectability accrues as the duration of the signal exceeds 500 msec. This can be understood by considering the detection process to be fluctuating because of the fluctuating properties of the background noise and, in some cases, of the signal and of the acuity of the listener. As the duration of the signal is increased, the listener has the opportunity of increasing the number of independent samplings of the background noise. Hence, detectability increases, but the gain is generally quite small beyond a few seconds.

To detect a pure tone in the presence of masking noise, the duration of the tone should

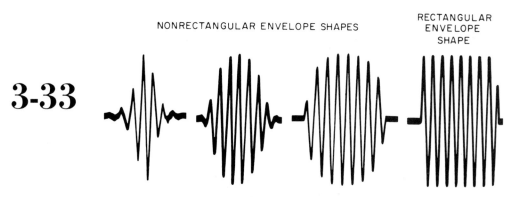

NONRECTANGULAR ENVELOPE SHAPES   RECTANGULAR ENVELOPE SHAPE

3-33

be no shorter than 300 msec. When tones are of shorter duration, signal intensity must be proportionately increased because, below about 300 msec, the product of time and intensity required for threshold is constant.

For short-duration sounds, the above rule can be generalized further, i.e., the time integral of the intensity is a constant, which provides a rule for determining an equivalent intensity and duration for sounds having nonrectangular envelope shapes (see Fig. 3-33). The effect of tonal duration on the masked threshold for bursts of tones of various frequencies having rectangular envelopes is shown in Fig. 3-34 (Garner and Miller, 1947).

Tones should last at least 100 msec, and never less than 10 msec, if an operator has to detect changes in pitch (Turnbull, 1944). Pitch sensitivity is slightly impaired for tones between 50- and 100-msec long and deteriorates rapidly as tonal duration is shortened below 50 msec. Tones shorter than 10 msec have very little pitch (Doughty and Garner, 1947) because, as a tone pulse is shortened, its spectrum spreads out and becomes more and more like a noise. The rule is that the width of the resulting spectrum, at its half-power points, is equal to the reciprocal of the duration ($\Delta f = 1/T$) where Δf is the effec-

tive bandwidth and T is the duration of the tone pulse (see Fig. 3-35).

3.4.2 *Multiple signals*

In many auditory signaling systems, it is necessary for a listener to monitor several different channels, either simultaneously or at different times. In the selection of signals for such systems, the techniques discussed in the following paragraphs should be considered.

USING MULTIPLE FREQUENCIES

When a listener must monitor several channels simultaneously, but ordinarily need attend to only one channel at a time, channels should be spaced at different frequencies (see Fig. 3-36). In addition, the frequencies of the channels should be spaced as widely as possible throughout the available spectrum to minimize the masking of signals from one channel by signals from another and make the identification of channels easier (see below). The designer should be cautioned, however, to avoid frequencies that are simple

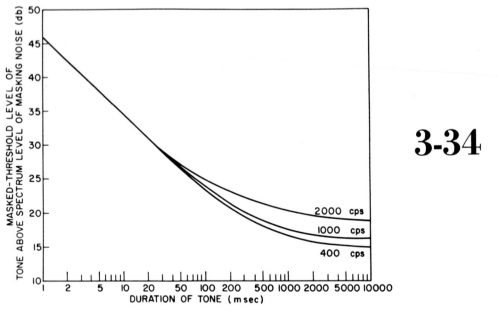

3-34

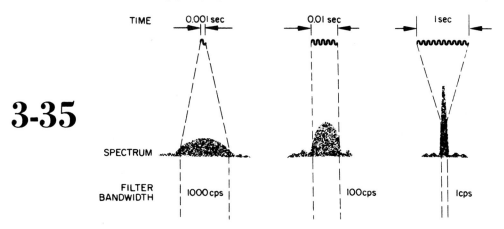

WIDTH OF SIGNAL IS INVERSELY PROPORTIONAL TO DURATION

3-35

multiples or submultiples of other frequencies (e.g., 2:1, 3:1, etc.) because they are easily confused.

SEQUENCING THE SIGNALS

When several active channels must be monitored under conditions in which urgent messages come in on two or more channels at the same time, separate operators must be provided for each channel. If the messages are not urgent, however, a system can be provided in which the messages can be stored and sequenced. Such a system is that known as RODMEX (Readout-on-Demand Message Expeditor), which records incoming messages on magnetic tape and actuates indicator lights to show the operator that a message is stored.

The operator can listen to these messages in any sequence he desires simply by pushing appropriate control buttons. Laboratory tests simulating a typical competing-message situation (in this case speech messages) showed the elimination of repeats by RODMEX resulted in a net gain in time and accuracy when compared with direct listening (Bertsch, et al., 1956).

IDENTIFYING THE SIGNALS

It is often desirable, or essential, for a listener to identify rapidly and correctly the channel presenting a message to him. The ability to make such an identification depends on the number of parameters available for coding the channels.

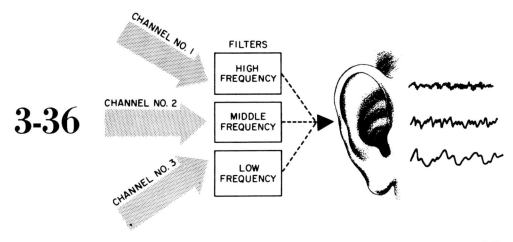

3-36

One- and Two-Dimensional Coding

If only one parameter can be used for coding the channels, no more than four or five channels can be correctly identified all the time. If intensity is the parameter, the limit is four; if frequency is the parameter, the limit is five.

In information-theory terms, coding by intensity alone yields 1.7 bits per stimulus, corresponding to nearly perfect identification of four levels. Coding by frequency alone yields about 2.3 bits, corresponding to perfect identification of five frequencies. To attain this performance, however, the stimulus range and intervals must be chosen carefully and the listeners must be well trained (Pollack, 1953).

Two-dimensional coding further increases the number of absolute identifications possible. Combinations of intensity and frequency, each divided on a five-step scale, have been shown to yield 3.1 bits per stimulus, corresponding to perfect identification of slightly over eight channels.

Multidimensional Coding

As additional parameters are combined to code channels, the number of channels, or signals, that can be correctly identified increases with practically no limit. For example, a listener can recognize hundreds of different voices and thousands of different sounds because these have many complex characteristics that serve as cues for their identification.

Experiments on the relative advantage of increased number of parameters versus increased number of steps per parameter indicate that it is better to use more parameters with fewer steps, e.g., a two-step, eight-parameter signal yielded about the same performance (6.9 bits per stimulus) as a five-step, six-parameter signal (7.1 bits per stimulus). The parameters used in these tests were direction, tone frequency, noise frequency, tone level, noise level, repetition rate, on-off time fraction, and duration (see Pollack and Ficks, 1954). When as many as six or eight parameters are used, about three steps per parameter is considered optimum.

4.

speech communication

THE STEPS INVOLVED in designing for speech communication can be listed as follows:

1. Requirements must be established. In addition to the requirements more or less common to all speech-communication systems, there are some special ones that are occasionally encountered. In some cases, messages from several sources must be transmitted simultaneously to a single listener. Some systems require speech communication at high altitudes; others require it under water. Section 4.5 of this chapter is devoted to a discussion of design for such special requirements, including communication through masks.

2. Performance criteria must be selected. Often the criteria for speech-communication systems include naturalness or quality of received speech and recognizability or identifiability of the talker, but the main criterion is intelligibility. Much of the information in this chapter has to do with answering the following question: how can the designer maximize the intelligibility of speech in a communica-

tion system? See section 4.2 for three methods of determining or predicting intelligibility, including one for face-to-face communication.

3. The relevant characteristics of the environment in which the communication system will operate must be determined. These include noise and reverberation. Because noise is probably the biggest problem, it is a major consideration throughout the chapter, but especially in section 4.3.

4. The characteristics of communication-system components must be specified. Microphones, transmitters, receivers, headsets, etc., are discussed in section 4.4.

5. At least one workable system configuration and, preferably, several alternate ones, must be conceived.

6. The effectiveness of system performance for each configuration must be evaluated. For factors affecting performance, see section 4.6.

7. The cost of each configuration must be estimated.

When the designer has in hand the information indicated above, he can evaluate and compare alternate system configurations in a straightforward way. If he can manipulate the variables in such a way as to maximize the difference between effective performance and cost, he can find the optimum design.

This chapter, drafted by Karl D. Kryter and J. C. R. Licklider of Bolt, Beranek and Newman, Inc., is based, in part, on material prepared by J. C. Webster of the U. S. Navy Electronics Laboratory and M. Hawley of Radio Corp. of America.

4.1 *Characteristics of Speech*

Before we examine the human-engineering data that bear on speech-communication problems, we should look at some of the characteristics of speech itself. Knowledge of these characteristics contributes to realistic designs of speech systems and is basic to the understanding of procedures for predicting, from the characteristics of the environment and the equipment, the intelligibility of speech that is transmitted over a system.

4.1.1 *Speech production*

When a person speaks, air moves from the lungs, past the vocal cords in the throat, into the mouth and nose, and out into the environment. If the vocal cords are tensed, they are set into vibration by this stream of air. Vibration of the vocal cords, in turn, modulates the air stream so that it becomes a rapid sequence of puffs or pulses—the primary source of vocal sounds. A secondary source of speech power is the turbulence produced as the air stream passes through narrow constrictions in the vocal passages.

4.1.2 *Representations of speech waves*

The speech wave can be regarded as a function of time only (waveform), as a function of frequency only (spectrum), or as a function of both time and frequency (intensity-frequency-time pattern).

TIME REPRESENTATION

The waveform is the function that relates the instantaneous speech pressure to time. The speech pressure is the force exerted by the speech wave on a unit area at an arbitrary, but specified, location with respect to the talker—usually normal to the line from his lips and 1 m away.

FREQUENCY REPRESENTATION

The spectrum corresponds to, and is a transformation of, the pressure waveform. It is a complex function of frequency only and can be resolved into two parts. One of these parts gives the amplitudes of the various frequency components of the speech signal; the other gives the phase angles of those components at some arbitrary instant in time. The phase part of the spectrum, however, is too complex to deal with when considering anything much longer than a single, fundamental speech sound. For most engineering purposes, one can neglect the phase part of the spectrum and consider only the amplitudes.

The distribution of pressure amplitudes as a function of frequency can be measured and depicted in several ways. The most widely used method is to transduce the acoustic speech signal into an electrical signal and pass it through a band-pass filter. Then the following computations are made:

1. The voltage output of the filter is squared and then integrated over time.

2. The integral is divided by the duration of the period of integration, and the square root of the result is taken.

3. This computation yields the root-mean-square (rms) voltage in the filter pass band, which is translated into an rms pressure with the aid of a calibration curve for the transducer in the analyzing system.

The numerical value of the rms pressure is the spectral coefficient corresponding to the center frequency of the analyzing filter. When octave-band or half-octave-band filters are used, stable spectra are obtained with integration periods as short as 1–2 min.

§ 4.1.1

Octave-Band Spectrum

When filters one-octave wide are used, the function relating the spectral coefficients to the center or boundary frequencies of the octave is called the octave-band spectrum. The spectral coefficients are transformed to a logarithmic scale and are expressed in decibels (db) relative to some convenient reference value such as microbars (μbar) or microbars per volt (μbar/v).

Spectrum Level

It often simplifies a calculation, dimensionally, to divide the rms pressure in each band by the width of the band in cycles per second (cps). When that quotient is translated into decibels, the result is called the spectrum level. The relationship among octave, one-half octave, one-third octave, and spectrum level is shown in Fig. 4-1. The octave-band level is arbitrarily taken to be 0 db.

Overall Level

It is usually helpful to give, in addition to the octave-band spectrum and the spectrum level, an indication of the overall level of speech. "Overall" indicates that the measurement of an unfiltered speech wave is made over all the audio-frequency range.

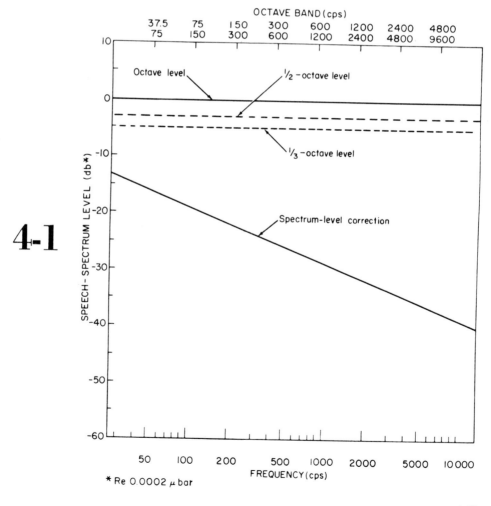

4-1

Results of Measurements

The octave-band spectrum and two curves relating spectrum level to frequency are shown in Fig. 4-2. The right-hand ordinate is appropriate for the octave-band spectrum and the left-hand ordinate is appropriate for the spectrum-level curves.

The solid curve in Fig. 4-2 is an idealized long-time average based on several experimental determinations in which octave-band and half-octave-band filters were used (French and Steinberg, 1947). The irregular dashed line represents the spectrum level determined in a typical set of measurements made on a 3-min sample of speech by a single talker with a 5-cps filter set at various places along the frequency scale (Stevens, et al., 1947). The solid curve is useful in engineering calculations, but the designer should keep in mind the fact, illustrated by the irregular dashed curve, that any particular sample of speech is likely to depart considerably from it.

The octave-band spectrum shown in Fig. 4-2 is an average based on three independent studies in which a total of 17 male talkers was used. The overall speech level is 65 db relative to 0.0002 μbar (see Chapter 3). These are reasonably representative for male speakers using a moderate level of vocal effort. The spectrum produced by female speakers is roughly similar in shape, but the overall level of female speech is, on the average, 2 or 3 db lower.

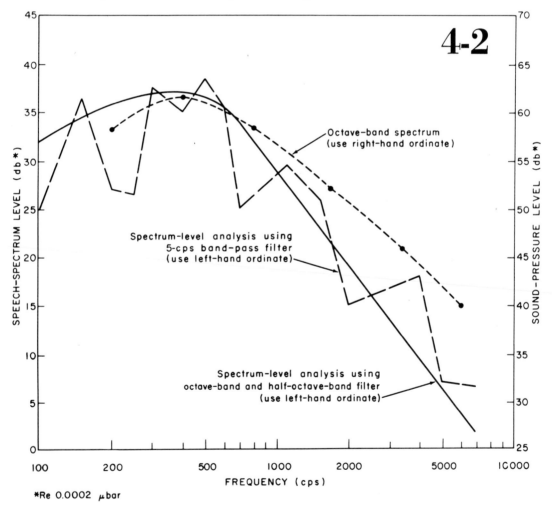

*Re 0.0002 μbar

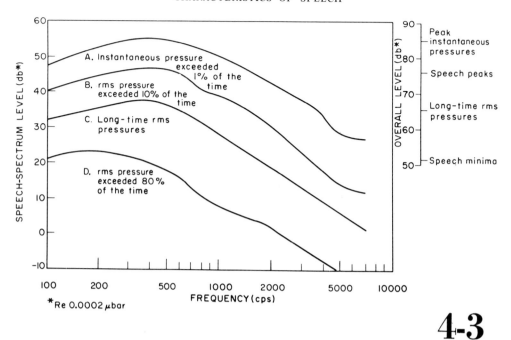

*Re 0.0002 μbar

4-3

4.1.3 *Time-varying characteristics*

The spectra of speech shown in the solid curve of Fig. 4-2 are "long-time spectra." Systematic changes in the function relating spectrum level to frequency would not have been observed had the duration of the measurement been decreased, but time does not appear as an independent variable.

For some purposes it is important to examine changes of speech pressure with time while simultaneously retaining the analysis of the speech wave into several or many bands of frequency. One way of accomplishing this is to divide the speech signal into a number of frequency bands (by means of band-pass filters) and then to divide the component signals—the individual signals in the several bands—into segments of 1/8-sec duration.

Measurements have been made in the manner described above with octave-band and half-octave-band filters. The maximum instantaneous pressure in each 1/8-sec segment, and, also, the rms pressure in each 1/8-sec segment, were determined. Spectrum levels were derived by dividing the squares of the instan-

taneous pressure and the rms pressure by the filter bandwidth and then converting the quotients into decibels.

Four curves relating sound-pressure level to frequency are shown in Fig. 4-3 (Dunn and White, 1940). Curve A shows, for each frequency band of 1-cps width, the instantaneous pressure that was exceeded in only 1% of the 1/8-sec intervals. This curve is, in a sense, a "peak-instantaneous-pressure" curve. Curve B shows, for each frequency band, the root-mean-square pressure that was exceeded in only 10% of the 1/8-sec intervals. We will call this one the curve of "speech peaks." Curve C is the long-time-rms pressure, which corresponds to the solid curve shown in Fig. 4-2.

Curve D in Fig. 4-3 shows, for each frequency band, the rms pressure that was exceeded in 80% of the 1/8-sec intervals. Inasmuch as about one-fifth of ordinary conversational speech is dead time, this lowermost curve represents, in a sense, the rms pressure of the weakest sounds. We will refer to this curve as the "speech minima" curve. At the right-hand side of Fig. 4-3 are represented the corresponding overall levels—the values for unanalyzed, unfiltered speech.

§ 4.1.3

165

Although the instantaneous speech pressure is usually below the rms pressure, the speech wave occasionally makes rather extreme excursions. One of the problems in designing a speech-communication system is whether or not to provide for faithful reproduction of these extremes. This problem will be discussed further when peak clipping is considered in article 4.5.2.

4.1.4 *RMS pressure of fundamental speech sounds*

In the foregoing discussion, no effort was made to relate the measurements and representations to the speech sounds being uttered. By making the intervals of time over which the squared pressures are averaged correspond directly to the intervals during which the specific vowels and consonants are spoken, we can relate the measurements to the individual sounds. The rms pressures of the fundamental speech sounds as measured by telephone engineers are shown in Table 4-1. The values are expressed in decibels relative to

the rms pressure of the weakest speech sound (the initial consonant, "th," of "thin").

4.1.5 *Dynamic range*

If the speech is too soft, it will be masked by noise in the communication system (see article 4.3.1). If it is too loud, it will overload the system. Dynamic range is the difference, in decibels, between the pressure level at which overload occurs (according to some overload criterion) and the pressure level of the noise in the system. Obviously, the dynamic range is not, in general, the same for all points in the communication system. Usually, it is the dynamic range at the listener's ear that is most important.

To determine the dynamic range required of a communication system, the engineer must take into account the variations in pressure level from speech sound to speech sound, condition to condition, and talker to talker. From Tables 4-1, 4-2, and 4-3 we note that:

a. The range of fundamental speech-sound levels is 0–28.2 db (see Table 4-1).

b. The range (difference) from speech minima with minimum normal vocal effort to

Table 4-1 Typical RMS Pressure Levels of the Fundamental Speech Sounds *

Key word	Sound	Pressure level (db)	Key word	Sound	Pressure level (db)
talk	o′	28.2	chat	ch	16.2
top	a	27.8	me	m	15.5
ton	o	27.0	jot	j	13.6
tap	a′	26.9	azure	zh	13.0
tone	ō	26.7	zip	z	12.0
took	u	26.6	sit	s	12.0
tape	ā	25.7	tap	t	11.7
ten	e	25.4	get	g	11.7
tool	ū	25.0	kit	k	11.1
tip	i	24.1	vat	v	10.8
team	ē	23.4	that	th	10.4
err	r	23.2	bat	b	8.0
let	l	20.0	dot	d	8.0
shot	sh	19.0	pat	p	7.7
ring	ng	18.6	for	f	7.0
me	m	17.2	thin	th	0

* Spoken by an average talker at a normal level of effort (Fletcher, 1953).

Table 4-2   Sound-Pressure Levels of Speech 1 m From the Talker

Measure of sound pressure	Whisper (db)	Normal level (db)			Shout (db)
		Minimum	Average	Maximum	
Peak instantaneous pressures	70	79	89	99	110
Speech peaks	58	67	79	87	98
Long-time rms pressures	46	55	65	75	86
Speech minima	30	39	49	59	70

peak instantaneous pressures with maximum normal effort is 60 db (39–99 in Table 4-2).

c. The range (difference) from speech minima to peak instantaneous pressures is about 40 db for a given level of vocal effort (such as average normal level in Table 4-2).

d. The range of variations of talkers in normal conversation is 20 db (see Table 4-3).

DESIGN RECOMMENDATIONS

Fortunately for the designer, the dynamic range usually required of a speech communication system is not the sum of the ranges just mentioned but, rather, can be stated as follows:

1. For very high-quality communication, the dynamic range should be 60 db.

2. For commercial broadcast purposes, the dynamic range can be 40–45 db.

3. If a mechanism for compensating for variations in average speech levels among talkers is provided in the system, a dynamic range of 30 db is adequate for essentially perfect speech communication.

4. With practiced talkers and listeners, communication can be quite effective in a system providing a dynamic range of only 20 db.

4.1.6 *Estimating speech level*

In most commercial radio, television, and recording work, the overall rms pressure is

Table 4-3   Distribution of Talker Levels for Persons Using the Telephone

Percent of talkers	Level range (db *)
7	Below 54
9	54–57
14	57–60
18	60–63
22	63–66
17	66–69
9	69–72
4	72–75
0	Above 75

* Above sound pressure of 0.0002 μbar at a point 1 m from the talker's lips (Fletcher, 1953).

approximated by reading either a special voltmeter, called a volume indicator or VU meter, or by reading a sound-level meter. Ordinarily, the sound-level meter is set for "slow" meter action and "flat" response. The meter can be calibrated to indicate, approximately, the rms pressure at the microphone location.

If the engineer takes the averages, by eye, of the highest deflections corresponding to the individual words for several spoken sentences, his reading will be, usually, about 4 db above the long-time rms-pressure level as measured by more elaborate and precise techniques. As can be seen from Figs. 4-2 and 4-3, the long-time rms-pressure level of normal speech, measured 1 m from the talker's lips, is about

§ 4.1.6

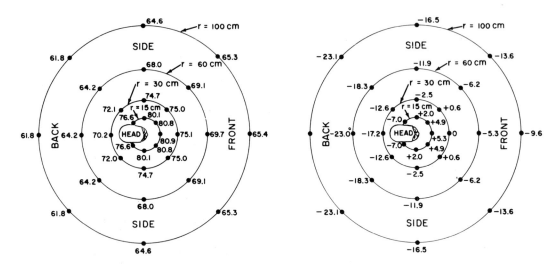

4-4 Speech-intensity levels around head of speaker. Numbers in left-hand diagram are for whole speech and are in decibels relative to 0.0002 μbar; numbers in right-hand diagram are for band of speech of 2,800–4,000 cps and are in decibels relative to level 30 cm in front of lips

65 db above the standard reference level of 0.0002 μbar (i.e., 9 db below 1 μbar or 129 db below 1 bar). The intensity of normal speech at different positions around the head of a talker is shown in Fig. 4-4 (Fletcher, 1953).

The long-time rms-pressure levels of Figs. 4-2, 4-3, and 4-4 are for speech uttered with normal effort when the talker is using a telephone or talking in a typical office. When the

talker is speaking to a listener only 1 m away and in a quiet place, the level of conversational speech is somewhat lower than the 65 db we have been calling normal—it is about 58 db. Because most communication systems include microphones and/or background noise, however, it is appropriate for our purposes to identify "normal" with 65 db, relative to 0.0002 μbar, one meter in front of the talker.

4.2 *Intelligibility in Speech Communication*

In designing a speech-communication system, many design decisions must be made on the basis of the intelligibility of speech in a given system. Two procedures are available for measuring speech intelligibility. One procedure, the one the design engineer can use most often, is characterized by calculating a predictive measure of intelligibility (see article

4.2.2). The other procedure involves measuring intelligibility directly through intelligibility testing (see article 4.2.1).

Both of the above procedures have their limitations. For example, the calculated, predictive measure of intelligibility breaks down under extreme conditions of noise masking, frequency distortion, and certain kinds of amplitude distortion and is not applicable to the evaluation of systems involving complex processing of speech. When confronted with such problems, it is necessary to resort to empirical data derived from intelligibility tests to provide the basis for engineering decisions, but intelligibility testing requires careful laboratory methods involving the control of a number of factors, and, unless the engineer is in a position to follow these methods carefully, intelligibility testing should not be attempted.

4.2.1 *Intelligibility testing*

To conduct an intelligibility test, proceed as follows:

1. Formulate the objective explicitly. Intelligibility-test scores are useful mainly as relative measures—as bases for comparison (see also Chapter 1). If the objective is to evaluate the system in relation to other systems of interest, or if the intelligibility test will be used to compare a system with other systems that will be tested later, be sure to test a reference system.

2. Analyze the communication situation. Be sure that the environmental conditions under which the tests are made match those under which the communication system will be used. The parameters of the noise are especially important. For example, if the system will be used in the vicinity of jet aircraft, or in the interiors of armored vehicles, the noise levels and spectra of those environments should be duplicated in the tests.

3. Plan a definite test schedule. In planning the test schedule, try to counterbalance the effects of learning, fatigue, and boredom during the tests (see Chapter 1). If word lists are used repeatedly, be sure to rearrange the random order of the words within each list each time it is used.

4. Select a group of listeners. They should have normal hearing, know thoroughly the language to be used, and be motivated to do their best.

5. Select a group of talkers. The talkers should have the following qualifications:

a. Be representative, with respect to accent, voice training, voice power, etc., of the actual talkers who will use the system. Ordinarily, this means that they should not have unusual regional accents or noticeable voice defects and that they should know thoroughly the language to be used in the tests.

b. Be motivated to work effectively, but not to go to unusual extremes (e.g., speak very slowly, abnormally accentuate words) to make themselves intelligible.

6. Train both talkers and listeners intensively (such as 2 hr a day for 5 days) in the proper use of the equipment. Ordinarily, this involves making sure of the following:

a. That the talker's lips touch the microphone (if a close-talking or noise-cancelling microphone is used).

b. That the talker's voice level either is kept constant from condition to condition (use an independent microphone and meter for monitoring) or is free to change as it would if the tests were being made with the actual communication system in its operational context.

c. That the listening level is representative of the level that will be used in the actual system.

d. That headsets, microphone noise shields, and ear-protective devices are fitted to the wearers in the same way they would be in the actual system.

7. Select the speech material to be used in the tests. If word lists are to be used, be sure that the listeners are familiar with the spelling and meaning of every word in the lists. Select test material that can be scored readily and unambiguously. It is usually best to select material that has been used in earlier tests, or that probably will be used in subsequent tests, to establish a basis for comparison with the findings of other intelligibility-testing programs.

8. In nonsense-syllable or word tests, have the talkers insert each test syllable or word in a "carrier" sentence, e.g., "You will write _____ now." The carrier sentence should be repeated with each new test item, the item being read in the position of the blank without undue stress or emphasis.

9. Have the listeners write down their best estimates, based on what they hear, of what

the talker transmitted to them, and then compare the listeners' records with the talkers'.

SELECTING TEST MATERIAL

Although many different types of intelligibility tests have been used at one time or another, most of the work on which our understanding of speech communication is based was done with one or more of the following three tests: nonsense-syllable tests, monosyllabic-word tests, and sentence tests. Examples of lists of items used in these tests are given in Tables 4-4 through 4-11.

The items in a nonsense-syllable test are usually random combinations of fundamental speech sounds in the pattern consonant-vowel-consonant. In monosyllabic-word tests, the items are usually drawn from a set of 20 lists of 50 words each in which the frequencies of occurrence of the various fundamental speech sounds are proportional to their frequencies of occurrence in everyday speech. These lists are called Harvard PB (phonetically balanced) word lists.

If only a few sentence tests are to be made, the sentences are usually drawn from a set of test sentences compiled for the purpose (see Egan, 1948). If extensive sentence testing is to be done, however, it is necessary to prepare a very large ensemble of sentences. The sentences can be drawn from any reasonably homogeneous source, but it is very important to select them at random from the ensemble for presentation in the tests, and no sentences should be used twice with the same listener.

Two variations of sentences can be used in sentence tests. One, illustrated in Tables 4-8 and 4-9, is a question that can be answered with a single word or short phrase. The other, illustrated in Tables 4-10 and 4-11, is an ordinary sentence in which certain "key" words have been designated.

SCORING TESTS

In the case of nonsense syllables, score each syllable correct if all its component sounds are correct. The percentage of the consonants heard correctly is called the "percent con-

Table 4-4 Nonsense-Syllable List No. 1 *

1. monz	26. dahf	51. zohm	76. duhm
2. nihf	27. fohf	52. gohn	77. map
3. nan	28. fook	53. pahz	78. zaf
4. ʒeef	29. kohth	54. thoop	79. puhf
5. dayth	30. thehʒ	55. dad	80. gahk
6. thayd	31. muhd	56. koof	81. pohd
7. gayf	32. kawd	57. pooth	82. nohg
8. thawf	33. zihg	58. fuhp	83. ʒuhg
9. dohp	34. kuhk	59. gehg	84. dihʒ
10. fayg	35. ʒihd	60. nood	85. pawg
11. meek	36. zehd	61. fehm	86. nawz
12. thuhn	37. ʒayp	62. dehz	87. mawʒ
13. geed	38. theez	63. mihth	88. fahd
14. kihp	39. fihn	64. faz	89. dawk
15. zahp	40. mehf	65. kaʒ	90. fawth
16. kayz	41. keem	66. nahʒ	91. gihz
17. pam	42. ʒehht	67. mahm	92. gawp
18. payʒ	43. nehk	68. kehn	93. neep
19. naym	44. ʒawm	69. goom	94. guhʒ
20. mayn	45. feeʒ	70. doon	95. zayk
21. deeg	46. peen	71. pihk	96. zeeth
22. ʒahn	47. thag	72. ʒak	97. zuhz
23. thahth	48. kahg	73. moog	98. gath
24. zawn	49. thihm	74. zooʒ	99. pehp
25. thahk	50. ʒohʒ	75. ʒooz	100. nuhth

* See Table 4-19 for symbols.

Table 4-5 Nonsense-Syllable List No. 2 *

1. neen	26. nehp	51. theeg	76. fawf
2. nahz	27. mood	52. thuhm	77. puhk
3. maym	28. ʒoog	53. fohk	78. fayd
4. kaz	29. poof	54. zohʒ	79. muhth
5. dehg	30. nihk	55. duhʒ	80. zeef
6. man	31. kook	56. dath	81. fehʒ
7. geeth	32. zahn	57. mahʒ	82. thawk
8. gawn	33. mawz	58. mihf	83. kahd
9. thad	34. gehd	59. ʒahm	84. meep
10. nohd	35. kehm	60. ʒayn	85. nayʒ
11. fag	36. ʒihth	61. thayth	86. gohm
12. dayf	37. mehk	62. mohg	87. payz
13. dawp	38. gihg	63. zuhg	88. zooz
14. dihz	39. fihm	64. gaf	89. kihn
15. thehz	40. guhz	65. ʒap	90. doom
16. thahf	41. nawg	66. ʒuhd	91. peem
17. kahf	42. gooʒ	67. gahp	92. kawth
18. zihd	43. fuhn	68. fahth	93. gayk
19. pawd	44. ʒohz	69. pehn	94. zawm
20. ʒeek	45. dohn	70. pahg	95. ʒehf
21. dahk	46. ʒawʒ	71. foop	96. deed
22. feez	47. nuhg	72. zehth	97. nooth
23. thihʒ	48. kayg	73. pohth	98. nam
24. keeʒ	49. thoon	74. thohp	99. kuhp
25. zayp	50. pihp	75. paʒ	100. zak

* See Table 4-19 for symbols.

§ 4.2.1

Table 4-6 Phonetically Balanced (PB) Word List No. 1

1. smile	14. box	27. are	40. fuss
2. strife	15. deed	28. cleanse	41. folk
3. pest	16. feast	29. clove	42. bar
4. end	17. hunt	30. crash	43. dike
5. heap	18. grove	31. hive	44. such
6. toe	19. bad	32. bask	45. wheat
7. hid	20. mange	33. plush	46. nook
8. creed	21. rub	34. rag	47. pan
9. rat	22. slip	35. ford	48. death
10. no	23. use (yews)	36. rise	49. pants
11. there	24. is	37. dish	50. cane
12. then	25. not	38. fraud	
13. fern	26. pile	39. ride	

Table 4-7 Phonetically Balanced (PB) Word List No. 2

1. gill	14. dab	27. mute	40. start
2. suck	15. earl	28. rib	41. bounce
3. perk	16. bean	29. awe	42. bud
4. fate	17. nut	30. trash	43. frog
5. five	18. ways	31. corpse	44. quart
6. need	19. wish	32. bait	45. rap
7. pick	20. pit	33. job	46. charge
8. log	21. cloud	34. hit	47. sludge
9. nab	22. scythe	35. hock	48. tang
10. else	23. blush	36. niece	49. them
11. gloss	24. shoe	37. tan	50. vamp
12. hire	25. snuff	38. vast	
13. bought	26. moose	39. our	

Table 4-8 Test Sentence List No. 1

Question	Answer
1. What do you saw wood with?	Saw
2. What letter comes after B?	C
3. What is the color of coal?	Black
4. Which is smaller, a dog or a horse?	Dog
5. What is the opposite of white?	Black
6. What comes between 2 and 4?	3
7. How many weeks are there in a month?	4
8. What do you hear with?	Ears
9. Does a cat eat bricks or mice?	Mice
10. What do you use to unlock a door?	Key
11. What letter comes before D?	C
12. Do elephants have a hump or a trunk?	Trunk
13. What is the opposite of wet?	Dry
14. What number comes before 12?	11
15. What day comes before Wednesday?	Tuesday
16. How many pennies are there in a dime?	10
17. Does a horse eat oats or chickens?	Oats
18. What do you spread butter with?	Knife
19. What number comes before 2?	1
20. What color is ketchup?	Red
21. What is the opposite of young?	Old
22. What month comes after March?	April
23. Does an eagle have wings or arms?	Wings
24. What number comes after 20?	21
25. How many wheels does a bicycle have?	2

Table 4-9 Test Sentence List No. 2

Question	Answer
1. What letter comes after C?	D
2. What is the opposite of narrow?	Broad, Wide
3. Which is higher, a hill or a mountain?	Mountain
4. What is the opposite of tall?	Short
5. What day comes after Tuesday?	Wednesday
6. How many months are there in a year?	12
7. What number comes after 5?	6
8. Does a man wear a hat or a table?	Hat
9. What do you chop wood with?	Axe
10. What letter comes before E?	D
11. What is the color of butter?	Yellow
12. What is the opposite of dry?	Wet
13. What day comes after Thursday?	Friday
14. What country is Moscow in?	Russia
15. What letter comes after B?	C
16. How many toes are there on each foot?	5
17. What do you tell the date by?	Calendar
18. What number comes before 3?	2
19. What is the opposite of love?	Hate
20. What color is the cloth on a pool table?	Green
21. What month comes after June?	July
22. How much is 1 and 8?	9
23. Does an owl lay books or an egg?	Egg
24. What number comes before 20?	19
25. Do palm trees grow in Alaska?	No

§ 4.2.1

Table 4-10   Test Sentence List No. 3

1. Deal the cards from the top, you bully.
2. Jerk the cord, and out tumbles the gold.
3. Slide the tray across the glass top.
4. Heat the rod and tap it against the skin.
5. The cloud moved in a stately way and was gone.
6. Light maple makes a swell room.
7. There were high jinks on the gala day.
8. Set the piece here and say nothing.
9. Gay lads make hay in the moonshine.
10. Drop that notion, and be a sport.
11. Stale bread is a waste in pudding too.
12. The gray paint clashed with the gaudy tints.
13. The stiff drink hit like a bolt of lightning.
14. Sell it short, and lose your money.
15. Dull stories make her laugh.
16. The clown moulded his pale face into a smirk.
17. Sew and knit, it helps evenings pass.
18. Men are but infants to a smart girl.
19. Dip the pail once and let it settle.
20. A stiff cord will do to fasten your shoe.

Table 4-11   Test Sentence List No. 4

1. Get the trust fund to the bank early.
2. A tight bow is not found in worn shoe-strings.
3. A mean child pulls wings from insects.
4. There is plenty of pork, but spring lamb is short.
5. Jean is a man trap in silk stockings.
6. Can such falsehoods be proved true?
7. The nude man was jailed by the angry cop.
8. She works in a boiled shirt factory.
9. A number of tunes tell of June nights.
10. Men dare not scorn a dab of lipstick.
11. Choose between the high road and the low.
12. A plea for funds seems to come again.
13. He lent his coat to the tall gaunt stranger.
14. There is a strong chance it will happen more than once.
15. The line will march until they halt or drop.
16. The duke rides the park in a silver coach.
17. The donkeys bray as the ghosts flit in the fields.
18. As the boys fought the cops brought the wagon.
19. Greet the new guests and leave quickly.
20. When the frost has come it is time for turkey.

sonant articulation." The percentage of the vowels heard correctly is called the "percent vowel articulation." The percentage of the syllables heard correctly is called the "percent syllable articulation."

Nonsense syllables are difficult to understand, even with a fairly good communication system, and are, therefore, sensitive to small amounts of noise and distortion and reveal small differences between systems. For example, the contribution to intelligibility of the speech components above 5,000 cps would be difficult to measure in quiet with sentences. With nonsense syllables, however, one can tell after a reasonable amount of testing that some intelligibility is lost when the components above 5,000 cps are removed from the signal.

In the case of word tests, score each recorded word on the basis of its phonetic agreement or disagreement with the corresponding word on the talker's list. The percentage of the words heard correctly is called the "percent word articulation" or the "percent word intelligibility." The PB-word tests are somewhat less sensitive than nonsense-syllable tests, but they are sufficiently sensitive for most purposes, and they do not require as much training time as do nonsense-syllable tests.

In the case of sentence tests, there are two ways of arriving at a score. The first way is to have an experienced scorer (or group of scorers) judge, for each transmitted sentence, whether the listener's record indicates that he did, or did not, get the essential sense of the sentence. The second way is to designate, ahead of time, five "key" words in each sentence. These words are then scored simply as words.

The "percent sentence intelligibility" is the percentage of the sentences of which the essence was understood correctly or the percentage of the key words recorded correctly. Experience indicates that the two scores usually approximate each other. Sentence-intelligibility tests yield rather high scores, even for systems in which there is a considerable amount of noise and distortion. The reason, of course, is to be found, in part, in the redundancy of the sentences.

INTERPRETING TEST RESULTS

In interpreting the results of intelligibility tests, take into account the vocabulary that will actually be used with the system: numbers, single words, short phrases, or complete sentences. Estimate what percentage of each kind of item must be heard correctly for the system to operate effectively. If the material used in testing is essentially the same as

§ 4.2.1

the material that will be transmitted over the system when it is in actual use, the test scores can be taken at face value. If the test and actual materials differ, as is more likely to be the case, it is necessary to make inferences. Figure 4-5 (French and Steinberg, 1947) will be of help in doing this; it shows the approximate relationship between the articulation index (see article 4.2.2) and the intelligibility of various types of speech-test materials.

Although intelligibility testing is simple in concept, it is actually an art with many ramifications. A person rarely obtains usable results in his first tests unless he has the supervision of others experienced in the field or takes rather full advantage of the published literature (see Fletcher and Steinberg, 1929 and Egan, 1948). The designer should consider using the measures described in article 4.2.2.

4.2.2 *Predicting intelligibility*

Many design decisions can be made on the basis of calculated, predictive measures of intelligibility. One such measure is the articulation index (AI), and there are two methods of calculating it; one (the 20-band method) is more detailed and accurate than the other (the weighted-octave-band method). A second measure is really an inverse measure of intelligibility and is called the speech interference level (SIL) of noise. The articulation index should be used in all carefully designed speech-communication systems. The speech interference level can serve as a rule-of-thumb guide in making some engineering decisions regarding face-to-face communication.

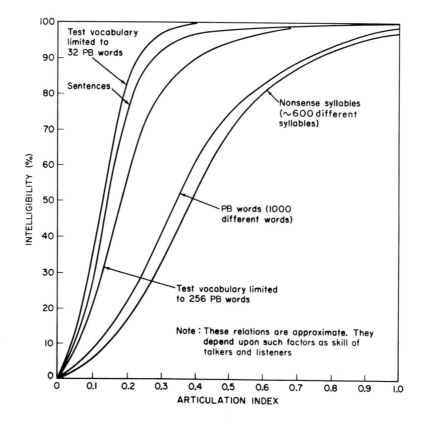

4-5

COMMUNICATION SYSTEMS

For speech-communication systems, the AI can be used as the predictive measure of intelligibility. The articulation-index formulation is based on the fact that, to obtain high intelligibility, one must deliver a considerable fraction of the total speech bandwidth to the listener's ear and, also, that the signal-to-noise ratio at the listener's ear must be reasonably high. If the speech peaks are 30 db or more above the noise throughout the frequency band from 200–6,100 cps, the listener will make essentially no errors (AI = 1.00). If the speech peaks are less than 30 db above the noise in any part of the speech band, the listener will make some mistakes (AI < 1.00). If the speech peaks are never above the noise at all (ratio of speech peaks to rms noise less than 0 db), the listener will rarely be able to understand anything (AI = 0).

Computing the Articulation Index

The ideas underlying the computation of the AI are simple. First, some parts of the frequency scale are inherently more important than others, insofar as contribution to intelligibility is concerned. Thus, the parts of the scale below 200 cps and above 6,100 cps are almost totally unimportant and can be neglected entirely. The remainder of the scale, 200–6,100 cps, can be divided into 20 bands, with cutoff frequencies being chosen in such a way that the contributions to intelligibility of the 20 bands are equal. The cutoff frequencies, midfrequencies, and widths of the 20 bands are given in Table 4-12.

Second, the contribution to intelligibility is 0.05 if the ratio of speech peaks to rms noise within each band is 30 db or greater, it is zero if the ratio within each band is 0 db or less, and it is proportional to the ratio in each band if that ratio is between 0 and 30 db. The contribution to intelligibility to be assigned to each band according to the ratio of speech peaks to background noise is presented in Fig. 4-6 (Beranek, 1957a).

Generally, the contributions made by the 20 bands, when added together, give us the

Table 4-12   Frequency Bands that Contribute Equally to Speech Intelligibility *

Band number	Frequency			Band-width
	Lower	Middle	Upper	
1	200	270	330	130
2	330	380	430	100
3	430	490	560	130
4	560	630	700	140
5	700	770	840	140
6	840	920	1,000	160
7	1,000	1,070	1,150	150
8	1,150	1,230	1,310	160
9	1,310	1,400	1,480	170
10	1,480	1,570	1,660	180
11	1,660	1,740	1,830	170
12	1,830	1,920	2,020	190
13	2,020	2,130	2,240	220
14	2,240	2,370	2,500	260
15	2,500	2,660	2,820	320
16	2,820	2,900	3,200	380
17	3,200	3,400	3,650	450
18	3,650	3,950	4,250	600
19	4,250	4,650	5,050	800
20	5,050	5,600	6,100	1,050

* Beranek, 1947.

AI for the communication system. It is necessary, however, to add two qualifications to this statement. First, the contribution to intelligibility is zero if the curve of speech peaks

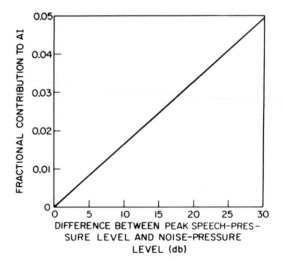

4-6

174

falls below the absolute threshold of hearing, and, although it is convenient to think of hearing in quiet as being limited by the inherent physiological noise of the auditory system, the abscissa of Fig. 4-6 applies, for all practical purposes, equally well to listening in quiet and to listening in noise. Second, any portion of the curve of speech peaks that exceeds a specified overload line (95-db spectrum level) makes no contribution to intelligibility, and additional qualifications and modifications are required to adapt the formula to these special circumstances.

Twenty-band method. To compute an articulation index by the 20-band method, proceed as follows:

1. Draw in a curve showing the speech-spectrum level as a function of frequency on a chart like that of Fig. 4-7.

2. Draw in a curve showing the spectrum level of the noise on the same chart. (As explained in article 4.3.1, it is necessary under some circumstances to use the "masking spectrum" of the noise instead of its acoustical spectrum.)

3. At every one of the lines numbered 1 to 20, measure the difference between the speech-peak level and the noise-spectrum level. If, at any line, the noise level is below the threshold of audibility, use the threshold curve rather than the noise curve. If, at any line, the speech-peak curve is above the appropriate limiting curves at the top of the figure, use that curve rather than the speech-peak curve.

4. Convert each of the differences measured in Step 3 to its fractional contribution to the AI by means of Fig. 4-6. Differences of

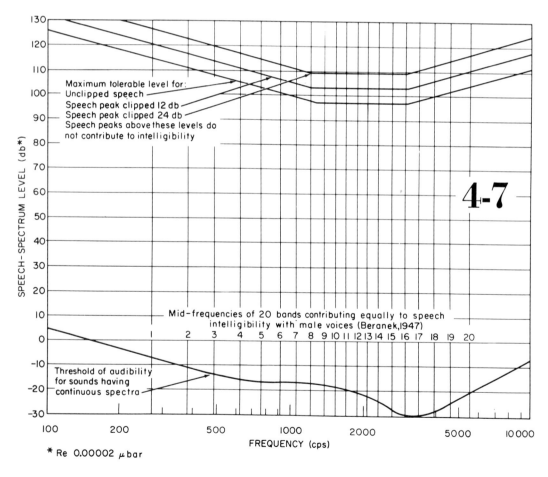

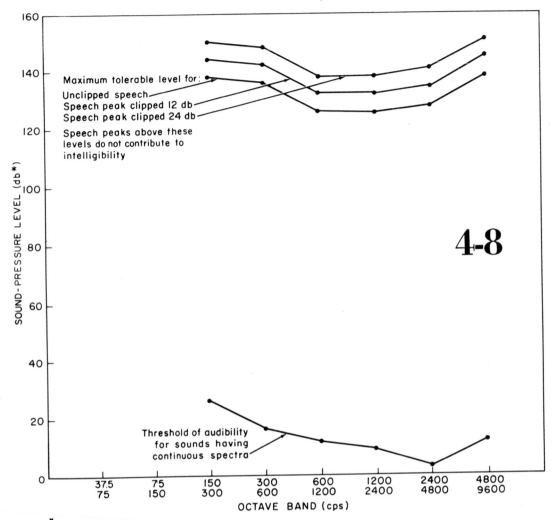

§ 4.2.2

30 db or greater are given a fractional contribution of 0.05, differences of 0 db or less are given a contribution of zero.

5. Add up all 20 fractional contributions to obtain the final AI.

Weighted-octave-band method. An index that usually approximates the AI obtained by the 20-band method can be computed from octave-band measurements of the speech and noise. A worksheet for plotting speech and noise measurements made with octave-band filters is shown in Fig. 4-8. The procedure for computing the AI is as follows:

1. Obtain the fractional contribution (W) of each octave band by entering Fig. 4-6 with the ratios of speech peaks to rms noise (or quiet threshold) in each of the octave bands of 150–300, 300–600, 600–1,200, 1,200–2,400, 2,400–4,800, and 4,800–9,600 cps.

2. Multiply W by one for octave bands of 150–300, 300–600, and 4,800–9,600; by five for octave bands of 600–1,200 and 2,400–4,800; and by seven for the octave band 1,200–2,400 cps.

3. Add the values obtained in Step 2. The sum is the AI.

If there is no appreciable frequency distortion present in the communication system to be evaluated, use the octave-band speech spectrum given in Fig. 4-2. Adjust the level to coincide with the level to be used in actual operation. Under these conditions, the only physical measurements required are octave-band measurements of the noise.

Limitations in the Use of the AI

The articulation index can be an immensely valuable aid to the design engineer; it makes possible the evaluation of many designs without having to resort to elaborate and time-consuming intelligibility testing (see article 4.2.1). The AI as thus far defined, however, does not predict well if the noise is of a "line-spectrum" type, if the noise power is concentrated in narrow bands, or if the frequency response of the communication system is extremely irregular (i.e., has pronounced peaks and valleys).

FACE-TO-FACE COMMUNICATION

There are many situations in factories, around military and commercial aircraft, aboard ship, etc., in which it is impractical to use an electroacoustic communication system between a talker and listener. In such cases face-to-face communication is just as important as communication carried out with the aid of equipment. It is useful, however, to think of face-to-face communication as communication via a system. Here are some rules to follow in designing man-machine systems in which men have to communicate with each other directly in noise:

1. Build into the system an inescapable instruction to the users to talk loudly, especially if they are wearing ear-protective devices (see article 4.3.3). A person talking in noise judges his vocal effort almost entirely by the sound of his voice. As shown in Fig. 4-9, the vocal effort used by a talker depends on the level of the background noise and on whether or not he is wearing ear-protective devices; when wearing ear-protective devices in noise, the talker tends to lower his voice by 1–2 db. Note that the maximum overall sound-pressure level a talker can develop at a distance of 1 m from his lips is around 95 db—about 30 db above conversational level in quiet. Even though instructed to make themselves heard, talkers are unable to raise their voices sufficiently to over-ride very intense noise.

2. Have the talkers and listeners wear ear-protective devices in intense noise. In noise

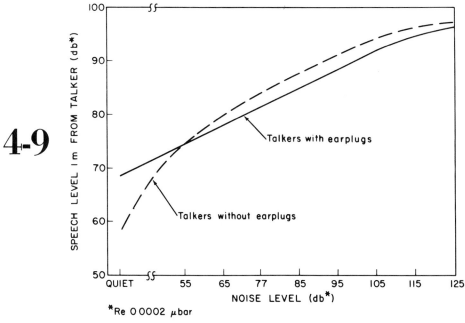

*Re 0.0002 μbar

above a certain intensity, the intelligibility of face-to-face communication is higher when the listeners and talkers wear ear-protective devices than it is when they do not.

3. Arrange the equipment so that the communicators can see one another's faces. People can understand one another better if they can receive visual cues.

Computing the Articulation Index

To compute the AI, and to predict the effect of a given noise environment on face-to-face speech communication, it is necessary to adjust the procedure previously described. Changes are required because shouted speech is not as intelligible as speech uttered at a more normal level of effort, even though a constant speech-to-noise ratio is maintained. This fact is illustrated in Fig. 4-10.

To compute the AI for face-to-face speech communication, proceed as follows:

1. Measure, or estimate from Fig. 4-9, the speech level 1 m from the talker.

2. Determine from Fig. 4-11 the effective speech level 1 m from the talker.

3. Drop 6 db for each doubling of the distance from the talker to determine the received-speech level of the listener (see below).

4. Plot the idealized speech-peak spectrum on a chart like that of Fig. 4-7 or Fig. 4-8, using the received-speech level determined in Step 3. (Note: The speech spectrum changes somewhat as vocal effort is varied. It is nevertheless sufficiently accurate for most engineering purposes to use the idealized speech spectrum and to adjust its level to correspond to the effective overall level found in Step 3.)

5. Plot on the above chart the spectrum of the noise at the position of the listener.

6. Complete the computation of the AI in the way previously described.

The Speech-Interference Level

A simpler, but less exact and less general, method for predicting the intelligibility of

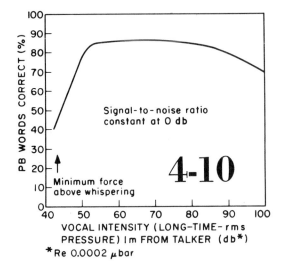

face-to-face speech communication has been devised for use in situations in which the noise has a relatively continuous spectrum (e.g., ventilation noise in offices, aircraft noise, the noise in most engine rooms, and the noise around milling machines). The method, called the speech-interference-level (SIL) method, yields the maximum noise level that will permit correct reception of 75% of PB words or about 98% of test sentences (see article 4.2.1). This criterion is equivalent to an AI of about 0.5.

To determine the SIL of a given noise, proceed as follows:

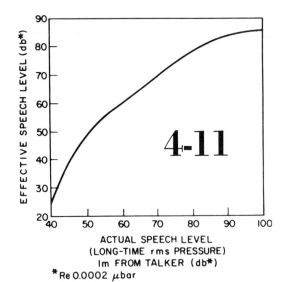

1. Measure the sound-pressure level of the ambient noise in octave bands of 600–1,200, 1,200–2,400, and 2,400–4,800 cps.

2. Determine the arithmetic average of the decibel levels in the three octave bands. (To convert spectrum levels to octave-band spectra or vice versa, see Fig. 4-1.) This average value is the SIL.

3. Consult Table 4-13 to find the maximum distance between talker and listener at which 75% of PB words will be heard correctly.

The Received-Speech Level

It is difficult to predict accurately what the received-speech level will be in a face-to-face communication situation because the communicators might move about, the talkers' vocal efforts might vary, etc. But reasonable estimates for engineering applications can be made. Adjustments in vocal effort normally made to compensate for variations in noise level can be estimated from Fig. 4-9.

The effect of variations in distance between talker and listener can be estimated with the aid of the "inverse distance law," which can be stated as follows:

$$\frac{P_1}{P_2} = \frac{d_2}{d_1}, \qquad (4\text{-}1)$$

where P_1 is the sound pressure at distance d_1 and P_2 is the sound pressure at distance d_2. The formula indicates that doubling the distance between talker and listener causes a halving (6-db decrease) of the sound pressure.

Equation (4-1) is an exact formula only if the sound is propagated in a free field (e.g., outdoors). In a room, there is reverberation (see article 4.4.3), and the formula can be no better than approximate. In addition, the formula should not be used in determining the speech level at any great distance from the talker.

It is best, of course, to make measurements of the speech and noise levels instead of depending on estimates of this type. For accurate values indoors at a distance from the

talker, actual measurements are indispensible. A word of caution, however: when making measures of speech levels, do not use so-called carbon microphones because the amplitude response of most carbon microphones is non-linear (see article 4.4.1).

To determine the level of received speech in intense noise, it is necessary to use the following procedure:

1. With a voltmeter or VU meter, record the electrical signal level produced by a magnetic, throat microphone worn by the talker. (The talker should be talking with the level of effort typically used in the communication situation under question.)

2. Turn off the source of the noise or take the talker into a relatively noise-free place that is in other respects acoustically similar to the one of interest.

3. Have the talker read the words or messages used in Step 1 in such a way that the throat-microphone signal causes the voltmeter or VU meter to indicate the same levels as recorded in Step 1.

4. Place a sound-pressure-level meter at the position of the listener, and record the peak level reached on each word.

5. Subtract 4 db from the arithmetic average of the decibel readings obtained from the sound-pressure-level meter. This gives, approximately, the long-time rms level of the speech at the position of the listener.

Table 4-13 Speech-Interference Levels that Barely Permit Reliable Conversation [1] at Various Distances and Voice Levels

Distance between talker and listener (ft)	Speech-interference level (db)			
	Normal [2]	Raised [2]	Very loud [2]	Shouting [2]
0.5	71	77	83	89
1	65	71	77	83
2	59	65	71	77
3	55	61	67	73
4	53	59	65	71
5	51	57	63	69
6	49	55	61	67
12	43	49	55	61

[1] Correctly hearing 75% of PB words.　　　　[2] Voice level.

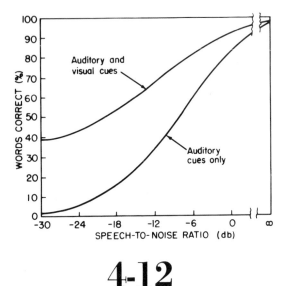

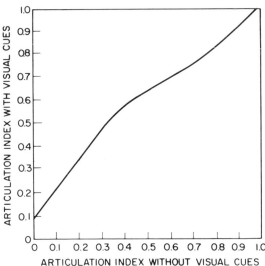

4-12

The Contribution of Visual Cues

Listeners obtain higher scores on speech intelligibility tests when they can see the lips and face of the talker than when they cannot, even though all other factors, such as the intensity of the received speech and the noise, are the same under both conditions of listening. The reason for this is that the average person is able to obtain some information by so-called "lip reading."

The increment in intelligibility contributed by visual cues is a function of the prevailing speech-to-noise ratio; if the speech-to-noise ratio is high, the listeners hear the words clearly and therefore cannot take advantage of the cues provided by lip reading; if the speech-to-noise ratio is low, they need, and they in fact use, the visual cues (see Fig. 4-12).

The effective AI for a given face-to-face communication situation in which normal visual cues are available can be estimated with the aid of Fig. 4-13. Proceed as follows:

1. Calculate an AI by the procedure outlined at the beginning of this article.

2. Read from Fig. 4-13 the effective AI that corresponds to the AI obtained in Step 1.

4.3 Noise in Speech Communication

Unwanted noise often masks our speech unless appropriate design features and operational procedures are used. The noise might come from the environment of the talker and/or listener or from electrical and/or electromagnetic interference within the system itself. As we will see later, the effects of noise on speech communication can be combated by the use of ear-protective devices (see article 4.3.3) and microphone noise shields (see article 4.3.4), noise-cancelling microphones (see article 4.4.1), signal control and processing (see article 4.4.2), and special headsets (see article 4.4.3).

Whenever it is feasible, the most effective way to protect speech from noise interference is to control and isolate noise at its source—to keep it out of the speech-communication system. It is assumed in the discussion to follow in this section that the communication engineer has applied noise control at the source. The discussion in this section concerns the noise that remains.

4.3.1 *The masking of speech by noise*

The masking spectrum of a noise is the curve that shows, as a function of frequency, how strong a sinusoidal signal must be to be just audible above the noise. As a practical matter, the masking spectrum of a *wide-band noise* is the same as the acoustical spectrum of the noise. This is the reason why we can use the acoustical spectrum in the calculation of AI, even though it is obviously what can be heard (and not the noise-pressure level *per se*) that is important in determining intelligibility. Accordingly, the AI for a communication system operating in the presence of wide-band noise can be computed directly, in the way outlined in article 4.2.1, from a plot of the speech and noise spectra.

How well AI predicted the performance of several systems in wide-band noise is shown in Fig. 4-14 (Egan and Wiener, 1946). The solid curve in Fig. 4-14 shows what nonsense-syllable scores theoretically should be obtained. The various points that are plotted represent scores actually obtained with the several systems described. The noise spectrum extended from 100–10,000 cps and was the same for all of the systems tested. The noise spectrum was uniform up to 400 cps and then fell at the rate of 10 db per octave above that frequency.

NARROW-BAND NOISE

Most industrial and military noises have approximately continuous spectra and exist in a more or less steady state for several minutes or hours. Sometimes, however, one encounters a noise that, although more or less steady, has its energy concentrated in relatively narrow bands of frequency.

The masking effect of narrow bands of noise on speech intelligibility cannot be estimated in the same way that the masking effect of wide bands of noise are estimated. In computing the AI for narrow-band noises, it is necessary to consider the spread of masking from noise components in one frequency band to speech components in another. In addition, the spread down the frequency scale sometimes must be taken into account.

Examples of Masking by Narrow-Band Noise

Intelligibility tests have been conducted with bands of noise of various widths added to normal, unfiltered speech. As examples, the speech spectra, noise spectra, and masking spectra of several of the bands of noise are plotted in Figs. 4-15 and 4.16 (Kryter, 1958). Note that the upward-spread-of-masking

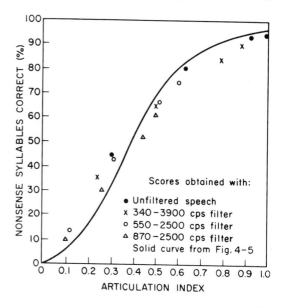

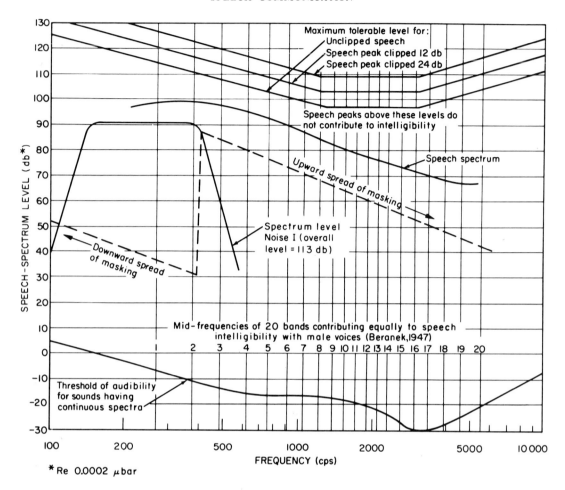

* Re 0.0002 μbar

4-15

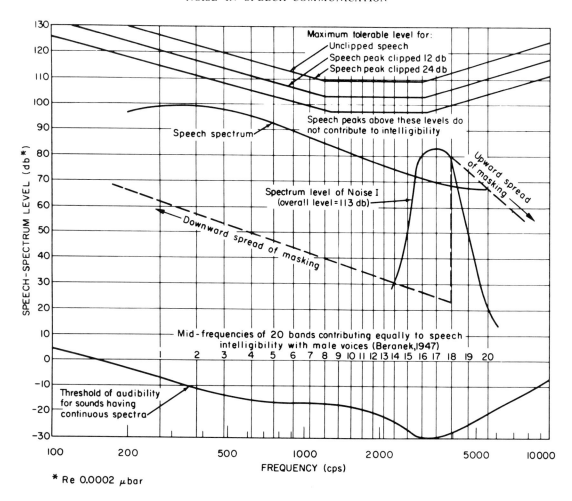

4-16

curve in Fig. 4-15 exceeds the acoustical spectrum of the noise, and that the downward-spread-of-masking curve in Fig. 4-16 exceeds the acoustical spectrum of the noise at the lower frequencies.

The scores predicted on the basis of the AI's that were calculated for various narrow bands of noise are shown in Fig. 4-17 (Miller, 1947b). The scatter of the actual scores around the curve of prediction is largely attributable to the inherent variability in experimental test scores. Considering that variability, the prediction is about as accurate as can be expected under the circumstances.

Computing the AI for Narrow-Band Noise

To compute the AI for narrow bands of noise or of noise containing intense peaks or line components, the curve for the speech peaks and the measured spectrum is plotted, and then the masking spectrum of the noise is plotted by raising the ends of the measured spectrum as follows:

1. Plot the measured noise spectrum on a chart like that of Fig. 4-7.

2. Begin the determination of the masking spectrum of a noise by locating the right-hand-most point at which a horizontal line, 3 db below the maximum of the noise spectrum, intersects the noise spectrum. Call this the "starting point."

3. Drop vertically 57 db from the starting point.

4. Draw a line to the left and upward with a slope of 10 db per octave. This line is the low-frequency part of the masking spectrum.

5. From the starting point, draw a line to the right and downward. The slope of this line depends on the frequency of the starting point and on the maximum spectrum level of the noise, as shown in Table 4-14. This line represents the high-frequency part of the masking spectrum.

6. To find the final masking-spectrum curve, in the region to the left of the starting

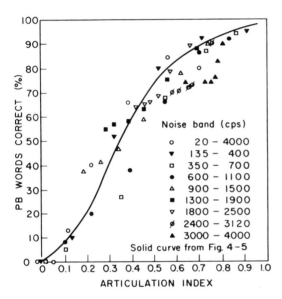

4-17

Table 4-14 **Downward Slope of Masking Spectrum for Various Noise Levels and Frequency Ranges**

Max. spectrum level of noise above 0.0002 μbar (db)	Downward slope of masking spectrum (db/octave)				
	50–800 *	800–1,600 *	1,600–2,400 *	2,400–3,200 *	3,200–5,200 *
46–55	45	40	40	40	40
56–65	35	30	25	25	20
66–75	25	23	20	15	5
76–85	20	18	15	10	0
86–95	15	13	10	5	0
>95	10	8	5	3	0

* Frequency of starting point (cps).

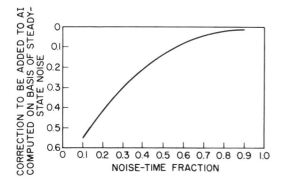

point, take the curve for downward spread of masking or the noise-spectrum curve, whichever is higher, and, in the region to the right of the starting point, take the curve for upward spread of masking or the noise-spectrum curve, whichever is higher.

The final part of the procedure is the same as in the 20-band procedure previously described (see article 4.2.2). When there are simultaneously present in a noise several narrow bands or line components at different points on the frequency scale, treat each one according to Steps 3 through 5 above, and then compute the AI by taking, for each band, the difference in db between speech peaks at the mid-frequency in each of the 20 bands and the highest masking spectrum at the mid-frequency of that band.

Editor's note: As we go to press, a revised procedure for estimating the spread of masking has been published that is based on recent research findings (see Kryter, 1962).

INTERMITTENT NOISE

Many of the noises encountered in communications are interrupted or intermittent. The degree to which such noises will interfere with speech communication can be estimated in the following way:

1. Plot on an AI chart (see Fig. 4-7 or 4-8) the spectrum of the speech peaks reaching the listener's ears.

2. On the same worksheet, plot the masking spectrum of the noise reaching the listener's ears.

3. Compute an AI in the standard way.

4. Note the average "noise-time fraction." The noise-time fraction is the fraction of the time, in a 2-min interval, for example, that the noise is on. As far as masking the speech is concerned, it does not make much difference whether the interruptions of the noise are regular or irregular in time.

5. Correct the AI obtained in Step 3. The correction is given in Fig. 4-18 (Miller and Licklider, 1950). Enter Fig. 4-18 with the noise-time fraction, and read out the correction. Then add the correction to the AI found in Step 3.

6. Measure the frequency of interruption of the noise (the average number of times per second).

7. On Fig. 4-19, draw a vertical line at the interruption frequency found in Step 6. Read the ordinate value corresponding to the point at which the vertical line intersects the curve having the value of AI closest to the AI value obtained in Step 5. The ordinate value is the effective AI of the speech-communication sys-

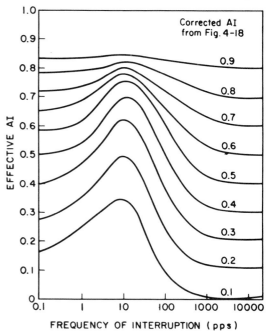

4-19

Effect of interruption rate on AI. Interruption rates between 10 and 25 pps are least effective in masking speech; those above 500 pps are most effective (Miller and Licklider, 1950)

§ 4.3.1

tem operating in the presence of the intermittent noise. This AI now can be converted into an intelligibility score by using Fig. 4-5.

The procedure for estimating or predicting the effects of intermittent noise should not be used with a communication system that imposes a great deal of frequency distortion on the speech signal. For typical communication systems however, the method is reasonably accurate.

4.3.2 *Criteria for communication in noise*

For signals of moderate intensity, it is usually the signal-to-noise ratio, and not the absolute level of the speech or the noise, that determines speech intelligibility. The design engineer has to think of the absolute level, however, as well as the signal-to-noise ratio. The absolute level is especially important in connection with the risk of damage to hearing caused by intense speech or noise and the tolerance for, and acceptability of, extreme levels of speech and noise under various working conditions.

DAMAGE-RISK CRITERIA

Intense speech can cause damage to the human hearing mechanism just as any other audio signal of sufficient intensity and duration (see Chapter 10 for a complete discussion of hearing damage). In intense noise, it can be dangerous to provide a sufficiently high signal-to-noise ratio for high intelligibility—the speech can become as great a source of danger to the ear as the noise.

If communication is to be frequent or long-continued, the overall long-time rms level of the speech signal should not exceed 115 db, relative to 0.0002 μbar, at the ears of the listener. Higher speech levels can damage hearing, and increasing the level of speech above 125 db does not improve intelligibility

even though it increases the signal-to-noise ratio (see Figs. 4-7 and 4-8). If the listeners wear earplugs, however, speech presented by the loudspeaker or the head set (worn over the earplugs) can be made stronger than 115 db by an amount equal to the actual earplug attenuation (see article 4.3.3).

INTELLIGIBILITY CRITERIA

Table 4-15 presents criteria that have been found to be useful as bases for estimating the acceptability of communication systems for which AI's have been calculated. The criteria are based, primarily, on experience with communication systems designed for military use.

Table 4-15   Intelligibility Criteria

An AI of . . .	Provides communications . . .
0.7 to 1.0	Satisfactory to excellent
0.3 to 0.7	Slightly difficult to satisfactory—up to 98% of sentences are heard correctly
0.0 to 0.3	Impossible to difficult—special vocabularies and radio-telephone voice procedures are required

NOISE CRITERIA

The effect of noise on people's efforts to communicate clearly has an important influence on their tolerance for noise. Other factors, such as the general annoyance of a continued high-pitched "hiss" and individual dislikes for particular noises, also influence this tolerance.

Acoustical noise criteria (NCA) are available that take into account both the effect of noise on speech communication and the annoyance factor. These criteria are useful in evaluating communication for offices, conference rooms, and factory workplaces. Figure 4-20 (Beranek, 1957) and Table 4-16 outline the criteria. These criteria should be used, however, only when the background noise is fairly steady and has a continuous spectrum.

To determine the NCA of a given communication environment, proceed as follows:

§ 4.3.2

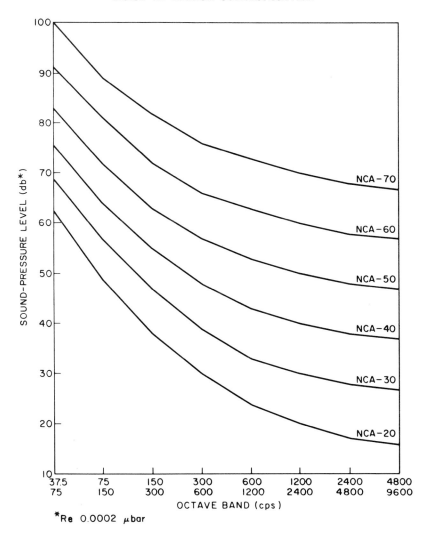

*Re 0.0002 μbar

4-20 Acoustical-noise-criteria curves. These curves are to be used with Table 4-16 in determining permissible sound-pressure levels in eight octave bands. Curves show maximum recommended when noise is steady and free of beats between low-frequency components

1. Measure the background noise in octave bands with work proceeding normally (but with no one talking) in the workplace.

2. Plot the octave-band spectrum of the noise on a worksheet like that shown in Fig. 4-8.

3. Find, in Fig. 4-20, the NCA curve next above the highest measured octave-band level as determined by the plot obtained in Step 2, and assign its number to the environment under study.

4. Enter Table 4-16 with the NCA number and read out a description of the communication environment.

Table 4-16   Noise Criteria (Acoustical) for Offices and Shop Areas *

NCA	Communication environment
20 to 30	Very quiet office, telephone use satisfactory, suitable for large conferences
30 to 35	Quiet office, satisfactory for conferences at 15-ft table, normal-voice range 10–30 ft, telephone use satisfactory
35 to 40	Satisfactory for conferences at 6–8 ft table, telephone use satisfactory, normal-voice range 6–12 ft
40 to 50	Satisfactory for conferences at 4–5 ft table, telephone use slightly difficult, normal-voice range 3–6 ft, raised-voice range 6–12 ft
50 to 55	Unsatisfactory for conferences of more than two or three people, telephone use slightly difficult, normal-voice range 1–2 ft, raised-voice range 3–6 ft
55 to 60	Very noisy office, telephone use difficult
60 to 70	Raised-voice range 1–2 ft, telephone use difficult
70 to 80	Raised-voice range 1–2 ft, shouting range 3–6 ft, telephone use very difficult
Above 80	Communication extremely difficult, telephone use unsatisfactory

* Noise measurements made for the purpose of comparing the noise in an office with these criteria should be performed with the office in normal operation but with no one talking at the particular desk or conference table where speech communication is desired, i.e., where the measurement is being made (Beranek, 1957).

4.3.3 *Ear-protective devices*

Personnel in extremely noisy environments might need to wear ear-protective devices to avoid damage to their ears and to make noisy environments more comfortable and habitable. See Chapter 10 for a complete discussion of ear-protective devices. We will confine our discussion here to their effect on intelligibility in speech communication.

EFFECT ON INTELLIGIBILITY

Figure 4-21 shows that, under most noise conditions, a listener can wear earplugs without reducing the intelligibility of speech. The earplugs attenuate the speech and the noise by the same amount so that the signal-to-noise ratio at the listener's eardrums is the same with the earplugs as without. If the ambient noise is sufficiently intense to override the "physiological noise" in the listener's ear, the AI is also the same.

To override the physiological noise, even after being attenuated by earplugs, the ambient noise must be 30–40 db above threshold in each of the 20 bands. Otherwise, the earplugs can reduce both the ambient noise and all or part of the speech in some bands to levels below the threshold of hearing. This is what happens when the noise has an overall level of 65 db or less; the use of earplugs in this case causes a decrease in speech intelligibility.

On the other hand, as Fig. 4-21 shows, when the speech level exceeds 85 db, the use of earplugs causes an increase in intelligibility, whether or not there is background noise. When the long-time-rms level of speech is 85 db, the speech peaks have a spectrum level of about 97 db. As mentioned earlier, at about 95 db the speech peaks start to overload the ear.

The effect of overload on speech intelligibility can, in fact, be more serious than is implied by the procedure for computing AI

§ 4.3.3

because, in this procedure, peaks above the overload level are assumed to make no further contribution to intelligibility. Actually, overload can impair reception, and any device that attenuates both speech and noise will reduce the speech-peak level and thus reduce the amount of overloading.

In addition, not only does the use of ear-protective devices improve the intelligibility of speech in the presence of intense noise, it also retards the decline in intelligibility that has been found to result from long-continued exposure to intense speech and noise.

WHEN TO USE THEM

In the quiet with no background noise and with maximum-attenuation (50 db) ear-protective devices, speech reception will be at least as good with the ears protected as with

them unprotected, if the long-time-rms level of the speech is 90 db or greater at the position of the listener's head. The following procedure indicates whether a given ear-protective device will improve, or interfere with, speech reception under specified noise conditions:

1. Plot, on Fig. 4-7, the noise spectrum under consideration.

2. Subtract from the noise spectrum the attenuation afforded by the ear-protective device.

3. Plot the result obtained in Step 2.

If the curve obtained in Step 3 exceeds the threshold of audibility, any speech signal, no matter how weak or intense, will be heard better with the ear protected than with the ear unprotected. In the case of very intense speech, the improvement in reception will be appreciable. If the curve obtained in Step 3 falls below the threshold curve at some points

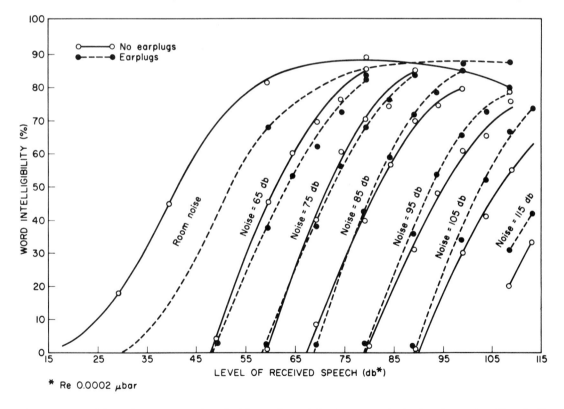

* Re 0.0002 µbar

4-21 Relation between PB-word intelligibility and speech level in various levels of masking noise with and without earplugs. (NDRC type V-51R earplugs were used.) Data show higher intelligibility in presence of intense noise with earplugs than without (Kryter, 1946)

on the frequency scale, very weak speech will not be heard as well when the ear protectors are worn as when they are not worn.

4.3.4 *Microphone noise shields*

When the talker is in an intense noise field, the microphone should be put in a noise shield. This applies to noise-cancelling microphones (see article 4.4.1) as well as to other microphones. A noise shield protects the microphone more from high-frequency than low-frequency noise (noise cancelling does just the opposite), but, as shown in Fig. 4-22 (Hawley and Kryter, 1957), a noise-cancelling microphone in a noise shield can attenuate noise by 30 db.

DESIGN RECOMMENDATIONS

Noise shields should be designed to meet the following requirements:

1. The shield should have a volume of at least 250 cm³ to permit a pressure-gradient microphone to function normally, if this is the type used.

2. The shield should not be so large as to be unwieldy.

3. The shield should fit tightly against the face to obtain a good seal with the pressure of the hand or the tension of straps.

4. A hole, or combination of holes, having a total area of 0.1 in.² should be provided in the shield to let the talker exhale while talking so that he does not build up pressure in the shield. The hole or holes should be as far as possible from the microphone.

5. A standing-wave pattern inside the shield should be avoided. Sound-absorbing material should be enclosed in acoustically transparent, waterproof material (such as thin-sheet polyurethane).

6. To provide good intelligibility, the shield should not impede the talker's voice effort, mouth or jaw movement, or breathing.

7. To obtain the data necessary for the prediction of intelligibility, the designer should measure the response of the shield and the microphone together.

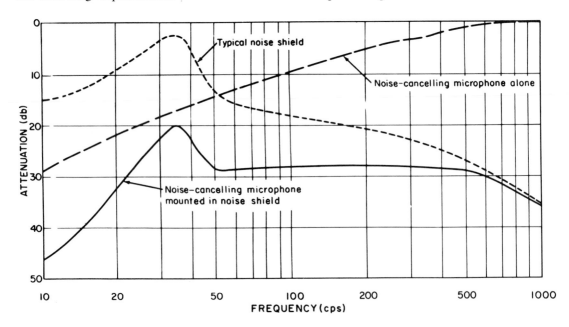

4-22

4.4 *Component Selection and Application*

The various components (microphones, amplifiers, headsets, loudspeakers, etc.) of a communication system often must function in noise, and some are better for this than others. Also, the components often distort the speech signal. Some distortions have adverse effects on speech quality and intelligibility, but others can be used to advantage in speech-communication systems. For instance, automatic gain control and clipping of the peaks of speech waves, under some conditions, yield improved communications (see article 4.4.2).

4.4.1 *Microphones*

The three most important characteristics to be looked for in a microphone can be listed as follows:

1. High sensitivity to acoustic speech signals.

2. Faithful transduction of the acoustic speech signal into an electric signal.

3. Ability to reject other acoustic signals and noises that are present at the location of the talker.

Many microphones are satisfactory insofar as frequency-response characteristics are concerned; few, however, are specifically designed to discriminate between the talker's speech signal and the ambient noise surrounding the talker. Microphones that are so designed are called noise-cancelling microphones.

NOISE-CANCELLING MICROPHONES

Some microphones have good noise-cancelling characteristics. These microphones, also called differential or pressure-gradient microphones, are so constructed that sound waves can reach the diaphragm from the back as well as from the front of the microphone. When a microphone is placed directly in front of the lips of a person who is talking, it is in the spherically expanding part of the speech wave pattern, and there is a large gradient of speech pressure between the front and back of the diaphragm. Noise, on the other hand, usually comes from more distant sources. With noise-cancelling microphones, this noise has equal access to both the back and front of the diaphragm and is thus largely "cancelled" whereas the speech is not. The amount of discrimination that is available from a typical noise-cancelling microphone placed ½ in. in front of the talker's lips is shown in Fig. 4-23 (Hawley and Kryter, 1957).

Design Recommendations

The following points are important in connection with the selection of noise-cancelling microphones:

1. For close talking, do not use the large pressure-gradient microphones that are usually called "velocity microphones." They are not designed as noise-cancelling microphones but as ordinary microphones that can be used at a distance of several feet from the sound source.

2. Use a close-talking noise-cancelling microphone when the problem is low-frequency noise (in the neighborhood of 100 db overall sound-pressure level).

3. Design the microphone mounting or grip so that talkers always speak along the axis of the microphone, i.e., along a line through the holes leading the sound to the active element. Most microphones are so designed that this is the "natural" way to use them, but do not count on the talker using the microphone correctly unless he cannot use it any other way.

§ 4.4.1

4. Design the microphone grip so that talkers always hold the microphone in such a way that none of the holes are covered by the talker's hand, clothing, etc.

5. Provide instructions for the talker to hold the microphone very close to his lips. Noise-cancelling microphones must be held very close to the lips if their noise discrimination properties are to be realized; in most cases they should just touch the lips when being used.

CONTACT MICROPHONES

Contact microphones are microphones placed directly in contact with the throat, forehead, jaw or surfaces of the head, in the ear canal, or on a tooth. Such microphones can be constructed and shielded to yield a good signal-to-noise ratio even though the talker is in an intense-noise field. Contact microphones tend to introduce distortion, however, because of the absorption of the high speech frequencies by body tissues and because different microphone locations favor certain speech sounds over others.

When the talker is in intense noise and the listener is in relative quiet, the best contact microphones provide as much intelligibility as most other types of microphones. When both talker and listener are in noise, however, contact microphones do not provide as much intelligibility as noise-cancelling microphones, even though the overall signal-to-noise ratios might be comparable.

DESIGN RECOMMENDATIONS

In the selection and application of any kind of microphone, the design engineer should observe the following general principles:

1. Choose a microphone with a smooth frequency-response characteristic that is as wide as that of the rest of the system (which should ordinarily extend from 200–6,100 cps for highest intelligibility).

2. Be sure that the dynamic range (see article 4.1.5) of the microphone, when working into the selected amplifier, is great enough to admit 50-db variations in signal input.

3. For close talking, consider only microphones that do not overload with signals as high as 125–130 db.

4. Avoid condenser microphones if the bias voltage (typically 200) would constitute a safety hazard.

5. Avoid carbon microphones in which "packing" of the carbon granules occurs.

6. Do not use carbon microphones if the quality criteria demand a truly linear response

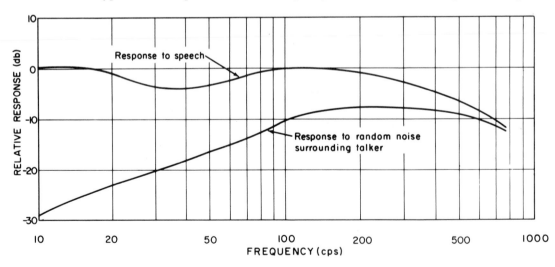

4-23

characteristic or very low background noise.

7. Do not use a ribbon microphone for close talking unless the microphone has been designed specifically for this kind of use.

8. If it is to be used for close talking, be sure that a microphone is provided with protection against breath blast, which may damage the microphone and will certainly make the reproduced-sound quality objectionable, and with protection against condensation of moisture, particularly saliva.

4.4.2 *Amplifiers, transmitters, and receivers*

In general, amplifiers, transmitters, and receivers to be used in speech-communication systems should have the following characteristics:

1. Sufficient bandwidth to provide a "flat" audio-frequency response from at least 250–4,000 cps (preferably 200–6,100 cps for intelligibility and 100–7,500 cps for quality of reproduction).

2. Sufficient dynamic range (see article 4.1.5) and gain to handle the range of instantaneous pressures found in speech and to develop the necessary signal level at the headset or loudspeaker terminals.

In addition, they should introduce less background noise than is introduced by the microphone.

Linear amplification is usually desirable for speech communication when both talkers and listeners are in relative quiet. In noise, however, it may be desirable to introduce nonlinearity deliberately. Two kinds of nonlinear amplification are of particular interest in this connection: automatic gain control (AGC), sometimes called automatic volume control (AVC), and peak clipping.

Automatic gain control and peak clipping have different actions and effects, but they can be used together. The one essential difference in the actions of the two is in their response times; ordinary AGC operates on

relatively long-time measures of the intensity of a signal whereas a peak clipper can be thought of as an AGC that operates instantaneously.

AUTOMATIC GAIN CONTROL

Essentially, an AGC system acts like a linear system during any interval that is short relative to the attack time (the time required for the AGC to adjust the gain to the level of the input signal) and the release time (the time it takes the gain to return to normal after the signal stops). This linear behavior is illustrated by waveforms A and B of Fig. 4-24. Note that input A is, on the average, of a greater intensity than input B, but the output, following AGC gain adjustment, is the same for both A and B.

The AGC system derives a measure of the average signal strength over a period of time, and this information is used to adjust the operating characteristic of the amplifier. Sustained, intense signals lead to reduction of the gain; sustained, weak signals lead to increase of the gain. The average output level is, therefore, about the same, no matter what the average input level. But AGC does not eliminate variations in intensity between parts of the signal that occur together in a short interval of time; the consonants remain weaker than the neighboring vowels, for example, because the AGC averages over an interval longer than a single speech sound.

The Uses of AGC

When AGC is used to maintain full modulation of a carrier, it is located between microphone and modulator. If the "side-tone" circuit through which the talker hears his own voice is controlled by the AGC, the AGC will tend to keep the level of the side tone (the talker's own voice) constant even though the input speech level is reduced. The natural reaction of the talker is to reduce his voice level even further. He will, of course, hear the signal-to-noise ratio decrease as he lowers his voice level, but, ordinarily, talkers do not pay much attention to the signal-to-noise ratio

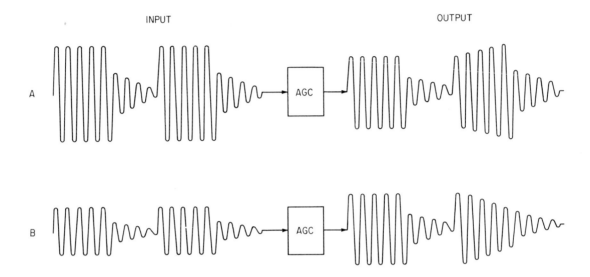

4-24 Effect of AGC amplifier on two signals. AGC action preserves intensive relations within short segments of signal, but it automatically de-amplifies stronger signal in A, and automatically amplifies weaker signal in B to give the same average long-term output.

of the side tone. This problem can be avoided by taking the talker's side tone from the system at a point ahead of the AGC.

AGC is also used to provide constant listening level without requiring the adjustment of a manual gain control. When the strength of the received signal varies, e.g., because of fading in radio transmission, AGC in the receiver will tend to keep the output constant.

In addition, AGC is used to maintain a constant signal-to-noise ratio in spite of variations in the ambient-noise level at the listener's location. A noise-controlled AGC system can provide high speech intelligibility during periods of intense noise and, at the same time, protect the hearing of the listeners from exposure to intense speech during periods of relative quiet.

As an example of a situation in which such a system would be desirable, aboard aircraft, communication sometimes is transmitted in a noise field by a powerful loudspeaker system that can generate a speech signal intense enough to be heard in the noise. In moments of relative quiet, however, the speech signal, if adjusted for audibility in the intense noise, sounds excessively loud, and intelligibility declines with continued presentation.

A noise-controlled AGC system has a "noise microphone" in the area where the listeners are located so that the intensity of the noise picked up by the noise microphone can control the gain of the speech amplifier. Speech intelligibility is not adversely affected by the variations in level introduced by a noise-operated AGC, even though the variations occur at rapid rates.

Attack and Release Times

The attack- and release-time constants usually employed in the "limiter" amplifiers used in commercial broadcast work are, typically, 10 msec and 600 msec, respectively. For some military communication systems designed to operate in noise, it has been found that an attack time of about 0.1 sec and a release time of about 10 sec are most satisfactory. (When the release time is made appreciably shorter, there is an objectionable fluctuation in the transmitted background noise.) But, because the optional time constants depend so greatly on conditions and requirements, it is best to determine the AGC time constants empirically for each new application.

PEAK CLIPPING

Peak clipping is, as the name implies, simply clipping the peaks off the speech signal and leaving the remainder. Ordinarily, peak clipping involves clipping both the positive (upward) and negative (downward) peaks. For all practical purposes, peak-clippers have no attack or release times; they operate instantaneously.

Peak clipping (alone) often tends to reduce the amplitudes of the intense parts of speech (usually the vowels) down to the level of the weaker parts (consonants). Because of this, peak clipping is often used to make the various speech sounds more homogeneous in amplitude. If we reamplify a signal that has been clipped so that the peak amplitude of the remnant is the same as the peak amplitude of the original wave before clipping (see Fig. 4-25), the intensity of the weak (consonant)

sounds is increased. This is true even though the peak level of the speech (and, therefore, the peak power requirements of the amplifiers, radio transmitters, etc.) is not increased. Figure 4-26 (Licklider, 1946) shows word intelligibility as a function of peak amplitude of received speech, with peak clipping as the parameter. As can be seen, with equal peak-to-peak amplitude, clipped speech is much better understood than unclipped speech.

The Optimum Amount of Clipping

The amount of peak clipping, if any, to be used in a communication system depends, mainly, on the noise conditions. For instance, as the amount of pre-clipping noise increases relative to the amount of post-clipping noise, the optimum degree of peak clipping decreases. Tests have been conducted with var-

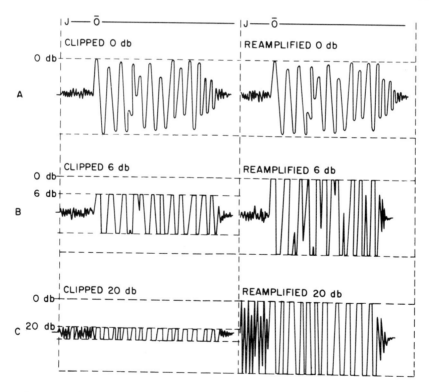

4-25 Schematic representations of word "Joe." A is undistorted, B is after 6-db clipping, and C is after 20-db clipping. Clipped signals in B and C are shown reamplified until their peak-to-peak amplitudes equal peak-to-peak amplitude of A (Licklider, et al., 1948)

195

ious amounts of peak clipping and with various amounts of noise introduced at various places into the communication system. The results are summarized in Table 4-17 and Fig. 4-27.

When it is possible to have the talker in a quiet environment, or to have him use a noise-cancelling microphone and noise shield, so that the signal-to-noise ratio coming from the microphone is greater than 10 db, Fig. 4-28 can be used to estimate the optimum amount of peak clipping and reamplification. To determine the amount of clipping to be used, first calculate the AI for the system without peak clipping; then, enter Fig. 4-28 with the

be aware that the consonants and other weak sounds in the speech are now louder, but, certainly, the speech is more intelligible. Such subjective appraisals of the quality of clipped and unclipped speech are shown in Table 4-18.

Low-frequency-attenuating filters between microphone and clipper are often helpful in reducing distortion products and in cleaning up the noisy sound of heavily clipped speech. High-pass filters cutting off everything below 300–400 cps are quite successful, but, where cost is a consideration, coupling circuits between the stages of pre-clipper amplifiers can be designed to provide 6-db-per-octave atten-

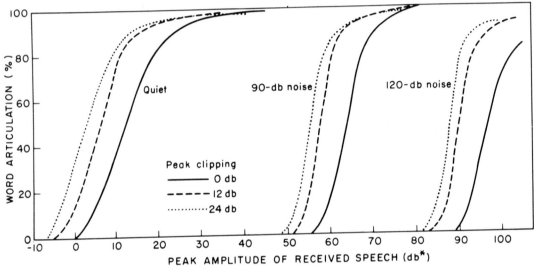

*Re threshold of audibility for undistorted speech in quiet

AI and read out the optimum amount of peak clipping and reamplification.

uation of frequencies below 1,000 cps with considerable improvement in the quality of the clipped speech.

Distortion Products

When listened to in quiet, speech that has been severely clipped has a harsh, unpleasant sound because of the distortion products that are introduced by the clipping. When listened to in noise that enters the system at a point following the clipper, the distortion products tend to be masked by the noise, and the speech sounds about as "clean" as unclipped speech in the same noise. The listener might

Heterodyne Clipping

Another way of avoiding some of the distortion products introduced by peak clipping is by using the following procedure (referred to as "heterodyne clipping"):

1. Use single-sideband suppressed-carrier modulation to shift the spectrum of the speech signal up the frequency scale by x cps.

2. Peak clip and then reamplify the single-

196

§ 4.4.2

Table 4-17 Optimum Amount of Peak Clipping for Various Noise Conditions and System Configurations

Environmental noise surrounding talker	System noise	Environmental noise surrounding listener	High-pass filter[1] after microphone	AGC after microphone	Peak clipping before modulation (db)	Low-pass filter[2] before modulation	AGC in receiver	Peak limiter in receiver
Negligible[3]	Negligible	Negligible	No	Yes	0	No	No	No
Negligible[3]	Negligible	Moderate	No	Yes	12	Yes	No	No
Negligible[3]	Negligible	Intense	No	Yes	18	Yes	No	No
Negligible[3]	Moderate	Negligible	No	Yes	12	Yes	Yes	Yes
Negligible[3]	Moderate	Moderate	No	Yes	18	Yes	Yes	Yes
Negligible[3]	Moderate	Intense	No	Yes	24	Yes	Yes	Yes
Moderate[4]	Negligible	Negligible	No	Yes	0	No	No	No
Moderate[4]	Negligible	Moderate	No	Yes	0	No	No	No
Moderate[4]	Negligible	Intense	No	Yes	8	No	Yes	No
Moderate[4]	Moderate	Negligible	No	Yes	6	Yes	Yes	Yes
Moderate[4]	Moderate	Moderate	No	Yes	8	Yes	Yes	Yes
Moderate[4]	Moderate	Intense	No	Yes	12	Yes	Yes	Yes
Intense[5]	Negligible	Negligible	Yes	No[6]	0	No	No	No
Intense[5]	Negligible	Moderate	Yes	No[6]	0	No	No	No
Intense[5]	Negligible	Intense	Yes	No[6]	6	Yes	Yes	No
Intense[5]	Moderate	Negligible	Yes	No[6]	0	No	Yes	Yes
Intense[5]	Moderate	Moderate	Yes	No[6]	6	Yes	Yes	Yes
Intense[5]	Moderate	Intense	Yes	No[6]	12	Yes	Yes	Yes

[1] 6db/octave.

[2] 5,000 cps.

[3] Or moderate with noise-cancelling microphone in noise shield.

[4] With noise-cancelling microphone not in noise shield or intense with noise-cancelling microphone in noise shield.

[5] With noise-cancelling microphone not in noise shield.

[6] If noise fluctuates widely in intensity, noise-operated AGC might be beneficial. If used, AGC should have release time greater than 15 sec.

§ 4.4.2

PROPOSED SPEECH-COMMUNICATION SYSTEMS FOR USE IN EXTREME-INTENSITY NOISE

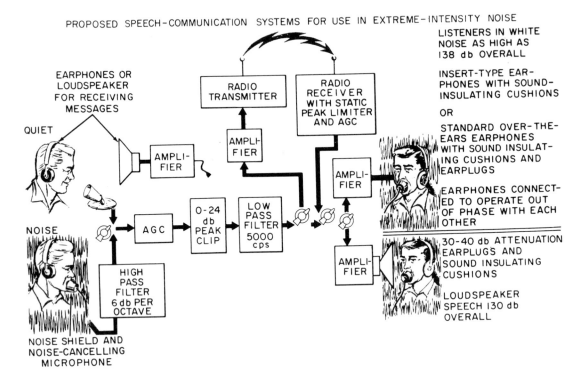

4-27

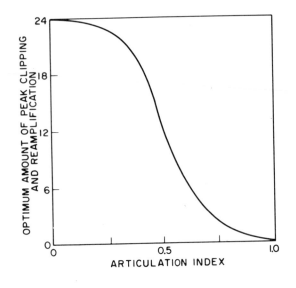

4-28

Table 4-18 **Quality of Clipped and Unclipped Speech** *

Clipping (db)	Sound in quiet	Quality
0	Normal	Excellent
6	Essentially normal, effect barely detectable	Probably acceptable as of broadcast quality
12	As though talker enunciated with special care	Usable for military communication
18	Sharp, "sandy"	Fair, usable for most military communication
24	Coarse, "grainy"	Poor, but usable if intelligibility is of paramount importance

* Licklider, 1946.

§ 4.4.2

sideband-modulated carrier by the desired amount.

3. Pass the resulting signal through a band-pass filter (*x* to *x* + 5,000 cps).

4. Use the signal in an ordinary single-sideband suppressed-carrier transmission or, if an audio signal is required, demodulate with the aid of standard single-sideband suppressed-carrier techniques.

Because the distortion-product noise introduced by peak clipping consists of harmonics and intermodulation products, it will be largely very high and very low in frequency, relative to the shifted speech frequencies, and will, therefore, fall outside of the band of the band-pass filter (*x* to *x* + 5,000 cps), and the transmitted signal will not contain the distortion products even though it has been clipped.

Such a process will make the received signal sound "cleaner" and less harsh to a listener in quiet. Elimination of the distortion products that lie outside the filter bands, however, will affect the shape of the transmitted wave in such a way that less power is actually transmitted than would be transmitted by an ordinary premodulation peak-clipping system. Thus, heterodyne clipping does not improve the intelligibility of the speech received in noise quite as much as does peak clipping the speech prior to modulation.

Computing the AI for Clipped Speech

The increase in intelligibility of noise-free speech that has been clipped and reamplified is closely related to the increase produced in the long-time rms of the speech signal by the clipping and reamplification, assuming that the signal is reamplified until the peak amplitude of the remnant is the same as the peak amplitude of the original speech signal. The relation between the amount of peak clipping and the increase in long-time-rms level is shown in Fig. 4-29.

It can be seen from Fig. 4-29 that, if, for example, we clip and then reamplify the speech signal by 24 db, the long-time-rms intensity increases by 12 db. And it is apparent from Fig. 4-26 that the peak ampli-

tude of the speech signal that has been clipped and reamplified 24 db can be about 12 db less than the unclipped speech and still be equally intelligible.

Because the AI of speech heard in noise is proportional to the speech-to-noise ratio (if it is between 0 and 30 db), we can compute an AI for a system that utilizes peak clipping —as long as the speech entering the clipper is relatively free of noise. If this condition prevails, the AI can be computed by proceeding as follows:

1. Determine from Fig. 4-29 the increase in the long-time rms of speech that results from the peak clipping and reamplification.

2. Add the result of Step 1 to the level of speech peaks that would reach the listener's ears without the peak clipping and reamplification.

3. Plot the result of Step 2 on an AI work-chart (see Fig. 4-7 or 4-8). Note that the maximum tolerable level for the speech is higher for clipped than for unclipped speech.

4. Plot the noise spectrum reaching the listener's ears on the AI worksheet being used, and proceed to compute an AI in the regular way.

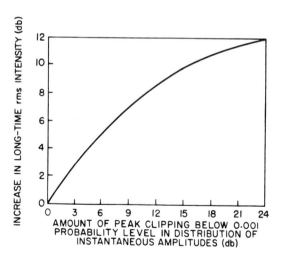

4-29 Increase in rms speech pressure as function of amount of clipping and reamplification. Speech intelligibility remains approximately constant with different amounts of peak clipping if long-time-rms pressure at output of clipper is held constant (Wathen-Dunn and Lipke, 1958)

4.4.3 *Loudspeakers and headsets*

The following paragraphs list the principal factors that determine the selection of one or the other type of receiving device. Loudspeakers should be used when any of the following conditions prevail:

a. Ambient-noise levels are low, and no special equipment need be worn.

b. Listeners must move around so much that a headset cable is impractical.

c. A large number of listeners should hear the same message.

d. Signals (e.g., warning or alerting signals) might have to be sent to people who would not be wearing headsets.

Headsets should be used when any of the following conditions exist:

a. Ambient-noise levels are so high that ear-protective devices are required to protect the ears of the listener.

b. Different listeners must receive different messages.

c. Reverberation interferes with loudspeaker listening.

d. The listener must wear special equipment such as an oxygen helmet.

e. The electric power available is inadequate to operate a loudspeaker.

LOUDSPEAKERS

From a human-engineering point of view, it makes little difference whether horns or direct-radiator loudspeakers are used or what kind of enclosure is provided. It is necessary to be sure only that the signal strength, sensitivity, bandwidth, and distance are such that an adequate signal-to-noise ratio exists at the listener's ears. The problem of reverberation, however, must be taken into consideration whenever loudspeakers are to be used.

Reverberation and echoes are both caused by reflection; the speech reaches the listener after reflecting off walls or other surfaces. This indirect (and therefore delayed) signal is superposed upon the signal received over the direct path. In the case of an echo, the delay is great enough so that the listener distinguishes two separate sounds. In the case of reverberation, the delayed signal (or, as is usually the case, the complex of variously delayed signals) fuses with the direct signal in the listener's perception.

Often the addition of the delayed components to the direct-speech waves interferes with intelligibility; the direct-speech sounds are, in effect, masked by the echoes or reverberation of preceding speech sounds. Some reverberation is desirable, however, to avoid the abnormal "dead" sound of a completely anechoic space.

The reverberation characteristics of a room usually are measured by determining the length of time required for a tone abruptly terminated at the source to decay 60 db in sound-pressure level. The longer the reverberation time, the greater is the masking effect of the reverberant sound, and reverberation is usually greater at the rear of a large space than at the front.

Much of the sound reaching the rear is reflected off of more than one surface. This reflection comes to the service of listeners in the rear of the space by distributing sound energy more or less uniformly throughout the space and keeping the signal from becoming excessively weak at great distances from the source.

Figure 4-30 (Farrell, 1958) gives the reverberation times (measured with a 500-cps pure tone) generally agreed upon by acoustical experts as being optimum for various types of rooms. Complete information on the effects of reverberation on speech reception is not available, but Fig. 4-31 (Fletcher, 1953)

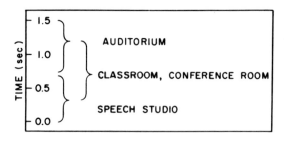

4-30

shows the main relation between reverberation time and speech intelligibility. The evidently deleterious effect on intelligibility has to be tempered with the observation, already mentioned, that a certain amount of reverberation is desirable because it makes speech sound "alive" and natural.

Computing the AI with Reverberation

The following procedure can be used to estimate the intelligibility of speech in a room with reverberation:

1. Calculate the AI using either the spectrum levels or octave-band spectra of the speech peaks and noise.

2. Correct the AI, if necessary, for intermittency of noise (see article 4.3.1), vocal effort of the talker, and peak clipping (see article 4.4.2).

3. Measure the reverberation times of the room in question at the positions to be taken by listeners, placing the test-signal source at the position normally used by talkers in the room.

4. From Fig. 4-32 (Fletcher, 1953), read the AI fractions corresponding to the reverberation times found in Step 3.

5. Subtract from the AI found in Step 1 or Step 2 the fractions obtained in Step 4. The differences are the effective AIs, which can be used in conjunction with Fig. 4-5 to estimate the intelligibility of various types of speech messages in the room.

Reducing Reverberation

To lessen the effect of undesired reverberation in large rooms, use several or many low-powered loudspeakers distributed throughout the area instead of a few powerful loudspeakers. The loudspeakers should be directional and should be oriented in such a way that they cover directly the most important parts of the room and so that overlap in coverage among the various loudspeakers is minimized. In addition, provide instructions for the talkers to speak slowly and deliberately and allow time for the echo of one word or phrase to decay before saying the next word or phrase.

Preventing Feedback "Squeal"

Public-address systems in highly reverberant rooms are inclined to go into oscillation and "sing" or "squeal" because of acoustical feedback from loudspeaker to microphone. To prevent this trouble, do the following:

1. Reduce the gain from microphone to loudspeaker, and put the talker closer to the microphone.

2. Use components with nearly uniform frequency-response characteristics.

3. Use a directional microphone.

4. Provide a booth for the talker or a shield around the microphone.

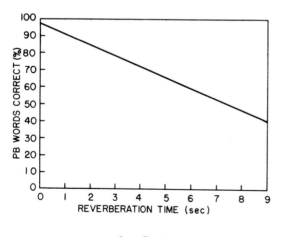

4-31

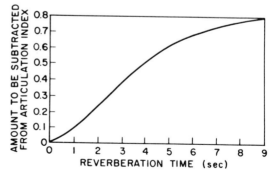

4-32

HEADSETS

The important human-engineering considerations in the selection and application of headsets can be listed as follows:

1. Choose a headset with a smooth frequency-response characteristic as broad as that of the remainder of the system.

2. Be sure that the dynamic range, without appreciable distortion, is at least 40 db and that the power-handling capacity is adequate to receive the peaks of the amplifier output.

3. Pick a combination of earphone and socket or cushion for which the earphone sensitivity and the earcap attenuation together will provide an adequate signal-to-noise ratio.

4. Select an earphone cushion that is comfortable enough to permit the user to wear it as long as necessary. (Comfort is sometimes a very difficult requirement to meet and is often neglected, with unfortunate consequences.)

Measuring Headset Characteristics

Frequency response. The cushions or sockets that hold the earphones influence the frequency-response characteristics of the earphones and, thereby, the fidelity with which the speech signal is reproduced. The characteristics of the earphone-and-socket combination can be measured with the earphone and socket on an "artificial ear" that simulates acoustically the head and ear cavity of a human being. When sinusoidal signals of various frequencies are applied at constant voltage across the earphone, the pressure developed in the artificial ear is measured with the aid of a calibrated microphone.

A more meaningful way to determine the characteristics of the earphone and its socket, however, is based on the equal-loudness judgment of actual people wearing the equipment, but the characteristics of equipment determined in this way, called "real-ear" response characteristics, require the responses of highly trained, sophisticated listeners. If this condition can be satisfied, proceed as follows:

1. Set up a loudspeaker and associated equipment as shown in Fig. 4-33 (Beranek,

1949). This equipment should produce a pure tone of variable frequency at a sound-pressure level of 80 db relative to 0.0002 μbar.

2. Set up a "transfer-standard" earphone, and alternately apply the test signal to it and to the loudspeaker.

3. Adjust the voltage applied to the transfer-standard earphone until its tone equals the loudspeaker tone in subjective loudness. This will require separate adjustments at several different representative frequencies.

4. Put earphone X (in its socket) to the ear with which the listener has been listening to the loudspeaker.

5. Deliver a test signal alternately to X and to the transfer-standard earphone.

6. Adjust the voltage applied to X until the loudness produced by the two earphones is equal.

Insofar as the assumption of "equal sound-pressure level for equal loudness" holds, earphone X is now developing, in effect, the equivalent of 80 db (re 0.0002 μbar) or 2 μbar. The "response" at each frequency tested is simply 2 μbar divided by the voltage required for equal loudness. This can be expressed in decibels relative to 1 μbar/v.

Typical results of real-ear and artificial-ear earphone measurements are shown in Fig. 4-34 (Wiener and Filler, 1945). Note that the response obtained with the artificial ear differs from the real-ear response. Usually, the latter offers a better basis for engineering decisions because it is free of the unevaluated errors inherent in the simulation of so complex a system as the human ear.

Noise attenuation. The noise-attenuation characteristics of an earphone and its socket are best measured by tests based on the "threshold of hearing" for pure tones. To perform this test, proceed as follows:

1. Place a listener in a soundproof, anechoic chamber with a loudspeaker on one side of him.

2. Plug the ear that is not oriented toward the loudspeaker.

3. Have the listener adjust the sound-pressure level of a pure tone until he can just detect its presence at several frequencies.

4. Have him place the earphones (in their sockets) on his ears as they would be worn

§ 4.4.3

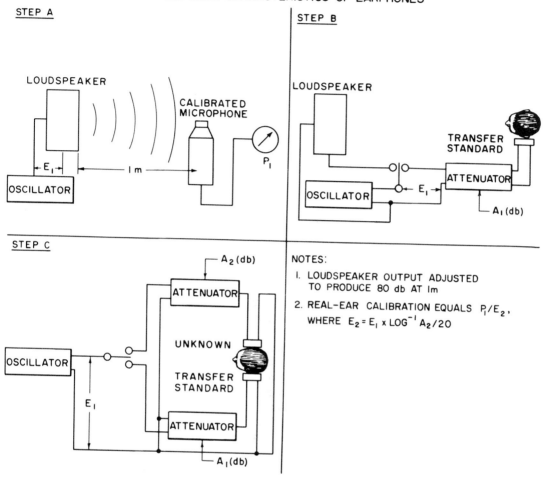

"LOUDNESS-BALANCE" METHOD FOR MEASURING "REAL-EAR"
RESPONSE CHARACTERISTICS OF EARPHONES

STEP A

LOUDSPEAKER

CALIBRATED
MICROPHONE

E_1

1 m

P_1

OSCILLATOR

STEP B

LOUDSPEAKER

TRANSFER
STANDARD

OSCILLATOR

E_1

ATTENUATOR

A_1(db)

STEP C

A_2(db)

ATTENUATOR

OSCILLATOR

UNKNOWN

TRANSFER
STANDARD

E_1

ATTENUATOR

A_1(db)

NOTES:

1. LOUDSPEAKER OUTPUT ADJUSTED
   TO PRODUCE 80 db AT 1m

2. REAL-EAR CALIBRATION EQUALS P_1/E_2,
   WHERE $E_2 = E_1 \times LOG^{-1} A_2/20$

4-33

§ 4.4.3

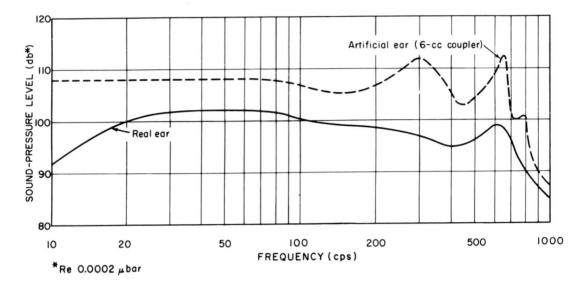

*Re 0.0002 μbar

normally, and again adjust the sound-pressure level until he can just detect the presence of a tone at each of the test frequencies. The difference between the open-ear and the covered-ear thresholds is the amount of attenuation or noise exclusion provided by the earphone and its socket.

Noise-attenuation characteristics also can be measured with the aid of an artificial or "dummy" head in which a calibrated microphone is located at the bottom of the "ear cavity." To perform this test, proceed as follows:

1. Place the earphone and socket on the dummy head.

2. Produce ambient sounds, preferably tones of known frequency and sound-pressure levels.

3. Read the voltage developed by the microphone in the dummy head.

4. Remove the earphones and repeat Steps 2 and 3.

5. For each test frequency, determine the ratio between the voltage generated by the microphone when the earphone and socket are not on the artificial head and the voltage generated when they are.

6. Convert this ratio into decibels. The result is the amount of sound attenuation afforded by the earphone and socket.

A comparison of typical real-ear and artificial-ear measurements of earphone-socket and -cushion attenuation is shown in Fig. 4-35 (Beranek, 1949). Note, again, the differences between the values for real-ear and artificial-ear measurements; the latter provide only a rough approximation.

Comfort vs. Performance

The sensitivity of an earphone depends in part on the size of the cavity formed by the earcap, earphone, ear canal, and any parts of the outer ear that are inside the earphone socket. The smaller this cavity is, the higher the sound pressure produced by a given power delivered to the earphone. But sensitivity (as well as power-handling capacity and attenuation) and comfort tend to be incompatible.

To achieve comfort with a headset, we might use large, light-weight earcaps that apply little pressure to the ears. The combination of low pressure and light weight, however, provides little attenuation, so that a strong signal is necessary to provide a satisfactory signal-to-noise ratio. But, a large earphone socket means a large cavity, and to get a strong signal in a large cavity, with leaks around the socket, requires high electrical power and, therefore, high power-handling capacity. But, high power-handling capacity means large, heavy earphones, and heavy earphones are uncomfortable.

§ 4.4.3

Obviously, compromises between comfort and performance tend to be at least partially unsatisfactory, but they must be made, nevertheless. The most common compromises are the following:

a. Large earphones and sockets mounted in a rigid helmet that has to be worn anyway (e.g., an oxygen helmet or diving helmet). The large socket surrounds the ear and presses very gently on the head bones. Such headsets can be worn for long periods of time, in some cases continuously for 20 hr, and provide adequate intelligibility if the noise level is low or if the helmet provides good attenuation.

b. Medium-size earphones and sockets mounted in a rigid or flexible helmet or on a headband. The socket is large enough to press tightly against the head bones, but it also rests lightly on the outer ear because the cavity size is not great enough for complete clearance. Such headsets can be worn for periods up to about 6 hr and provide high intelligibility if the sockets have good attenuation.

c. Small earphones and sockets mounted on a headband or in a telephone handset or radioset. Here, the earcap presses tightly against the outer ear. Such headsets can be worn for only a short time, usually less than an hour, but they are convenient for intermittent use and provide high intelligibility with small electrical power.

d. Insert earphones attached to a very light headband. Such earphones are very small and light and are attached to small insert or semi-insert tips that partially enter the ear canal. These headsets can be worn for several hours if properly fitted. For the insert tips, this usually means custom fitting for each person because ear canals vary widely in size and shape. Even then, the tips might be unsatisfactory medically (they might start or aggravate infections in the ear canal) or physically dangerous (a blow to the earphone might damage the ear). On the other hand, this headset gives high intelligibility with low electrical power, especially if covered with an earmuff or rigid helmet.

Design Recommendations

The following recommendations should be observed when designing headsets:

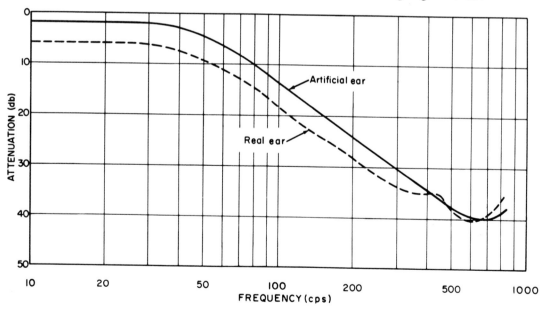

1. Connect earphones to operate out of phase. Slightly better intelligibility can be obtained in ambient noise when the earphones are so connected. "Out of phase" means that the diaphragm of one earphone moves toward the center of the listener's head while the diaphragm of the other earphone moves away from it. This is just the opposite of the normal way of connecting earphones. Electrically, it is quite simple. The improvement in intelligibility, relative to that obtained with in-phase connection of the earphones, is only about 5%, but even this amount can be helpful.

2. Delay the speech signal reaching one ear. Delaying the speech signal delivered to one ear relative to the signal delivered to the other ear by 500 μsec results in about the same degree of improvement as the out-of-phase connection. The effect of the two (time-delay and phase-reversal) are obviously related, but their joint effect on speech intelligibility is not known.

3. Use binaural rather than monaural headsets if the listeners will be in intense noise. Single-ear listening (e.g., the common telephone) is quite satisfactory under good listening conditions, but somewhat less effective than binaural listening under conditions of noise stress or signal distortion. The advantage of binaural over monaural listening is the superior discrimination achieved with two ears and not, as might be thought, to the elimination of masking of the speech heard through the telephone ear by ambient noise heard through the open ear. Noise reaching the uncovered ear has little or no effect on the intelligibility of speech delivered to the covered ear, unless the noise level at the uncovered ear is 40 or 50 db higher than the noise level at the covered ear. Even then, the effect probably is not truly an interaural interaction, but appears to be caused by transmission of the noise through the tissues of the head to the covered ear.

4. Provide that the talker's side tone meets certain characteristics. The signal from the talker's microphone is usually returned to the talker via his earphones. This feedback signal, mentioned earlier, is called the side tone. The following are some ways in which the talker's speech can be manipulated by varying the side tone:

a. Talkers usually adjust their vocal effort (speech intensity) in such a way as to compensate, within limits, for changes in the level of the side tone. The more intense the side tone, the less intense the talker's speech. To maintain a high signal-to-noise ratio, keep the side tone weak. Talkers tend to speak slowly when the side tone level is low because of the increased vocal effort required to restore "normal" side tone—especially in high-noise conditions.

b. Talkers tend to increase their vocal effort somewhat and to enunciate their speech more precisely and at a slower rate if the side-tone signal is passed through either a high-pass or a low-pass filter before the signal enters the binaural headset. Duplex binaural headsets in which only one channel is either high-pass or low-pass filtered usually yield even more intelligible speech than simple binaural headsets.

c. Talkers tend to increase their level of effort and to talk at a slower rate if the electric side tone is slightly delayed. A delay of 0.05 sec can be introduced intentionally to produce this effect.

4.5 Special System Requirements

Special requirements often enter in the design of communication systems, and these can pose unusual problems. Some examples of special requirements are the following:

a. The listener must receive messages from several sources at the same time.

b. The talker and/or listener must be at high altitudes.

c. The talker and/or listener must be submerged in water.

d. The talker must communicate through a mask.

4.5.1 *Multichannel listening*

Voice communications from many outlying stations might have to funnel into one central position for decision and action. For example, an air-traffic controller might have to receive voice communications from several aircraft, from other controllers, and from his supervisor, or a taxi dispatcher might have to receive incoming messages from several roving taxicabs and from customers calling in for cabs.

A listener cannot listen to two simultaneous, nonredundant messages and receive the full content of both messages. He has to switch his attention from one message to the other—with some loss of information in both messages—or pay attention to one message and ignore the other. Listening to two messages at once is more complicated than listening to speech in noise because of the semantic similarity between the messages. The listener might start out listening to one message and end up listening to the other.

DESIGN RECOMMENDATIONS

If the system cannot be designed so that only one message will be heard at a time, do the following:

1. Use a separate loudspeaker for each speech channel, and locate the loudspeakers in such a way that they are at different angles from the listener or listeners (see Fig. 4-36).

2. If there are two speech channels, feed one channel into one ear and the other channel into the other ear so that the listener can switch his attention to one channel or the other.

3. Use frequency-selective filters to give the signals heard through the several channels characteristic timbres (see Fig. 4-36). If there are three channels involved, leave one channel unfiltered, use a high-pass filter (with 1,000-cps cutoff) in the second channel, and use a low-pass filter (with 2,500-cps cutoff) in the third channel.

4. Use a visual signal to show which channel is in use.

5. If feasible, use a message-storage device to record and store on magnetic tape all incoming messages (see Chapter 3). Use a separate recording channel for each communication channel, and set up switching arrangements that will allow the listener to review the messages that have been received. In addition, after a period of time, the oldest messages on the tape should be automatically erased to make recording space available for new incoming messages.

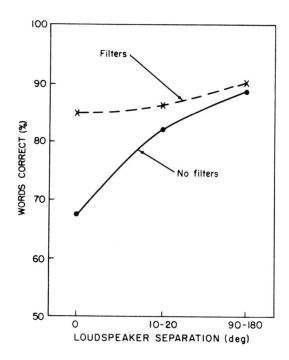

4-36 Effect of angular separation of loudspeakers on multichannel speech intelligibility. Comparing dashed curve with solid curve shows effect of inserting low-pass filter in channel feeding one loudspeaker and high-pass filter in channel feeding the other (Spieth, et al., 1954)

§ 4.5.1

4.5.2 *Communication at high altitudes*

Personnel and communication equipment in unpressurized or partially pressurized aircraft will be subjected to low ambient pressures when the aircraft fly at high altitudes (see Chapter 10). The human voice and earphones and loudspeakers become less efficient generators of sound, and microphones become somewhat less sensitive at certain frequencies, as the ambient pressure is reduced. These effects become appreciable at altitudes above 10,000 ft.

The effect on talker, microphone, and earphones of reducing the ambient pressure from that at sea level to that at 40,000 ft is shown in Fig. 4-37 (Kryter, 1944). The upper solid curve represents the overall acoustic-pressure response of the interphone as a function of frequency when tested at sea level.

The dotted curve in Fig. 4-37 is the overall acoustic response when the microphone-mask combination was tested at 40,000 ft while the other components of the interphone remained at sea level. This curve reflects the changes in sensitivity of the microphone as a function of high altitude. The dashed curve is the overall acoustic response with the entire interphone calibrated at 40,000 ft.

The above three curves were obtained with a constant input signal. The fourth, the lower solid curve, shows the drop in voice level to be expected when the speaker, wearing an A-14 oxygen mask at 40,000 ft, talks with the same effort that he would use at sea level.

It can be seen from Fig. 4-37 that the sound-pressure level of speech reaching the listener's ears is reduced about 25 db if the effort used by the talker and the gain of the speech amplifier are kept constant. The average talker cannot raise his voice enough to compensate fully for this decrease in level.

DESIGN RECOMMENDATIONS

To maintain intelligibility nearly equal to that available from a given system at sea level, do the following:

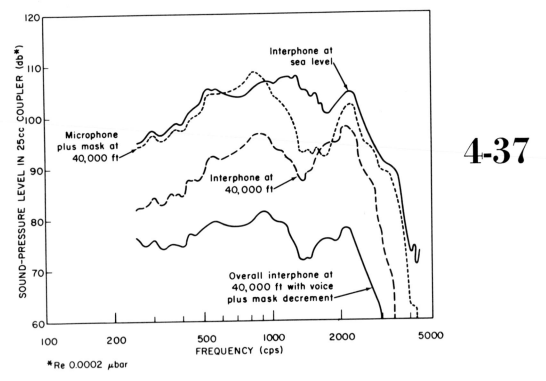

4-37

1. Use a pressure-sensitive device to adjust the gain of the amplifier as the ambient pressure changes.

2. Use microphones and earphones designed to have uniform frequency-response characteristics at all altitudes in which they are expected to operate.

4.5.3 *Underwater communication*

Frogmen and skin divers sometimes need to speak to one another when underwater. Also, a person underwater outside a vessel might need to communicate with people inside the vessel. In both cases, communication is beset by problems of listening and talking underwater.

LISTENING UNDERWATER

Hearing underwater is limited by the following factors:

a. Reverberation of sound caused by reflections off the bottom, surface, and such gradients and discontinuities in the water as are due to thermal and salinity conditions, micro-organisms, fish, etc.

b. Noises made by movement of the water, fish, vessels, and the listener himself.

c. An increased absolute threshold of hearing. (The threshold is raised about 40 db by the impedance mismatch between the water and the air in the middle ear.)

Design Recommendations

When designing a speech-communication system for listening underwater, the following recommendations should be observed:

1. Use an amplifying system and an underwater transducer (loudspeaker) to compensate for the increased threshold of the listener's hearing.

2. Use a directional receiver to discriminate against reverberation and noise that comes from directions other than the talker's.

§ 4.5.4

TALKING UNDERWATER

The problem of talking underwater is more difficult than the problem of listening underwater for the following reasons:

a. Because speech is generated by exhaling air, bubbles are emitted when a person talks, and the noise accompanying these tends to mask his speech. Consequently, the listener might hear little else but vowel sounds mixed with bubble noise.

b. If a diver has to hold the end of his air hose between his teeth, he cannot move his jaw or close his lips freely when he speaks. Consequently, his pronunciation of consonants is generally poor, and he cannot use the sounds "b" (as in bat) and "p" (as in pat) at all.

Design Recommendations

The following recommendations should be observed when designing for underwater talking:

1. The diver should be provided with an air-exhaust tube that is long enough to delay the release of the air bubble into the water until after the word or phrase is completed.

2. The diver should be instructed to say only one word or phrase at a time and to wait before saying the next word until the bubble that goes along with the previous word escapes and the bubble noise dies away.

3. Restrict the vocabulary for underwater communication to a few words, keep the messages simple, and devise a special code that uses only vowel sounds.

4. If possible, provide the diver with a full-face mask that contains a microphone connected to an amplifier and transducer (underwater loudspeaker).

4.5.4 *Communication through masks*

Speech communication is often of great importance in situations that require the wear-

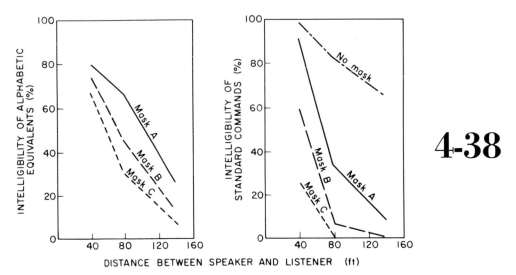

4-38

ing of gas masks. Gas masks are typically so constructed that the wearer must talk through the mask, whether face-to-face or to a microphone. The distortion and attenuation introduced by the mask reduces the intelligibility of the speech and the distances over which it can be heard. The effects of various masks on speech intelligibility are illustrated in Fig. 4-38 (Egan, et al., 1943).

Most of the sound transmission through ordinary masks takes place through the exhaust valve, especially when it is opened by exhaled air. To improve the sound transmission and divorce it from the valve action, it is desirable to equip masks with diaphragms especially designed to transmit speech. Masks A and B of Fig. 4-38 were equipped with such diaphragms; mask C was not.

4.6 Factors Affecting the Performance of Communication Systems

The performance of a speech-communication system depends to a great extent on the size of the message set or vocabulary that is used, the degree of standardization of the messages, and the familiarity of personnel using the system with the messages and with the equipment. Heavy information loads and poorly trained personnel are as hard on system performance as are noise and distortion.

4.6.1 Personnel selection and training

The selection and training of personnel to man a system often involve procedures and policies over which the engineers who are responsible for the design of the system have

210

no control. It is imperative, therefore, that design engineers know how greatly the selection and training of operators can affect the performance of a communication system. For example, it has been found that there are large differences in fundamental intelligibility among individual talkers and listeners, and these differences tend to persist even through practice and training. Proper training, however, can produce significant improvements.

4.6.2 *Language factors*

Intelligibility, and, hence, performance, is greatly affected by the language, by the nature of the message, and by the set of messages that is sent over the speech-communication system. Important language factors can be considered under the following headings:

a. The information content of individual words.

b. Sentence or phrase structure.

c. The size of the message set.

d. Situational constraints.

e. The interaction of the characteristics of certain speech sounds.

INFORMATION CONTENT OF WORDS

Other things being equal, the more frequently a word occurs in everyday usage, the more readily it is correctly identified when transmitted over a speech-communication system. As Fig. 4-39 shows, the length of the word also influences its intelligibility—the longer the word, the more readily it is correctly identified. This is because the listener is able to "make out" a long word by hearing one or more portions of it, particularly if it is a familiar and probable word, whereas missing one syllable of a short word is more likely to prevent the identification of the entire word. Both frequency and length factors are strong; they can change by 10–15 db the signal-to-noise ratio required for a given level of intelligibility.

SENTENCE OR PHRASE STRUCTURE

An effect somewhat similar to word length arises as words are formed into phrases and sentences. The grammar and syntax of the phrase or sentence dictate to some extent what words must go with other words. Listeners get the meaning of a meaningful message at a signal-to-noise ratio, or with a distortion, that would prevent the correct reception of an equal number of unrelated words. This fact is reflected in Fig. 4-5; under conditions that permit correct reception of about 75% of PB words, over 95% of test sentences are correctly understood.

THE SIZE OF THE MESSAGE SET

Related to the frequency and familiarity factors is the size of the set or ensemble of messages—the words, phrases or sentences that will be used in a given operational situation. Speech intelligibility is greatly dependent on the size of the message set; the smaller the set, other factors being equal, the easier it is for the listener and talker to communicate.

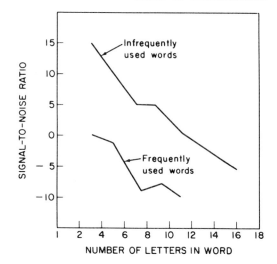

4-39 Relation between length of word (number of letters) and signal-to-noise ratio required for 50% intelligibility. Infrequently used words require higher signal-to-noise ratio than frequently used words when word length is held constant (Howes, 1957)

To take advantage of limited message-set size, both the talker and the listener must study the set and know it thoroughly. Radio-telephone procedure for aircraft control offers an example of deliberately setting limits to the messages and message forms that will be used for communication. The set includes digits and short, well-known phrases such as "LaGuardia tower: this is American 625 over Perth Amboy. Request landing instructions." These short phrases are highly stereotyped, and, when what the talker sends conforms to the listener's expectations, they are more intelligible than words in sentences.

The progressive reduction in the size of the message set from the domain of conversation to the domain of operational communication is illustrated diagrammatically in Fig. 4-40 (Frick and Sumby, 1952). The uncertainty of alphabetical sequences in words is assigned a value of unity, and the uncertainty of control-tower communications is seen to be only 0.04 in this study.

SITUATIONAL CONSTRAINTS

Although the effects of situational constraints on the efficiency of speech communication have not been fully quantified, we do know that the performance of many communication systems is influenced by the "extra" information that is contained in *a priori* knowledge of various aspects of the prevailing situation. For example, a pilot approaching a control tower to land is helped in the operational context to "hear" and understand messages concerned with landing instructions. The particular arrangement of the air field, the wind conditions, and the time of day, all contribute.

Table 4-19 Phonetic Symbols

Key word	Dictionary symbol	BTL[1] symbol	IPA[2] symbol
t oo l	$\overline{oo}$	ū	u
t o ne	ō	ō	o or ou
t a lk	ä	ó	ɔ
t a r	à	a	a
t a pe	ā	ā	e or ei
t ea m	ē	ē	i
t oo k	oo	u	ʊ
t o n	u	o	ʌ
t a p	a	á	æ
t e n	e	e	ɛ
t i p	i	i	I
t i me	ī	ī	aI
t ow n	ou	ou	aʊ
t oi l	oi	oi	ɔI
f e w	ū	ew	ju
w oo	w	w	w
y ou	y	y	j
h ow	h	h	h
l ate	l	l	l
r ate	r	r	r
m ate	m	m	m
n ate	n	n	n
si ng	ng	ng	ŋ
v oice	v	v	v
f un	f	f	f
z ero	z	z	z
s it	s	s	s
th en	th	th	ð
th in	th	th	θ
a z ure	zh	zh	ʒ
sh ip	sh	sh	ʃ
b at	b	b	b
p at	p	p	p
d en	d	d	d
t en	t	t	t
j udge	j	j	dʒ
ch ur ch	ch	ch	tʃ
g oat	g	g	g
c oat	k	k	k

[1] Bell Telephone Laboratories.
[2] International Phonetic Association

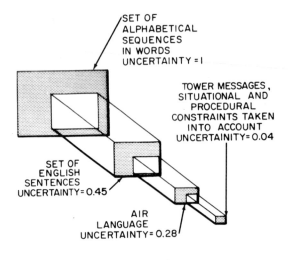

SET OF
ALPHABETICAL
SEQUENCES
IN WORDS
UNCERTAINTY = 1

TOWER MESSAGES,
SITUATIONAL AND
PROCEDURAL
CONSTRAINTS TAKEN
INTO ACCOUNT
UNCERTAINITY = 0.04

SET OF
ENGLISH
SENTENCES
UNCERTAINTY = 0.45

AIR
LANGUAGE
UNCERTAINTY = 0.28

4-40

§ 4.6.2

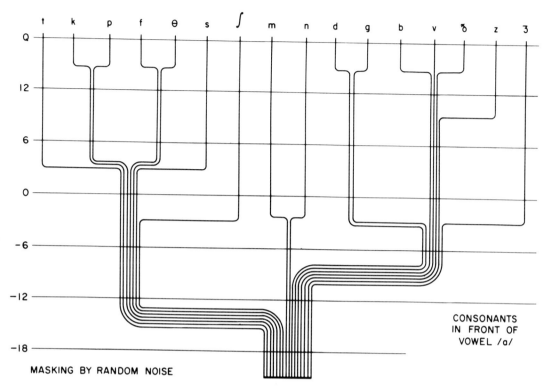

CONSONANTS
IN FRONT OF
VOWEL /a/

MASKING BY RANDOM NOISE

INTERACTION OF SPEECH SOUNDS

The interaction between the characteristics of certain speech sounds and the given communication system or environment usually is not considered in the "engineering" of a language for specific systems. Usually, the design engineer must design his system for use with normal, everyday speech. Situations can arise, however, in which the noise level is so great, the time available for communication so brief, or the requirement for communication so critical that it is necessary to specify the elemental speech sounds to be used in building a set of messages.

Fundamental Speech Sounds and Symbols

Before considering relevant data, we must distinguish and identify the fundamental speech sounds, and the individual letters of the alphabet are not adequate for this purpose. Most letters of the alphabet can be pronounced in any of several ways depending on

the words in which they appear. For example, compare the sounds of the "a" in "apply," "may," and "any." To deal with this situation, phoneticians have devised a special set of phonetic symbols to refer to the basic sounds used in spoken language. Table 4-19 (Fletcher, 1953) lists and defines, by "key" words, these phonetic symbols and relates them to the dictionary symbols (letters with diacritical marks).

Confusion Among Speech Sounds

Figure 4-41 (Miller and Nicely, 1955) shows a "tree of confusions" characteristic of a wide-band communication system that is limited only by random background noise at the signal-to-noise (S/N) ratios indicated at the left-hand side of the illustration. Note the following:

a. At S/N = −18 db, all consonants are confused with one another.

b. At S/N = −12 db, the voiced consonants (m, n, d, g, b, v, ð, z, and ʒ) are confused

§ 4.6.2

with one another, and the unvoiced consonants (t, k, p, f, θ, s, and ʃ) are confused with one another, but the consonants in the first group are seldom confused with those in the second group.

c. At S/N = −6 db, although the "m" and "n" are confused with each other, they are clearly distinguishable from the other consonants.

d. At S/N = 0 db, there are seven groups of easily recognizable consonants.

e. At S/N = 12 db, all of the consonants are readily distinguished.

Figures 4-42 and 4-43 (Miller and Nicely, 1955) show similar trees of confusion for communication channels in which there is high-pass and low-pass filtering, respectively. In general, the wider the spectrum passed, the greater the intelligibility of individual sounds.

Conversely, the greater the amount of filtering (either high-pass or low-pass), the more frequent the confusions.

Although consonants carry most of the intelligibility of speech, vowels represent most of the measurable acoustical energy. Each vowel can be specified and recognized fairly well on the basis of two of the frequency intervals (formants) that contain the greatest energy. Figure 4-44 shows the first and second formants of the English vowels. Note that confusions often occur between I and U, ε and ʌ, and æ and a; that they frequently occur between i and u and æ and ɔ; and that they sometimes occur between ε and I, ε and U, ε and a, etc. Thus, if intelligibility depends on the correct recognition of certain vowels, vowels should be chosen that are not interconnected in Fig. 4-44.

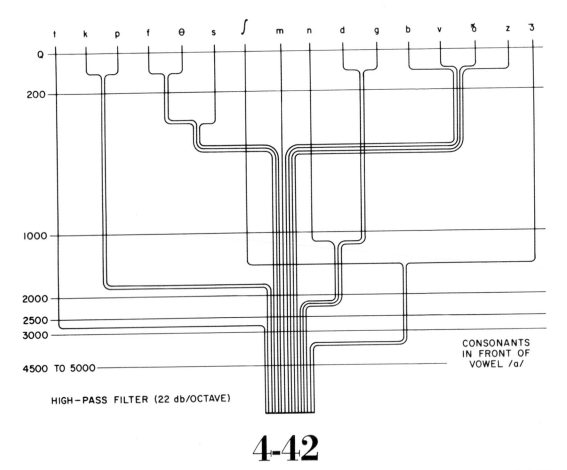

4-42

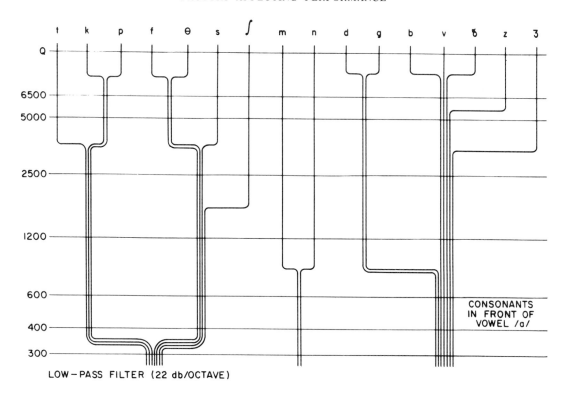

LOW—PASS FILTER (22 db/OCTAVE)

CONSONANTS
IN FRONT OF
VOWEL /a/

Word-Spelling Alphabets

Under very noisy conditions, or over extremely bad audio circuits, words can be almost wholly unintelligible. But, even in such

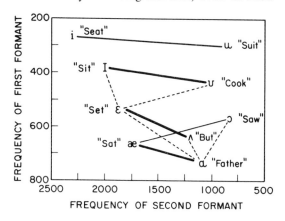

4-44 Locations of English vowels on plot of frequency of first formant versus frequency of second formant. Confusions tend to occur among vowel sounds that are interconnected by solid heavy lines (Miller and Nicely, 1955)

extreme circumstances, communication still can be maintained by spelling the words out with the aid of a word-spelling alphabet. This technique works and works well. Its chief disadvantage is that it is extremely slow.

The word-spelling alphabet given in Table 4-20 is used by the International Civil Aeronautics Organization and the U. S. Armed Forces. It is the product of extensive research and is designed to yield high intelligibility when used by talkers and listeners of any nationality represented in NATO (North Atlantic Treaty Organization).

DESIGN RECOMMENDATIONS

The use of standard phrases or words can mean the difference between poor communication and good communication. Standard phraseologies provide a margin of safety for emergency conditions if there are a sufficient number of words and phrases in the message set to deal with such emergencies. Nevertheless, the designer should place emphasis first

215

Table 4-20 International Word-Spelling Alphabet *

A—Alpha	N—November
B—Bravo	O—Oscar
C—Charlie	P—Papa
D—Delta	Q—Quebec
E—Echo	R—Romeo
F—Foxtrot	S—Sierra
G—Golf	T—Tango
H—Hotel	U—Uniform
I—India	V—Victor
J—Juliet	W—Whiskey
K—Kilo	X—X-Ray
L—Lima	Y—Yankee
M—Mike	Z—Zulu

* Moser and Bell, 1955.

on so designing the communication system that it will provide adequate intelligibility without the need of a special language or voice procedure. A special language or voice procedure should be used only as a supplement to the best possible equipment design.

Five general rules for building up standard words and phrases for communication purposes are listed as follows, in order from most to least important:

1. Provide context for critical words by embedding them in phrases or sentences. This is a technique many people use in ordinary telephone conversations. Under noisy conditions, the word "fire," by itself, occasionally might be confused with "tire," "dire," "mire," "sire," or "pyre." It is much less likely to be misheard in a sentence like "Your house is on fire."

2. Use familiar words rather than unfamiliar ones. Familiar words are much more likely to be heard correctly than unfamiliar ones. The "Teacher's Word Book" (Thorndike and Lorge, 1944) lists the 30,000 most common English words in order of frequency of use.

3. Use as small a total vocabulary as possible. The fewer the alternatives, the greater the intelligibility. If the listener knows that a critical word can be one of only eight possible words, for example, he is more likely to hear it correctly than if the word is one of a larger vocabulary.

4. To obtain words that are easily distinguished, select polysyllables; the more syllables in a word, the more likely it is to be heard correctly. Although "no" and "yes" are familiar words, they are frequently misheard when they are spoken by persons with certain regional accents and drawls. On the other hand, the words "negative" and "affirmative," although less often used, are much less likely to be misunderstood.

5. Avoid words that contain sounds that are easily confused.

4.6.3 *Feedback to the talker*

An important requirement in the design of communication systems is that the system should provide feedback to the talker. Feedback is important for the following reasons:

a. The talker can be sure that the system is operating properly. An example of such feedback information is the dial tone on a telephone; it tells the caller that the system is prepared to accept his call. The ringing sound after a number has been dialed tells the caller that the system has accepted and is processing the call.

b. The talker can be sure that the listener is receiving the message. Without feedback, the talker cannot be sure that his message is being received.

c. The talker can be more confident that his message is correctly understood. In critical cases, it might even be necessary to have the listener repeat the message back to the talker to insure that it is received correctly.

d. The talker can be sure that appropriate action is taken. An example of this type of feedback information is the helmsman advising the officer of the deck that he has carried out a command to change bearing.

In addition, there are other advantages in two-way communication. For instance, the morale of both talker and listener tends to be higher, particularly in emergency situations. Also, problems can be solved faster and better, particularly if separate pieces of information are being held at different stations, and strategic and tactical decisions can be arrived at more quickly and effectively.

5

man-machine dynamics

THIS CHAPTER identifies and discusses the factors affecting human performance in tracking and in vigilance (watchkeeping) tasks and makes design recommendations for improving the performance of man-machine systems with which these tasks are carried out.

Whenever these recommendations are the direct outgrowth of published research, the appropriate studies are cited. The chapter is divided into the following three sections: The Closed-Loop Manual-Tracking System, Human Dynamics, and Machine Dynamics.

5.1 *The Closed-Loop Manual-Tracking System*

A *closed*-loop system is one in which information about an output is fed back to an earlier stage in the system. In an *open*-loop system, no such feedback is present. Manual tracking is the process by which an operator continually attempts to minimize some meas-

ure of the difference between a desired and an actual system output. In a manual-tracking system, the operator acts, primarily, as an "error corrector," and, as such, his task is comparable to that of a servomechanism.

This similarity between manual tracking and the servomechanism has led to the practice of describing operator performance in manual-tracking systems by using servo terminology. Thus, operator *input* is the informa-

This chapter was drafted by Jerome H. Ely, Hugh M. Bowen, and Jesse Orlansky of Dunlap and Associates, Inc.

217

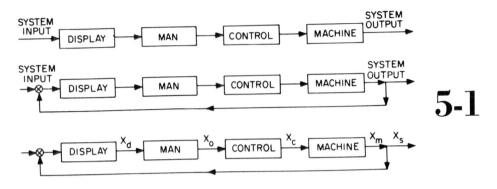

5-1

tion that is received (sensed) by the operator, and operator *output* is the action taken by the operator.

Figure 5-1 shows diagrams of open-loop and closed-loop man-machine systems. In both kinds of systems, there is a display that usually portrays (X_d) continuously changing information. The operator senses this information, ordinarily through his eyes or ears, and moves (X_o) his control or controls accordingly. The output of the operator's control (X_c) produces some action in the machine. The output of the machine (X_m) is the system output (X_s). As used here, "machine" refers to all the components in the system other than the display, the man, and the controls that the man operates. In the closed-loop system, information about the performance of the system is fed back to the display; the display, therefore, combines information about the system input and the system output.

5.1.1 *Pursuit and compensatory tracking*

In both pursuit and compensatory tracking, the operator's task is to match an actual output with a desired (or ordered) output. The two kinds of tracking differ only in the type of display used with each. Although not covered as a separate topic in this section, a single display can be a combination of both pursuit and compensatory displays.

THE PURSUIT DISPLAY

A pursuit display contains two moving elements: one representing an actual output (X_m) and the other the desired output (X_d). There is no separate indicator representing error (ϵ); error is estimated from the difference between the elements representing actual and desired output $(\epsilon = X_m - X_d)$.

The circular dial in Fig. 5-2 is an example of a pursuit display. It has a moving pointer that indicates the actual output and a moving index on its periphery that indicates the desired output. The operator's task is to keep the pointer on the index.

THE COMPENSATORY DISPLAY

A compensatory display contains only one moving element, representing error (ϵ), the difference between an actual output (X_m) and the desired output (X_d). The vertical dial in Fig. 5-2 is an example of a compensatory display. It has one moving index that indicates error on a fixed scale. The operator's task is to keep the index centered on the display at the zero mark (the point at which

PURSUIT
DISPLAY

COMPENSATORY
DISPLAY

218

error is zero, i.e., where the actual output is the desired output). Because many compensatory displays have a single index and a zero mark, a compensatory display is sometimes called a null indicator.

ANTICIPATION IN TRACKING

A pursuit display permits the operator to see a time-varying desired output (e.g., target course) and an actual output and to estimate the rate and acceleration of each. From such information, he can estimate where his desired output will be in the future, i.e., anticipate future conditions, and he can initiate corrective actions slightly before they are required. Thus, his responses are no longer limited by his own reaction time (see article 5.2.3). In general, his actions are determined, not merely by the immediate momentary state of the display, but, also, by the continuing information that is available.

A compensatory display, on the other hand, provides information about error only. Perfect tracking with such a display would result in *no* movement of the movable element. When the movable element does depart from the zero-error position, however, the operator cannot tell whether the error is caused by a change in the desired output, a change in the actual output brought about by his control movement, or a change in both. Thus, he cannot anticipate the future state of the desired output.

With training, the operator can learn the relation between his control movement and the moving display element, and, by mentally subtracting actual output from the error appearing on the display, he can estimate the change in desired output. This is a difficult task, however, especially for higher-order systems (see article 5.3.1).

Thus, as far as anticipation is concerned, a pursuit display is superior to a compensatory display in helping the operator to learn the nature of the desired output and to anticipate future conditions. For higher-order control systems, the pursuit display is better at helping the operator learn the dynamics of the machine because, with a pursuit display, he

can always observe the relation between his control motion and the machine output.

In addition, an inexperienced operator might be unaware of the lags present in the tracking system. In correcting a very simple input (see article 5.2.2) with a compensatory display, he might generate his own errors without realizing it and "track himself" for some time. Such a condition cannot arise with a pursuit display.

5.1.2 *Factors affecting display selection*

The following factors affect the kind of display (i.e., pursuit or compensatory) that should be selected:
   a. The complexity of the output.
   b. The dynamics of the machine.
   c. The rate of the movable element.
   d. The clarity of the background.
   e. Whether or not aided tracking is used.
   f. The size of the display.

OUTPUT COMPLEXITY

When there is only one desired output (e.g., maintaining a given heading), both kinds of display are equally good. The superiority of the pursuit display in helping the operator anticipate future conditions is not needed because the desired output is not time-varying. As the desired output increases in complexity, however, pursuit displays become increasingly better than compensatory displays because the output interacts with machine dynamics (Chernikoff, et al., 1956; Poulton, 1952; and Senders and Cruzen, 1952).

MACHINE DYNAMICS

With position control (see article 5.3.1), pursuit displays are superior as long as the desired output (or input) is time-varying. With rate control, pursuit displays are superior except when the cutoff frequency is about 0.1 cps or less (Chernikoff and Taylor, 1957). With higher-order control systems, pursuit displays are superior, and their superiority is directly related to the frequency of the desired output (i.e., the higher the frequency, the more superior is the pursuit display).

MOVABLE-ELEMENT RATE

When the movable elements of the display (e.g., pointers) move very slightly or slowly, the operator's ability to estimate rate of movement is poor. Under such conditions, he cannot accurately predict future positions, and the superiority of a pursuit display is nullified (Senders, 1953). Slow or slight rates of movement can result from a desired output that changes very slowly or from a display that is so small that even large output changes are represented by small pointer movements. Thus, when the display must be very small or when change in desired output is very slow, pursuit displays tend to lose their superiority.

BACKGROUND CLARITY

The prime advantage of a pursuit display results from the operator's seeing *two* moving indicators. If the display background was completely unstructured so that the two pointers were the only visible objects (in a darkened room), the operator could easily observe relative movement but would have difficulty in discerning whether the first, the second, or both indicators were moving. This difficulty would disappear if he also could see a stationary structured background behind the indicators. For a pursuit display to be effective, therefore, the background should be sufficiently well defined that the operator can easily observe the movement of each indicator relative to the background (Senders, 1953).

AIDED TRACKING

The value of an aided-tracking system (see article 5.3.2) is that the machine automati-

cally supplies the proper derivative terms when the operator corrects positional errors. Thus, with aided tracking, the operator performs best by making his corrective response proportional to error only. This is his normal mode of response with compensatory displays. With pursuit displays, however, he usually "anticipates" and responds to both error and error rate, which is undesirable in an aided system. Here, a compensatory display is best.

DISPLAY SIZE

A pursuit display normally must show the entire range of desired and actual outputs. When the range is limited or when high precision is not required, the size of the display is not a critical matter. When the range is great or when precision requirements are high, however, then either the display must be enlarged considerably, both the actual and desired output must have more than one moving element each (e.g., a counter-pointer combination), or each output step must be represented by a very small distance on the display.

A compensatory display normally does not have to show the entire range of outputs, but only those of immediate concern to the operator. Thus, it can display output steps in an enlarged form without increasing the total size of the display. Also, if there is a nonlinear relationship between control and display, a nonlinear scale can be used (see Chapter 2). For example, for submarine depth, the display need only show the depth range within which the submarine is operating, and a nonlinear scale is an effective display for maintaining depth within the required accuracy (see Fig. 5-3). In this situation, however, some means must be provided for setting the desired depth into the display system.

5.1.3 *Selecting the display*

As was indicated in the preceding article, neither a pursuit nor a compensatory display is always superior to the other. The one to use depends on the requirements of the specific task at hand. The general conditions under which each should be used are discussed in the following paragraphs.

To be effective, a pursuit display should be sufficiently large, and the background sufficiently structured, that the movement of both indicators can be seen easily. If this requirement is satisfied, pursuit displays should be used when any of the following conditions is present:

a. The course contains high frequencies.

b. It is a zero-order control system (see article 5.3.1).

c. The operator must know the actual output and not just the error.

Either a pursuit or a compensatory display can be used when the following conditions are present:

a. The course is simple.

b. Machine dynamics (see section 5.3) are simple.

c. The operator needs to know only the error and not the actual output.

A compensatory display should be used when either of the following conditions is present:

a. The system is quickened or aided (see section 5.3).

b. The display must be kept small, but the output range is large and/or the precision requirements are high.

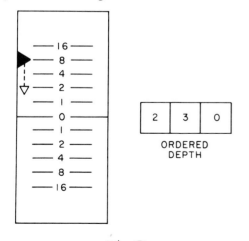

5-3

5.1.4 *Intermittency in the display of information*

In certain situations an operator receives information from a display intermittently rather than continuously. This article will discuss the causes of such intermittency, its effects, and design recommendations for minimizing these effects.

CAUSES OF INTERMITTENCY

Intermittency as a display condition can result from the nature of the system (from the method of instrumentation), from the requirements of the task, from operator behavior that is undesirable and is not required by the task, or from some combination of these three causes. Each of these causes is discussed in the paragraphs that follow.

The Nature of the System

In some systems, the display presents input information intermittently. A very common example is a PPI radar scope with a slow sweep rate and a low persistence phosphor (see Chapter 2). The picture that is painted on the scope during one sweep will decay before the next sweep.

In other systems, the input information is received directly from the external world by the operator without requiring a special display, but the nature of the input is such that the operator only can view it intermittently. An example of this would be an aircraft being tracked visually through cloud formations.

The Requirements of the Task

In some systems, information is presented continuously, but the operator can receive it only intermittently. In one case, the operator might be required to view a number of displays. To do this, he must set up a scanning pattern that permits him to look at each display periodically but none continuously. The relatively slow operator performance found in multidisplay situations such as this one is due, partly, to the time taken up by eye movements and, partly, to the mental lags (see article 5.2.3) associated with switching attention from one display to the other, the latter being of the order of 0.2 sec (Broadbent, 1951b and 1955).

In another case, special considerations might prohibit the operator from receiving the information that is continuously available. For example, under black-out conditions, he may be allowed to light his instrument panel only at infrequent intervals and for short durations.

Undesirable Operator Behavior

Regardless of the nature of the system and the requirements of the task, the operator always is capable of behaving in an undesirable and an uncalled-for manner. Such behavior can consist in failure to pay attention, in permitting himself to be distracted by loud flashes and noises, in involuntary eye blinks, etc. The latter, eye blinks, normally occur at a rate of about one every 3 sec when a person is not attending to any task, and each blink can obscure vision up to 0.25 sec. When performing a difficult tracking task, however, operators normally inhibit their blinking (Byrnes, 1951).

THE EFFECT OF INTERMITTENCY

In general, intermittency degrades tracking performance. Although the operator probably will be unaware that he is performing more poorly (Humphrey, et al., 1953), nevertheless, as the percent of time that the operator can view his display decreases, his performance decreases in an approximately linear manner (Battig, et al., 1955). This holds true whether the intermittency results from a few relatively long looks at the display with a long period elapsing between looks or a number of relatively short looks at the display with a short period elapsing between looks. In most

cases, a system that provides for relatively short looks, with short periods between them, is preferable.

The effect of intermittency, i.e., degraded performance, is modified, however, by input complexity and display brightness. If the target moves slowly and changes course infrequently, the operator can predict its present and future positions relatively well with only occasional views of the display. As the target's course (display input) becomes more complex, however, the operator must observe the display more often to track satisfactorily. Thus, the more complex the input, the more will be the degradation in performance caused by display intermittency.

When the intermittency is caused by a flashing display, the flash duration usually

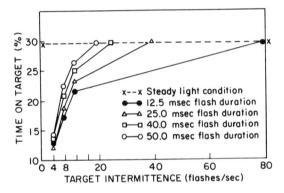

affects target brightness (Voss, 1955). When flash duration is short, brightness tends to be less than when flash duration is long. The decrease in brightness interacts with flash rate to further degrade performance, as shown in Fig. 5-4 (Senders, 1955). In general, a brightness of the order of 0.005 mL results in poorer performance than a brightness of 0.05 mL, which, in turn, results in poorer performance than a brightness of 10 mL or above (Voss, 1955).

DESIGN RECOMMENDATIONS

If the inputs shown on the display are simple, and the operator need not respond to the inputs quickly and precisely, an intermittent display will not have harmful effects on the system. But, if any display input is complex (i.e., has high rates and frequent changes in direction), and the operator must track with a high degree of precision, intermittent display of this information will degrade performance. In this situation, all causes of intermittency should be eliminated.

If intermittency cannot be completely eliminated, the harmful effects of intermittent displays should be reduced by carrying out as many of the following recommendations as are possible within the restrictions set by the overall system design:

1. Anticipatory information should be provided by the display. Effective means include using a pursuit display (see article 5.1.1) and alerting devices (see article 5.2.3).

2. The brightness level of the display should be kept high (Voss, 1955).

3. Eliminate all sources of distraction.

4. When intermittency results from the operator's having to scan a number of displays, the displays should be designed and arranged to minimize the time required to view each display and to shift from one display to another. (Specific recommendations for display design and arrangement are covered in Chapters 2 and 7, respectively.)

5. The duration of each intermittent signal should be as long as possible, and the rate of presentation should be as fast as possible.

6. Aiding or quickening should be used when applicable (see articles 5.3.2 and 5.3.3).

5.2 *Human Dynamics*

5.2.1 *Human transfer functions*

For automatic, closed-loop control systems, considerable work has gone into developing mathematical descriptions of the behavior of the system and of its various components. Such descriptions permit the designer to manipulate the system conceptually rather than physically. In like manner, the description of human performance in a tracking system would save the designer the requirement of measuring such performance for the design of each new system.

Transfer functions describe such input-output relationships. Hence, a "human transfer function" would describe the operator's outputs (e.g., control movements) in a tracking task as a function of his inputs. If his behavior were "linear," it would be describable by a linear differential equation, and, most important, his response to complex inputs would be easily predictable.

"Linearity" implies that the operator's output to a complex input that is the sum of a

series of simple inputs is the sum of his responses to each of the simple inputs. This superposition of solutions is useful in that the operator's inputs can, by a Fourier analysis, be separated into a series of sine waves. Thus, if it were known how an operator tracks sine waves of all frequencies and amplitudes, his tracking performance for any complex input could be predicted (Ellson and Gilbarg, 1948).

Linear models show that the human operator performs best when his task is no more complex than that of a low-pass filter with a time lag, i.e., within a limited bandwidth of input frequencies, his output is proportional to his input but with some lag in between. But, although generally useful as approximations of human tracking behavior, linear models are somewhat incomplete in that they fail to account for the following characteristics of operator performance:

a. It varies from person to person.

b. It varies from time to time for any one person. This is due, in part, to learning and, in part, to subtle factors such as motivation, fatigue, operating instructions, etc.

c. It is affected by the total context of the situation rather than by any single input-output relationship (Ellson and Wheeler, 1949). Thus, in correcting an error, the operator's response is affected by his previous experiences in tracking as well as by the immediate error.

d. It is often uneven ("jerky"). The unevenness is, possibly, one way in which the operator receives feedback information that helps in his learning the nature of the system.

e. In tasks such as controlling aircraft pitch, trained pilots tend to initiate corrective actions for pitch-rate errors only after these errors have reached a degree far greater than threshold (i.e., far greater than the point at which the pilot is first able to detect the error), and they tend to hold their control at some fixed position, after having made a correction, until the pitch error approaches zero (Goodyear, 1952).

5.2.2 *Human responses to various inputs*

There are many different types of inputs. Typical ones include steps, ramps, and sine waves and complex inputs, which are combinations of these (see Fig. 5-5). Human responses to each type of input are described in the following paragraphs.

STEP INPUTS

Three typical responses to step inputs with position control (see article 5.3.1) are shown in Fig. 5-6. In all three, there is, first, a lag before the operator starts to move his control. Such lags are generally between 0.25 and 0.40 sec (Craik, 1948; Ellson and Hill, 1948; and Vince, 1948), but they are affected by many factors and can vary considerably. (See section 5.2.3 for more detailed coverage.)

Following this initial lag, the operator takes an additional period of time to move his control to the desired position. His first movement (called "primary movement," "gross

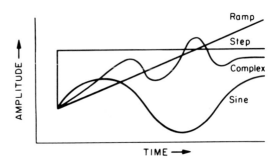

adjustment" or "slewing") might bring him exactly to the desired position (A in Fig. 5-6). Unless he is highly practiced, however, he usually either overshoots (B) or undershoots (C) and must, therefore, make a second movement (called "fine adjustment" or "secondary movement") to reach the desired position (Craig, 1949).

Factors Affecting Response

Performance in correcting a step input, like all control movements, is affected by control design. Among the important factors in design are the kind and amount of resistance and the amount and direction of control and display movement. (These factors are covered in detail in Chapter 6.) Other factors affecting human response to step inputs are amplitude and presentation rate.

Amplitude. Although the correction of large step inputs takes longer than that of small step inputs (because the control must be displaced a greater amount), the velocity of control movement tends to increase as the amplitude of the input increases. As the magnitude of the required corrective movement

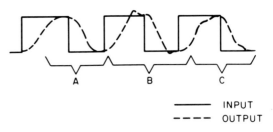

| INPUT |
| OUTPUT |

5-6

increases, the operator tends to apply more force to the control in both starting and stopping, to apply force faster, and to maintain its application over a longer period of time (Searle, 1948; Slater-Hammel and Brown, 1947; and Taylor and Birmingham, 1948).

In correcting a series of step functions of varying amplitude, operators tend to undershoot the larger errors and to overshoot the smaller ones. This "range effect" is a function of the relative amplitudes of errors and is independent of their absolute magnitudes. Thus, the operator is responding to a total situation, and any mathematical description of his input-output relationships must take into account the entire situation rather than a single input.

Presentation rate. When correcting a rapid series of step inputs, the operator's performance is affected by the rate of presentation of the inputs. Depending on the time interval between adjacent inputs, the operator might do any one of the following:

a. Respond to each input individually and at the proper time.

b. Respond to several inputs as if they comprised a single input.

c. Respond to each input individually but spread out in time.

d. Fail to respond to some inputs.

Selecting the Control Order

Figure 5-7 shows an "ideal" operator response to a step input with position control, rate control, and acceleration control (see article 5.3.1). The minimum number of control movements increases by one with each succeeding control order. When the amplitude of the step input is sufficiently small that it can be corrected by a single movement of the control, position control is better than rate control, which is better than acceleration control, etc. (Hick and Bates, 1950).

RAMP INPUTS

In tracking a ramp input, once the operator recognizes the nature of his input (i.e., real-

izes that it will continue to change at a constant rate), his performance can improve to the point where he tracks continuously with little error. Essentially, he learns to anticipate the future movement of the target and to respond in such a manner that both present and future errors will be minimized.

The "range effect," present for step inputs, is also present for ramp inputs. For steeper ramps (higher rates), the operator tends to undershoot or to lag behind; for ramps that are less steep (slower rates), he tends to overshoot or to "lead" (Young, 1951).

Theoretically, when using rate control for tracking a ramp input, the operator would make one control movement that would impart the proper rate, and, then, the machine would continue, automatically, to match input

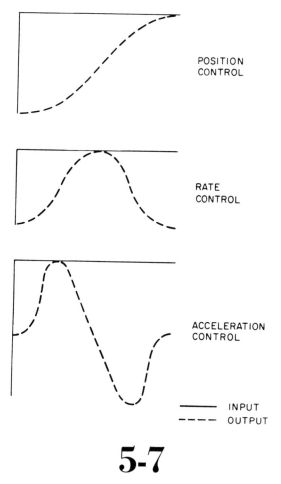

POSITION CONTROL

RATE CONTROL

ACCELERATION CONTROL

——— INPUT
- - - - OUTPUT

5-7

§ 5.2.2

with output. In practice, however, the operator has some finite reaction time that results in an initial lag. With rate control, he must impart a rate greater than that of the input to catch up, and, then, gradually slow down until the two rates match. With position control, however, he must continue to move his control at some constant rate. Also, with position control, the greater the target velocity, the greater will be the force applied by the operator to correct the resulting error. Thus, although rate control also requires frequent control adjustments, it is superior to position control for ramp inputs (Gibbs, 1954). In either case his response time is relatively independent of the slope (velocity) of the ramp (Young, 1951).

SINE-WAVE INPUTS

When tracking sine inputs (or any other repetitive input) with frequencies in the region of $\frac{1}{4}$–$\frac{1}{2}$ cps, an operator can learn to do an excellent job (Ellson and Gray, 1948; Ellson and Hill, 1947; Fitts, et al., 1953; and Noble, et al., 1953). Although there are individual differences, movements become smoother and more continuous with training, and time lags due to reaction time and move-

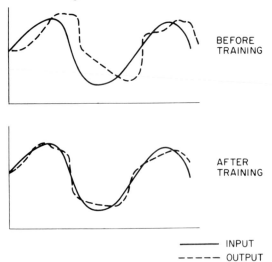

BEFORE
TRAINING

AFTER
TRAINING

——— INPUT
----- OUTPUT

5-8

ment time tend to disappear because the operator learns to anticipate the future desired positions. Shown in Fig. 5-8 is a typical example of an operator's response to a sine-wave input with position control, before and after training.

Theoretically, the operator's output in a perfect tracking performance would be the same whether he had position control or some higher-order control, with only a phase shift required for a change in control order (the curves in Fig. 5-9 indicate a perfect response to a sine input for various control orders). In practice, however, tracking a relatively high-frequency sine-wave input is considerably better with position control, and higher-order control becomes increasingly superior as frequency decreases. For frequencies between $\frac{1}{6}$ and 4 cps, with position control, time-on-target falls off as frequency increases (Noble, et al., 1955).

COMPLEX INPUTS

Responses to complex inputs are similar to those for simple inputs (Elkind, 1956). Characteristically, there is a time (phase) lag, which is reduced when the operator has information that permits him to anticipate the future behavior of the input. (For discussion of ways to present anticipatory information, see article 5.2.3 following.)

Generally, as cutoff frequency increases, performance becomes poorer (Elkind, 1953), but, for very low frequencies, rate control enables an operator to track better than does position control. As input frequency increases, however, there is a shift so that position control becomes better (Chernikoff and Taylor, 1957).

5.2.3 Human time lags

Human time lags contribute to the total operating time of man-machine systems. The importance of such lags depends on the extent to which operating time affects the overall mission of the system. For some systems,

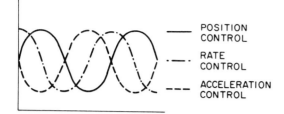

POSITION CONTROL

RATE CONTROL

ACCELERATION CONTROL

time requirements are unimportant, provided that the assigned tasks are carried out with the required degree of precision (for example, the calibration of delicate measuring devices). In other systems, however, total operating time is critical for the success of the mission, and human time lags can become very important and, on occasion, the determining factor of the mission's success.

An example of this latter situation would be the following. As an aircraft comes out of a cloud, its pilot sees another aircraft approaching him on a collision course, and, under some conditions, the approximate times involved in his taking corrective action can be listed as follows (Byrnes, 1951: Milton, 1947; and Strughold, 1949):

1. The pilot detects the object, and his eyes move to center and focus on it (approximate time, 0.3 sec).

2. He sees the object clearly and interprets the image (0.6 sec).

3. He selects a course of action (0.5 sec).

4. He makes a control movement (0.3 sec).

Here, a total of 1.7 sec transpires before the pilot moves the control, and then there is some additional time (aircraft-response time) before the aircraft changes its course and/or speed. If both aircraft are flying at 1,800 mph, they will approach each other at a rate of 1 mi/sec. In view of the fact that visual-detection range varies widely as a function of atmospheric and illumination conditions (see Chapter 2), a collision could occur without either pilot being able to avoid it.

ELEMENTS OF REACTION TIME

"Human time lag" is used synonymously with "reaction time" in this chapter. It is the time interval elapsing between the beginning of the signal (stimulus) and the completion of the operator's response. Hence, it includes the time required by the operator to sense the signal (sensing time), plus that required to decide what response to make (decision time), plus that required to respond (response time). Some authorities define reaction time as ending when the operator starts to make his response rather than when he finishes making it. In this chapter, reaction time includes the completion of the response.

Sensing Time

The time required to sense a signal is a function of the properties of the signal (e.g., size, intensity, duration) and of the particular sense stimulated. Under simple conditions, sensing time is a few hundredths of a second.

Response Time

The time required to respond to a signal is a function of the complexity of the response (e.g., force, displacement, and precision requirements) and of the body member being used. Very simple responses (e.g., pushing a button) involve a few hundredths of a second, but more complex responses (e.g., positioning a lever precisely) take a few tenths of a second. With the simplest tasks, i.e., where no decisions are required, the minimum reaction time resulting only from the sensing and response times is about 0.15 to 0.20 sec, depending on the senses used (pushing a button in response to a light signal: 0.18 sec).

Decision Time

Decision time varies widely, depending on the complexity of the decision to be made. When the decision is extremely simple, there is a slight increase in total reaction time (e.g., voluntary eye blinks take approximately 20% longer than involuntary ones). In general, decision time is proportional to the logarithm of the number of alternative choices.

§ 5.2.3

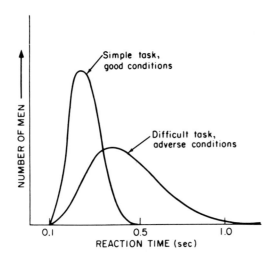

VARIATION IN REACTION TIME

No single value can adequately represent the reaction time for a given task. Given the identical task, there will be variations among individual people and, with any one person, from one time to another. These differences among people tend to increase as the task becomes more difficult or exacting and as the conditions of work become more adverse (see Fig. 5-10). Thus, the extent of variation in reaction time depends on the particular environmental conditions (see Chapter 10) as well as the person involved (Woodworth and Schlosberg, 1954).

This situation is exemplified when one considers the reaction-time variations among people of different age and sex. Older people (from the mid-fifties on) have a slightly longer reaction time than younger people (especially those in their twenties). Males have a slightly shorter and more consistent reaction time than females. Figure 5-11 (Kennedy, et al., 1952) shows the influence of age and sex on the time required to make a simple response to a visual and to an auditory signal.

FACTORS AFFECTING TIME LAGS

Some of the factors that affect human time lags can be listed as follows:

a. The sense used.

b. The characteristics of the signal.
c. The complexity of the signal.
d. The signal rate.
e. Whether or not anticipatory information is provided.
f. The response characteristics of the body-member used.

The Sense Used

Figure 5-12 (Teichner, 1954) shows the average simple reaction time for seven sense modalities. Although these times are useful in making comparisons among the senses, the times shown are not typical of those expected in practice because other factors are usually present that tend to increase reaction time. For example, in responding to a warning light, a pilot's reaction time might be much longer than 0.2 sec because he is attending to other tasks and might not see the light immediately, and, once he does see the light, the decision

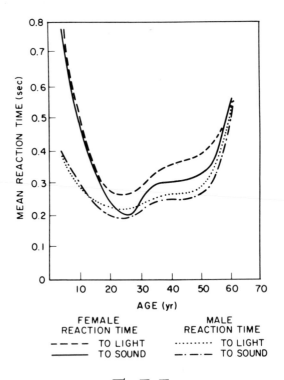

5-11

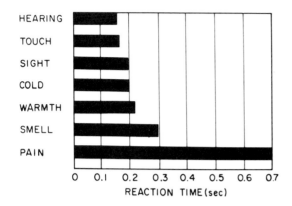

he must make is quite complex and, therefore, takes additional time.

In spite of the above precaution, however, the following conclusions can be drawn from Fig. 5-12:

a. All signal-action processes have time lags.

b. For the three senses most likely to be used (viz., hearing, touch, sight), the differences in time lags are small and probably insignificant for most, if not all, applications.

c. Smell and pain, which are physiological warning devices, have long reaction times.

The reaction time for combined signals (signals going to two or more senses simultaneously) is no shorter than for the one signal giving the fastest reaction time. In addition, it is of small value to select the sense to be used in any design situation solely on the basis of reaction time; other design considerations are nearly always more important. For example, auditory signals are poor when the ambient noise level is high; visual signals are poor when they appear outside the normal viewing area of the operator.

Signal Characteristics

Some of the signal characteristics that affect human time lags can be listed as follows:

a. Size. The larger the size of a visual signal, the faster will be the reaction time, up to some limiting value (Teichner, 1954 and Woodworth and Schlosberg, 1954).

b. Intensity. The greater the intensity of a signal, the faster will be the reaction time,

up to some limiting value. A typical curve for either light or sound is shown in Fig. 5-13 (Teichner, 1954 and Woodworth and Schlosberg, 1954).

c. Duration. The duration of a signal has very little effect on reaction time if the signal is easily visible or audible. Very short signals (0.1 sec or less) might produce longer reaction times, but their main disadvantage is the likelihood that they might not be noticed at all (Teichner, 1954).

d. Quality. Although no general relationships have been established, the quality of certain signals does evoke faster reaction times. For example, high-frequency sounds have a slightly faster reaction time than low-frequency ones (Broadbent, 1954).

e. Location. There is a faster reaction time to visual signals that strike the center rather than the periphery of the eye. That this is so can be seen from the data displayed in Fig. 5-14 (Teichner, 1954).

f. Intermittency. There is no difference in simple reaction time to flashing or steady signals. However, when one intermittent signal has to be distinguished from another by its flash rate, or when an intermittent signal has to be distinguished from a steady one, reaction time is directly related to the flash length of the intermittent signal because flashing and steady signals are indistinguishable until the flash is ended (Gerathewohl, 1954 and Gibbs, et al., 1955).

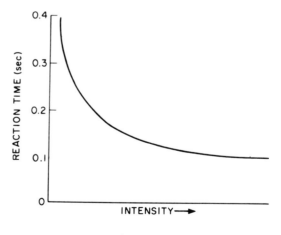

5-13

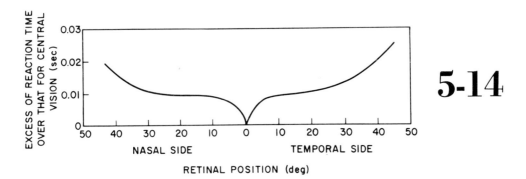

5-14

RETINAL POSITION (deg)

Signal Complexity

The two aspects of signal complexity that will be considered here are discriminability and number of signals. Reaction time is generally increased more when discriminability is reduced than when the number of signals is increased.

The discriminability of signals. In some instances the signals that are to be responded to are not perfectly discriminable (distinguishable) from each other. The act of discrimination takes time; the more difficult the discrimination, the longer the time (Crossman, 1955; Reid and Holland, 1954; and Woodworth and Schlosberg, 1954). Figure 5-15 demonstrates the change in reaction time when judging which of two lines is longer. Reaction time continues to decrease after the person is able to discriminate perfectly. Reaction time is a sensitive measure of the observer's uncertainty; when he is just barely capable of making a correct judgment, the extra effort is reflected in a longer reaction time (Woodworth and Schlosberg, 1954).

For signals that can be quantified in familiar and meaningful terms (e.g., area, size, length), the following formula approximates the reaction time (T_r) to discriminate between two signals (S_1 and S_2):

$$T_r = \frac{c}{|\log_{10}S_1 - \log_{10}S_2|} + T_m, \quad (5\text{-}1)$$

where c is a constant that varies with the type of task and the type of signal and T_m is movement time (Crossman, 1955). For a given type of task and signal, c can be determined from one or two trials, and the equation can then be used for all values of S_1 and S_2. Movement time might be difficult to separate from decision time because the decision might be continuing while the movement is being made. Thus, if the total reaction time is less than 0.2 sec, movement time should be disregarded.

The number of signals. As the number of available signals increases, the time required to respond to any one signal also increases (Hick, 1952 and Hyman, 1953). Figure 5-16

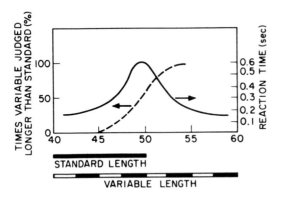

STANDARD LENGTH

VARIABLE LENGTH

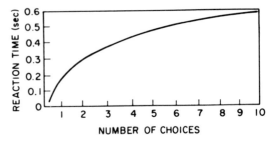

NUMBER OF CHOICES

5-16

shows how reaction time increases as the number of signals increases when each signal and response are perfectly paired and distinct, when there are no variables or distractions in the situation except the array of signals, and when the operator is practiced and well motivated. This curve is defined by the following formula (Hick, 1952):

$$T_r = c \log_{10} (n + 1) + T_m, \quad (5-2)$$

where T_r is the reaction time, n is the number of choices, c is a constant, and T_m is the movement time. For completely discriminable signals and ungraded responses, c will vary from 0.5 to 0.65, but, when practice is extremely prolonged, the value of c can approach zero.

The three important situations in which the above equation does not apply are the following:

a. When all possible signals are not equally likely to occur. Here, the most likely signals will have the shortest reaction time, and the least likely signals will have the longest (Crossman, 1953).

b. When the signals can be grouped in some meaningful way. Here, reaction time will tend to be proportional to the number of groups rather than to the number of separate signals (Krulee and Weisz, 1954).

c. When the signals are sequentially arranged. Here, once the operator learns the arrangement, reaction time will be a function of the number of signals that can occur at the next sequential step.

Signal Rate

This discussion covers only those situations in which signals are independent and are not "stored" by the operator for future response. Thus, tasks such as typing and piano playing are not considered.

"Psychological" refractory period. In tracking tasks, the maximum rate of response by the operator is 2–3/sec regardless of how high the demand rate might be. This maximum rate is due, in part, to man's inability to respond to a new signal while the previous

signal and its associated decision are being processed, i.e., man is in a "psychological" refractory period (Davis, 1948 and Welford, 1952). This differs from the "absolute" refractory period, which results from neural impulses being limited in transmission to a rate of about 1/msec.

Intervals between successive signals. When two successive signals occur within 0.1 sec, they are most likely to be treated as one signal requiring a double response, and the double response takes longer to start than a response to the first signal alone would take (see top diagram in Fig. 5-17). When the successive signals occur within about 0.1–0.5 sec of each other, each is responded to individually, but the psychological refractory period

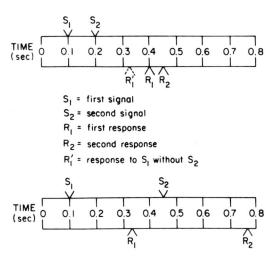

S_1 = first signal
S_2 = second signal
R_1 = first response
R_2 = second response
R_1' = response to S_1 without S_2

is present, and the second response takes appreciably more time than the first (see bottom diagram in Fig. 5-17). When the interval between successive signals is greater than about 0.5 sec, the operator is capable of responding to each without exhibiting any refractory period, but, on occasion, there is a slight facilitating effect that results in the second signal being responded to somewhat faster than the first (Davis, 1948 and Welford, 1952).

In addition to the time interval between signals, other factors affect the degree of refractoriness; precision of response, number of choices, and other factors influencing the difficulty of the decision all increase the time lag. Figure 5-18 shows the general relationship between time interval between successive signals and response time to the second signal (R_2) as compared with that of the first (R_1) under different conditions of task difficulty.

Operator behavior when overloaded. If signals arrive at a rate too fast for the operator to handle, he can keep himself current with new signals by omitting a certain percentage of responses, or he can lag behind the current signals and, by relying on his memory, hope to catch up when the arrival rate slackens. The latter strategy commonly is used to overcome peak signal densities, such as those encountered in air-traffic-control operations, but it is unsuccessful when the signal rate remains too high. Total failure often follows such a crisis, and all contact with incoming signals is lost (Conrad, 1951 and 1955b).

When any one signal source presents signals infrequently, but a number of such sources are present, chances are high that, at certain periods, the signals will be bunched in time. During these periods the operator's task is complicated further by the requirement that he switch his attention from one signal source to another, which takes a minimum of about 0.2 sec (Mackworth and Mackworth, 1956).

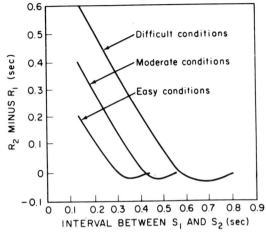

For signals that occur in succession, the action signal is also the alerting signal for the next action signal. When the interval between signals is constant, human time lags fall off until they approach zero. The most accurate performance occurs when the operator can impose rhythm on his movements; this is easiest when intervals are short (about 2 sec), but intervals should never be less than 0.3 sec (Leonard, 1954).

If the interval between the alerting and action signal is variable, the operator's reaction time is longer and more variable than it would be if the interval were fixed. Because the operator learns to expect the action signal at some average interval after the alerting signal, signals that occur distantly from the average one result in poorer performance (Klemmer, 1956).

In some systems it is possible to provide complete or partial advance information to indicate where and/or when the action signal will occur. As with regular alerting signals, the time interval between such signals that results in the best performance is from 2 to 8 sec for isolated tasks and from 0.3 to 2.0 sec for sequential tasks. As indicated above very short alerting signals (less than 0.1 sec) are worse than none (Klemmer, 1956).

For continuously varying signals, or for successive discrete signals that occur in unpredictable patterns, advance information permits the operator to prepare a response before he must make it. When responding to bunched signals coming from one or more

Anticipatory Information

A proper alerting signal preceding an action signal enables the operator to anticipate the occurrence of the action signal and reduces the time required for him to respond to it. Simple reaction times can be reduced 40% by an alerting signal (Teichner, 1954).

For a single signal, the alerting signal should come between 2 and 8 sec before the action signal, with preference given to the shorter period. If the time interval between the two signals is too long (greater than 8 sec), the operator's ability to anticipate the time of arrival of the action signal is reduced. If the time interval between the two signals is too short (less than 0.1 sec), his lag time is greater than if no alerting signal were provided (Woodworth and Schlosberg, 1954).

channels, an operator with advance information can spread his responses over time but still respond to each signal; without such information, he must respond to each signal as it appears.

Response Characteristics

There are only small differences in reaction time between the hands and feet; for simple tasks, it takes about 20% longer to respond with the feet than with the hands. Response with the preferred limb (e.g., the right hand for right-handed people) is about 3% faster than with the nonpreferred limb (Teichner, 1954). Thus, when controls must be selected entirely on the basis of speed of activation, the order of selection for right-handed operators should be the right hand, left hand, right foot, and left foot.

As the required precision of adjustment increases, control-movement time also increases, primarily because of the fine-positioning movement required. Also, if considerable force must be applied by the operator, his response time will increase. Similarly, his response time will increase when his output is the removal of a holding force (e.g., lifting his hand from a displaced, spring-centered lever).

Other Factors

Motivation. The value of improved motivation is dependent on the degree to which the operator exercises control over the system output. If he has no opportunity to benefit from practice or to exercise any judgment concerning the machine, motivating factors will have little influence. Motivation is a significant factor only when system output is considerably affected by operator performance.

In addition, the operator's motivation increases when given knowledge about good performance. This information not only aids in learning the job but, also, acts as an incentive for improved performance. Thus, feedback of such information should be provided, and the operator should get it as quickly as possible.

Practice. Human time lags tend to be reduced with practice. If the operator's speed of response, initially, is very high (e.g., about 0.2 sec), there will be little room for improvement. But if it, initially, is relatively slow (e.g., 1–2 sec), response speed will increase.

The general effects of practice depend on the task and the conditions of work. Simple tasks performed under good working conditions result in small time lags that are reduced very little with practice (see Fig. 5-19). Performance times for complex tasks, however, do show improvement, which results from a reduction in decision time, a dropping of irrelevant movements, and a refining of essential movements (Woodworth and Schlosberg, 1954). In highly complex tasks, response speed can continue to increase over a long period of time, but most of the improvement will take place during the initial practice period of days or, perhaps, weeks (Chapanis, et al., 1949).

When the same signal occurs at a constant rate, with practice, the operator can learn to

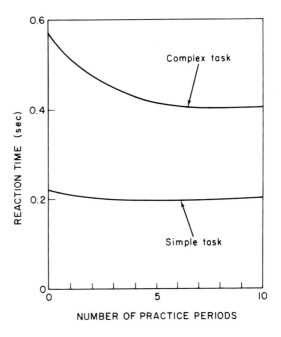

NUMBER OF PRACTICE PERIODS

5-19

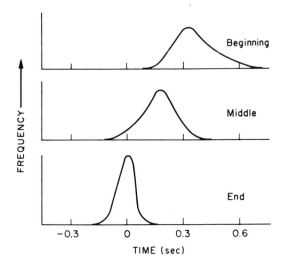

anticipate the occurrence of the signal and to reduce his time lag drastically. This is exemplified in the typical performance curves for a group of operators shown in Fig. 5-20. In this task, a light comes on every 5 sec, and the operator must turn it off by pressing a button.

Note that at the beginning of the task, the average time lag is approximately 0.3 sec. In the middle of the task, the average lag has decreased as the operator learns to anticipate the signal, and there are a few "negative" lags (i.e., some operators have anticipated that the signal will appear before it actually does and have responded accordingly). At the end of the task, the average lag is approximately zero, and there are as many "negative" lags as there are positive ones.

Pacing. When setting his own speed, the operator can operate faster than when a regular pace is set by the machine, or he can operate at the same speed but with fewer errors. Although his reaction time to the same signal will vary from time to time, when self-paced, such variations do not matter; he can benefit from an extra fast reaction time by not having to wait for the next signal to appear, and he can avoid being penalized for an extra long reaction time.

Self-pacing is particularly beneficial when the task is prolonged because the deleterious effects of increased variability in performance are minimized (Broadbent, 1953). Simple, repetitive operations will also benefit from

self-pacing, as, for instance, in inspection operations in which each item moves into the inspection point at an adjustable rate set by each inspector rather than at a permanently fixed rate.

DESIGN RECOMMENDATIONS

The following design recommendations to minimize human time lags should be observed whenever possible:

1. Wide variations in signal rate should be avoided.

2. If bunching of signals cannot be avoided, some means should be provided whereby the operator can anticipate them, and/or the signals should remain on until each has been responded to.

3. Signals should not occur at a rate faster than 2/sec unless some means of anticipating the signals is provided.

4. The use of many signal sources (channels) should be avoided. Operator performance will be better (i.e., the total number of signals that can be handled by the operator will be greater) with few channels and a relatively high signal rate rather than with many channels and a relatively low signal rate (Conrad, 1955a).

5. Alerting signals should be provided.

6. Alerting signals should precede action signals by 2.0–8.0 sec for isolated signals and by 0.3–2.0 sec for a number of signals occurring in sequence.

7. Very short alerting periods (less than 0.1 sec) should be avoided.

8. Alerting periods should be kept as constant as possible.

9. Alerting signals should be used to restrict the number of choices.

10. Advance information should be provided for tracking tasks and/or for bunched signals.

11. The operator should be provided with immediate knowledge of his own performance (feedback).

12. For best performance, practice periods should be provided—particularly for complex tasks.

13. Each operator should be allowed, as far as possible, to work at his own pace. Rigid

pacing of the person's task should be avoided.

5.2.4 *Human time lags in watchkeeping*

Watchkeeping is that task in which the operator monitors some condition such as the status of automatic equipment. Typically, he is required to respond to signals that might occur at any time during the watch, whereas the rest of the watch period is devoid of incidents and demands for action. When the signals occur infrequently, the task is called a "vigilance task," and, because performance tends to decline under such conditions, the term "vigilance decrement" has come into use.

Studies of vigilance problems, carried out on radar and similar apparatus, have indicated that the longer the watch period, the more likely that some signals will be missed, and, when signals are detected, response times will be long and variable (Deese, 1955; Lindsley, 1944; and Mackworth, 1950). Further studies confirm these findings, but also show that the vigilance decrement is not inevitable and that it can be controlled, to some extent, by varying the conditions of work.

FACTORS IN WATCHKEEPING

Some of the factors that affect performance in watchkeeping can be listed as follows:
  a. The frequency of signals.
  b. The magnitude and duration of signals.
  c. The search area.
  d. The precision required in the task.
  e. The duration of the task.
  f. The sense used.
  g. The environment.
  h. Variation among men.

Signal Frequency

Variation of the number of signals within a watch period has a marked effect on performance; the greater the number of signals, the better will be the average performance

and the less will be the decrement with time (Bowen, 1956; Browne, 1953; Deese, 1955; Deese and Ormond, 1953; and Jerison and Wallis, 1957a). It appears that observers raise their level of attentiveness according to when they expect a signal to occur, and it is easier to estimate short time spans. Thus, observers can estimate better the expected time of occurrence of the next signal when there are more signals in a given period of time.

Signal Magnitude and Duration

The magnitude and duration of a signal have a marked effect on performance; the more intense, bright, loud, or large the signal, the easier it is to detect and respond to rapidly (Adams, 1956; Bakan, 1955; Broadbent, 1953; and Davis, 1948). Signals that are large in magnitude or prolonged in time are not only easier to detect initially but, also, lead to little or no deterioration of performance over long periods of time (see Fig. 5-21). Signals that are difficult to detect, however, lead to relatively large vigilance decrements.

Flashing (repetitive) signals show no superiority over steady signals in terms of performance when the operator is fresh, but flashing signals become superior as the task is extended in time. A fast flash rate (e.g., 1 pps) generally maintains performance better than a slow flash rate (Bowen, 1956).

Search Area

The area of search for a signal not only directly influences the time required for an

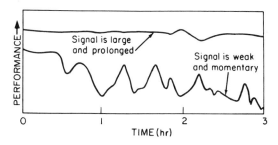

5-21

observer to detect a signal, but it also interacts with his vigilance behavior. For instance, on PPI radar scopes, operators show a progressive tendency to concentrate their attention on the center of the sweep so that signals appearing on the periphery of the scope either are missed or a long time is taken to respond to them. Similarly, pilots, toward the end of a long mission, tend to focus their attention on their primary indicators to the exclusion of the remainder so that they miss some important indications (Davis, 1948 and Jerison and Wallis, 1957b).

Task Precision

Tasks requiring a high degree of precision are degraded more with time than tasks requiring a low degree of precision. The reason for this effect is that the operator tends to become more variable in his response with time (Chapanis, et al., 1949).

Task Duration

For at least some vigilance tasks, long watch periods are harmful. It has been customary to limit many vigilance tasks to about 30–45 min, and this practice has proved satisfactory in most cases. When work conditions are good, an operator might be able to continue for a number of hours without serious vigilance decrement. To aid his performance in such a situation, he should be informed about the length of his watch and should be allowed rest periods of up to 5 min every half hour (Mackworth, 1950). A typical example of performance on a difficult vigilance task with and without rest periods is shown in Fig. 5-22.

Sense Used

Under conditions of relative quiet, an auditory signal is more likely to be attended to than a visual signal, but, a visual signal is superior in terms of the amount of information that can be presented by a single signal (see Chapter 2). A combination of the two (e.g., so that the operator's attention is obtained by an auditory signal and quantitative information is presented visually) is superior to either one individually.

Environment

Environmental factors can degrade watchkeeping performance either by causing too little or too much incidental stimulation of the man. When there is too little environmental stimulation, the conditions are similar to those that man contrives for himself just prior to sleep (Kleitman, 1939). Such conditions encourage lack of attentiveness and bring about quickly deteriorating performance (Bexton, 1954 and Fraser, 1953). Thus, an operator should not be isolated in a dimly lit, soundless compartment when required to perform a vigilance task such as monitoring a radar scope.

Overstimulation also can cause deterioration in performance. Various environmental conditions are noxious or distractive in their effects (see Chapter 10); in particular, noise (above 90 db) and excessive heat and humidity are conditions to be avoided (Broadbent, 1951a; Jerison and Wing, 1957; Mackworth, 1947 and 1950; and Pepler, 1950). In general, it is desirable to place a man in a reasonably lit workplace, with some sounds in the background, and in the company of other men so that some occasional interactions can take place. He also should be permitted means of refreshment, such as cigarettes, coffee, etc.

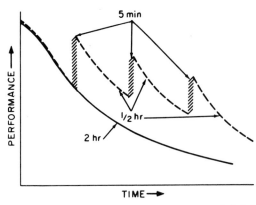

§ 5.2.4

Variation Among Men

Performance in watchkeeping situations varies widely from person to person and, to a lesser degree, from day to day for the same person. The ability to be vigilant over prolonged periods of time does not appear to be strongly related to any measurable personality trait or ability, although there is some indication that good watchkeeping performance is positively related to an introverted disposition (Bowen, 1956). When high penalty rates are attached to errors (viz., either reporting a signal that is not there or failing to report one that is there), vigilance is enhanced, but the degree to which this is effective very much depends on the person involved.

DESIGN RECOMMENDATIONS

Although the performance of operators in vigilance tasks is difficult to predict, there are certain steps that can be taken to minimize the vigilance decrement that accompanies prolonged watchkeeping activities. These can be listed as follows:

1. The signal should be as large in magnitude (e.g., brightness, size, intensity, length) as is reasonable under the conditions encountered.

2. The signal should persist until it has been responded to or for as long as possible.

(The minimum signal period should be 2.0 sec.)

3. The area in which the signal can appear should be restricted.

4. For flashing signals, the flash rate should be high (at least 1 pps) with the "on" period being at least 0.5 sec.

5. Insofar as signal frequency is controllable, it should be kept high. For 1–10 signals per hour, expect considerable decrement; for 10–20 signals per hour, expect moderate decrement; for over 20 signals per hour, expect little decrement.

6. Some means of giving anticipatory information should be provided whenever possible.

7. Feed-back information concerning the operator's proficiency should be provided.

8. The work environment (noise, temperature, humidity, etc.) should be maintained at a comfortable level (see Chapter 10).

9. The observer should not be isolated from other people nor deprived entirely of incidental stimulation (e.g., smoking, coffee, postural adjustments, minor interruptions).

10. When long watch periods are unavoidable, the observer should be provided with 3–5 min rest periods every half hour.

11. Watch periods ordinarily should not exceed 1 hr and, when working conditions are poor, should not exceed 30 min.

12. Whenever possible, group members should be rotated among jobs every 30 min.

5.3 Machine Dynamics

Machine dynamics, as used here, comprises the changes in machine output resulting from a control movement made by the operator. Mathematically, the dynamics of a machine can be described completely by one or a set of equations showing the relationship between machine input and output. As indicated in article 5.2.1, this relationship is commonly called the transfer function. Fortunately, we know something about transfer functions.

5.3.1 Machine transfer functions

The simplest kind of control order is a zero-order control linkage in which the con-

This article was drafted by Alphonse Chapanis of The Johns Hopkins University.

§ 5.3.1

ZERO-ORDER (POSITION) CONTROL

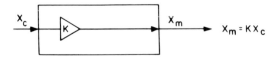

$$X_m = K X_c$$

trol output (X_c) directly determines the machine output (X_m). This is commonly called position control, and K is a constant representing the gain, amplification, or gearing ratio (see Fig. 5-23).

In the top diagram of Fig. 5-24 (Chapanis, 1960) are two sets of hypothetical control movements. Both show a sequence of movements starting with the control at a neutral (or zero) position. The control is displaced in one direction (to a or c), held at that position for a short period of time, and then returned to the neutral (or zero) position. After another short period of time, the control is then displaced in the opposite direction (to b or d), held there for a short period of time, and returned once more to the neutral position. The control movements on the left are mathematically exact step inputs.

Although no control operates with such instantaneous precision, this artificial example helps to illustrate the nature of the control dynamics in each of the systems discussed. The sequence of control movements on the

right is somewhat more realistic because it shows the control moving gradually from one position to another. Notice that the total displacement for the control movements on the right, that is, from 0 to c or from 0 to d, is only half those on the left, that is, from 0 to a or from 0 to b.

The curves in the second diagram of Fig. 5-24 show the system output for each of these sequences when the control is in a zero-order system. The curves representing the machine output have exactly the same shapes as those representing the control output but merely are reduced by K (0.5 in this example). The factor K could, of course, be greater than 1, in which case the system output would be greater than the control output.

The next level of complexity, a first-order control (see top diagram of Fig. 5-25), is one in which the control output directly determines the rate of change of the machine output. This is commonly called a rate or velocity control. The third diagram of Fig. 5-24 shows the machine output of a rate-control system for each of the two control sequences in the top diagram. Note that a displacement of the control produces a rate of change of position in the machine, and the rate of change in the machine is proportional to the displacement of the control. Except for time lags and certain other minor complicating

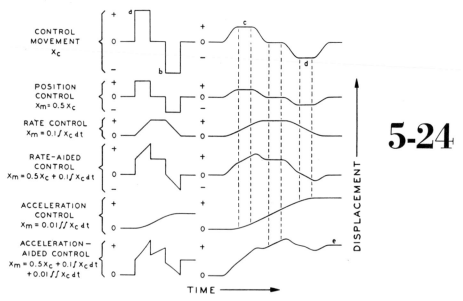

5-24

FIRST-ORDER CONTROL

RATE (OR VELOCITY) CONTROL

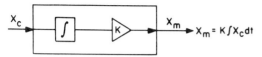

$$x_m = K \int x_c \, dt$$

RATE-AIDED (OR VELOCITY-AIDED) CONTROL

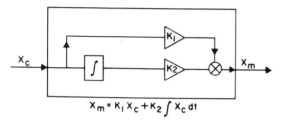

$$x_m = K_1 x_c + K_2 \int x_c \, dt$$

factors, an automobile approximates a first-order control system; a fixed displacement of one of the controls (the accelerator) produces a constant velocity in the system output (the forward movement of the automobile).

First-order control systems very often include the zero-order, position control as well, in which case they are called rate-aided or velocity-aided control systems (see bottom diagram of Fig. 5-25). The output of such a control system, illustrated by the curves in the fourth diagram of Fig. 5-24, is the alge-

SECOND-ORDER CONTROL

ACCELERATION CONTROL

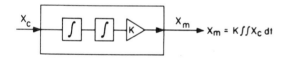

$$x_m = K \int\int x_c \, dt$$

ACCELERATION-AIDED CONTROL

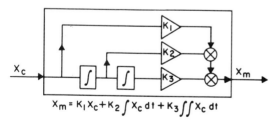

$$x_m = K_1 x_c + K_2 \int x_c \, dt + K_3 \int\int x_c \, dt$$

5-26

braic sum of both the position and the velocity components of the system (i.e., the two curves in the fourth diagram are the sums of the curves on the two lines immediately above).

In the design of rate-aided systems, an extremely important consideration is the proper selection of values for the constants K_1 and K_2, or, to be more exact, the ratio K_1/K_2, called the *rate-aiding constant*. A considerable amount of research has gone into determining the best all-around value for this ratio and an acceptable range (see article 5.3.2). The values used in Fig. 5-24 were selected for purposes of illustration; they are inappropriate for any real control system.

Still more complexity is shown in the second-order control system (see top diagram of Fig. 5-26). Here, the output of the operator's control determines the acceleration of the machine output. The schematic representation of such a system output is shown in the fifth diagram of Fig. 5-24. Note that when the operator's control is displaced and held in a fixed position, machine movement continues to increase at a faster and faster rate. When the operator's control is returned to its neutral position after an initial displacement, the machine continues to change its position at a constant rate. To stop the machine's movement, the operator must make another displacement in the opposite direction.

Second-order control systems frequently include both of the lower-order terms, one for position and one for rate. Such systems (illustrated in the bottom diagram of Fig. 5-26) are commonly called acceleration-aided systems. The performance of such a system is shown in the bottom diagram of Fig. 5-24. As in the case of the rate-aided system, the selection of the appropriate constants is a critical matter if the system is to be used effectively. Again, the constants used in Fig. 5-24 were selected for purposes of illustration and are unsuited for any real control system.

5.3.2 *Aided tracking*

Rate aiding is the simplest and most common type of aided tracking. It is a first-order system combining position control and rate control. Thus, a change in the control output (X_c) imparts a change in both position and rate to the machine output (X_m). The prime advantage of aiding is that a simple operator response controls a complex machine output. For ramp inputs, for example, rate aiding will reduce the number of responses made by the operator and improve system performance.

THE AIDING CONSTANT

The fraction K_1/K_2 is known as the "aided tracking time constant" or "aiding constant." Because K_2 is a number divided by a time interval, usually in seconds, the aiding constant is usually reported in seconds. Proper selection of this constant is critical for effective rate-aided tracking, and, because of the numerous factors affecting the optimum aiding constant and because of its importance in improving tracking performance, the constant should be confirmed experimentally for each specific situation.

For Continuous Inputs

For inputs that are presented to the operator continuously, the optimum constant has been estimated to range from 0.2 to 0.8 sec. Experimental evidence suggests that 0.5 sec approaches the most satisfactory single value, but additional evidence indicates that the optimum constant is a function of input frequency and complexity and of the type of display (Chernikoff, et al., 1955 and Lincoln and Smith, 1952).

For Intermittent Inputs

For inputs that are presented to the operator intermittently (e.g., radar displays), the optimum constant is the time interval between corrections (Mechler, et al., 1949). Thus, for a radar with a sweep rate of 0.1 cps, the optimum aiding constant is 10 sec if the operator makes corrections every sweep and 20 sec if he makes corrections every other sweep. If he

responds in an unpredictable manner, the constant should be set by a computer mechanism.

The Effects of Degrading Factors

The above values are applicable only when there is no time lag, backlash, or other degrading factor in the system. The introduction of lags at any point will result in interactions with other system parameters and will affect tracking performance (Rockway, 1954). Backlash has a somewhat similar effect as certain types of time lags, and thus might also change the optimum aiding constant (Ely, 1957; Helson, 1945; and Senders and Bradley, 1956).

EFFECTIVENESS OF AIDED TRACKING

A characteristic of aiding is that the operator must make more control movements to obtain a simple machine output than he would in unaided tracking. For step inputs, therefore, aided tracking is more difficult than simple position control. If, as has been suggested (Chernikoff and Taylor, 1957), in tracking complex high-frequency inputs, "the operator's ability to follow continuously is taxed to the point where the tracking problem begins to resemble that posed by a course composed of a succession of step function changes," then aided tracking for such situations should result in poorer performance than position control. Evidence to date tends to confirm this hypothesis.

The effectiveness of aiding is also a function of the type of display being used (see section 5.1). For displays that enable the operator to estimate derivative information as well as error information, aiding loses its effectiveness. To be used most effectively, aiding requires that the operator make a response that is directly proportional only to the magnitude of error; if the operator's response is proportional to a combination of error plus error rate, the prime value of aiding is lost, and the operator might perform more poorly than he would if there were no aiding present.

ADDING HIGHER DERIVATIVES

When course input changes very slowly, additional terms (beyond position and rate) will aid performance. For inputs with a constant rate, an acceleration term added to the position and rate terms will permit the operator to track with a minimum number of control movements. In like manner, for inputs with a constant acceleration, a fourth term (viz., rate of change of acceleration) can be added.

Under conditions of no lag or backlash, an optimum ratio in the range of $1:2:8$ to $1:4:8$ for the first three terms (K_1, K_2, and K_3) has been shown to be superior to others (Searle, 1951), but, here again, the designer should confirm the optimum ratio experimentally for his given conditions because they might depart significantly from those for which the above-quoted ratios were determined.

DESIGN RECOMMENDATIONS

When providing aided tracking, the following design recommendations should be observed if possible:

1. Aiding should be used when the input (desired output) has a constant rate, a constant acceleration, or some constant higher derivative.

2. The number of terms used in aiding should exceed by one the derivative of the input that is constant. Thus, for a constant input rate, there should be three terms in the aiding (viz., position, rate, and acceleration); for a constant input acceleration, there should be four terms in the aiding; etc.

3. The aiding constant should be confirmed experimentally for each specific situation.

5.3.3 *Quickening*

Quickening, unlike aiding, does not affect system output but only changes the information displayed to the operator. A quickened display reduces the complexity of the operator's task by eliminating his need to make complex mental calculations. Rather, it continuously displays to him where to position his control to achieve some desired system output. Quickening is most valuable in controlling higher-order systems.

Higher-order control systems composed of pure integrations tend to be more difficult to control than lower-order ones. A third-order system, as exemplified by helicopter pitch control, is extremely difficult to control under conditions of instrument flight when the pilot is provided with only an attitude display (Bailey and Sweeney, 1955). A fourth-order system, as exemplified by submarine depth control, is impossible to control when the operator (planesman) has only a depth gage.

In many systems, particularly those involving the control of a vehicle, control order is determined by the relationship between the control surface or surfaces and the machine output. For example, in fleet-type submarines with a single planesman controlling depth (see Fig. 5-27), the position of his control directly affects the rate of change (first derivative) of plane angle (the control surface); plane angle directly affects the acceleration (second derivative) of pitch; and pitch directly affects the rate of change of depth. Hence, the planesman controls the fourth derivative of depth (i.e., there are four integrations between operator output and system output). One integration can be eliminated by redesigning the machine so that the operator di-

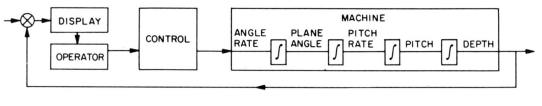

5-27

rectly controls plane angle rather than plane angle rate, but, as long as submarine depth is controlled primarily by planes, there will always be at least three integrations present.

Normally, the higher-order systems just described are controlled by providing the operator with an array of displays. One display gives output information and the rest provide derivative information about the output. For example, for one-man depth control of a submarine, the operator might be provided with displays showing depth (output), depth rate or pitch (either being the first derivative of output), pitch rate (second derivative of output), and plane angle (third derivative of output).

With such an array, the operator's task is quite difficult; he must know how each indicator moves to achieve a desired output. To perform his task well, the operator must reach a high level of skill and attend constantly to his displays. The general purpose of quickening is to simplify the operator's task by providing him with a single display requiring a minimum of mental computation on his part to achieve the desired output. The design of quickened displays is discussed in the paragraphs that follow.

QUICKENED-DISPLAY DESIGN

Complete quickening consists of a single display that provides the operator with immediate knowledge of the results of his own control actions before they would become available by sensing the system's actual output. The moving indicator on the display (X_d) represents the sum of the machine output (X_m) and its derivatives (see Fig. 5-28). This information (X_d) is obtained by placing feedback loops between the machine output and each of its derivatives and the display.

The mathematical expression for this is as follows:

$$X_d = K_1 X_m + K_2 \dot{X}_m + K_3 \ddot{X}_m + K_4 \dddot{X}_m,$$

(5-3)

where the K's are the weighting constants for the various terms, and $\dot{X}$ is the first time derivative of X, $\ddot{X}$ is the second, and $\dddot{X}$ is the third.

Although time derivatives of the machine output are often used, this procedure is not essential. Space derivatives (i.e., those showing how output changes per unit of distance rather than per unit of time) also can be used.

In a perfectly quickened system, the display tells the operator where to position his control. With a compensatory display (see section 5.1), the magnitude of the error is directly proportional to the distance that the operator must move his control, and, because his task is to minimize error, he behaves like a simple amplifier. The error indicator responds immediately to his control movement, thereby making his task very simple (Birmingham and Taylor, 1954).

The weighting constants ($K_1, K_2, \ldots K_n$) are very important in the proper design of a quickened display. An improper selection of constants can result in an uncontrollable system (Bailey and Sweeney, 1955). To some extent, the selection of the constants determines the manner in which the machine achieves its desired output. For example, the constants might be such as to cause the machine to correct for a step input very rapidly but with some overshooting, rather than slowly but with no overshooting.

The most desirable set of constants can vary with certain factors, such as speed. For example, the optimum set of constants for a vehicle moving at a slow speed might not be the optimum one for the same vehicle moving

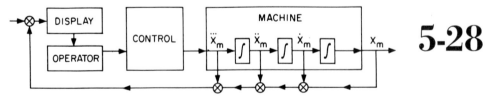

5-28

at a fast speed. It frequently is desirable, therefore, to make such terms nonlinear to improve system performance. In general, however, for quickened systems, the weighting constants affect output in the same manner as they do for fully automatic systems.

There is, as yet, no simple, general, analytical method that will permit the designer to determine these constants for all systems. With complex systems, the most effective method is an empirical one in which all weighting constants are varied simultaneously on a simulator (e.g., analogue computer) until the system responds in the desired manner.

PARTIAL QUICKENING

Ideally, there should be one term in the quickened display for each order of the control system. Thus, for a third-order system, there should be four terms determining the quickened display (viz., machine output plus its first three derivatives). In some systems (e.g., certain guided missiles), it is impossible to sense directly some of the derivatives of output, and it is extremely difficult to obtain these derivative measures indirectly by such means as differentiating the output or installing rate gyros. Such systems cannot be fully quickened, but there remains some advantage in partially quickening the display.

The number of derivative terms that must be present for partial quickening to be effective has not been determined. In general, the more terms that are present, the better will be the partial quickening. The terms closest to the machine output (viz., position, then rate, etc.) are more essential than higher-order terms. Skipping any term (e.g., omitting the first derivative term but including the second) will generally result in system instability.

MAJOR ADVANTAGES

The major advantages of a quickened display are as follows:

1. It simplifies the operator's tracking task and results in improved performance, except in those cases where either the original task is very simple or the operator has already reached a high level of skill in performing it (Birmingham, et al., 1954).

2. It minimizes the time required to train an operator (Holland and Henson, 1956).

3. It frees some of the operator's time so that he can perform other duties concurrently (Birmingham, et al., 1954).

4. It eliminates most of the detrimental effects resulting from "reversal errors" (i.e., from the operator's starting to move his control in the wrong direction when correcting an error) and, thereby, reduces the importance of such human-engineering considerations as direction-of-movement (see Chapter 6) and frame-of-reference relationships (Birmingham and Taylor, 1954).

5. It permits the operator with less ability to perform the tracking task, and, thereby, facilitates the selection problem by permitting operators to be drawn from a larger population.

6. It permits the execution of a desired maneuver in a very short time, the limiting factor being the performance capabilities of the vehicle rather than the skill of the operator.

7. It permits repeatability so that a desired maneuver will occur in the same way each time it is performed.

8. It makes system performance much less dependent on human performance; the designer, rather than the operator, determines what the performance characteristics of the system will be.

9. It permits "safety" terms to be incorporated into the display (e.g., in an aircraft, a nonlinear term from a g-sensing mechanism can be fed into the display so that, in properly responding to his display, the pilot will never pull excessive g-forces).

MAJOR DISADVANTAGES

The following are the major disadvantages of a quickened display:

1. It does not provide the operator with information about the actual state of the system. (The system might be in a dangerous

condition without the operator's being aware of it.)

2. To be useful when there are high frequencies present in the input, additional circuitry must be provided (Birmingham and Taylor, 1954).

3. Under some conditions, it is less satisfactory than a fully automatic system.

4. Although, theoretically, it reduces to one the number of displays required by the operator, in actual practice, it usually adds an extra display because the "normal" displays showing the actual state of the system will, in most cases, still be desired by operators.

5. If the operator achieves a perfect tracking performance when using the quickened display, he will always achieve his desired output in the same manner (e.g., by following the same flight path), but the best manner for any one situation is not necessarily the best for others (e.g., under some conditions, he must change his output very rapidly even though this results in overshooting, whereas, under other conditions, overshooting is intolerable).

6. It is possible to use a quickened display and still vary the manner in which the final output is achieved. For example, the operator can deliberately cause his indicator to move beyond the desired position before correcting it to reach his desired output quickly. This type of operation, however, requires additional training and is risky because the operator does not know precisely what his control movement is making the system do.

AIDING VS. QUICKENING

Aiding (see article 5.3.2) and quickening are alike in that both simplify the operator's task and involve placing loops around the integrators in the machine. They differ in that aiding directly affects machine output whereas quickening normally is thought of as directly affecting the input to the operator.

With aiding, the operator's display shows the actual state of the system, but his output is changed so that he can control an aided system with simpler responses than those required to control the same system when un-

aided. With quickening the operator's display shows what he should do with his control but not the actual state of the system. Quickening, in itself, does not affect output. To achieve a desired output, the operator should make the same set of responses that he would if the system were not quickened.

DESIGN RECOMMENDATIONS

No general set of rules can be provided that will state the conditions under which quickening should be used, but the list of advantages and disadvantages enumerated in the preceding paragraphs should aid the designer in determining whether quickening is appropriate for his particular design problem. When a quickened display is to be used, however, the following requirements should be met:

1. As many derivative terms as necessary should be included.

2. The weighting constants for all terms should be determined empirically.

3. If the operator requires information about the actual state of the system he is controlling, auxiliary displays should be provided.

4. A lower derivative should never be skipped, e.g., a third derivative should not be included without also including the first and second derivatives.

5.3.4 *The effects of machine dynamics on operator performance*

It is useful to examine the dynamics of a machine in terms of certain discernible attributes. Insofar as they affect performance, important ones are lag, gain, and integration (Fig. 5-29 shows the effects of each on a simple sine-wave input), which are covered in this article. There are other important attributes, however, that are not covered in this article, e.g., differentiation and analog addition, which have not been studied sufficiently to be covered, and control resistance, which is covered in the next chapter (see Chapter 6).

THE EFFECTS OF LAG

There are various kinds of lag, and these can appear in various parts of the system. Examples of three kinds are shown in Fig. 5-30. Transmission lags normally degrade performance with a compensatory display even though the lags might be so small (e.g., 0.06 sec) that the operator is unaware of them (Warrick, 1949). Backlash (free play) and transmission lag are similar in their initial effects on operator performance (Ely, et al., 1957). This is to be expected because both affect the system, initially, in a similar manner. With either present, a certain period elapses before the system starts to respond to the operator's initial control movement (Senders and Bradley, 1956).

Exponential and sigmoid lags either can improve or degrade performance, depending on their interactions with other attributes of machine dynamics. For example, when the gain is optimally set, the addition of an exponential lag between control output and machine output will degrade performance. But, if the gain is too high (e.g., if it causes continual overshooting), the addition of a lag will serve to reduce output amplitude and, thereby, improve performance (Rockway, 1954).

THE EFFECTS OF GAIN

In zero-order control systems, gain is one of the most critical factors affecting tracking performance. (A detailed discussion of its importance and of procedures for setting it is presented in Chapter 6.) In higher-order control systems, the *relative* gain (or sensitivity) of each output term (viz., position, rate, acceleration, etc.) also is of prime importance. Gain also interacts with other attributes of machine dynamics as shown in the example in the paragraph above.

EFFECTS OF INTEGRATION

As explained in article 5.3.1, the number of integrations between control output and machine output determines the control order of the system (e.g., no integration is zero-order control, one integration is first-order control). The optimum number of integrations depends on the input frequency and the availability of feed-back and feed-forward loops around each integrator. Under most circumstances the number of integrations should be minimized, but, for very slow input frequencies, first-order control (one integrator) is superior to zero-order control (Chernikoff and Taylor, 1957). Also, if feed-back or feed-forward loops can be supplied to "aid" or to "quicken" the system, then at least two and, on occasion, four or five integrations are desirable to assist the operator in the performance of his task.

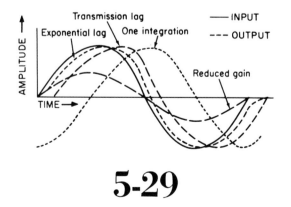

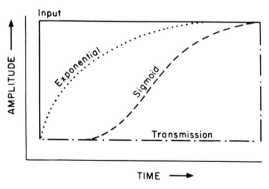

5-29

6
design of controls

THE PROPER DESIGN of controls is an important factor affecting operator performance in most man-machine systems. This chapter provides a compilation of human-engineering recommendations concerning various aspects of control selection and design. Wherever these recommendations are the direct out-growth of published research in this field, the appropriate studies are cited. The chapter is divided into the following four sections: Selecting the Best Control, Important Factors in the Design of Controls, Design Recommendations for Hand and Foot Controls, Design Recommendations for Specific Controls.

6.1 *Selecting the Best Control*

There are no "good" or "bad" controls as such; the suitability of any control depends on its appropriateness for the task to which it is assigned. A control that is satisfactory for one task might be inadequate for another. The purpose of this section is to aid the designer in selecting the best control for any given task.

This chapter, except for one section, was drafted by Jerome H. Ely, Robert M. Thomson, and Jesse Orlansky of Dunlap and Associates, Inc.

The first step in selecting the best control is to determine the following:

a. The function of the control. This includes its purpose and importance to the system, the nature of the controlled object, the type of change to be accomplished, and the extent and direction of change.

b. The requirements of the task. This includes the precision, speed, range, and force requirements for using the control and the effect of reducing one of these requirements to improve another.

247

c. The informational needs of the operator. This includes the operator's requirements for locating and identifying the control, determining control position (setting), and sensing any change in control position.

d. The requirements imposed by the workplace. This includes the amount and location of available space in which the control can be placed and the importance of locating the control in a certain position for proper grouping and/or association with other equipment, controls, and displays (see Chapter 7).

The second step is to apply the following general rules for control selection:

1. Select controls that permit each hand or foot to be used effectively (see section 6.3). When an operator is involved in a complex task, the controls should be distributed so that no one limb will be overburdened.

Controls requiring rapid, precise setting should be assigned to the hands. Controls requiring large or continuous forward applications of force generally should be assigned to the feet. Many controls of various types can be assigned to the hands, but, whenever possible, not more than two controls, of even the simplest type, should be assigned to each foot.

2. Select controls the movements of which conform to those of the associated display, equipment component, or vehicle. The direction of movement of the control (see article 6.2.2) should be consistent with that of the controlled object or display (see Chapter 2). The general situations in which linear (or near-linear) and rotary controls should be used are shown in Fig. 6-1.

3. Use multirotation controls when high precision is required over a wide range of

ACCEPTABLE CONTROLS FOR VARIOUS TYPES OF SYSTEM RESPONSES

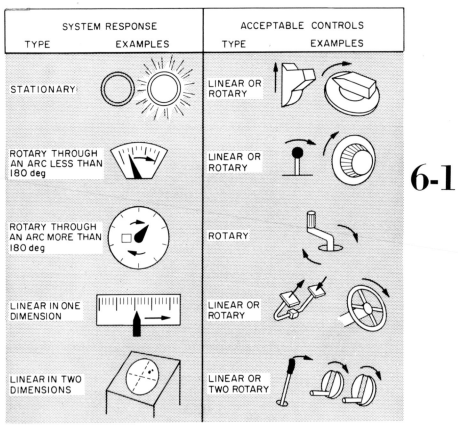

248

Table 6-1 Recommended Controls for the Case Where Both Force and Range of Settings are Important

For SMALL forces and . . .	Use . . .
Two discrete settings	Hand pushbutton, foot pushbutton, or toggle switch
Three discrete settings	Toggle switch or rotary selector switch
Four to 24 discrete settings	Rotary selector switch
Small range of continuous settings	Knob or lever
Large range of continuous settings	Crank

For LARGE forces and . . .	Use . . .
Two discrete settings	Detent lever, large hand pushbutton, or foot pushbutton
Three to 24 discrete settings	Detent lever
Small range of continuous settings	Handwheel, rotary pedal, or lever
Large range of continuous settings	Large crank

adjustments. Linear movements can be made as precisely as rotary ones, hence, for small adjustments of the controlled object, either a linear or a rotary control is satisfactory. But, because the range of movement of a linear control is generally limited, this type of control does not permit high precision over a wide range of adjustments. With a multi-rotation control, any desired precision can be obtained by appropriate gearing (although this might affect operating time).

4. Use discrete-adjustment (detent) controls rather than continuous-adjustment (non-detent) controls when performance requirements are such that the controlled object can be adjusted in a limited number of discrete steps. Discrete-adjustment controls (i.e., controls that snap into place for a limited number of positions), when properly designed, can be positioned with one gross adjusting movement; continuous-adjustment controls are generally positioned in two steps (a slewing movement and a fine adjustment).

5. Continuous-adjustment controls should be used when precise adjustments are needed along a continuum, or when a large number of settings (usually more than 24) is required. When a limited number of settings is required, however, or when precision requirements are so gross that a limited number of settings can represent an entire continuum within the required accuracy, discrete-adjustment controls are preferred (Jenkins, 1953).

6. When force and range of settings are the primary considerations in control selection, use the controls recommended in Table 6-1.

7. Combine functionally related controls when they reduce reaching movements, aid in sequential or simultaneous operation of controls, or economize in the use of panel space. Be careful, however, not to violate other hu-

man-engineering principles (see, especially, Chapter 7), and the hazard of accidental activation also should be considered (see article 6.2.5).

8. Select controls that can be easily identified. All controls should be identifiable, primarily by standardizing their locations but also by other means when appropriate (see article 6.2.4). Primary and emergency controls should be identifiable both visually and by touch. Identification should not hinder the operator in manipulating his controls or increase the likelihood of their being accidentally activated.

6.2 *Important Factors in the Design of Controls*

This section describes the following important factors that should be considered in the design of controls:

   a. The control-display (C/D) ratio.
   b. Direction-of-movement relationships.
   c. Control resistance.
   d. Preventing accidental activation.
   e. Control coding.

General recommendations are made in this section that are applicable to most types of controls. Design recommendations for hand and foot controls and for specific controls are presented in sections 6.3 and 6.4, respectively.

6.2.1 *The control-display ratio*

The control-display (C/D) ratio is the ratio of the distance of movement of the control to that of the moving element of the display (pointer, cursor, etc.). The C/D ratio is a critical design factor affecting operator performance; a good C/D ratio has been shown to save from 0.5 to 5 sec in positioning time (Jenkins and Connor, 1949; Jenkins and Karr, 1954; Jenkins, et al., 1950; and Jenkins and Olson, 1952).

For linear and near-linear controls (e.g., levers) that affect linear displays, the C/D ratio is usually defined as the ratio of the linear distance of control displacement to the distance of the resulting display movement, with control displacement being measured from the point where the operator's hand grasps the control (see Fig. 6-2). For small rotary controls (e.g., knobs) that affect linear displays, the C/D ratio is usually defined as the ratio of the number of control rotations to the distance of display movement.

OPTIMIZING THE C/D RATIO

In positioning a continuous-adjustment (non-detent) control, the operator makes the following movements:

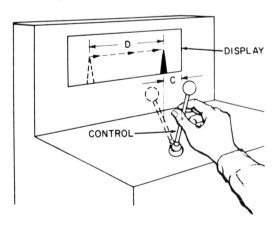

a. A slewing movement (also referred to as "travel," "gross adjusting movement," and "primary movement") in which he rapidly moves his control close to the final, desired position. An increase in the C/D ratio will increase slewing time because of the longer movements required. For linear controls, however, slewing time is only slightly greater for long movements than for short ones (Barnes, 1936; Brown and Slater-Hammel, 1949; Brown, et al., 1948; and Peters and Wenborne, 1936).

b. A fine adjusting movement (also referred to as "adjusting movement" or "secondary movement") in which the operator places his control precisely in the final, desired position. Fine-adjusting time is reduced either by increasing the C/D ratio or by easing the tolerance requirements, i.e., increasing the maximum acceptable error in positioning the control (Jenkins and Connor, 1949). The optimum C/D ratio is that which minimizes the total time (slewing plus fine adjusting) required to make the desired control movement (see Fig. 6-3).

FACTORS AFFECTING C/D RATIO

In many design situations, the designer will be unable to determine the optimum C/D ratio from available research data. Hence, whenever possible, he should determine the optimum C/D ratio experimentally, keeping in mind that it can be affected by the following factors:

a. Display size. With tolerance (see below) kept constant, changing the size of the display might change the total adjustment time.

b. Tolerance. Fine adjusting time is reduced directly by easing the tolerance requirements. Slewing time probably also is reduced because the operator tends to move his control into position more slowly when he knows that it will have to be positioned precisely. Thus, changing tolerance might change the optimum C/D ratio.

c. Viewing distance. Research to date suggests that viewing distance does affect performance and that it might also change the optimum C/D ratio, although no definite rela-

tionships have been established as yet (Shackel, 1954).

d. Time delay. The type and extent of any time delay in the system might affect the optimum C/D ratio. For exponentially shaped time delays that occur between the control movement and the resulting display response, the longer the time delay, within reasonable limits, the smaller will be the optimum C/D ratio (Rockway, 1954).

6.2.2 Control-display relationships

To be correct, the direction of movement of the control must be related appropriately to the change that it induces in the associated display, the equipment component, and/or the system as a whole. Correct direction-of-movement relationships will improve system performance by improving the following:

a. Reaction or decision time.

b. The correctness of initial control movements (i.e., it will reduce movement in the wrong direction, called reversal error).

c. The speed and precision of control adjustment.

d. Learning time.

These improvements are relatively unimportant if the operator has a simple, repetitive task, but their importance increases directly with the following:

a. The complexity of the task.

b. The discontinuity, or number of interruptions, in the control sequence.

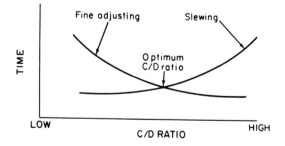

6-3

c. The degree of stress or anxiety experienced by the operator.

The direction-of-movement relationships recommended in this article are made to satisfy one or more of the following three basic requirements: a) natural relationships, b) existing design practice, and c) standardization and consistency. Natural relationships refer to control-movement habit patterns that are consistent from person to person without special training or instructions, i.e., they are responses that individuals make most often and are called "population stereotypes." For example, an upward movement of a toggle switch is almost always related to "on" as opposed to "off."

GENERAL RULES

The following general rules are applicable in all situations:

1. The direction of movement of the control must be considered in relation to all of the following factors:

a. The location and orientation of the operator relative to the control and to a moving vehicle.

b. The position of the display relative to the control and the nature and direction of the display response.

c. The change exhibited by an equipment component as a result of the control movement—either in terms of motion for moving components (landing gear, gun turret, etc.) or in terms of power for stationary components (volume of a radio receiver, brightness of a radar scope, etc.).

2. Control movements should be consistent for all equipment that the same operator is likely to use (see Chapter 1).

3. The direction of movement of controls and displays should be related to the purpose underlying each control movement rather than to any particular mechanism or method of actuation used to perform the desired function. For example, if the operator wants to lower temperature, opening a vent that will admit cool air or closing a vent that has been admitting hot air need not be related, by itself, to the control movement. The control movement should be related to the basic purpose: to raise temperature (upward movement, clockwise movement, etc.) or to lower temperature (downward movement, counterclockwise movement, etc.).

4. Direct movement relationships should be used whenever possible, particularly when they result in vehicle movement. Thus, a movement of a control to the right should result in a movement to the right of an instrument pointer, a right turn or right bank of the vehicle, etc. (Recommended relationships between control movement and system or component response are shown in Fig. 6-4.)

5. Controls that are related to the direction of movement of the vehicle in which they are mounted should not be located so that the operator faces rearward. In such situations, movement relationships are ambiguous with respect to left-and-right, fore-and-aft, etc. An operator inside a vehicle controlling its direction of movement should face in the direction in which the vehicle normally moves.

SPECIFIC RECOMMENDATIONS

The following paragraphs give specific design recommendations for rotary and on-off controls. Push-*pull* controls, which project from the panel surface on which they are mounted (e.g., a hand choke on an automobile, a throttle on some types of small aircraft), are not recommended because the pushed-in position on these controls is generally associated with "off" or "decrease," and this control movement, particularly when the control is mounted on the front plane, conflicts with the usual forward-to-increase control movement. Even more important in some applications is the fact that it is usually difficult to tell how a push-pull control is set just by looking at it or feeling it. These objections, of course, do not apply to push-*button* controls.

Rotary Controls

When using rotary controls, the operator orients himself with a certain point on the

RECOMMENDED RELATIONSHIPS BETWEEN CONTROL MOVEMENT AND SYSTEM OR COMPONENT RESPONSE

CONTROL MOVEMENT	SYSTEM (OR EQUIPMENT COMPONENT) RESPONSE				
	DIRECTIONAL				NONDIRECTIONAL
	UP	RIGHT	FORWARD	CLOCKWISE	INCREASE*
UP	RECOMMENDED	NOT RECOMMENDED	CONDITIONALLY RECOMMENDED	NOT RECOMMENDED	RECOMMENDED
RIGHT	NOT RECOMMENDED	RECOMMENDED	NOT RECOMMENDED	CONDITIONALLY RECOMMENDED	RECOMMENDED
FORWARD	SEE TEXT	NOT RECOMMENDED	RECOMMENDED	NOT RECOMMENDED	RECOMMENDED
CLOCKWISE	SEE TEXT	SEE TEXT	SEE TEXT	RECOMMENDED	RECOMMENDED

*INCREASE REFERS TO INCREASE IN POWER OUTPUT, BRIGHTNESS, rpm, ETC., AND TO "ON" OR "START" AS OPPOSED TO "OFF" OR "STOP."

6-4

control; he perceives the control as moving in the direction in which this point is moving. With rotary control movements in a horizontal plane, the operator orients himself with respect to the forward point of the control (see Fig. 6-5). With rotary control movements in a vertical plane, the operator orients himself with respect to the top of the control (see Fig. 6-6). With these points in mind, the following recommendations should be observed:

1. When the control affects the direction of movement of a vehicle, the point of the control with which the operator is oriented should move in the same direction as the desired direction of the vehicle.

2. The axis of rotation for the control should parallel the corresponding axis of rotation of the vehicle (provided that the resulting control movements do not cause undue operator discomfort).

3. With a rotary display that has a moving pointer and a stationary dial, a clockwise rotation of the rotary control should result in a clockwise rotation of the display pointer.

4. A rotary display that has a moving dial and a fixed pointer usually will cause direction-of-movement ambiguities and should be replaced, when feasible, by a fixed dial and moving pointer (see Chapter 2). If it cannot be replaced, the following are recommended for the case where the indicator (pointer) is fixed at the 12 o'clock position (Bradley, 1954):

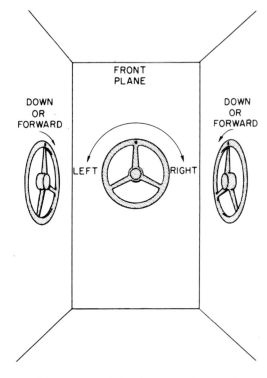

a. If the control-display combination is not related directly to the movement of the vehicle and if the operator always views the display when operating the control, scale numbers on the display should progress in a clockwise direction, and a clockwise rotation of the control should result in a clockwise rotation of the display.

b. If the control directly affects the movement of the vehicle and if the operator does not have to view the display when operating his control, scale numbers on the display should progress in a clockwise direction, and a clockwise movement of the control should result in a counterclockwise movement of the display.

5. A rotary control should be on the concave side of a rotary display when the display movement traverses less than a full circle (see Fig. 6-7).

6. When a rotary control and a linear display are in the same plane, the part of the control adjacent to the display should move in the same direction as the moving part of the display (see Fig. 6-8).

7. A rotary control should not be placed

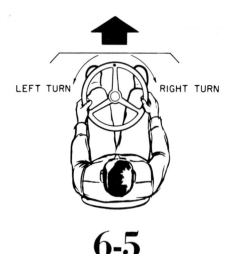

6-5

above *any* display or to the left of a *vertical* display. This avoids conflict between the principle above and the principle that a clockwise control movement should result in either an upward or rightward movement of the pointer.

8. When there is a direct linkage between control and display (e.g., the frequency-selector knob of a radio directly affects the pointer indicating each station), the following recommendations apply (Warrick, 1947):

a. If the indicator moves through an arc of more than 180 deg, a rotary control should be used (see Fig. 6-9).

b. If the indicator moves through an arc of less than 180 deg, a linear control may be used, provided that the path of control movement parallels the average path of the indicator movement and the indicator and control move in the same relative direction (see Fig. 6-10).

On-Off Controls

The direction of linear control movements for on-off (or increase-decrease) controls, such as levers and toggle switches, is deter-

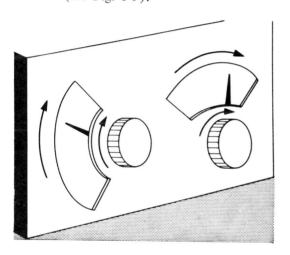

6-7

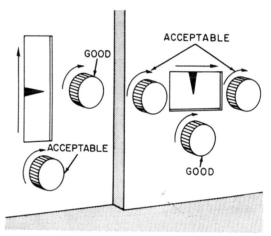

6-8

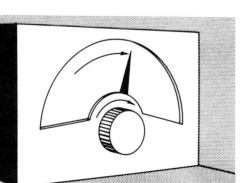

6-9

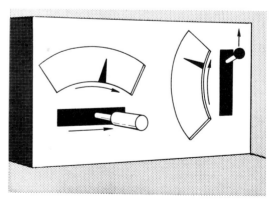

6-10

mined by the location of the panel on which these controls are mounted. Therefore:

1. For controls mounted on vertical panels, "on" or "increase" should be an upward movement, "off" or "decrease" a downward movement.

2. For controls mounted on horizontal panels, "on" or "increase" should be a forward movement, "off" or "decrease" a rearward movement.

3. For controls mounted on sloping panels, there is no sharply defined division between up-and-down and fore-and-aft control movements. When panels are below eye-level, this is unimportant because forward and upward movements both require the operator to apply force in the same general direction. For panels above eye-level, however, a forward movement is opposite that of an upward movement so that, to avoid ambiguous situations, the following recommendations should be observed:

a. For overhead panels tilted *less* than 45 deg from the vertical, controls should be actuated as if the panel were *vertical* ("on" or "increase" should be an upward movement).

b. For overhead panels tilted *more* than 45 deg from the vertical, controls should be actuated as if the panel were *horizontal* ("on" or "increase" should be a forward movement).

6.2.3 *Control resistance*

Some force must always be applied to make a control move. The kinds of resistance offered by the control (and the device to which it is coupled) can be listed as follows:

a. Elastic (spring loading).
b. Static and sliding friction.
c. Viscous damping.
d. Inertia.

Rarely, if ever, is control resistance of a single kind. All controls have some mass and, hence, some inertia; most controls move on a slide, shaft, or pivot and, hence, have some static and sliding friction. In addition, in terms of operator performance, there are inter-

actions among the various kinds of resistance; friction or viscous damping, for example, can be helpful in counteracting the adverse effects of excessive inertia.

Depending on the kind and amount, resistance can affect the following:

a. The precision and speed of control operation.

b. The "feel" of the control.

c. The smoothness of control movement.

d. The susceptibility of the control to accidental activation and to the effects of shock, vibration, g forces, etc.

The designer should build into the control the kind or kinds of resistance that best satisfy performance requirements. The following paragraphs discuss the most important characteristics of the four major kinds of resistance. (See sections 6.3 and 6.4 for specific design recommendations.)

ELASTIC RESISTANCE

Elastic, or spring-loading, resistance has the following characteristics:

a. It varies directly with control displacement but is independent of velocity and acceleration.

b. It applies force toward the null position when the control is displaced; hence, it aids in identifying the null position and in making adjustments around it.

c. It returns the control automatically to the same (null) position when the operator's hand or foot is removed; hence, it is ideal for momentary-contact or "dead-man" switches.

d. It permits quick changes in direction to be made.

e. It allows the operator's hand or foot to rest on the control without activating it if there is sufficient resistance (preloading) at the null position.

f. It reduces the likelihood of undesired activation caused by accidental contact with the control or by shock, g forces, vibration, etc.

g. It provides the operator with feedback information ("feel") concerning control position.

h. It provides constant or adjustable spring tension.

i. It permits the force gradient to be modified to provide special cues about the critical positions of the control (e.g., resistance suddenly increases as a limit is approached).

FRICTIONAL RESISTANCE

Static- and sliding-friction resistance has the following characteristics:

a. It decreases sharply to a constant value when the control starts to move smoothly and continuously but is independent of displacement and acceleration.

b. It tends to hold the control in position.

c. It reduces the likelihood of undesired activation caused by accidental contact with the control or by shock, g forces, vibration, etc.

e. It allows the operator's hand or foot to rest on the control without activating it, provided that there is sufficient static friction.

f. It makes difficult designing to insure a constant amount of friction, but a "locking" device, by which friction can be varied, is easily provided.

VISCOUS-DAMPING RESISTANCE

Viscous-damping resistance has the following characteristics:

a. It varies directly with control velocity but is independent of displacement and acceleration.

b. It resists quick gross movements.

c. It reduces the likelihood of undesired activation caused by accidental contact with the control and by shock, g forces, vibration, etc.

d. It assists the operator in making smooth control movements.

e. It permits rapid changes in direction and small changes in position.

f. It provides the operator with feedback information ("feel") about the velocity of control movement. (It is questionable, however, whether the operator can use this information precisely.)

INERTIAL RESISTANCE

Inertial resistance has the following characteristics:

a. It varies directly with control acceleration but is independent of displacement and velocity.

b. It resists sudden changes in velocity; hence, it aids in making smooth movements or gradual changes in velocity.

c. It reduces the likelihood of undesired activation caused by vibration, etc.

d. It requires that large forces be applied to stop or start control movements quickly; hence, it hinders any changes in direction of movement.

e. It provides the operator with feedback information ("feel") about the acceleration of control movements. (It is questionable, however, whether the operator can use this information precisely.)

f. It increases the difficulty of making precise adjustments quickly because of the danger of overshooting.

6.2.4 Control coding

The primary purpose of coding controls is to make them easy to identify. Making controls easy to identify will decrease the number of times a wrong control is used and will reduce the time required to find the correct control. The proper application of control coding will be reflected not only in improved operator performance but also in reduced training time.

There are a number of methods of coding controls. (See Chapter 2 for a detailed discussion of visual coding.) The five most common methods of coding controls are shape, size, mode-of-operation, labeling, and color. These methods are self-evident except for mode-of-operation, which refers to coding on the basis of the type of movement associated with the control (e.g., vertical movement against tension is typical of and reminds one of a toggle switch; rotary movement with detent action is typical of and reminds one of a rotary selector switch). The following rules

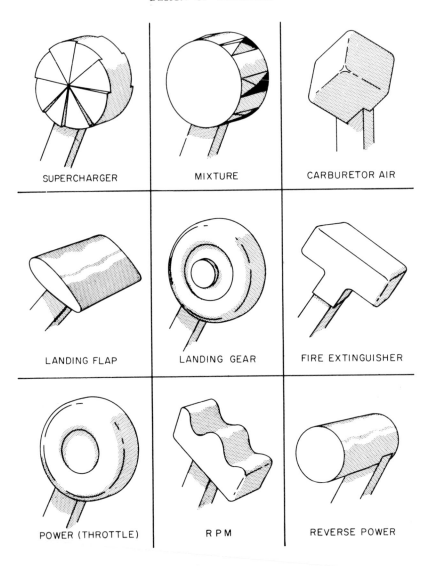

SUPERCHARGER · MIXTURE · CARBURETOR AIR

LANDING FLAP · LANDING GEAR · FIRE EXTINGUISHER

POWER (THROTTLE) · R P M · REVERSE POWER

6-11

should be used in selecting which method, if any, to use:

1. Use standard codes whenever possible.
2. Combine several methods of coding whenever possible.

To some extent, control coding is the natural result of good workplace design (e.g., standardized control positions aid in identification). When the primary purposes of control coding have not been met by other means, however, coding is in order. The specific method or methods of coding to use depend on the following:

a. The total demands on the operator during the time when the control must be identified.

b. The extent and methods of coding already in use.

c. The illumination of the operator's workplace.

d. The speed and accuracy with which controls must be identified.

e. The space available for the location of controls.

f. The number of controls to be coded.

SHAPE CODING

Shape coding improves visual and tactile identification of controls. When feasible, it is desirable to select functional shapes that suggest the purpose of the control because the effectiveness of shape coding depends on the ease with which shapes can be identified. A number of knob shapes that can be used for shape coding are presented in article 6.4.3; other examples are shown in Fig. 6-11. The following rules should be observed in designing shape-coded controls:

1. Use standardized shapes.
2. Avoid sharp edges on the parts of the control that must be grasped (Brennan and Morant, 1950).

SIZE CODING

Controls can be coded by size, but the number of sizes that can be used is limited (see Chapter 2). The ability to discriminate

shape, however, is relatively independent of size so that size coding can be superimposed on shape coding (Eriksen, 1954). Both size and shape coding are less effective, however, if the operator wears thick gloves.

Information is available for "relative" (as against "absolute") size discrimination. Figure 6-12 shows the diameters required for two round knobs when the operator must compare each by touch alone before deciding which is larger. The larger knob should always be about 20% larger than the smaller one for knobs ranging from $\frac{1}{2}$ to 6 in. in diameter.

When the operator cannot compare the sizes of all controls before selecting the proper one, only two or three different sizes of controls should be used (viz., small, medium, and large). When the operator always compares two controls before selecting the proper one, three, four, or five different sizes of controls can be used (Hunt, 1953).

MODE-OF-OPERATION CODING

The mode of operation of a control is a useful method of identifying it. This method of coding can always be used with other methods. Its most severe limitation is that the operator must activate the control (or at least attempt to do so) to identify it.

To use this method most effectively, the designer should vary one or more of the fol-

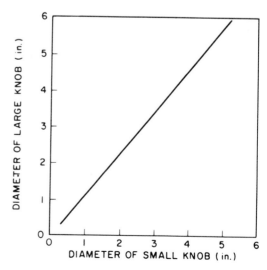

lowing: the direction of movement, the amount of displacement, and the type and amount of resistance. None of these, however, should be varied to the extent that other design principles are violated.

LABELING

Labeling is always an effective means of identifying controls and requires no special training of the operator. The two main prerequisites for using this method are adequate space and lighting (Chapanis, et al., 1949). In addition, the following recommendations should be observed:

1. The label should be either on the control or immediately adjacent to it.

2. The label should be brief, but only common abbreviations should be used.

3. The label should tell what is being controlled (e.g., landing gear, brightness).

4. Common words should be used, and technical words should be used only when they are familiar to all operators.

5. Abstract symbols (squares, stars, etc.) should not be used when they require special training of the operator. Common symbols, used in a conventional manner, are acceptable (e.g., plus, minus, arrow).

6. Letter and numeral style should be standard (see AND 10400) and easily legible (see MIL-C-10812).

COLOR CODING

Color coding is most effective when a specific meaning can be attached to the color (e.g., red for danger). The use of color coding depends, largely, on the color of the illuminant (see Chapter 2). In general, color should not be used as the primary method for coding controls, but it is effective when combined with other methods. Color coding should conform with existing standards (see Chapter 2).

In general, only the following five colors should be used for color coding: red, orange, yellow, green, blue. Additional colors can be used when essential, but, even under ideal conditions, an operator has difficulty in effectively recognizing more than 10 or 12 colors. He can recognize many more colors but is limited primarily by his ability to attach a name to each.

6.2.5 *Preventing accidental activation*

It is always necessary to reduce the possibility of the accidental activation of controls. In some situations, controls might be located in such a way that they are susceptible to being moved while reaching for, or operating, another control. In other situations, the incorrect activation of a control might have such serious implications that it becomes desirable to design the control so that it cannot be operated in haste.

In the application of any of the methods of physically protecting controls against inadvertent activation, it is necessary to consider the extent to which other human-engineering design recommendations are compromised. (For example, in some instances, even though the method provides protection against accidental activation, it might increase the time required to operate the control to such an extent that it is unacceptable.)

Some methods for physically protecting controls against inadvertent activation are as follows:

a. Recessing. Controls can be recessed into the control panel so that they do not protrude above its surface. The major disadvantage of this method is the relatively large amount of panel space that must be used. A related technique is that of placing raised barriers around the control.

b. Location. Controls can be located so that they are unlikely to be hit accidentally. This can be accomplished by isolating one control from the others, or by arranging controls so that the sequence of operations is not conducive to accidental activation.

c. Orientation. The direction of movement of the control can be oriented along an axis

THIS   **NOT THIS**

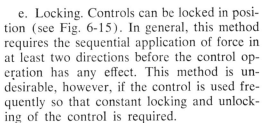

in which accidental forces are least likely to occur (see Fig. 6-13), but care should be taken to insure that recommended direction-of-motion relationships are not violated (see article 6.2.2).

d. Covering. Protective covers or guards can be placed over each control (see Fig. 6-14). If the control is to be operated frequently, however, this method probably should not be used.

e. Locking. Controls can be locked in position (see Fig. 6-15). In general, this method requires the sequential application of force in at least two directions before the control operation has any effect. This method is undesirable, however, if the control is used frequently so that constant locking and unlocking of the control is required.

f. Operation Sequencing. A series of interlocks can prevent Step 2 from being performed before Step 1, Step 3 before Step 2, Step 4 before Step 3, etc. There are two variations of this method. In the first, all the steps prior to the last one have a direct effect on system output. (For example, a bomb-release control that cannot be operated unless the control that arms the bomb has already been activated.) This variation should not be used when the sequence of operation might vary from situation to situation. In the second variation, the steps prior to the last one have no direct effect on system output other than to permit the next control operation to be performed. In the simplest situation, a preliminary operation (e.g., pushing a button, squeezing a trigger) releases the control for its normal operation.

g. Resistance. Use of the proper kind or kinds and amount of resistance prevents accidental forces (below the breakout force) from activating the control. A detailed discussion of the various kinds of resistances can be found in article 6.2.3.

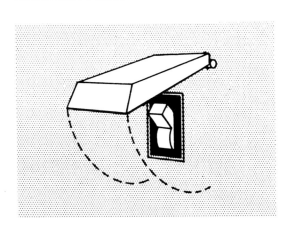

6-14

6-15

6.3 *Design Recommendations for Hand and Foot Controls*

The design recommendations contained in this section have been derived from anthropometric and biomechanical data (see Chapter 11). It is sometimes difficult to evaluate these data. This is especially so if they are the result of only one study. So many variables affect human capabilities in operating controls that the results of one study cannot be generalized or, even, applied to an apparently similar situation. A few differences between, for example, one workplace layout (see Chapter 7) and another might have a decisive effect on the operator's performance on identically designed controls.

In the present state of the art, therefore, these recommendations for control design should be considered more as general guides than as established rules. When more precise values are needed, and they cannot be derived from the data given, the engineer will have to seek help from a human-engineering group (see Chapter 11).

6.3.1 *General principles of control design*

The following general principles apply to the design of all types of controls, whatever their purpose or mode of operation:

1. The maximum force, speed, accuracy, or range of body movement required to operate a control should not exceed the limits of the least capable operator, and normal requirements for control operation should be considerably less than the maximum capabilities of most operators.

This section by Albert Damon, Howard W. Stoudt, and Ross A. McFarland of Harvard University.

2. The number of controls should be kept to a minimum, and the control movements should be as simple and as easy to perform as possible.

3. Control movements that seem "natural" for the operator are more efficient and less fatiguing than those that seem awkward or difficult.

4. Control movements should be as short as possible, consistent with the requirements of accuracy and "feel."

5. Controls should have sufficient resistance so as to reduce the possibility of inadvertent activation by the weight of a hand or foot.

6. For controls requiring single applications of force, or short periods of continuous force, a reasonable maximum resistance is half of the operator's greatest strength. For controls operated continuously, or for long periods, resistances should be much lower.

7. With some types of equipment, such as high-speed aircraft or space vehicles, in which an operator cannot apply enough force, unaided, to operate the controls and power-boosted or fully powered control systems are necessary, artificial resistance cues should be provided.

6.3.2 *Hand controls*

Hand controls should be used in preference to foot controls in the following situations:

a. If accuracy of control positioning is important.

b. If speed of control positioning is required.

c. If continuous or prolonged application of moderate-to-large forces (20 lb or more) is *not* necessary.

WHAT TYPE TO USE

For start-stop or on-off controls, use either pushbuttons or toggle switches. When speed of operation is important, use pushbuttons, but if the controls must be spaced closely together (less than 1 in. between centers), use toggle switches with small dimensions and relatively large resistance to prevent inadvertent operation (Bradley and Wallis, 1959).

For fine-adjustment tasks requiring small forces, such as radio tuning, use either finger- or hand-operated rotary knobs. For discrete control settings operated by applying moderate-to-large forces, such as gear shifting or hand braking, use control sticks or levers. For continuous-adjustment or tracking tasks, sticks, levers, or wheels may be used, but, where very precise control settings are necessary, or in tracking fast-moving targets, hand-wheels or cranks should be used that have high wheel speeds and low gear ratios.

ONE VS. TWO HANDS

For precision and speed, one-hand controls are preferable to those operated with both hands, except for large-diameter handwheels with reciprocal rotary motion (such as vehicle steering wheels), which are best operated with two hands. Controls requiring large forces should be operated with two hands (which, for most controls, about doubles the amount of force that can be applied) depending on control type and location and on the kind and direction of movement as follows:

a. When two hands are used on wheel controls, rotary forces are effectively doubled in most cases (Provins, 1955).

b. When two hands are used on stick or lever controls located along the body midline, *pull* is generally almost doubled, *push* is doubled near the body but is only slightly stronger at distances away from the body, and *push right* or *left* is increased about 50%.

c. When two hands are used on stick or lever controls located on either side of the body midline, at or beyond the shoulder, *pull* is approximately doubled, *push* is not greatly increased except at close distances, *pull right*

on controls located to the left is slightly better with two hands than with only the right hand, and *push right* on controls located to the right is slightly better with two hands than with only the left hand.

DIRECTION OF MOVEMENT

A major requirement is that a control move in the "expected" direction, producing a machine or display movement in a similar direction. For example, a control movement to the right or clockwise should cause the machine or display to which it is linked to move to the right or clockwise (see article 6.2.2). In addition, the movement should not change in direction, but, if it does, continuous, curved movements should be used.

Where great strength must be exerted on a control, push-pull movements should be used. Rotation produces the next highest force, followed in descending order by up-down and right-left movements. In the weakest direction (right-left), control movements are only about one-third as strong as those exerted in the strongest direction (push-pull).

For precision, a single control moving in two or three dimensions is better than separate ones, each moving in one dimension (Orlansky, 1948). Right-handed operators move indicator knobs most precisely between 9 and 12 o'clock with the right hand and between 12 and 3 o'clock with the left hand (Chapanis, 1951b). Where possible, control movement should be terminated by a fixed, mechanical stop rather than by muscular control guided by sight or touch (Barnes, 1936).

SPEED OF MOVEMENT

For speed in control movement, the required precision of movement should be as low as possible because increasing the precision required increases the operating time. Generally, control resistance should be minimal, though a pound or two makes little difference, because control speed decreases as the load increases. For instance, pilots can move "joysticks" at rates up to 75 in./sec with resistances of less than 35 lb, 50 in./sec with a resistance of 35 lb, and 10 in./sec with a resistance of 100 lb (Orlansky, 1948).

The distance moved should be as short as possible because longer movements take more time. Longer movements take proportionately less time, however. For instance, a 4-in. movement will take 0.8 sec, whereas a 16-in. movement will take only 1.0 sec. This is because reaction time (see Chapter 5) and starting time are constant regardless of distance moved, and longer movements permit increasing rates of movement.

The preferred direction of movement for most hand controls is horizontal rather than vertical and fore-and-aft rather than lateral. Horizontal movements generally are faster than vertical ones (Woodson, 1954), and right-left movements are slightly faster than left-right for right-handed operators (Brown and Slater-Hammel, 1949); but, for short linear movements of about 2–3 in. long that require precision, vertical movements are fastest, followed by lateral and fore-and-aft movements (Herbert, 1957).

Handwheels are turned most rapidly when the wheel is nearly vertical (Lehmann, 1958). For handwheels and cranks, speed of movement varies with control resistance and radius (slower speed with larger resistance and radius), but 180 rpm is a good "average" speed (Helson, 1949 and Reed, 1949). Handwheels and cranks should be turned forward or clockwise for maximum speed and efficiency (Provins, 1953 and Baines and King, 1950). Two-hand, simultaneous, positioning movements are fastest when reaching about 30 deg to the left and right of the midplane of the body (Barnes and Mundell, 1939).

RESISTANCE

A hand control should offer some resistance to movement to reduce the possibility of accidental operation (see article 6.2.5), but the resistance should not be so great that it prevents some operators from using it satisfactorily. In general, resistance for hand controls (except finger-operated controls) should not be less than 2 lb. Even below 5 lb, the

pressure sensitivity of the hands is poor (Orlansky, 1948). If the full weight of the arm and hand rest on a control, the minimum resistance should be 10–12 lb; if only the forearm and hand, 5 lb; if only the hand, 2 lb (Dempster, 1955). See section 6.4 for minimum resistances for specific controls.

Limits for maximum resistance for hand controls are difficult to determine because of wide variations in operating populations; type and location of controls; and frequency, duration, direction, and amount of control movement. For example, there is more than a fourfold difference in the push exertable on a control stick depending on whether it is located on the midline of the body away from the operator (maximum), or to the left near the (right-handed) operator (minimum). In spite of this, some recommendations for maximum control resistance can be given and will be found among the recommendations for specific controls (see section 6.4).

HANDGRIPS

A handgrip where thumb and forefinger overlap is much better than a wider grip separating the two (Fox, 1957). Handgrips may be either round or oval in cross-section or contour moulded to the shape of the hand. The best diameter for a handgrip is between ¾ and 1½ in. (Müller, 1934). Minimum diameters depend on the forces exerted: for 10–15 lb, the diameter should be no less than ¼ in. (preferably larger); for 15–25 lb, a minimum of ½ in.; for 25 or more lb, a minimum of ¾ in. Maximum diameters should not greatly exceed 1½ inches, and the length of a handgrip should be at least 3¾ in. to accommodate the full breadth of the hand.

For whole-hand grasping or "trigger" grips in which two elements are squeezed together, the fingers should be placed around the main shaft and the heel of the hand used to close the movable part (Dupuis, et al., 1955). Maximum force can be applied when 2½ in. separate the "trigger" and the heel in the open position (Hertzberg, 1955). In the closed position, this distance should be 1½–2 in. (Dupuis, et al., 1955).

§ 6.3.2

6.3.3 *Foot controls*

Foot controls, rather than hand controls should be considered in the following situations:

a. When a continuous control task is required (if precision of control positioning is not of primary importance).

b. When the application of moderate-to-large forces (greater than about 20–30 lb), whether intermittently or continuously, is necessary.

c. When the hands are in danger of becoming overburdened with control tasks.

Pedals on which pressure is applied by the whole leg, such as an automobile brake pedal, should be used when forces above 10–20 lb are required. Pedals on which pressure is applied mainly from the ankle, such as an automobile accelerator pedal, should be used when small forces (about 10 lb or less) and continuous operation are required. Foot pushbuttons, such as headlight dimmer switches, are advantageous where small forces and intermittent operation are required. For all foot controls, the direction of movement should be down (or away from the body) and in line with the long axis of the lower legs or roughly parallel to the midplane of the body.

6.4 *Design Recommendations for Specific Controls*

This section presents design recommendations for most commonly used controls, i.e., pushbuttons, toggle switches, rotary selector switches, knobs, cranks and levers, handwheels, and pedals. The design of controls similar to these can be helped by extrapolating from the recommendations given here. Recommendations for combined controls (e.g., a hand pushbutton mounted on a lever) can be established from the recommendations given for individual controls.

Along with recommended size and displacement (range of control movement), recommended amounts and kinds of resistance to be built into each control are given. For toggle switches, handwheels, cranks and levers, resistance is described in terms of linear resistance (i.e., the resistance at the point where the operator applies force to the control) rather than torque. For these controls, operator output normally can be considered as a force relatively independent of control radius. For circular knobs, resistance is described in terms of torque. The force that can be brought

to bear on these controls is a function of the "efficiency" of the operator's grasp (i.e., the amount by which the fingers must be spread, etc.), which, in turn, is related to knob diameter.

6.4.1 *Pushbuttons*

Hand pushbuttons are of three major types: push-on-release-off, push-on-push-off, push-on-lock-on. They require only a small amount of space for their location and operation and they can be coded by color or size (see Table 6-2). They can be operated quickly and simultaneously with other pushbuttons in an array (see Fig. 6-16) and are identified easily by their position within an array or by their associated display signal, but control setting (whether "on" or "off") is not identified easily either visually or nonvisually (Hunt, 1953 and Orlansky, 1949). Although they can be very quickly activated, operating time

§ 6.4.1

Table 6-2 Comparison of the Characteristics of Common Controls

Characteristic	Hand push-button	Foot push-button	Toggle switch	Rotary switch	Knob	Crank	Lever	Hand-wheel	Pedal
Space required	Small	Large	Small	Medium	Small-medium	Medium-large	Medium-large	Large	Large
Effectiveness of coding	Fair-good	Poor	Fair	Good	Good	Fair	Good	Fair	Poor
Ease of visual identification of control setting	Poor[1]	Poor	Fair-good	Fair-good	Fair-good[2]	Poor[3]	Fair-good	Poor-fair	Poor
Ease of tactile identification of control setting	Poor	Poor	Good	Fair-good	Poor-good	Poor[3]	Poor-fair	Poor-fair	Poor-fair
Ease of check reading in array of like controls	Poor[1]	Poor	Good	Good	Good[2]	Poor[3]	Good	Poor	Poor
Ease of operation in array of like controls	Good	Poor	Good	Poor	Poor	Poor	Good	Poor	Poor
Effectiveness in combined control	Good	Poor	Good	Fair	Good[4]	Poor	Good	Good	Poor

[1] Except when control is backlighted (see Chapter 2) and light comes on when control is activated.
[2] Applicable only when control makes less than one rotation and when round knobs have pointer attached.
[3] Assumes control makes more than one rotation.
[4] Effective primarily when mounted concentrically on one axis with other knobs.

266

§ 6.4.1

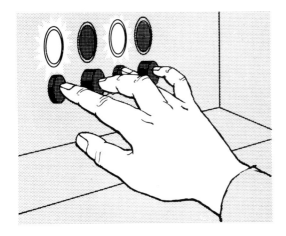

increases with excessive displacement and/or resistance.

Foot pushbuttons are of two major types: push-on-release-off, and push-on-push-off. They leave the hands free for other operations, but require a large amount of space for their operation because of the swept volume of the foot (see Table 6-2). Because it usually cannot be seen or felt (without danger of activating it), neither the control nor its setting (whether "on" or "off") is easily identified, but it is quickly activated when the foot is

on it. Operating time increases with increase in required displacement and/or resistance, and toe-operated controls are activated slightly faster than heel-operated ones (Barnes, et al., 1942).

HAND PUSHBUTTONS

Some design recommendations are given in Table 6-3; others are listed as follows:

1. Use elastic resistance (aided by a slight amount of sliding friction if necessary) starting low and building up rapidly with a sudden drop to indicate that the control has been activated (see Fig. 6-17). Minimize viscous-damping and inertial resistance.

2. The top of the pushbutton should be concave to fit the finger (see Fig. 6-18).

Table 6-3   Design Recommendations for Pushbutton Controls

Activated by	Fingertip	Ball of foot
Diameter		
Minimum	$\frac{1}{2}$ in.[1]	$\frac{1}{2}$ in.
Maximum	—	—
Displacement		
Minimum	$\frac{1}{8}$ in.	$\frac{1}{2}$ in.[2]
Maximum	$1\frac{1}{2}$ in.	$2\frac{1}{2}$–4 in.[3]
Resistance		
Minimum	10 oz	4–10 lb[4]
Maximum	40 oz	20 lb

[1] Emergency controls that can be activated by thumb or heel of hand should have minimum diameter of $\frac{3}{4}$ in.

[2] For operator wearing heavy boots, minimum displacement should be 1 in.

[3] First number is for controls activated by ankle flexion only; second number is for controls activated by leg movement.

[4] First number is for case where foot will *not* rest on control; second number is for case where foot *may* rest on control.

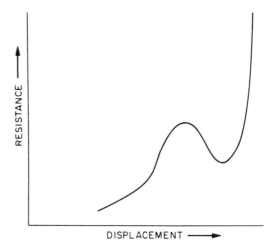

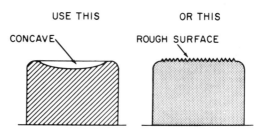

USE THIS   OR THIS

CONCAVE   ROUGH SURFACE

6-18

§ 6.4.1

When this is impractical, it should have a rough surface to prevent slipping.

3. To indicate that the control has been activated, an audible click should be provided if the working environment is not too noisy for the click to be heard.

FOOT PUSHBUTTONS

Some design recommendations are given in Table 6-3; others are listed as follows:

1. Use elastic resistance, aided by static friction, to support the foot. The resistance should start low, build up rapidly, then drop suddenly to indicate that the control has been activated. Minimize viscous-damping and inertial resistance.

2. Design for toe-operation (by the ball of the foot) rather than heel-operation.

3. Where space permits, foot pushbuttons should be replaced by pedals hinged at the heel. This device serves as a pushbutton and also aids in locating and activating the control.

6.4.2 Switches

Toggle switches usually have two positions; they may have more, but speed and ease of

operation are sacrificed if they do. These switches require only a small amount of space for their location and operation (see Table 6-2). They can be operated quickly and simultaneously with other toggle switches in a row (see Fig. 6-19) and are identified easily by their proximity to the associated display or by their location within an array. Control setting (position) is identifiable both visually and nonvisually, provided that it has a small number of positions (preferably two, but three are acceptable).

Rotary switches usually have between three and 24 settings (positions). They may have more, but speed and accuracy of setting and checking are sacrificed if they do (Chapanis, 1951b and 1951c). These switches require a medium amount of space for operation because of the swept volume of the hand (see Fig. 6-20). When a large number of discrete settings is needed, however, one rotary selector switch requires less space than an array of pushbuttons or toggle switches. Rotary switches are quickly activated and easily coded by color or shape, and control setting (position) can be identified visually and nonvisually if properly designed (see Table 6-2).

Rotary switches can have either a moving pointer and fixed scale or a moving scale and fixed index, but a moving pointer with a fixed scale is preferred for most tasks (see Chapter

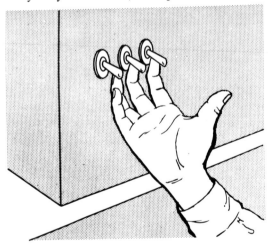

6-19

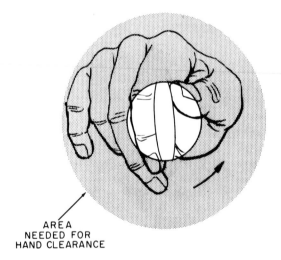

AREA
NEEDED FOR
HAND CLEARANCE

6-20

§ 6.4.2

6-21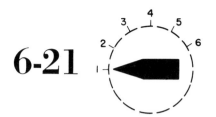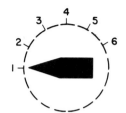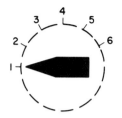

2). The moving-pointer type can conform with direction-of-motion relationships (see article 6.2.2) without violating other principles, and it facilitates check reading control position for individual controls and for arrays of controls (see Fig. 6-21). With the moving-scale type, the setting always reads from the same position (see Fig. 6-22),

but the index can be located at any one of the four cardinal points, depending on which is most desirable for the specific situation. In addition, a small segment of the entire scale is all that need be shown. With the open-window arrangement shown in Fig. 6-23, the clutter of numbers on the panel is reduced to a minimum.

TOGGLE SWITCHES

Some design recommendations are given in Table 6-4; others are listed as follows:

1. Use elastic resistance in such a way that it builds up and then decreases as the desired position is approached so that the control will snap into position and not stop between adjacent positions.

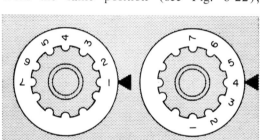

6-22

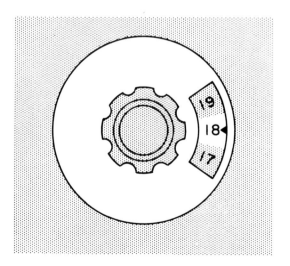

6-23

Table 6-4   Design Recommendations for Toggle-Switch Controls

Lever-tip diameter [1]	
Minimum	$\frac{1}{8}$ in.
Maximum	1 in.
Lever-arm length [1]	
Minimum	$\frac{1}{2}$ in.
Maximum	2 in.
Displacement [1]	
Minimum	40 deg [2]
Maximum	120 deg [3]
Resistance	
Minimum	10 oz
Maximum	40 oz
Number of positions	
Minimum	2
Maximum	3

[1] See Fig. 6-24.
[2] Between adjacent positions.
[3] Total displacement.

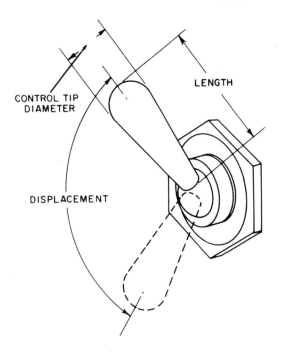

CONTROL TIP DIAMETER

LENGTH

DISPLACEMENT

Table 6-5 Design Recommendations for Rotary Selector-Switch Controls

Type	Pointer [1]	Knob [2]
Width or diameter		
Minimum	—	1 in.
Maximum	1 in.	4 in.
Depth		
Minimum	$\frac{1}{2}$ in.	$\frac{1}{2}$ in.
Maximum	3 in.	3 in.
Length		
Minimum	1 in.	n.a.
Maximum	—	n.a.
Displacement [3]		
Minimum	15–30 deg [4]	15–30 deg [4]
Maximum	40 deg [5]	40 deg [5]
Resistance		
Minimum	12 oz	12 oz
Maximum	48 oz	48 oz
Number of positions		
Minimum	3	3
Maximum	24	24

[1] Moving pointer, fixed scale (see Fig. 6-25).
[2] Moving scale, fixed index (see Fig. 6-26).
[3] Between adjacent detents.
[4] First number is for visual positioning; second number is for tactile positioning.
[5] When special requirements demand large separations, max. should be 90 deg.

2. Minimize frictional and inertial resistances.

ROTARY SWITCHES

Some design recommendations are given in Table 6-5; others are listed as follows:

1. Provide detents at each control position (setting).

2. Use elastic resistance that builds up and then decreases as each position (detent) is approached so that the control will fall into each detent and cannot easily stop between adjacent detents. Minimize frictional and inertial resistances.

3. Round knobs should not be used for detent controls because they are not effective for the application of large torques.

4. It is undersirable for a rotary selector switch to have more than 24 positions. When more than 24 positions must be made available, the minimum separation between adjacent positions should be $\frac{1}{4}$ in. at the index marks.

5. Control positions should not be 180 deg from each other (see Fig. 6-27). If followed, this rule will help to reduce errors in setting

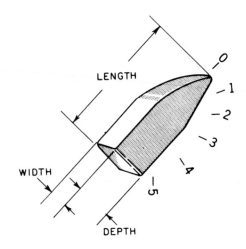

LENGTH

WIDTH

DEPTH

0
1
2
3
4
5

6-25

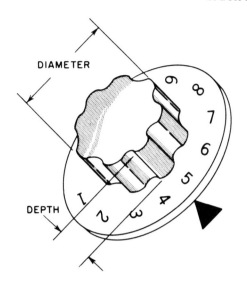

and reading the wrong end of the moving pointer.

6. Stops should be placed at the beginning and end of the range of control positions. This will facilitate blind-positioning by enabling the operator to count the number of settings (by the feel of the detent action or by the sound of the click) from a starting position.

7. Moving pointers should be bar-type knobs with tapered tips.

6.4.3 *Knobs*

Knobs are effective for making small turning operations that do not require the application of large forces, and they require only a small-to-medium amount of space for their operation because of the swept volume of the hand (see Fig. 6-28). They are easily coded by color, size, or shape (see below), and control setting (position) is visually identifiable if the control makes less than one rotation and has a pointer or marker attached (see Table 6-2).

Knobs can have an unlimited range of control movement, and, with proper gearing, they can be used for either gross or fine positioning over a wide range of adjustments. In addition, a folding crank handle can be at-

tached to the knob to aid in rapid slewing (see Fig. 6-29). Knobs can be "ganged" by mounting them on concentric shafts. Mounting more than two knobs on the same shaft, however, is likely to be wasteful of panel space, but it might be desirable for other reasons such as facilitating a sequence of operations.

Knobs lend themselves well to shape coding. For shape-coding purposes, knobs can be divided into the following three classes (Hunt and Craig, 1954):

a. Those for twirling or spinning (more than one full turn is required) for which knob position is *not* important (Class A).

b. Those for which less than one full turn is required and knob position is *not* important (Class B).

c. Those for which less than one full turn is required, and knob position *is* important (Class C).

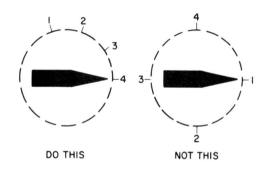

DO THIS   NOT THIS

6-27

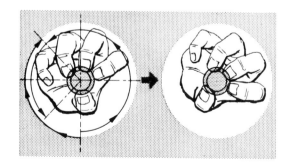

6-28

Figure 6-30 shows examples of all three classes. Each knob can be identified by touch alone with the bare hand or while wearing lightweight gloves. All of these knobs can be used together without confusing one with the other, with the following exceptions:

a. Do not use knobs of class A-3 with those of B-4.

b. Do not use knobs of class B-1 with those of B-5.

c. Do not use knobs of class B-2 with those of B-3 or B-4.

DESIGN RECOMMENDATIONS

Within the ranges recommended in Table 6-6, knob size is relatively unimportant provided the C/D ratio is optimum, the resistance low, and the knob easily grasped (Jenkins and Connor, 1949). When panel space is limited, the use of minimum values for knob size will not degrade performance, provided that knob resistance is very low (Stump, 1953).

Knob diameters have little effect on speed and accuracy. Diameters of ½–2 in. are generally acceptable (Jenkins and Connor, 1949 and Craik and Vince, 1945). Diameters of 2

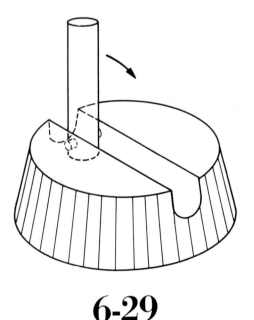

6-29

Table 6-6   Design Recommendations for Knob Controls

Grasp	Fingertip	Palm of hand
Diameter		
Minimum	¼ in.	1½ in.
Maximum	4 in.	3 in.
Depth		
Minimum	½ in.	
Maximum	1 in.	
Displacement	Depends on C/D ratio	
Resistance		
Minimum	—	—
Maximum	4½–6 oz *	

* First number is for 1-in.-diameter knobs; second number is for larger knobs.

in. provide smooth operation at any resistance, though smaller diameters can be used with moderate resistances (1¾–3½ oz or less). If resistances are above 5¼–7 oz, knob diameters should be at least 1½ in. in diameter (Bradley and Arginteanu, 1956).

For concentric, ganged knobs, the best arrangement is with knobs greater than ½ in. in diameter and ¾–1¼ in. between their edges (Bradley, 1957). Where three knobs are concentric, the best diameters are ½–1 in. for the front or top knob, 2 in. for the middle one, and 3¼ in. for the back or bottom one (Bradley and Stump, 1955). Minimum knob depth should be about ½ in., and the best depth is about ¾ in.

The kind or kinds of resistance that should be provided depends, primarily, on performance requirements. When other kinds of resistance are satisfactory for precise positioning tasks, changes in inertial resistance have little practical effect on performance until an excessive level is reached (Jenkins, et al., 1951), but the addition of inertial resistance can counteract some of the harmful effects of friction, and vice versa (Searle and Taylor, 1948).

When bracketing is used for locating a visual or auditory null position (e.g., tuning a transmitter), the knob should move through

§ 6.4.3

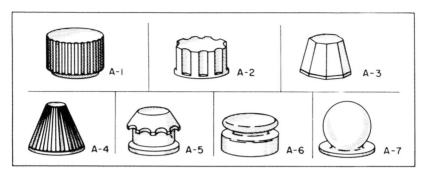

CLASS A

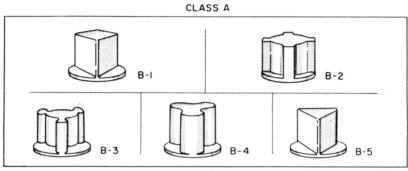

CLASS B

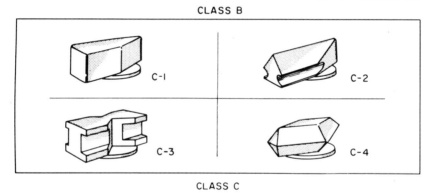

CLASS C

6-30

an arc of 30–60 deg on either side of the null position for a misalignment to be just noticeable (Craik and Vince, 1945). Finger-operated knobs used for fine adjustment should have 1–2 in. of pointer movement for one complete turn of the knob. If less pointer movement is required, lower ratios (less pointer movement per turn of knob) should be provided; for more pointer movement, higher ratios should be provided. In general, accuracy increases as the ratio decreases (Jenkins and Connor, 1949).

6.4.4 *Cranks and levers*

Cranks are effective in making adjustments on a continuum when large distances must be covered and high rates of turning are required; for slower rates, a knob or handwheel is more effective (Baines and King, 1950; Helson, 1949; and Reed, 1949). Cranks require a medium-to-large amount of space for their location and operation (turning) because of the swept volume of the hand (see Fig. 6-31).

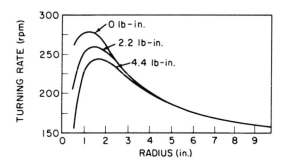

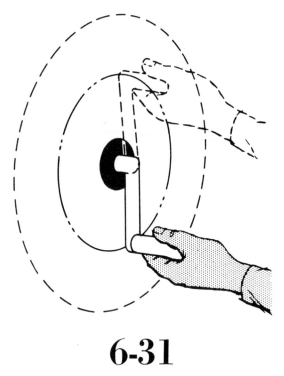

6-31

Because cranks are usually multirotational, the position of the crank handle generally does not indicate the control setting (position). Cranks can have an unlimited range of control movement, and, with proper gearing, can be used for either gross or fine positioning over a wide range of adjustments (see Table 6-2).

Cranks can be attached to knobs or handwheels to increase the versatility of that control. Under no-load conditions, small cranks can be turned more rapidly than large ones. As the load increases, however, the crank size that maximizes turning rate also increases (see Fig. 6-32). For rotating cranks at a constant rate, larger cranks (about 4½ in. in radius) are better than smaller ones (Foxboro, 1943).

Levers include "joysticks," gear shifts, and controls such as aircraft throttles. Levers are usually designed to move when force is applied, but they also may be designed to remain fixed in one position. For these "rigid" (or "pressure") controls, the amount of force being applied is used as the input to the system. Both rigid and spring-loaded levers are characterized by their elastic resistance. Spring-loaded levers are generally preferred because their control positions (settings) can be determined visually and because they provide the operator with feedback information about both control position and resistance (thus giving him better "feel"). The primary advantage of rigid levers is that they require no extra space for displacement.

Spring-loaded levers require a medium-to-large amount of space for their location and operation; they are easily coded by color, size, or shape; and control setting (position) can be identified fairly well, both visually and

274

nonvisually (see Table 6-2). Because they generally have a limited range of movement, however, levers are usually unsatisfactory for precise positioning over a wide range of adjustments. For making large fore-and-aft movements, a long lever is usually more desirable than a short one because the movements of a long lever are more nearly linear.

CRANKS

Some design recommendations are given in Table 6-7; others are listed as follows:

1. Cranks, rather than knobs or handwheels, should be used for tasks involving at least two rotations of control movement; knobs and handwheels are better when the task requires less movement.

2. For tasks involving large slewing movements plus small fine adjustments, a crank handle may be mounted on a knob or handwheel for fine adjusting. (An alternative practice would be to provide rate-control rather than position-control for such tasks.)

3. For small cranks (less than $3\frac{1}{2}$ in. in radius) for rapid, steady turning, the minimum resistance should be 2 lb and the maximum 5 lb.

4. For large cranks (5–8 in. in radius) for rapid, steady turning, the minimum resistance should be 5 lb and the maximum 10 lb.

5. For large cranks for precise settings (adjusting between one half and one rotation),

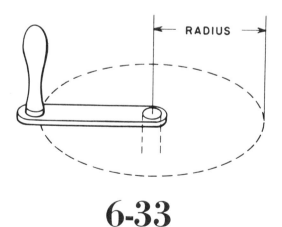

6-33

6-34

Table 6-7 Design Recommendations for Crank and Lever Controls

Control	Crank	Lever
Radius [1] or length		
Minimum	$\frac{1}{2}$ in.	—[2]
Maximum	$4\frac{1}{2}$–20 [3]	—[2]
Handle diameter [4]		
Minimum	1 in.	1 in.
Maximum	3 in.	3 in.
Handle depth [4]		
Minimum	3 in.	3 in.
Maximum	—	—
Displacement		
Minimum	n.a.	—
Maximum	n.a.	14–38 in.[5]
Resistance	See text	See text

[1] See Fig. 6-33

[2] Depends on mechanical advantage required.

[3] First number is for light loads; second number is for heavy loads.

[4] See Fig. 6-34 above.

[5] First number is for fore-and-aft movements; second number is for lateral movements.

the minimum resistance should be $2\frac{1}{2}$ lb and the maximum 8 lb.

6. The kind or kinds of resistance to be provided depends, primarily, on performance requirements. In general, however, any resistance will decrease the maximum rate of turning (about 275 rpm). Friction of 2–5 lb

275

reduces the effects of shock (Hick, 1945), but friction degrades performance in rotating cranks at constant rates: primarily at low rates (3–10 rpm), slightly at moderate rates (about 30 rpm), and negligibly at high rates (above 100 rpm). Inertial resistance aids performance in rotating cranks at constant rates, particularly for small cranks and at low rates.

7. The crank handle should be designed so that it turns freely around its shaft (see Fig. 6-35).

LEVERS

Some design recommendations are given in Table 6-7; others are listed as follows:

1. The minimum resistance for a lever grasped by the hand (rather than the fingers) should be 2 lb.

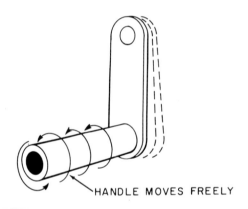

HANDLE MOVES FREELY

2. The maximum resistance for one-hand push-pull (fore-and-aft) movements with the control along the midline of the body should be 30–50 lb, depending on how far away the control is from the body (the farther away, the greater the recommended resistance).

3. The maximum resistance for two-hand push-pull (fore-and-aft) movements should be twice as much as for one-hand operation.

4. The maximum resistance for one-hand, right-left (lateral) movements should be 20 lb.

5. The maximum resistance for two-hand right-left movements should be 30 lb.

6. The kind or kinds of resistance that should be provided depends primarily on per-

formance requirements, but for any guidance "joystick," elastic resistance that increases nonlinearly may be used to improve stick "feel" for the operator.

7. Levers are most effective when they move through an arc of not more than 90 deg (see Fig. 6-36), but in any event, the range of movement should never exceed the convenient reach of the arm.

8. When the knob on the lever is spherical (see Fig. 6-37), it should have a minimum diameter, for finger grasp, of ½ in. and, for hand grasp, of 1½ in. In addition, its maximum diameter should be 3 in.

9. For making fine adjustments, support should be provided for the body part being used: elbow support for large hand movements, forearm support for small hand movements, and wrist support for finger movements.

10. In making very fine adjustments with a small "joystick," operators rest their wrists on the control panel and grasp the control pencil-style below the tip rather than on it. For such situations, the pivot point should be recessed below the surface on which the wrist rests (see Fig. 6-38).

11. When levers are used as discrete adjustment controls, if the lever arm is longer than 6 in., the minimum separation between control positions should be 2 in. (see Fig. 6-39). When the control also serves as a visual indicator (see Fig. 6-40), control positions may be placed closer to each other, their minimum separation being largely determined by the operator's ability to see them (see Chapter 2).

6.4.5 Handwheels and pedals

Handwheels are useful for exerting greater rotary force than is possible with knobs and cranks, but they require a large amount of space for their location and operation (see Table 6-2). They can be coded by color effec-

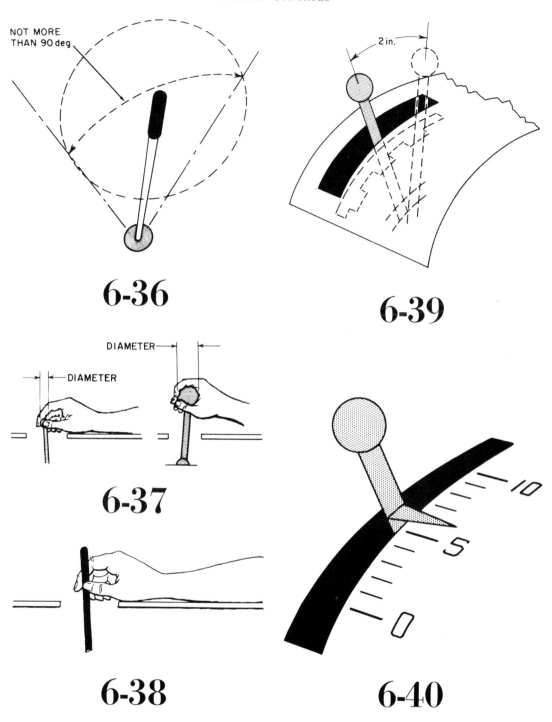

6-36

6-39

6-37

6-38

6-40

tively, but identification of control setting (position) is poor or impossible if multiple rotations are permitted.

Pedals are of three major types: rotary, reciprocating, and translatory (see Fig. 6-41). They require a large amount of space for their location and operation, and, because they usually cannot be seen or felt (without danger of activating them), neither the controls nor their settings (positions) are easily identified (see Table 6-2). Pedals permit more force to be applied, but with less precision and speed, than do hand controls. Rotary pedals have unlimited range of control movements and, with proper gearing, can be used for either gross or precise positioning over a wide range of adjustments. Reciprocating and translatory pedals have limited ranges of control movement and are unsatisfactory for precise positioning over a wide range of adjustments.

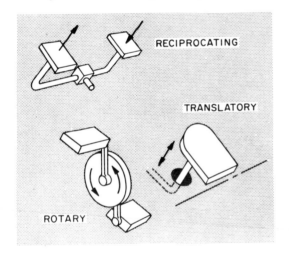

RECIPROCATING

TRANSLATORY

ROTARY

HANDWHEELS

Some design recommendations are given in Table 6-8; others are listed as follows:

1. For most effective use, handwheel displacement should not exceed ±60 deg from the normal (null) position because larger arcs require the hands to shift position on the control (see Fig. 6-44).

2. Displacement should be determined by the desired C/D ratio. When the handwheel must move through a large arc, the C/D ratio can be increased either by increasing the number of control rotations per unit movement of the controlled object or by increasing the handwheel diameter. When handwheel movement is limited to small arcs, the C/D ratio can be increased by increasing the handwheel diameter. In the latter situation, control movements are nearly linear, so that increasing the extent of control movement will increase the C/D ratio even though the arc of rotation is not increased.

3. The diameter of the handwheel rim should not exceed $\frac{3}{4}$–2 in.

4. The kind or kinds of resistance that should be provided depends, primarily, on performance requirements, but, for controls moving through small arcs, inertial resistance should be minimized, and, for aircraft handwheels, resistance should be elastic and increase nonlinearly from 5 to 30 lb.

5. Contour molding should be provided on the handwheel rim to aid in holding it.

6. When the maximum displacement is less than 120 deg, only the two sections of the handwheel that the operator grasps need be provided (see Fig. 6-45). These parts are usually the chords of arcs, each approximately 6 in. long, across from one another. Eliminat-

Table 6-8 Design Recommendations for Handwheel and Pedal Controls

Control	Handwheel	Pedal
Size		
Minimum	7 in. dia.	$3\frac{1}{2} \times 3$ in.[1]
Maximum	21 in. dia.	—
Displacement		
Minimum	—	½ in.
Maximum	120 deg	2–7 in.[2]
Resistance		
Minimum	5 lb	4–10 lb[3]
Maximum	30–50 lb[4]	10–200 lb[2]

[1] See Fig. 6-42.

[2] First number is for controls activated by ankle flexion only; second number is for controls activated by leg movements (see Fig. 6-43).

[3] First number is for case where foot will *not* rest on control; second number is for case where foot *may* rest on control.

[4] First number is for one-hand operation; second number is for two-hand operation.

§ 6.4.5

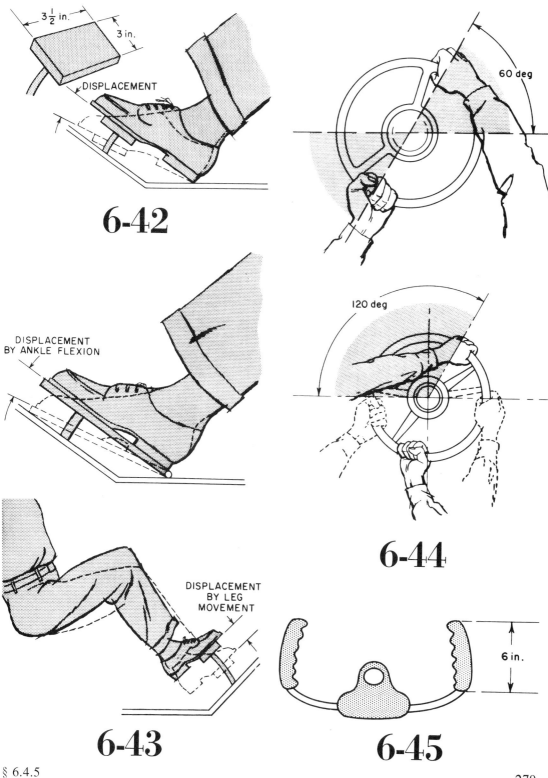

$3\frac{1}{2}$ in.

3 in.

DISPLACEMENT

6-42

60 deg

120 deg

6-44

DISPLACEMENT
BY ANKLE FLEXION

DISPLACEMENT
BY LEG
MOVEMENT

6 in.

6-43

6-45

ing the rest of the control increases the visual and pedal areas (see Chapter 7).

PEDALS

Some design recommendations are given in Table 6-8; others are listed as follows:

1. The kind or kinds of resistance that should be provided depends, primarily, on performance requirements, but, in most situations, the pedal should return to its null position when force is removed.

2. Maximum pedal resistance should never exceed the maximum pressure exertable by the weakest operator. Accordingly, for male military personnel and for most male workers, resistance for leg-operated (as opposed to ankle-operated) pedals should not exceed 200 lb for single, brief applications (Elbel, 1949 and Hugh-Jones, 1947).

3. For frequently but not continuously used leg-operated pedals, a force of about 30% of the maximum exertable is reasonable (Dupuis, et al., 1955).

4. For ankle-operated pedals in continuous use, such as an automobile accelerator, maximum resistance should be about 10 lb (Dupuis, 1958).

5. The minimum resistance for leg-operated pedals should be about 10 lb to exceed by a good safety margin the 7-lb average force exerted on the pedal by the weight of the leg alone (Orlansky, 1948).

6. Minimum resistance for ankle-operated pedals may be about 4 lb less than that for leg-operated pedals.

7. The optimum range of resistance for leg-operated pedals is 8–60 lb (Orlansky, 1948).

8. For ankle-operated pedals, the optimum resistance is $6\frac{1}{2}$–9 lb (Lehmann, 1958).

9. Pedals operated by the entire leg generally should have a 2–4 in. displacement, except for an automobile-brake type of pedal, for which an additional 2–3 in. of travel may be added (Dupuis, et al., 1955). Caution: displacements of 3–4 in. or more should never be coupled with resistances of less than 10 lb.

10. Pedals operated by ankle action should have a maximum travel of about 2 in., corresponding to a motion angle of about 10–12 deg. Caution: no motion angle greater than 30 deg should be used because this is about half the total range of ankle movement (Dupuis, et al., 1955 and Dupuis, 1958).

11. Heavy footgear makes it difficult to gauge pedal travel, and excessive movement and force usually result. Under such conditions, pedal travel should be increased (Clark and Weddell, 1944). The minimum should be increased by at least $\frac{1}{2}$ in. (Ely, et al., 1956).

12. The angulation of most pedals operated by leg action at the hip and knee should permit the foot to be placed on the pedal surface with the ankle at a 90-deg angle, but pedal angulation will vary considerably with vertical and fore-and-aft pedal location. For example it has been found that the forces applied to aircraft brake pedals dropped off sharply as the pedal angle (with the vertical) decreased below 20 deg or increased above 40 deg, and maximum forces were at pedal angles of about 30 deg (Hertzberg, 1954).

13. The angulation of most pedals operated by ankle action also varies widely with vertical and fore-and-aft location. In general, however, the angle of the pedal surface should permit the foot and lower leg to form an angle of at least 90 deg but never more than 130 deg. Foot-leg angles of less than 90 deg should be avoided, except when greater forces are needed for brief intervals.

14. Most pedals should be as wide, or almost as wide, as the sole of the shoe, i.e., at least $3\frac{1}{2}$ in. What the maximum width is matters little as long as there is enough clearance between adjacent pedals.

15. Pedals used intermittently or for short periods should be at least 3 in. long. Pedals used continuously or for long periods should be 11–12 in. long.

16. Pedal shape is not very important; it can be square, rectangular, circular, or oval as long as it is flat and affords a large enough area of contact with the shoe.

17. For pedals with which large forces must be exerted, i.e., 200 lbs or more, a pedal bar (or recessed heel section) will prevent the foot from slipping off the pedal and will assist the operator in locating the pedal by feel. (This is particularly advantageous in cold weather or with large, heavy boots.)

§ 6.4.5

7

layout of workplaces

MANY DETAILS affecting men and equipment must be considered in the layout of workplaces, but it is seldom possible to provide optimum conditions throughout the design. The recommendations presented in this chapter, therefore, are intended to guide the designer in making the best possible compromise in each case. It is not the purpose of this chapter to cover the topic of system analysis; this subject is covered in Chapter 1.

To make the fullest use of the information contained in this chapter, the following steps should be taken:

1. Establish a clear and explicit set of requirements.

2. Make sure that all design requirements have been considered.

3. Keep the design "tentative" until you are sure about the facts.

4. Use mockups to evaluate alternate layouts and to check the final layout.

The designer should obtain information about requirements before beginning to design

the workplace. Unless the following information is available, the designer might include undesirable characteristics that are not detectable until late in the development stage:

a. The purpose or mission of the system.

b. The mission profile or detailed steps in conducting typical and atypical missions.

c. The tolerances allowable in the performance of the system—accuracy, speed, etc.

d. The effects on system performance when various tolerances are not met.

e. The specific tasks that the operator must perform—sequences to be followed, relative importance of each task, relative frequency and time duration for each task.

f. The inputs to the operator—information that he needs to accomplish his specific tasks.

g. The outputs of the operator—data provided by the operator to influence the system.

h. The anticipated environmental conditions—temperature, humidity, noise, illumination, vibration, ventilation, radiation, altitude, body position, accelerative forces, etc. (see Chapter 10).

i. The specific pieces of equipment already committed to the design.

j. Maintenance access and clearance requirements (see Chapter 8).

This chapter was drafted, for the most part, by Jerome H. Ely, Robert M. Thomson, and Jesse Orlansky of Dunlap and Associates, Inc.

281

7.1 *General Rules*

Specific rules for various aspects of the workplace are presented in later sections. The following general rules for workplace layout should be observed (Kennedy, et al., 1952):

1. Retain the same relative grouping for major controls and displays in all similar models of equipment, and design similar controls and displays so that they operate in the same manner. If, for any reason, this cannot be accomplished, make any exception obvious and drastic; this procedure reduces confusion in shifting from one device to another, thus minimizing the possibility of error.

2. Make special provisions for emergency controls and displays in the following ways:

a. Distinguish between emergency controls or displays and those used during normal operations by physically separating normal controls and displays from emergency ones. If physical separation would result in an inaccessible or poorly placed control (see below), provide the normal control with an emergency mode or special operating position. This can be accomplished by adding an emergency release, going through a detent, exceeding a minimum force, etc.

b. Place emergency controls in locations that are easily accessible, regardless of the momentary body attitude of the operator.

c. Place emergency controls and displays within 30 deg of the operator's normal line of sight (see Fig. 7-1).

d. Provide special measures (guards, color coding, etc.) for emergency controls to aid in identification and to prevent inadvertent operation (see Fig. 7-2).

3. When one hand or foot must operate two or more controls in sequence, arrange the controls to allow for continuous limb movement (from left to right, through an arc, etc.). This recommendation, however, should not take priority over basic rules for locating controls (see section 7.3) and proper direction-of-movement relationships (see Chapter 6).

4. Distribute the controls in such a way that none of the operator's hands or feet will be overburdened and each will be used most effectively. The following should be observed:

a. Assign to the hands controls that require precision and/or speed of operation.

b. When there is only one major control that at times must be operated by either or

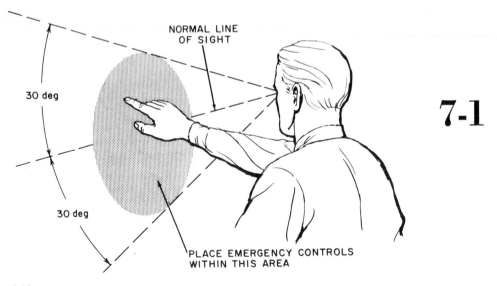

NORMAL LINE OF SIGHT

30 deg

30 deg

7-1

PLACE EMERGENCY CONTROLS WITHIN THIS AREA

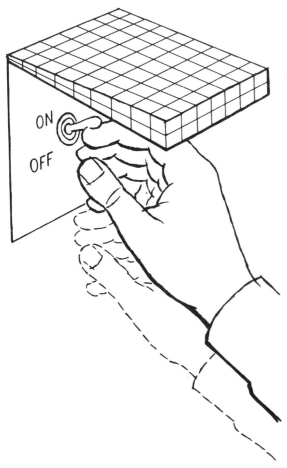

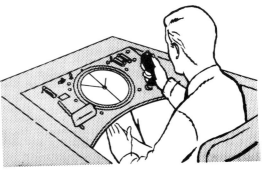

7-3

both hands, place the control in front of the operator, midway between his hands.

c. When the primary control is to be operated by one hand it should be located on the operator's right for right-hand operation (see Fig. 7-3).

d. Assign the major load to the right hand because most people are right-handed.

e. Assign to the feet controls that require large applications of force.

5. When the seated operator must apply a force of more than 5 lb to a control with one hand, provide the operator with a support, e.g., backrest for pushing and footrest for pulling.

6. Design the workplace so that the operator can move his trunk or entire body, particularly when heavy forces (more than 30 lb) or large movements (more than 15 in. in the fore-and-aft direction) must be made with the hands. If seated, the operator should be able to bend forward from the waist.

7. When controls must be positioned precisely, provide a support for the hand or foot being used. Such support should permit the limb to slide smoothly (see Fig. 7-4). For finger-operated controls provide a rest for the wrist or heel of the hand. For hand-operated controls, provide an armrest, either as part of

7-4

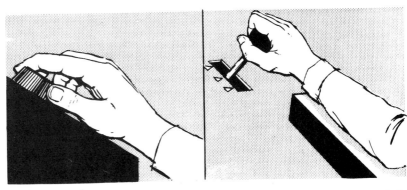

the seat or, if there is sufficient space, on the panel itself.

8. When the operator is on duty for long periods of time, arrange the workplace so that he can change his posture and so that the larger body members (arms, legs, trunk), as well as the hands and feet, can be moved about freely.

7.2 *Workplace Dimensions*

Proper workplace layout requires that consideration be given to various workplace dimensions. Controls and displays should be located with due regard to the operator's size, his position (seated or standing), the directions in which he can look most easily, and the spaces in which he can manipulate controls best. Consideration also should be given to special influences such as protective clothing and accelerative forces. For instance, the supine position is used to counteract accelerative forces and/or to reduce the vertical height or silhouette of a vehicle, but the fully supine position (flat on the back) is not useful because it greatly reduces the operating capacity of the body members and blocks off forward vision. The semisupine position, however, is equivalent to the seated position with a large backward tilt, and workplace dimensions for the seated position should include positions varying from the upright to a backward tilt of 60 deg to include the semisupine position.

The following workplace dimensions are given in this section:

a. Optimum dimensions. These dimensions define the most desirable space for the location of controls and displays, and the most important controls and displays should be placed within this space.

b. Overall dimensions. These dimensions define the acceptable, but not necessarily the most desirable, space for the location of controls and displays. (The overall dimensions will always include and be larger than the space bounded by the optimum dimensions.) All normally used controls and displays should be located within this space; controls that are outside this space are either too close or too far from the operator.

The dimensions given in this section will include about 90% of the operator population. Extreme dimensions are represented by the 5th percentile (small operator) and the 95th percentile (large operator). Operators outside this range will be accommodated but not as comfortably. Operator dimensions are based on personnel who are generally different from the population at large, but the techniques described for determining limiting dimensions are applicable to any population; the designer must choose dimensions from the appropriate population. This he can do by referring to Chapter 11 of this Guide.

7.2.1 *Seated operators*

The seated position is superior to the standing position in the following ways:

a. In the reduction of fatigue. The operator can perform light work with his arms and heavy work with his legs for a much longer time when seated than he can when standing.

b. In increased stability and equilibrium. The operator's body is protected against vibration, rolling, jolting, etc., and his arms and legs are free to operate controls. When the operator's platform is subjected to violent maneuvers and/or appreciable accelerative forces, some form of body support (seated, semisupine, or semiprone) is mandatory.

c. In the effective operation of pedal controls. The operator can use both feet simultaneously, he can operate controls over a greater range with either foot, he can exert much greater force, he can operate pedal controls faster, and he can operate more controls with either or both feet.

VISUAL AREAS

The following terms will be used throughout this chapter:

a. Line of sight. This is an imaginary line from the bridge of the nose to the object on which the eyes are fixed, regardless of head position. For precise visual measurements, this line runs from the cornea of the eye, but, because both eyes are involved simultaneously, the bridge of the nose is a satisfactory approximation for workplace-layout dimensions.

b. Standard line of sight. This is the line of sight that is perpendicular to both the lateral and vertical axes of the operator's head, independent of eye movement. For a seated or standing operator, the vertical axis of the head is tilted slightly forward because of normal slump (assumed to be about 5 deg), and, therefore, the standard line of sight is about 5 deg below the horizontal (see Fig. 7-5). For the supine operator it is tilted upward from the horizontal, the exact amount depending on the position of the operator's head.

c. Normal line of sight. The line of sight with the eyes at rest is 10 deg below the standard line of sight because the eyes naturally assume a small downward cast (about 15 deg downward for a seated operator).

d. Viewing distance. This is the distance from the bridge of the nose to the object being viewed, i.e., the length of the line of sight.

e. Optimum viewing angle. This is the solid angle, measured horizontally and vertically from the standard line of sight, through which the operator can view displays or controls with speed and accuracy by eye rotation alone. Shifts from one visual point to another are accomplished most quickly by eye rotation alone when they involve several such shifts in close succession and only a small angular change (less than 15 deg). Changes in the point of fixation lasting more than a few

seconds or requiring a greater angular change in the line of sight generally involve both head and eye motion.

f. Maximum viewing angle. This is the angle through which the operator can view displays by combined head and eye rotation without straining his neck or eye muscles. It also is measured horizontally and vertically from the standard line of sight.

g. Visual area. The dimensions of the visual area are defined by the viewing angle and the viewing distance.

Dimensions of Visual Areas

Viewing distances. For displays that are located close to their associated controls,

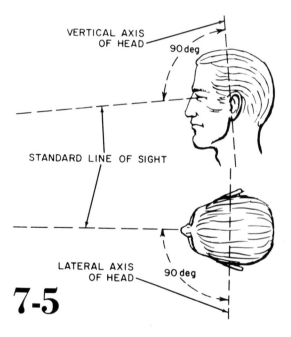

7-5

viewing distance is limited by reach distance and should not exceed $29\frac{1}{2}$ in. (see Fig. 7-6), otherwise, there is no maximum limit other than that imposed by practical space limitations, provided the display is properly designed (see Chapter 2). Viewing distance to displays should never be less than 13 in., however, and, preferably, not less than 20 in. because a small viewing distance places an undue strain on the eyes.

§ 7.2.1

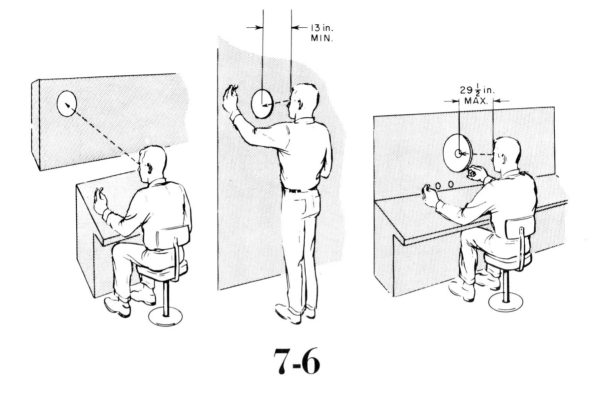

7-6

Table 7-1 Viewing Angles for the Seated, Standing, and Supine Positions

Body member rotated	Direction	Lateral angle *		Direction	Vertical angle *	
		Opt.	Max.		Opt.	Max.
Head only	Left	0	60	Up	0	50
	Right	0	60	Down	0	50
Eyes only	Left	15	35	Up	0	25
	Right	15	35	Down	30	35
Head and eyes	Left	15	95	Up	0	75
	Right	15	95	Down	30	85

* In deg from the line of sight, which is assumed to be horizontal. Any shift in the line of sight from the horizontal will rotate these dimensions by a similar amount.

§ 7.2.1

Viewing angles. Table 7-1 gives optimum and maximum viewing angles for the seated and supine positions, but restrictions to visual areas (see below) must be taken into consideration before the data can be used.

Restrictions to Visual Areas

Certain equipment can restrict the visual areas in the following ways:

a. Head rotation can be reduced because of the weight and bulk of a helmet, mask, headphone, etc.

b. Eye rotation is unrestricted, but vision will be cut off by equipment that projects into the visual area (see Chapter 8).

c. In the seated position, upward head rotation will be restricted by a headrest, particularly when the operator is strapped to his seat so that his head is normally in contact with the headrest.

d. In the semisupine position, where the operator's head is tilted forward by a headrest, upward head rotation is eliminated, and downward head rotation is reduced by the amount (X deg) that the operator's head is tilted forward from alignment with his trunk (see Fig. 7-7).

e. In the semisupine position, downward head rotation is unrestricted but vision can be cut off by the operator's knees. This effect can be partially corrected by lowering the front edge of the seat pan, thus increasing the angle between the seat and backrest, which angle should not exceed 120 deg (see Fig. 7-8).

MANUAL AREAS

The following terms will be used throughout this chapter:

a. Optimum manual area. This is the space, defined by optimum dimensions, that is most desirable for the location of hand controls, both in their neutral position and when displaced in any direction. This is an

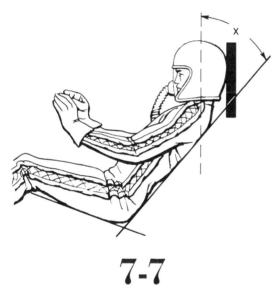

7-7

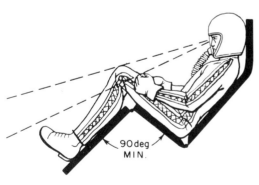

OBSTRUCTED VISUAL AREA . . . . . .

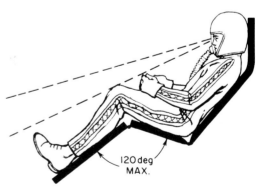

REMOVED BY LOWERING SEAT PAN

7-8

"ideal" area (reserved primarily for manual controls that must be seen and used frequently) in which the operator's ability to locate, operate and see the controls is optimized. (Important controls should be placed so that they can be located and operated without having to be seen, but it should be possible to see them easily in emergency situations.)

b. Overall manual area. This is the space, as defined by limiting dimensions, in which all hand controls should be located, both in their neutral position and when displaced in any direction.

c. Seat reference point (SRP). This is the point where the midlines of the seat and the backrest intersect. This point does not necessarily fall on the surface of the seat, e.g., in seats with recessed pans and backs for kits and "chutes" the seat reference point is a point in space that might not fall within the seat structure (see Fig. 7-9).

Dimensions of Optimum Manual Areas

Recommended areas. As shown in Fig. 7-10, the width of the optimum manual area is about 24 in. (Ely, et al., 1956). Other dimensions are given in Fig. 7-11, which shows variations in seat tilt from the upright (0 deg) to 60 deg. The shaded areas in Fig. 7-11 represent the vertical fore-and-aft cross sections of the optimum manual area when the backrest of the operator's seat is at various angles of tilt.

This optimum area is bound by the following four principal points: near low, near high, far high, and far low (each represented as the center of the operator's fist). The near low is determined with the operator's elbows next to his body and his forearms horizontal, the near high with the operator's elbows next to his body and his forearms flexed upward about the elbow 15 deg, the far high with the operator's arm extended horizontally from the shoulder, and the far low with the operator's arms extended and lowered until his hand is at the level of his elbow when in the near-low position (see Fig. 7-12).

The top curve in Fig. 7-11, marked "far high," shows the arc generated by the center of the fist, held at shoulder height with the arm extended, as the operator swings backward from the upright position (0 deg) through 60 deg. The position of the center of his fist is indicated at successive 10-deg intervals along the arc. Similarly, the arcs generated by the center of the fist at the far-low, near-low, and near-high positions (as the operator's backrest swings from the upright to a 60-deg tilt) are also marked at successive 10-deg intervals. At each 10-deg interval, the four bounding points have been joined and

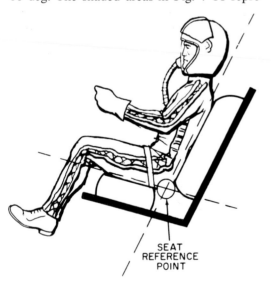

SEAT
REFERENCE
POINT

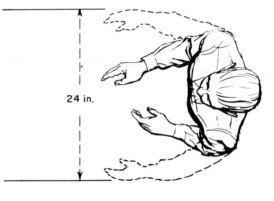

24 in.

7-10

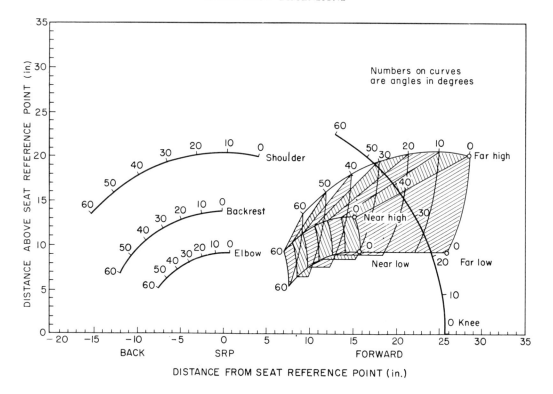

7-11

shaded in, showing the vertical cross section of the optimum manual area.

Arcs marked in 10-deg intervals are also shown in Fig. 7-11 for the operator's shoulder, backrest, and knee as the backrest tilts from the upright position back to 60 deg. The knee position, however, is directly dependent on the angle of the seat pan, i.e., if the seat pan remains set at a stationary position the operator's knees will remain in the same position regardless of the angle through which the backrest is tilted.

In Fig. 7-11, knee position is shown as the arc generated by the knee as the seat pan is tilted with the backrest. This will enable the designer to determine clearance for the knees and the amount by which the knees will obstruct the optimum manual and visual areas if the seat pan is not lowered.

Alternate areas. When all important controls cannot be placed within the optimum manual areas, locations immediately adjacent

to the optimum areas are more desirable than those farther away. As a general rule, the desirability of a control location for the seated position decreases as either or both of the following distances increase:

a. The distance above shoulder level or below waist level (see Fig. 7-13).

b. The distance to the side and away from the optimum areas (see Fig. 7-14).

Dimensions of Overall Manual Areas

The maximum dimensions of overall manual areas can be determined from the data for maximum reach of the small (5th percentile) man in Chapter 11. When movement of the operator's elbows is unrestricted, the surface of his body (or clothing) forms the minimum limits to manual reach. Thus, controls may be placed close to the operator, with the following exceptions:

§ 7.2.1

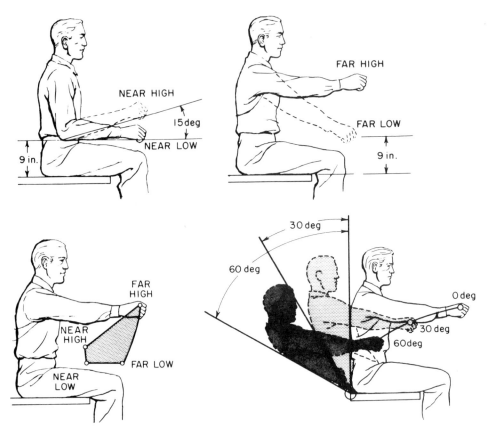

7-12

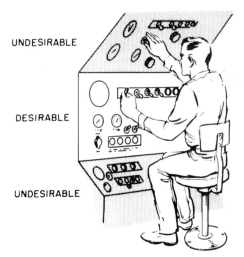

7-13

a. Tight or bulky clothing can prevent the operator from manipulating controls next to his body because he is limited in the extent to which he can bend his elbows.

b. The strength and accuracy of certain movements (especially rotary) close to the body are severely limited.

When a backrest or other obstruction interferes with the rearward movement of the elbows, no control should be placed within 16 in. (in any direction) of the resting position of the elbow (see Fig. 7-15).

Factors Affecting Manual Areas

Seat adjustment. All reach dimensions for the seated and supine positions in Chapter 11 are given with respect to the seat refer-

§ 7.2.1

7-14

ence point. For these dimensions to be applicable to the entire population, this reference point should be adjustable at least 3 in. in the fore-and-aft directions and 5 in. in the up-and-down directions.

Acceleration. The following recommendations apply to the relatively prolonged g forces in one direction that are found in aircraft during sharp turns or pullouts as well as to the sudden changes in g forces (jouncing, pitching) encountered in trucks, tanks, small naval craft, etc. (see Chapter 10). Controls that must be used while the operator is subject to acceleration forces above 2g should be located to accomplish the following:

a. The operator's hand or foot is always in contact with the control, i.e., no reaching is required.

b. As many controls as practicable are assigned to the same hand or foot. This is best accomplished by the use of combined controls (several control functions mounted on a single shaft) so that movement from one control to another is avoided.

c. Linear controls operate perpendicularly to the direction of the g forces. This eliminates the necessity for the operator to compensate for g forces acting along the line of control

movement. (Rotary control movements are little affected by g forces.)

PEDAL AREAS

The following terms will be used throughout this chapter:

a. Optimum pedal area. This is the area that is most desirable for the location of foot controls when in their neutral position and when displaced in any direction.

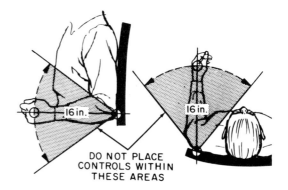

7-15

§ 7.2.1

b. Overall pedal area. This is the area beyond which foot controls should not be located whether in their neutral position or displaced in any direction.

Dimensions of Optimum Pedal Areas

Figures 7-16 and 7-17 show, respectively, vertical and horizontal fore-and-aft cross sections of the optimum pedal areas. In each figure, separate areas are indicated for heel- and toe-operated controls.

The shaded areas in Fig. 7-16 represent the vertical cross sections of the optimum pedal areas for toe-operated and heel-operated controls when the backrest of the operator's seat is vertical and the seat pan is horizontal. In this graph, the optimum areas are bounded by the following four principal points (see Fig. 7-18):

a. Near low. This is the position of the heel or *retracted* toe when the upper leg is raised 15 deg from the seat pan, and the lower leg is at a 90-deg angle with the upper leg.

b. Near high. This is the position of the heel or *retracted* toe when the upper leg is raised 15 deg from the horizontal, and the toe is level with the plane of the seat pan.

c. Far high. This is the position of the heel or *extended* toe when the upper leg is horizontal, and the lower leg is extended 60 deg from the vertical.

d. Far low. This is the position of the heel or *extended* toe when the upper leg is horizontal, and the lower leg is vertical.

When the seat pan is tilted upward from the horizontal, the lower legs and feet swing upward and forward, with the center of rotation being the seat reference point. Thus, if the seat pan is raised 30 deg from the horizontal, a 30-deg arc with its center at the SRP and extending upward from the "far low heel" point in Fig. 7-16 will locate the position of the "far low heel" point when the seat pan is tilted 30 deg (see Fig. 7-19). The remaining bounding points can be located in the same way.

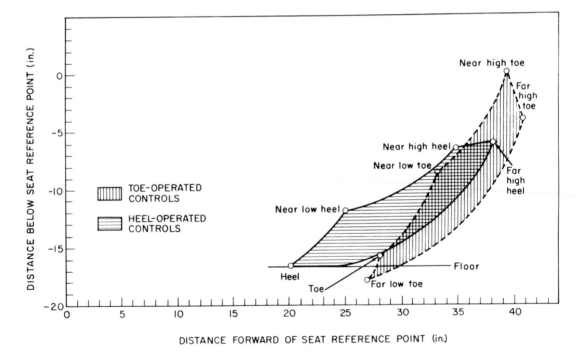

7-16

§ 7.2.1

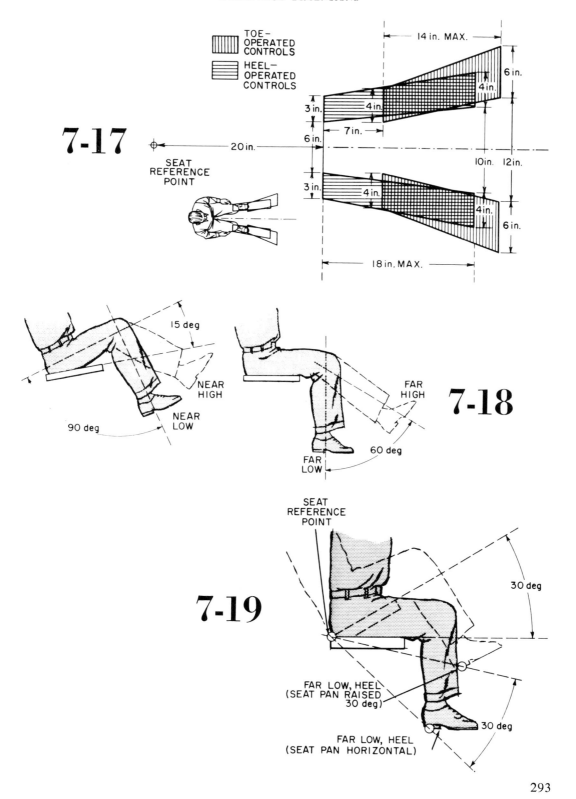

7-17

TOE-OPERATED CONTROLS

HEEL-OPERATED CONTROLS

14 in. MAX.

6 in.

3 in.

4 in.

4 in.

7 in.

6 in.

20 in.

SEAT REFERENCE POINT

10 in. 12 in.

3 in.

4 in.

4 in.

6 in.

18 in. MAX.

15 deg

NEAR HIGH

90 deg

NEAR LOW

FAR HIGH

7-18

60 deg

FAR LOW

7-19

SEAT REFERENCE POINT

30 deg

FAR LOW, HEEL (SEAT PAN RAISED 30 deg)

30 deg

FAR LOW, HEEL (SEAT PAN HORIZONTAL)

Dimensions of Overall Pedal Areas

The horizontal cross sections of the overall pedal areas are shown in Fig. 7-20 (Ely, et al., 1956). Measurements represent the horizontal reach that 95% of the population can attain without strain and without altering the normal operating position of the trunk of the body.

The shaded areas in Fig. 7-21 represent vertical cross sections of the overall pedal areas for toe-operated and heel-operated controls when the backrest of the operator's seat is vertical and the seat pan is horizontal. The control areas are each bounded by the following four principal points (see Fig. 7-22):

a. Far high. This is the position of the heel or *extended* toe when the upper leg is resting on the seat pan, and the lower leg is horizontal.

b. Far low. This is the position of the heel or *extended* toe when the upper leg is resting on the seat pan, and the lower leg is at a 90-deg angle with the upper leg.

c. Near high. This is the position of the heel or *retracted* toe when the upper leg is raised 25 deg from the seat pan, and the lower leg is horizontal.

d. Near low. This is the position of the heel or *retracted* toe when the upper leg is raised 25 deg from the seat pan, and the lower leg is at a 90-deg angle with the upper leg.

When the seat pan is raised, the bounding points can be located by the same method described for the optimum pedal areas.

7.2.2 *Standing operators*

The standing position is considered here to be a standing-and-walking position, i.e., the operator is free to move in various directions. If this freedom is not available, the workplace should be designed so that the operator either sits or shifts between a seated and standing position (see article 7.2.3).

The standing position is superior to the seated position in the following ways:

a. In increased mobility. By taking one or more steps in any desired direction, the operator can bring within his visual and manual areas displays that he could not read and controls that he could not operate from a stationary seated position.

b. In increased manual force. The operator can make large control movements such as those demanded by a large lever or handwheel. The standing position is of particular advantage when the operator must make a

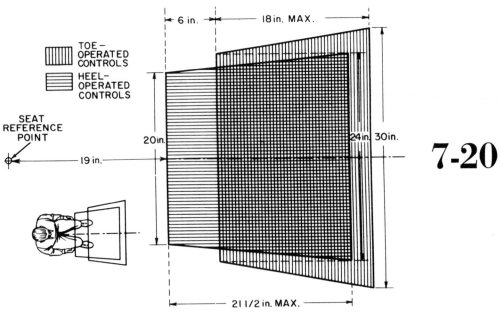

TOE-OPERATED CONTROLS
HEEL-OPERATED CONTROLS
SEAT REFERENCE POINT
6 in. — 18 in. MAX.
20 in.
19 in.
24 in. 30 in.
21 1/2 in. MAX.

7-20

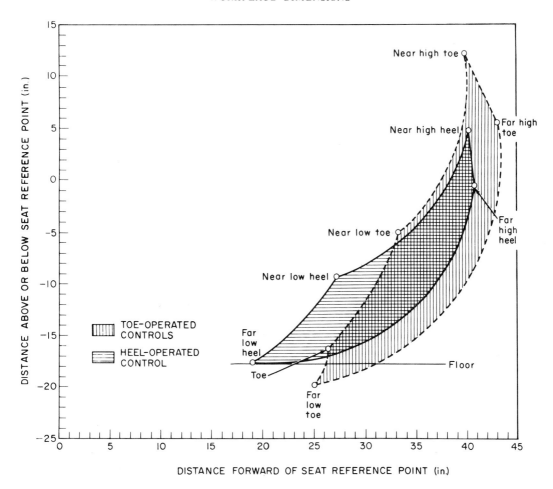

7-21

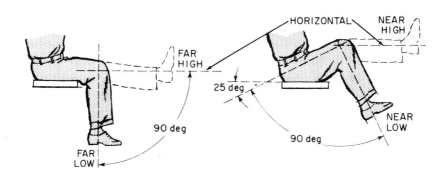

7-22

control movement that requires a large force over a long distance.

The standing position is particularly useful in the following situations:

a. When the operator must be free to walk. This situation can occur when controls and displays are so numerous, space consuming, or otherwise widely separated that they cannot be attended to and operated from a single, stationary position.

b. When no special provisions are made for leg room. This situation can occur either when all controls are mounted on a wall or bulkhead or when the console has no indentations for knee room and is too wide to be straddled. If the operator is seated directly facing such a console, few, if any, controls will lie inside the optimum manual area.

c. As an alternative or change-over from the seated position. Designing a workplace that permits the operator to sit or stand allows him to shift his posture at will, thereby reducing the muscular fatigue that results from prolonged effort in any one position. In this situation, the workplace must be designed to conform to the operator's visual, manual, and pedal areas in the more restricted of the two positions: seated position for visual and manual areas and standing position for pedal areas (see article 7.2.3).

VISUAL AREAS

The *vertical* viewing angles given in Table 7-1 also apply to the standing position. The *lateral* viewing angles in Table 7-1 only apply to groups of displays that are read in close succession or in conjunction with the operation of related controls. Optimum and maximum *lateral* viewing angles need not be specified for unrelated displays because the operator can walk at will to the front of any display. In addition, the operator can face equally well in any direction, and, therefore, so long as constant attention in any one direction is not always demanded, displays that require occasional reading may be placed (at the proper height) anywhere around him.

In general, for the standing position, it is preferable to keep together a group of related

displays (which might move some of the important displays out of the optimum visual area) rather than to take the important displays out of each group and concentrate them in the optimum visual area (as it might be necessary to do for an operator for the seated position).

MANUAL AREAS

Figure 7-11 closely approximates the vertical fore-and-aft cross section of the *optimum* manual area, but, instead of using the seat reference point, the reference is the horizontal line between the near-low and far-low points, which should be about $43\frac{1}{2}$ in. above floor level. The lateral dimension of this area is about 30 in. for any one operating station. (An operator in the standing position may be responsible for more than one operating station at the same time.)

Theoretically, the limits of the *overall* manual area extend from floor level (for an operator bending down) to the highest point that a small (5th percentile) operator can reach and still manipulate controls (78 in.). In practice, however, the following limitations should be accepted:

a. The minimum floor-to-ceiling clearance for a tall operator is 76 in., which leaves only 2 in. for overhead controls. Therefore, controls should not be placed on the overhead directly above passageways and/or working positions (see also Chapter 8).

b. In its lowest position (maximum displacement), a control should be at least 32 in. above the floor (the knuckle height of a tall operator) to prevent excessive stooping. This is particularly important for controls that are used frequently or that require heavy forces for operation.

c. When the operator must reach over an object (table, console, work bench, etc.) to reach a control, the height that he can reach is limited accordingly. The operator can bend over and increase his forward reach by about 16 in., but as the point of reach rises to above shoulder level, the gain by bending the trunk decreases progressively to zero at a point directly overhead (see Fig. 7-23).

PEDAL AREAS

In the seated position, the feet should be used to exert large forces and to relieve the hands from repetitive, routine operations that do not require precise adjustment (Barnes, 1950). In the standing position the legs and feet are needed to maintain balance and to increase the operator's range of manual-control capabilities. Thus, for the standing position, pedal controls should be avoided whenever possible, except for occasional "in-between" operations.

operator population in both seated and standing positions if the dimensions of the average (50th percentile) operator are used rather than those of the short (5th) and tall (95th) operators. This increased operating area is slightly larger than the optimum manual area for the seated position; hence, the standing, tall operator will have to reach slightly below elbow level for the lowest control, and the standing, short operator will have to reach slightly above shoulder level for the highest control.

DESIGN RECOMMENDATIONS

The following design recommendations should be observed when providing for the

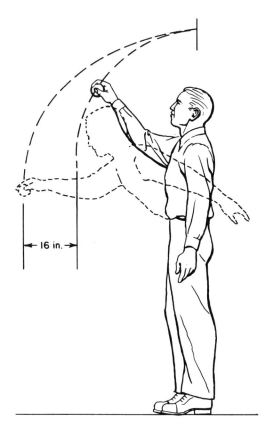

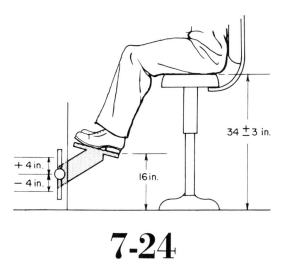

7-24

operator to alternate between the seated and standing positions:

1. When the operator alternates between the seated and standing positions, a raised seat should be provided, the seat pan of which should be 34 in. above floor level and adjustable ±3 in. (see Fig. 7-24). In addition, the seat should be easily movable into and out of position.

2. A footrest should be provided for the seated position. The top of the footrest should be 16 in. above floor level and adjustable ±4 in. If the operator is working at a console-type workplace, the footrest may be made part of

7.2.3 *Alternating between sitting and standing*

The size of the optimum visual and manual areas will be a maximum for the entire

the console (rather than the seat) to remove it as an obstacle to a standing operator (see Fig. 7-24).

3. The location of pedal controls for the operator when seated should be higher than that for the operator when standing. Hence, pedal controls should *not* be used when the operator is free to sit or stand.

7.3 *Locating Controls and Displays*

This section deals with the general location of individual controls and displays within the spaces allotted to them as determined by the workplace dimensions given in the preceding section. The following three major factors will be considered:

a. Priority. The most important controls and displays should be assigned to the optimum areas.

b. Grouping. Controls and displays should be grouped into logical units.

c. Association. A correct and consistent relation (correspondence) should be established between each control and its related display.

The rules given in the following three articles are general ones and cannot be expected to apply, explicitly, in all cases. In the event that two rules conflict with each other, the designer must determine a compromise that is based, primarily, on the needs (or specific requirements) of the system being designed.

7.3.1 *Establishing priority positions*

The first step in the procedure to follow in establishing priority positions is to analyze how the control or display is used by the operator and what is its ultimate effect on system performance. The priority of the control or display then can be measured in various ways. The most common ways involve determining one or more of the following:

a. The frequency and extent of its use.

b. The accuracy and/or speed with which the display must be read or the control positioned.

c. The decrease in system performance and/or safety resulting from an error or delay in using it.

d. The ease of manipulating certain controls (in terms of the force that can be applied and the precision and speed of adjustment) in various locations.

In establishing priority positions, the following rules should be observed:

1. Primary (highest priority) controls and displays should be placed within the optimum areas.

2. Emergency controls and displays should be placed in readily accessible positions (see section 7.1 for detailed information), but they usually will not be located in the optimum areas in preference to primary controls and displays. In some systems, however, the nature of an emergency is so critical that emergency controls and displays should be given top priority in location.

3. Secondary controls and displays (less important than primary ones but used periodically during normal operations) should be placed within the overall areas but not necessarily within the optimum areas. Their exact location should be determined, primarily, by

proper grouping and association (see articles 7.3.2 and 7.3.3). Standardization is essential whenever a large number of such controls and displays must be used by one operator.

4. Adjustment and calibration controls and displays that are used infrequently before the operator begins his primary tasks or during any convenient slack period normally should be given lowest priority in assigning locations. They may be located outside of the operator's normal workplace unless they are used with other controls or displays in the workplace.

5. The sharing of controls and/or displays by more than one operator requires special considerations. Among these are the following (see also section 7.7):

a. If primary controls or displays must be used by two operators, duplicate sets should be provided wherever there is adequate space; otherwise, controls or displays should be centered between the operators.

b. If secondary controls or displays must be used by two operators, they should be placed between the operators. If they are of equal importance to both operators, they should be centered between them; if they are more important to one operator, they should be nearer the one to whom they are more important.

c. Whenever direction-of-movement relationships are important, and controls or displays must be shared by more than one operator, the operators should all face in the same direction.

7.3.2 *Grouping controls and displays*

The following two general methods of grouping controls and displays should be used whenever possible:

a. Functional grouping. With this method, all controls or displays are grouped together that are identical in function, or are used together in a specific task, or are related to one system component (e.g., all controls and displays pertaining to Engine No. 1).

b. Sequential grouping. With this method, all controls or displays that are operated or observed in sequence are grouped together, and they are arranged in their normal order of use.

When grouping controls and displays, the following rules should be observed (Woodson, 1954):

1. Displays should be grouped so as to facilitate check reading.

2. When displays and controls are to be used sequentially, they should be aligned so that they are observed or operated in the following sequence:

a. Horizontally from left to right.

b. Vertically from top to bottom.

c. In rows from top to bottom and from left to right within a row.

3. When displays or controls are to be used sequentially, the following rules should be observed:

a. They should be grouped as close together as possible.

b. Unless important control-display associations are violated (see article 7.3.3), controls and displays should be aligned horizontally, provided that they do not extend beyond the visual and manual area (see Fig. 7-25).

c. If a *large* number of displays must be viewed in sequence, they should be arranged in rows rather than columns. In any case, the direction in which they are aligned (horizontally, vertically, or in rows) should be determined, primarily, by the correct control-display association.

d. When controls are operated sequentially by the same hand, they should be arranged so that the operator moves his arm horizontally from one control to the next (provided that control-display and/or control-component locations do not result in violations of the association rules).

e. When they cannot be aligned horizontally, controls should be arranged vertically from top to bottom.

4. When concentric (ganged) knobs are to be used sequentially, the control should be designed so that the front (smallest) knob is used first and the back (largest) knob last (see also article 7.5.3).

DO THIS

NOT THIS

7-25

7.3.3 Control-display associations

Whenever an operator must use a large number of controls and/or displays, their location and arrangement should aid him in determining the following:

a. Which controls are used with which displays.

b. Which equipment component each control affects.

c. Which equipment component each display describes.

When locating controls and displays by association, the following rules should be observed:

1. When a group of equipment components has the same function (e.g., the engines of a multi-engine aircraft), the positions of the related (associated) controls and displays depend on the direction the operator faces (relative to the normal direction of movement of the vehicle), and the following rules apply:

a. If the operator of a vehicle normally faces in the direction in which the vehicle

moves, the positions of the controls and displays should correspond to the spatial orientation of their associated equipment components (see A in Fig. 7-26).

b. If the operator of a vehicle normally faces sideward, controls and displays may be located in front of or on either side of the operator. When equipment components are arranged from left to right in the vehicle, their associated controls and displays should be located so that their arrangement would correspond spatially to their associated equipment components if both operator and panel were rotated to face in the direction the vehicle moves (see B in Fig. 7-26). When equipment components are arranged from front to rear in the vehicle, their associated controls and displays should be arranged to correspond spatially to their equipment components without "rotating" the operator and panel.

c. If the operator of a vehicle normally faces rearward, he should not control equipment components that have definite spatial orientations. If he must control equipment components that are arranged from left to right in the vehicle, however, the arrangement of controls and displays should be such that they would correspond spatially to their associated equipment components if both operator and panel were rotated to face in the direction of forward vehicle motion (see C in Fig. 7-26).

2. When a control is always associated with a specific display, the control should be located so that the operator's hand does not block his view of the display. Controls operated by the left hand should be located below their associated displays (they also may be located to the left of their displays provided that the direction-of-movement relations set forth in Chapter 6 are not violated), and controls operated by the right hand should be located below or to the right of their associated displays (see Fig. 7-27).

3. When a large number of displays are on the same panel, they normally should be arranged in *either* of the following two ways (Nystrom and Grant, 1954):

a. Place each display directly above its associated control (see A in Fig. 7-28). All control-display combinations should be located close together so that wrong associations are not made (e.g., controls should be associated with the displays above them, not below them).

b. Place all displays in the upper portion and all controls in the lower portion of the panel, with each control occupying the same

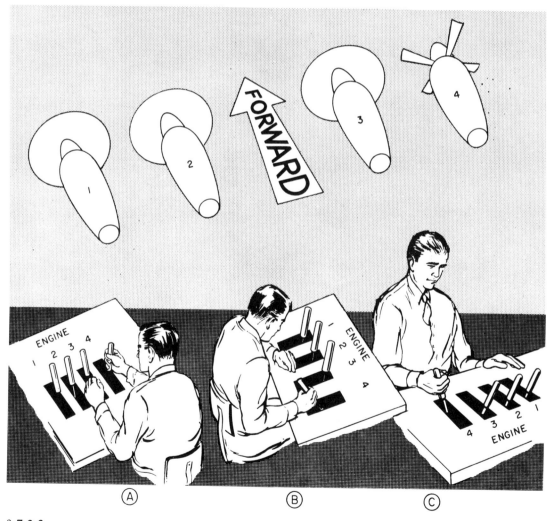

7-27

relative position as its associated display (see B in Fig. 7-28). This last is most important; any arrangement that changes the relative positions among controls or among displays (such as that resulting from reversing the positions of two controls) will seriously degrade operator performance. Such a change can result in a four-fold (or more) increase in both time and errors in selecting the proper control for a given display, either for skilled or unskilled operators.

4. When concentric (ganged) knobs must be associated with displays, the displays should be arranged in a row from left to right with the front (smallest) knob controlling the left display, the middle knob the middle display, and the back (largest) knob the right display (see Fig. 7-29).

5. When *rows* of displays *must* be associated with *columns* of controls, and vice versa, left should correspond with top, and right with bottom (see Fig. 7-30).

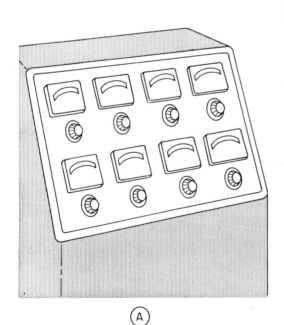

Ⓐ

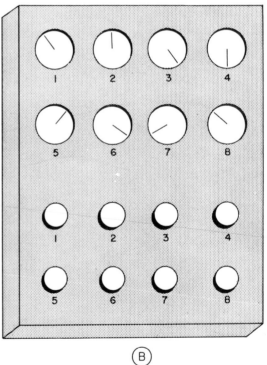

Ⓑ

7-28

§ 7.3.3

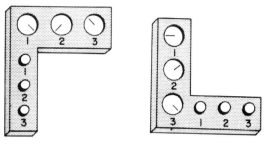

7-30

7-29

6. When two or more rows of displays must be associated with one row of controls, and vice versa, the general arrangement shown in Fig. 7-31 (right) should be used.

7. When all controls are on one panel and their associated displays are on another panel, good control-display associations still can be maintained if the following rules are observed:

a. The controls on one panel should occupy positions corresponding to those of their associated displays on the other panel.

b. The two panels should never face each other.

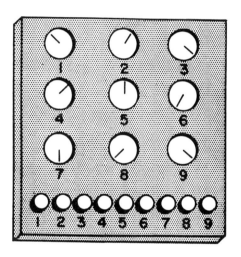

7.4 *Display Layout*

After individual displays have been designed properly (see Chapter 2), they must be located and arranged in a way that best suits the operator. This section takes up problems of display arrangement and combination. Related information on layout of controls is given in the next section (7.5).·

This section was drafted, in part, by Charles A. Baker and Walter F. Grether of the Air Force Systems Command.

§ 7.4.1

7.4.1 *General layout considerations*

There are some general requirements that should be kept in mind in planning the layout of a display panel. These can be listed as follows:

a. Visibility. The operator should be able to see all displays from his normal working position.

b. Identification. It should be easy for the operator to find the display he needs.

c. Grouping. Displays should be arranged in functional or sequential groups (see also article 7.3.2).

d. Association. Display arrangements should be compatible with the functions they display and with the controls that affect the readings. Special problems arise when the panel is in a different spatial plane than the controls, components, or equipment with which it must be compatible, or if the operator is facing other than forward in a moving vehicle. (For a discussion of these problems, see article 7.3.3.)

e. Combination and integration. Combining and integrating several indications into a single display is discussed in Chapter 2.

7.4.2 *Layout for good visibility*

For a seated operator, the optimum visual area centers around the normal line of sight (see section 7.2). The overall visual area, with the body stationary, is considerably larger. Although exact limits are not rigidly defined (and vary somewhat according to the task), it is generally agreed that the overall visual area ranges from just below eye level downward 60 deg and 30 deg to either side of the midplane of the body (see Fig. 7-32). Within this area, the operator can shift his attention easily from one section to another.

The standing operator has the same field of view except that he is free to turn his body to see anywhere around him. Nevertheless, it still is desirable to group all primary displays within one optimum visual area as if the operator were in a fixed position; then, additional display groups can be established at one or more other locations.

VIEWING ANGLE

The plane in which the display lies should be perpendicular to the line of sight whenever possible, and the operator's view should be unobstructed by bezels, light shields, or other projections. In any case, the line of sight to the plane of the display should never be more than 45 deg from the perpendicular.

The optimum viewing angle is from 10–30 deg laterally or vertically from the horizontal (see Table 7-1). And the most important displays should be located at the eye level of the small (5th percentile) operator (see Chapter 11). If additional vertical room is needed, the location may be raised to the eye-level of the average (50th percentile) operator.

VIEWING DISTANCE

Viewing distance need be limited only if the operator is required to manipulate controls on the panel from his normal position. In this case, this distance should never be less than 13 in. nor more than 29½ in. from the eyes for vertical panels. The display size (see Chapter 2) must be increased proportionally for longer viewing distances.

The difficulty of shifting the eyes between displays increases with separation distance. Vertical eye movements are more difficult than horizontal shifts but, in any case, the distance between displays should be minimized.

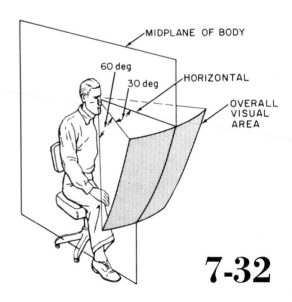

MIDPLANE OF BODY

60 deg

30 deg

HORIZONTAL

OVERALL VISUAL AREA

7-32

7.4.3 *Layout for identification*

All displays should, of course, be properly labelled. Even so, a busy operator is likely to read the wrong indicator, or lose valuable time trying to find an indicator, unless the following identification aids also are employed:

a. Location and separation. Location on the panel is one of the best aids to identification. When several displays are identical in appearance and function but represent different components (e.g., rpm for different engines), they should be arranged in a pattern corresponding to the location of the components. Where functions are similar but location by components cannot be applied (e.g., cabin pressure altimeter and aircraft altimeter), separated locations are desirable.

b. Functional grouping. By grouping indicators in terms of their functional use, the designer can reduce the area over which the operator must search to find a display. As a general rule, place displays in groups according to their functional use (see also article 7.4.4).

c. Standardized location. Very often the same operators (e.g., pilots, tank drivers, gunners) will make frequent transfers from one work station to another (e.g., one vehicle to another). In such cases, the time for retraining and the chances of identification errors will be much reduced by the standardized arrangement of common elements in the different work stations. The general rule is as follows: wherever possible, standardize the location of displays, or functional groups of displays, that are common to different work stations among which there is frequent interchange of operators.

7.4.4 *Grouping displays*

The benefits of grouping displays as an aid to identification has already been discussed above. There are, also, other ways that grouping displays can help the operator. These are discussed in the following paragraphs.

GROUPING FOR CHECK READING

Some displays (such as some engine indicators) maintain stable values for given operating conditions, and are used, primarily, for monitoring purposes. Readings are of special interest only when they deviate from desired values. The monitoring of such displays is aided if they are arranged in rows and columns with horizontal pointer alignment, as shown in Fig. 7-33.

Here the pointer tips are aligned at the 9 o'clock position for the most critical reading condition. For simple check reading, the grouping shown in Fig. 7-33 would be equally good if the pointers were aligned vertically, i.e., in the 12 o'clock position, but judgement as to the amount of deviation (too high or too low, etc.) is better with horizontal alignment. In addition, the same general effect can be obtained with vertical straight-scale indicators placed side by side.

GROUPING FOR FLOW DIAGRAMS

Often, indicators or simple signal devices (see Chapter 2) can be shown as parts of a

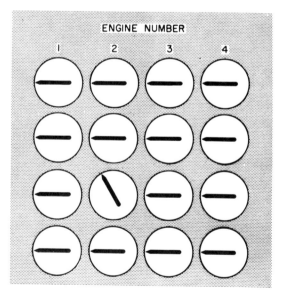

7-33

flow-diagram display. This shows the operator from what parts of the overall system the information is coming (identification) and helps him to interrelate the different things displayed. Such diagrammatic displays are particularly suitable, and are extensively used, to show indicators as parts of electrical, gas, and liquid flow systems; they also are used for showing railroad switch positions and train movements. If the illumination is suitable, color coding can be used to advantage to differentiate different types of lines.

A limitation to the use of flow-diagram displays is the additional space required for the connecting lines. On crowded panels, displaying many different types of unrelated information, such an application often is not feasible.

7.4.5 *Compatible space relationships*

Many displays present information about positions and movements in space. For these to be correctly interpreted by the operator, their location in the workplace must be compatible with the space relationships they display and with the movements of controls that change the displays. Similarly, the grouping or arrangement must be compatible with the geometric relationships among the controls and with the components that the displays represent. All this would be fairly easy to accomplish except for one difficulty: space has three dimensions, display panels have only two. Because of this, many of the relationships must be displaced to another plane.

The problem of space relationships arises whether the operator is in a fixed workplace on the ground or in a moving vehicle, but, in the case of a moving vehicle, a further complication arises: the direction in which the operator is facing in the vehicle. Such relationships as fore and aft and right and left are changed if the operator faces sideways. On a vertical side panel, there is no true right or left relative to the vehicle—only up and down and fore and aft.

Two kinds of space relationships have to be

represented in displays: linear (up and down, right and left, fore and aft) and rotational (about the vertical and horizontal axes). The linear relationship is important, primarily, for the position of indicators relative to one another so that they correspond with the position of components (engines, hatches, fuel tanks, flaps, generators, etc.).

It sometimes is more convenient to speak of the rotational relationships as right or left turn (yaw), right or left bank, and up or down pitch. Along with rotational movement, we include angular deviations as described by the terms azimuth angle, bank angle, and pitch angle. Compatibility in rotational representation is important, primarily, in the design and mounting of indicators (heading, pitch, bank, antenna angle, etc.) rather than their arrangement.

DESIGN RECOMMENDATIONS

The following design recommendations concerning the compatibility of space relationships should be observed:

1. Displays should be arranged in patterns that duplicate the directional relationships (up and down, right and left, fore and aft) of the movement of the vehicle or components they represent.

2. When the true space relationships cannot be duplicated because of the plane of space of the display panel (most panels are vertical), conventional or standard transformations should be used. The following rules will cover most situations:

a. For a forward-facing operator with a vertical panel, "fore" should be up on the panel and "aft" down.

b. For a sideward-facing operator with a vertical panel (or side panel for a foreward-facing operator), "left" and "right" should correspond to the operator's left and right as he faces the panel. This will, of course, be 90 deg from the right-left axis of the vehicle.

c. Do not place an operator in a rearward-facing position if his duties require good orientation with respect to the left-and-right and fore-and-aft dimensions of the vehicle. In this case, left and right relative to his body is 180 deg from left and right relative to the vehicle —a particularly confusing situation.

3. When panels are sloping, or mounted at odd angles, the space relationships that apply are the same as those for the vertical or horizontal plane of space that the panel comes closest to. A panel that is less than 45 deg from the vertical should be treated as if vertical. If it is greater than 45 deg from the vertical, it should be treated as if horizontal.

7.5 *Control Layout*

7.5.1 *The effects of body position and limb used*

The design and location of the operator's controls should not require him to expend energy merely to maintain his body position. Control movements are easiest when the limb used is moderately flexed; extreme body positions should be avoided. The neutral position of a control should correspond to the operator's most comfortable body position. For many kinds of repetitive or continuous control operation, muscular activity should be distributed about the body rather than concentrated in one part. Thus, arm movements in key punching are less tiring than wrist or finger movements alone.

HAND CONTROLS

Hand controls should not be operated from awkward or uncomfortable positions, such as when stooping, kneeling, or crouching, unless such situations are unavoidable. The seated position is preferable to the standing—especially if the controls are to be operated for any length of time. Standing is more fatiguing

This section by Albert Damon, Howard W. Stoudt, and Ross A. McFarland of Harvard University.

and usually results in less efficient, weaker, or less accurate control movements.

Hand controls can be operated from the prone or modified prone position, but, from the true prone position, only 71% of the strength obtainable when seated can be exerted on the controls (Hunsicker, 1955). A modified prone position (see Fig. 7-34), on the other hand, permits upward and lateral movements stronger than those obtainable from the seated position (Brown, et al., 1949a). From any body position, however, forces greater than those exertable in a single effort can be applied if the operator can reposition his body and hands to better advantage during the course of the control movement (McFadden and Swearingen, 1958).

Where speed, accuracy, or strength of the control movement is important, use the preferred hand (right for right-handed operators) if possible. In operating handwheel or lever controls, the entire arm should be used, including the shoulder—not just the elbow

§ 7.5.1

and wrist or wrist alone (Orlansky, 1948). Using the entire arm reduces fatigue, especially when large resistances must be overcome, and handwheels can be turned from the shoulder with 50% greater force than from the elbow (Provins and Salter, 1955).

FOOT CONTROLS

Whenever possible, foot controls should be operated from the seated position because more force can be exerted on the pedal, and less effort is required to keep the body upright and balanced (Koch, 1941). If the standing position is used, however, maximum forces can be exerted when the body is directly over the pedal (Koch, 1941).

There is little difference between the right and left legs with regard to strength, speed, or accuracy, but, for most people, the right leg is slightly preferable, especially for critical tasks. For tiring, noncritical tasks, it should be possible to use the feet interchangeably (Koch, 1941).

For all but light pedal pressures (under 10–20 lb), the foot should be applied to the pedal in such a way that the long axis of the lower leg is immediately over, and in line with, the axis or pivot of the pedal, and the long axes of the foot and lower leg should form a 90-deg angle (see Fig. 7-35). This position requires the least muscular effort to hold the foot in position.

The next-best position is with the arch of the foot over the pedal axis (Lauru and Brouha, 1957). The toe and heel are least effective for heavy pressures (Clark and Weddell, 1944 and Müller, 1936). For small pressures, however, the toe can be used satisfactorily. Indeed, where rapid, continued pedal movements are required, the pedal should be toe operated, with the fulcrum at the base of the heel (Barnes, et al., 1942).

For the most comfortable position when operating controls that require the application of small forces (0–50 lb), the upper and lower leg should form an angle of 105–110 deg (see Fig. 7-35). When moderate forces (50–100 lb) must be exerted, the upper and lower leg should form an angle of at least 120 deg (Orlansky, 1948). When large forces (over 100 lb) must be exerted, the control should be located on a level with the seat pan or slightly (but not more than 4 in.) below it, and, during maximum exertion of force, the upper and lower legs should form an angle of 135–155 deg (Müller, 1936). Control operations requiring quite small forces (0–20 lb) over a short distance (less than 2½ in.) can be accomplished by ankle movements alone.

7.5.2 *Locating controls*

In any control layout, the most critical and important controls should be given priority in location. The less important controls then can be fitted into the remaining space that is available. The following paragraphs give design recommendations for hand and foot controls.

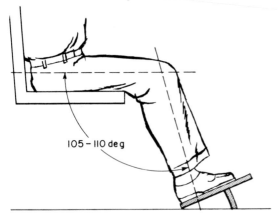

105 – 110 deg

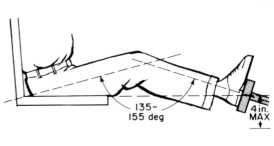

135–155 deg   4 in. MAX

HAND CONTROLS

The area for locating hand controls is much larger than that for foot controls because the arms and hands have a greater range of movement. Although hand controls can be placed anywhere within the overall manual area (see article 7.2.1), critical and frequently used controls take precedence and should be placed where they can be operated most easily, i.e., in the optimum manual area.

Fore-and-Aft Location

Outer limits. The maximum distance from the operator that controls can be located varies with arm reach, body movement, vertical and lateral location of the control, and type of control. Ideally, all forward distances should be measured horizontally from the seat reference point, but, because the backrest angle influences reach distance, the following recommendations are measured from the surface of the backrest at shoulder height (or the back of the shoulder if no backrest is provided:

1. Controls operated with the whole hand should be located no farther away than 27 in. from the back of the shoulder.
2. Finger-operated controls should be located no farther away than 29½ in. from the back of the shoulder. In general, controls located at or near these maximum distances should not be critical or frequently used ones (except for controls requiring maximum pull).

Best location. Controls should not be located at the outer limits of the workplace, where their operation becomes awkward and tiring, but, rather, they should be located where the operator can handle them with his elbow at angles of 90–135 deg. This comfortable, efficient position can be obtained if the following recommendations are observed:

1. Hand-operated controls should be no farther away than 20 in. from the back of the shoulder.
2. Finger-operated controls should be no farther away than 22½ in. from the back of the shoulder.

Location for application of greatest force. Generally, the best elbow angle for exerting force from a *seated* position is about 120 deg, with the following variations for certain kinds of movement:

a. Push-pull forces are strongest when the controls are farthest from the operator, i.e., at or near the full extension of his elbow (Hunsicker, 1955; Hugh-Jones, 1947; and Caldwell, 1959a).

b. Push-only forces are strongest at elbow angles of 150–160 deg (Caldwell, 1959b).

c. Up-and-down forces are maximum at intermediate (120-deg) locations (Hunsiker, 1955) or when closest to the body (Caldwell, 1959b).

d. For right-left movements, fore-and-aft location makes little difference, although forces are slightly stronger closer to the body (Hunsicker, 1955 and Caldwell, 1959b).

e. For rotary movements, there is little difference at most fore-and-aft locations, although the farthest points should be avoided.

From the *prone* position, the best fore-and-aft locations for applying force that are different from those in the seated position are as follows:

a. Push-pull forces are greatest at intermediate-to-far distances (i.e., elbow angles of 120–180 deg) and are least close to the body (Hunsicker, 1955).

b. Up-and-down movements are strongest close to the body and weaken as the distance increases (Hunsicker, 1955).

c. For right-and-left movements, fore-and-aft location makes little difference, although forces are somewhat stronger close to the body (Hunsicker, 1955).

Location for speed and accuracy. The speed and accuracy of visually controlled positioning movements are greatest when controls are close to the operator (7 in. from the body) and become progressively less as the distance increases (Briggs, 1955).

Vertical Location

The best vertical area for the location of hand controls is between the shoulder and elbow (Caldwell, 1959b). In this area, controls can be reached quickly and operated most accurately and efficiently. The best single vertical location is probably at elbow height, although waist level seems better for handcranks (Provins, 1953). Push is strongest at shoulder level, but, for right-handed operators, left movement is strongest around waist level, and right movement is little affected by vertical location (Caldwell, 1959b).

Some controls can be located above the shoulder or below the waist if they are not critical or frequently used and if speed and accuracy are not important. Controls that should be located outside the shoulder-to-waist area are those that require maximum up-and-down pull. Pull-down controls are best placed 12–24 in. above shoulder level (Ross, 1956; Garry, 1930; and Lehmann, 1927), and pull-up controls should be located below seat level (Hugh-Jones, 1947). From the semiprone position, the best vertical location for hand controls is 5 in. below shoulder level (Brown, et al., 1949a).

Lateral Location

Hand controls in frequent or continuous use should be located in front of the operator in the area between the shoulders (Herbert, 1957). This is an area about 16–18 in. wide. Controls for the right hand should be within 8–9 in. to the right of the body midline; controls for the left hand, should be within the same distance to the left of the midline. If both hands are used in positioning movements, the controls should be located directly in front of the operator's midline (Briggs, 1955).

Where strength is important, left-and-right movements are strongest when the hand is directly in front of the shoulder, down movement and push are strongest at about 30 deg to the side. Lateral location makes little difference for up movement and pull.

It sometimes might be desirable to support the forearm with a horizontal armrest, especially to reduce the effects of acceleration (see Chapter 10). Under such conditions the control grip should be located 9–12 in. from the operator's midline (Brissenden, 1957).

FOOT CONTROLS

Whenever possible, foot controls should be operated from the seated position. More force can be exerted on the pedals thereby, and less effort is required to keep the body upright and balanced (Koch, 1941). When the seated position is used, a backrest should be provided, and, if both feet are not used full time for control operation, a footrest should be provided as well (see article 7.6.1). If the standing position is used, maximum force can be exerted when the body is directly over the pedal (Kock, 1941).

Seated Operators

In the paragraphs that follow, location within the optimum and overall pedal areas is specified with reference to the Seat Reference Point (SRP) as defined in article 7.2.1. Location is also specified with reference to the operator's height, and, therefore, these dimensions assume that an adjustable seat is provided (see article 7.6.1).

Fore-and-aft location. The SRP-to-pedal distance is an important determinant of the amount of pressure exertable on a foot control. In general, the shorter the distance, the greater the force that is exertable (Martin and Johnson, 1952), but this distance must always be less, by at least 2–4 in., than the length of the outstretched leg when the pedal is about at seat height. As seat height increases above the pedal, the SRP-to-pedal distance must be correspondingly decreased (Müller, 1936).

Because fore-and-aft SRP-to-pedal distance bears a definite relationship to leg length, and, consequently, to stature, this distance can be estimated from the latter measurement (see Chapter 11). Where maximum pedal pressures are required, the SRP-to-pedal distance should be about 47.5% of the operator's height. Where maximum pressures are not required, the SRP-to-pedal distance should be increased for greater comfort, and a distance of 55% of the operator's height is satisfactory.

Vertical location. For maximum pressures, the center of the pedal surface should be at or *above* the SRP level but never more than 4 in. above or below seat level (Müller, 1936). The best vertical SRP-to-pedal distance is about 3.5% of the operator's height.

Where comfort is more important than maximum pressures, pedals should be placed *below* the SRP by vertical distances that vary with the type of task and the subjective evaluation of comfort, but this distance should never exceed 16 in. and normally should be less. For tractors, it has been recommended that the center of the pedal be about 5½ in. below the SRP (Dupuis, et al., 1955).

Lateral location. The farther pedals are located away from the midline of the body laterally, the more the maximum exertable force decreases and discomfort increases. Force is greatest and discomfort least when the pedal is located directly ahead of the body midline. The maximum force exertable falls to 90% when the pedal is placed 3 in. to either side of the midline, to 73% with a 6.7-in. shift, and to 63% with a 10.2-in. shift.

Thus, if midline location is not feasible, as it would not be when two pedals are required, pedals should be located 3–5 in. from the midline, or about in front of the legs (Dupuis, et al., 1955). Pedals should never be located more than 12 in. laterally from the midline, however, and even this distance is uncomfortable and inefficient for forces greater than a few pounds (Dupuis, et al., 1955).

Standing Operators

Pedal controls to be operated while standing should be limited to operations that are performed while the hands are stationary and that relieve the hands from exerting large forces. The operator should be able to reach the pedal by a natural, short, stepping or walking, leg movement, i.e., with a minimum lifting of the foot and knee. Preferably, only one pedal control should be assigned to an operator at any one operating station. (In the standing position, there can be more than one operating station for a single operator.)

For normal forces (less than 30 lb), the pedal should be located along the midplane of the station, so that it (preferably, a broad "tie-bar" pedal extending at least 7 in. laterally to either side of the midline) can be operated by either foot, or dual controls should be provided (with centers 4 in. from the midline), and the control or controls should be 4–8 in. forward of the operator's toe when he is in the normal standing position (see Fig. 7-36). For heavy forces (greater

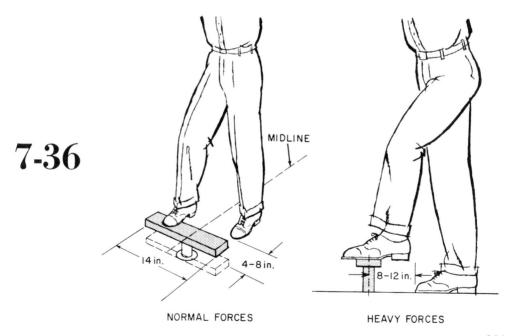

7-36

MIDLINE

14 in.   4–8 in.

8–12 in.

NORMAL FORCES   HEAVY FORCES

than 30 lb), the pedal should be designed as described above, but it should be 8–12 in. forward of the toe in the normal standing position.

The part of a hinged pedal nearest the operator's foot should be at least 1 in. above the floor or platform to provide the operator with a good cue that his foot is in contact with it (see Fig. 7-37). Nonhinged pedals operated from a standing position should never be more than 10 in. from the floor or platform and, preferably, 8 in. or less (Koch, 1941).

7.5.3 Spacing between controls

In determining the proper spacing between controls within a given area, the following factors should be considered:

a. Requirements for the simultaneous or sequential use of controls.

b. The body member being used.

c. The size of the control and the amount of movement (displacement or rotation).

d. Requirements for "blind" reaching (i.e., being able to reach for and grasp the control without seeing it).

e. The effects on system performance of inadvertently using the wrong control.

f. Personal equipment that might hinder control manipulation (e.g., pressure suits, gloves, boots).

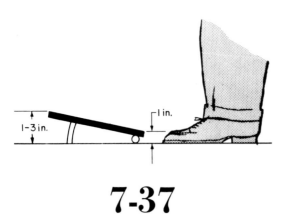

1–3 in.

1 in.

7-37

DESIGN RECOMMENDATIONS

The specific distances separating controls is so much a function of the task being performed (and the space available) that rigid adherence to a single set of specifications is not advisable. The following recommendations are offered as guides:

1. Foot controls should normally be spaced farther apart than hand controls.

2. When "blind" reaching might be required, there should be greater separation between controls than when the operator can look at the control (Fitts and Crannell, 1950). The separation distance of hand controls located at arm's length and in forward areas below shoulder level should be at least 6 in. For areas behind the operator or above his shoulder to either side, the separation distance should be 12 in. Both distances can be reduced, however, for highly trained operators (Fitts, 1947).

3. Figure 7-38 presents recommended separations for various types of controls. Unless stated otherwise, separations are measured between adjacent edges of two controls regardless of control size. The minimum separation is the least acceptable distance between adjacent controls when the operator is in a stationary workplace with good environmental conditions and when the controls are located within the optimum manual or pedal areas. The desirable separation is the preferred distance between adjacent controls that are operated intermittently or are in a moving vehicle where the operator is subjected to jolting, vibration, etc. If the operator is wearing gloves, heavy shoes, a pressure suit, or any other type of clothing that interferes with his movements, the recommended separation between controls should be increased.

4. To conserve limited panel space or to aid in sequential operations, two or three knobs may be mounted on concentric shafts, but chances of accidental operation are increased if either the knob diameters or thicknesses are too large, too small, or differ by too small an amount. Figure 7-39 (Bradley, 1954) shows recommended dimensions for concentrically mounted knobs when accidental operation must be guarded against.

RECOMMENDED SEPARATIONS FOR VARIOUS TYPES OF CONTROLS

CONTROL	TYPE OF USE	MEASURE OF SEPARATION	RECOMMENDED SEPARATION (in.)	
			MINIMUM	DESIRABLE
PUSH BUTTON	ONE FINGER (RANDOMLY)[1]		1/2	2
	ONE FINGER (SEQUENTIALLY)		1/4	1
	DIFFERENT FINGERS (RANDOMLY OR SEQUENTIALLY		1/2	1/2
TOGGLE SWITCH	ONE FINGER (RANDOMLY)		3/4	2
	ONE FINGER (SEQUENTIALLY)		1/2	1
	DIFFERENT FINGERS (RANDOMLY OR SEQUENTIALLY		5/8	3/4
CRANK AND LEVER[2]	ONE HAND (RANDOMLY)		2	4
	TWO HANDS (SIMULTANEOUSLY)		3	5
KNOB	ONE HAND (RANDOMLY)		1	2
	TWO HANDS (SIMULTANEOUSLY)		3	5
PEDAL[3]	ONE FOOT (RANDOMLY)		d = 4	6
			D = 8	10
	ONE FOOT (SEQUENTIALLY)		d = 2	4
			D = 6	8

[1]WHEN FINGER- OR HAND-OPERATED CONTROLS ARE USED RANDOMLY OR ARE "POSITIONED BLIND", THEY SHOULD BE SEPARATED BY AT LEAST 5 in. WHEN MOUNTED IN THE OPTIMUM MANUAL AREA. THIS SEPARATION SHOULD BE PROGRESSIVELY INCREASED TO 12 in. AS THE LOCATION OF THE CONTROL APPROACHES THE PERIPHERY OF THE LIMITING MANUAL DIMENSIONS.

[2]WHEN A GROUP OF LEVERS ARE USED SIMULTANEOUSLY BY THE SAME HAND, THEIR MAXIMUM SEPARATION SHOULD BE 6 in. OR LESS

[3]EITHER DIMENSION d OR DIMENSION D SHOULD BE MET, PREFERABLY d.

7-38

§ 7.5.3

313

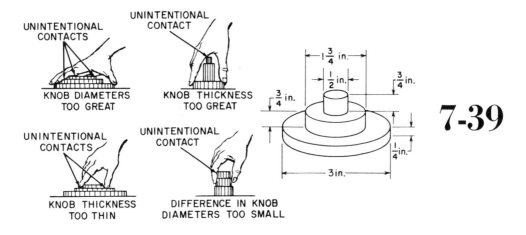

7-39

7.6 Seat and Panel Design

7.6.1 Seat design

Seats should vary in design according to their intended purpose and the physical characteristics of their users. For example, "executive" and typist chairs and seats for school children and aircraft pilots differ markedly in size, shape, construction, and materials. All seats, however, should accommodate as many of the using population as possible.

Adjustable seats are desirable so that controls and displays will always be within the operator's visual and manual areas. Such seats, in a properly designed work station, provide easy accessibility to operators varying widely in height, reach, etc. In any event, it should be remembered that good seating design is generally low in cost compared to the total equipment cost per operator, but it can be a very important factor in operator efficiency.

This article was drafted, in part, by Albert Damon and Howard W. Stoudt of Harvard University.

THE SEAT PAN

Seat height above the floor, measured vertically to the front of the sitting surface, is a major determinant of comfort. Most seats in current use are 17–18 in. above the floor, but a better dimension for the general-purpose seat is 15–16 in. Many fixed (as opposed to adjustable) seats are too high. As a rule, tall people can accommodate to a low seat more easily than short people can accommodate to a high seat. If forced to choose between too low and too high a seat, the lower should be chosen, but a seat that must be high can be made comfortable by footrests.

Seat length (or depth) is measured from the front edge of the seat to the intersection of the rear edge with the backrest, if there is one. Too long a seat pan presses into the leg behind the knee, causing discomfort and possibly danger (from blood clotting), unless the sitter can shift his position forward. Current seats vary considerably in length, e.g., from the 13 in. of a typist's chair to the clearly excessive 24 in. or more of some upholstered furniture. The best general-purpose-seat length is about 17 in.

Seat width matters only as a minimum, not a maximum, dimension. Current seat widths range from 14 through 19 in., although any width below 17 in. is too small. A reasonable dimension for seat width is 18 in.

Tilting back the entire seat pan or its surface prevents the operator from sliding forward on the seat and permits the backrest to support part of the body weight. The current range of inclination varies from zero (horizontal) to 12 deg, but the best angle is around 6–7 deg.

SEAT HARDNESS AND SHAPE

The skin immediately over the bony protuberances upon which one sits has a blood supply better adapted to support the body's weight than the rest of the buttocks (Edwards and Duntley, 1939). This anatomical fact has led some designers to prescribe firm seat surfaces on which the bony protuberances carry most of the body weight (Darcus and Weddell, 1947 and Åkerblom, 1954). Common experience and actual tests (e.g., Randall, et al., 1946 and Slechta, et al., 1957), however, show that most people perform more efficiently for longer periods in soft seats—not "supersoft," but, certainly, cushioned (1–2 in. of compression will suffice).

Most seat pans should be flat rather than shaped because of the varied conformation of the human buttocks and adjacent regions as well as because of the difficulty of changing position in a shaped seat (Darcus and Weddell, 1947). Preliminary studies of seats in which the occupant is virtually immobile for many hours, however, indicate that seats with cut-outs or depressions under the bony protuberances are more comfortable and efficient than flat seat pans (Hertzberg, 1955).

THE BACKREST

The backrest should extend at least 18–20 in. above the seat pan, i.e., high enough to

provide back support up to the shoulder area; head support will require a backrest 34 in. high. Small-of-the-back support, as in a typist's chair, is provided by a backrest 5–6 in. high that has its bottom edge 7–8 in. above the seat pan.

Where the seated operator can rest or relax, at least a 20-in. wide backrest will provide full support across the shoulders. In seats in which only small-of-the-back support is needed, a width of 12–13 in. will suffice.

For most seated positions, a backrest inclined 103 to 115 deg will be comfortable. Backrests that afford only small-of-the-back support should have a lateral curvature equivalent to the arc of a circle $7\frac{5}{16}$ in. in radius (Darcus and Weddell, 1947). For backrests at shoulder or head height, any curvature should have a radius of 16–18 in. and never less than 12 in. (Floyd and Roberts, 1958), but such backrests need not be curved at all.

ARMRESTS AND FOOTRESTS

When armrests do not interfere with necessary body movements, they should be provided to increase the operator's comfort. Armrest height, the most critical dimension, should be 8–10 in. above the seat pan, but, whenever possible, the operator's arm should be supported so that it lies in the same plane as the work surface (see article 7.6.2). This arrangement will support the arm without forcing the operator to raise or depress his shoulder.

The operator should always be provided with a footrest that allows each foot to be about normal (90–100 deg) to the lower leg (Brown, et al., 1949b). If the footrest is at an angle of more than 20 deg from the horizontal (see Fig. 7-40), a heel support should be provided to prevent the foot from sliding downward (Ely, et al., 1956), and this support should be between 1 and $1\frac{1}{2}$ in. thick to minimize interference with leg movements.

ADJUSTABILITY

Seats should be adjustable whenever the operator has to do the following:

§ 7.6.1

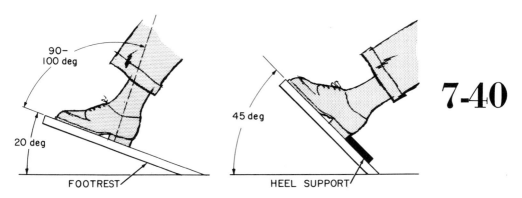

7-40

a. Have his eyes at a critical height to see a specific display.

b. Operate critically important controls, either by hand or by foot.

c. Use his hands and feet simultaneously.

d. Use pedal controls.

For seats in a moving vehicle, both fore-and-aft and vertical adjustability is recommended.

Fore-and-aft adjustability of 6 in., in increments of 1 in. or less, will bring most operators into adequate contact with hand and foot controls and with the work surface. Fore-and-aft adjustability of 8 in. will include the extremes of the general population, both male and female. To bring the eyes to a desirable level, or to place the hands at a given working level, 6 in. of *vertical* adjustment, in 1-in. increments, will fit the entire civilian population, and, for an all-male group, 4 in. will suffice.

CLEARANCES AROUND THE SEAT

The following clearances will accommodate over 99% of the general population when sitting still; for body movements, more clearance will be required:

1. For clearance above the head, 40 in. should be allowed above the seat surface for operators wearing helmets or hats.

2. For lateral clearance across the body, at least 24 in. should be allowed for heavily clothed operators and 21 in. for those lightly clothed.

3. For fore-and-aft clearance between the backrest and the front of the knees, 26½ in. will accommodate almost everyone.

4. At waist level, 15 in. of fore-and-aft clearance should be allowed for heavily clothed persons and 13½ in. for those lightly clothed.

5. A vertical distance of 12 in. is desirable between the seat and work surface, with a minimum of 24½ in. between the floor and the underside of the work surface.

6. When the seat is so constructed that the operator's feet cannot be placed under it, the clearance that should be provided between the front edge of the seat and any foot controls is 4 in. for heel-operated controls and 12 in. for toe-operated controls (see Fig. 7-41).

7.6.2 Panel design

This article pertains only to panel surfaces designed for a single operator. Workplace layout for groups of men and machines is covered in Chapter 8.

PANEL SHAPE

The general shape of panels may be flat, curved, or sectional (see Fig. 7-42). Following are the advantages and disadvantages of each type:

a. Flat surface. This type is easy to construct but is the poorest to use when the panel is large because the outer edges might be beyond the maximum visual and manual dimensions or the center of the panel might be too close to the operator (less than the minimum visual and manual dimensions).

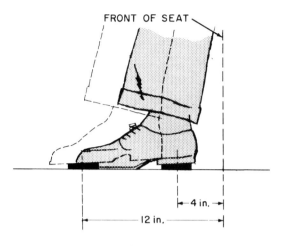

FRONT OF SEAT

|← 4 in. →|

|← 12 in. →|

PANEL CONTOUR

The following recommendations for designing panel contours will aid the designer in determining the proper size, shape and slope of panels. These recommendations apply only when the operator is standing or is seated with his backrest tilted no more than 20 deg from the upright. The contour of every panel, whether flat or sectional, is divided into the following three sections (see Fig. 7-43):

a. Upper section. This section should be from zero to 20 deg from the vertical, with its lower edge no more than 30 deg below the horizontal line of sight. This section should be used primarily for displays; controls can be located in this section if they are within reach but should be restricted to indicator setup or adjustment controls.

b. Middle section. This section should be from 30 to 50 deg from the horizontal and extended downward to a maximum of 45 deg below the horizontal line of sight. This section should be used, generally, for displays and their associated controls. Controls located in this section should lie within the optimum manual area.

b. Continuous-curved surface. This type is difficult to construct but, theoretically, the best to use. It can be designed so that all points are within the overall manual dimensions and so that all surfaces are perpendicular to the line of sight.

c. Sectional surface. This is the type of panel in which several flat surfaces are mounted at appropriate angles. It is easier to construct and has most of the advantages of a continuous-curved panel.

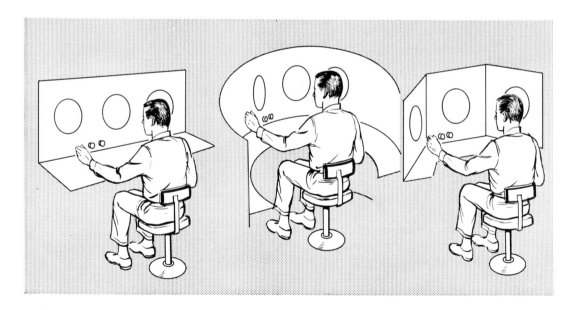

7-42

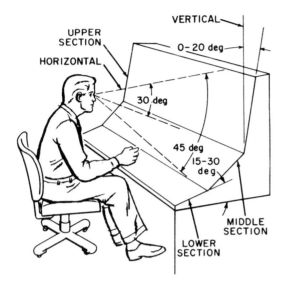

c. Lower section. This section should be from 15 to 30 deg from the horizontal and extended from the middle section to the near limits of the optimum manual area. This section should be used for controls and miscellaneous equipment, and as much of the section as possible should lie within the optimum manual area.

The vertical side of the panel is the recommended location for setup and adjustment controls, light switches, and other controls that are seldom used other than at the start or finish of the operating period. This surface can be recessed to safeguard against inadvertent operation.

7-43

7.7 *The Location of Shared Controls and Displays*

Up to this point, we have considered, mainly, the situation in which the controls and displays are used by a single operator. Before we bring this chapter to a close, we must consider those situations in which some controls and/or displays are shared by two operators or by an operator and a mobile observer.

7.7.1 *Those shared by two operators*

Secondary controls, such as on-off switches and setup and adjustment knobs, and displays

can be shared easily and present few design difficulties. Such controls may be located outside the optimum manual and visual area of either operator and within nearby overlapping areas. On the other hand, the sharing of primary controls and displays, which should be in the optimum areas, should be avoided wherever possible because of the following disadvantages inherent in shared controls and displays:

a. The optimum manual areas do not overlap for two persons seated side by side (see Fig. 7-44) because the width of the optimum areas is about 24 in. (see article 7.2.1), which is less than the recommended lateral allowance for seating of 26 in. (see Chapter 8).

b. The possibility of the operators sitting at some angle to each other might exist for some applications, but, to keep display position compatible for both operators, both

This section was drafted by Robert M. Thomson, Bernard J. Covner, and Herbert H. Jacobs of Dunlap and Associates, Inc.

§ 7.7.1

should face in nearly the same direction, i.e., within 30 deg of each other, because as this angle approaches 45 deg, display position becomes ambiguous (see Fig. 7-45). This situation is particularly undesirable where any two-dimensional tracking task is involved. Thus, if any such task must be shared, it is recommended that two displays be provided

so that each operator can face his own display squarely.

c. Controls that are shared must be used by the left hand of one operator and by the right hand of the other. This situation might lead to confusion, particularly if they change places or if the same operator is required to fill either position. For instance, with controls placed in the shaded area of Fig. 7-46, control movements in the direction of the arrows represents forward to operator A and left to operator B.

d. When continuously monitored primary controls must be shared (as in multi-engined aircraft), a duplicate set of such controls should be provided for each operator. But, to insure proper coordination of both sets of controls, this arrangement leads to the additional complication of requiring either a system of interlocks or a special operating procedure (which requires special training).

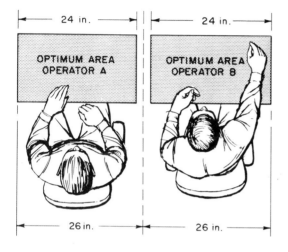

7-44

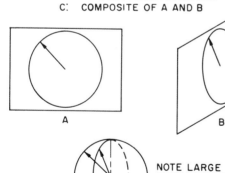

POINTERS SET AT 315 deg POSITION
A: AS SEEN FROM HEAD ON
B: AS SEEN FROM AN ANGLE
C: COMPOSITE OF A AND B

NOTE LARGE
DISPLACEMENT IN
APPARENT POSITION

7-45

7.7.2 *Those used by a stationary operator and a mobile observer*

When considering the location of controls that are to be used by an operator stationed at

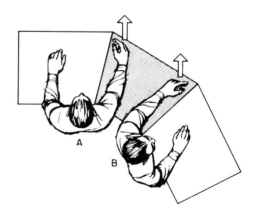

7-46

a fixed workplace but that must occasionally be monitored and/or operated by mobile observers, first priority should be given to the requirements of the stationary operator; if the controls are of primary importance to his job, they must be placed within his optimum manual area. In addition, the controls should be located in relation to other controls and displays in a manner consistent with the design principles given in the preceding sections.

As an exception to the above rule, a *single* control sometimes can be taken out of the context of related controls and displays. The learning problem, or the probability of making control errors, is seldom increased by a single exception. Indeed, by its uniqueness, the exception tends to reinforce learning associations (see Chapter 1). In general, however, only emergency controls should be separated from their associated displays. And, although the removal of controls from their normal context might make them more accessible to supervisors and/or other operators, too much separation makes for a hard-to-operate arrangement.

Displays that must be used by both an operator and a mobile observer (e.g., supervisors, liaison officers) cannot be optimumly located for both at the same time; hence, a compromise is always involved, and the stationary operator, who is not at liberty to find an acceptable position, should receive primary consideration. Thus, primary displays should be located within the stationary operator's optimum visual area, even at the expense of some inconvenience to the observer, because the latter is mobile and, thus, more adaptable. Indeed, there is almost no location for a display within the operator's visual area that an observer cannot get in a position to see.

To get the best view of the operator's activities, the observer will stand to one side and slightly to the rear of the operator and look over his shoulder. The best location within the operator's optimum visual area for displays that the observer must see is the upper right or left corner of the area, depending on which side of the operator the observer will stand (see Fig. 7-47).

AREA MOST EASILY SEEN BY SUPERVISOR

OPERATORS OPTIMUM VISUAL AREA

7-47

8

arrangement of groups of men and machines

THE ORGANIZATION, layout, and arrangement of man-machine systems represents a large complex of decision-making problems, and no entirely adequate or objective methodology for treating such problems has evolved. It generally is believed, however, that quantitative methods probably are best reserved for studying those design aspects that are believed to have profound significance to the accomplishment of the mission. Qualitative methods, on the other hand, probably are best for resolving a large number of more or less superficial problems that enter into any complex system-design problem. An example of such a qualitative method is link analysis, which is discussed in the following section.

8.1 *Link Analysis*

Link analysis is a technique for arriving at the best arrangement, for a particular purpose, of the men and machines in a system. It presupposes that firm decisions have been made about the exact items of equipment to be used in the system, the exact number of men who will operate it, and the functions that will be performed by these operators. The critical

This chapter was drafted by Robert M. Thomson, Bernard J. Covner, Herbert H. Jacobs, and Jesse Orlansky of Dunlap and Associates, Inc.

point is that the "best arrangement" can be found only in terms of some criterion (such as, perhaps, the distance between men, convenience of communications, and/or some other criterion) that is thought to be important in the particular system being designed; there is probably no one overall "best arrangement" for the entire system.

The term "link" as used here refers to any connection between a man and a machine or between one man and another. If, for example, one man must talk to another, this need is represented by a link between them. Similarly, if a man must see the display on a machine or operate a control on a machine, he has a link to the machine. Ordinarily, any links between machines can be neglected if the length of the

2. From a knowledge of the use men make of such machines (if it is necessary to make actual studies of real or simulated systems to find out this information, refer to Chapter 1) draw connecting lines (links) between each man and each equipment and between each man and any other man or men who have any direct connection in the operation of the system (see Fig. 8-1).

3. Redraw the resulting diagram to reduce to a minimum the number of crossing links. If necessary, redraw it several times until the simplest possible arrangement has been obtained (see Fig. 8-2, top of next page).

For many systems, this procedure practically completes the link analysis, which now shows how to place those men and equipments

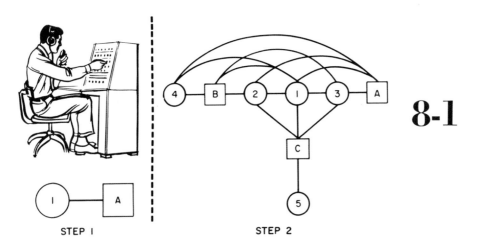

STEP I   STEP 2   **8-1**

link is of no importance in the system being considered.

To make a link analysis of a man-machine system, proceed as follows:

1. Draw a circle for every man in the system and label it with a code *number* for his particular function (e.g., "1" for radio operator, "2" for navigator, "3" for plotter, etc.), and draw a square for every item of equipment used by a human operator and label it with a code *letter* (e.g., "A" for radio, "B" for plotting board, "C" for compass, etc.). It makes little difference how the circles and squares are arranged at this point as long as there is some room between them (see Fig. 8-1).

together that belong together and how to separate those that have little relation to each other in the operation of the system. In this case, one would skip the next two steps and continue with step 6.

Where the preceding steps yield many crossings that reveal conflicting requirements for the proximity of men and machines, it is necessary to evaluate the frequency of use, and the importance, of each link. When this is true, proceed as follows:

4. Evaluate each link by one or more of the following methods:

a. Where the *importance of each link* is the criterion, have an experienced person—someone who knows thoroughly the operation of

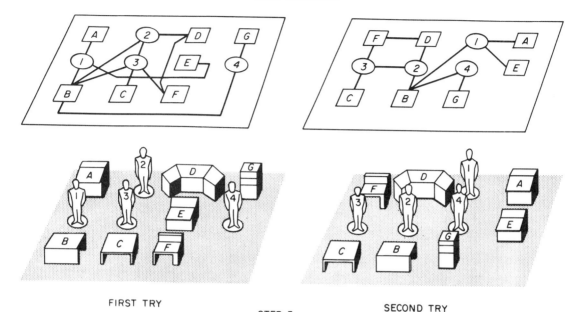

FIRST TRY

STEP 3

SECOND TRY

the system—rank each link according to its relative importance (assign low numbers to low rankings and high numbers to high rankings), and enter these rankings on the links (see Fig. 8-3).

b. Where *frequency of use* is the criterion, obtain data, from the simulated or operational use of the system, on the frequency of use of a link or the time it is in operation; use these data to rank each link according to the amount

of use each gets, and enter these rankings on the links.

c. Where *both* frequency of use and importance of a link must be considered, have experienced observers judge the relative weights to be given to frequency of use and importance so as to be able to assign a single value to each link.

5. Redraw the diagram so that the links having the higher link values are shorter than

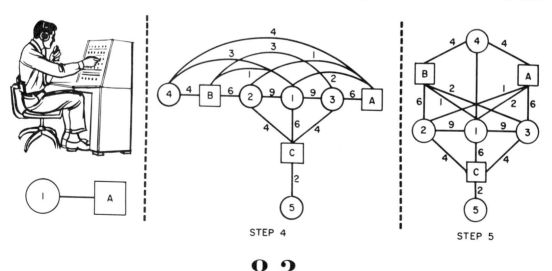

STEP 4

STEP 5

8-3

those having lower link values and reduce the number of crossing links (see Fig. 8-3). This is the optimum link diagram.

At this point a word of caution is in order. Analysis based on structural, rather than functional, criteria is a very useful device for a preliminary schema, but it is hardly the last word. No real meaning can be attached to the length of the lines or to the number of crossings; we suppose that performance data will go along with the appearance of the line structure, but it is by no means a "sure thing." It is, however, the handiest method available. But, to continue:

6. Redraw the link diagram, as necessary, to fit it into the available space, or, preferably, design the space to suit the shape of the diagram.

7. Confirm the final link analysis on a scale drawing of the actual positions of the men, machines, and spaces comprising the system. Such a drawing enables the designer to visualize the physical dimensions of the system and to discover any difficulties that are not revealed in link analysis. An example of a link diagram superimposed on the scale drawing of a Navy communications and control center is shown in Fig. 8-4 (below).

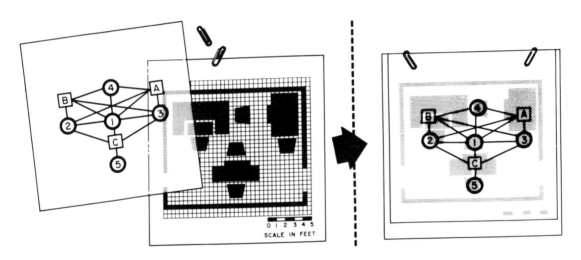

8.2 *Compartment Layout*

The layout of compartments is considered here from the point of view of its effect on human performance. For this reason, it will be assumed that the following factors are fixed (at least provisionally):

   a. The mission of the system.
   b. The design of individual equipments.
   c. The number of equipments.
   d. The number of personnel.
   e. The function of individual personnel.

8.2.1 *Factors affecting compartment size and shape*

Compartment size and shape will depend, primarily, on the total size and shape of the working units (men and machines) that must go into the compartment. Working-space tol-

324

§ 8.2.1

erances within the compartment are determined by both personnel and equipment requirements.

HUMAN-BODY SIZE AND DYNAMICS

The human-body dimensions that most directly affect compartment size and shape are given in Chapter 11. Although the data presented in Chapter 11 describe, for the most part, the nude body, they are acceptable for lightly clothed persons. When special clothing or equipment is worn, however, it is recommended that a mockup be made and space tolerances be determined empirically. Heavy clothing or encumbering equipment generally will have the following two important effects on nude dimensions:

a. It *increases* the static dimensions, e.g., trunk thickness, thigh clearance.

b. It *decreases* the dynamic dimensions, i.e., arm span, arc of leg movement, and forward arm reach.

Design Recommendations

The following recommendations apply to the use of lateral dimensions:

1. Use the 95th percentile when the size of the operator to be stationed at any particular equipment cannot be predicted in advance.

2. Add 4 in. to either side of lateral dimensions to allow for normal "elbow room" to take into account activities, such as rotary movements, that require several pounds of torque when the forearm is used.

CREW SIZE AND MOBILITY

A large crew imposes certain conditions on design not required by a small crew. For instance, the following are affected by the size of the crew:

a. Communications. As crew size increases, unaided voice communications decrease in effectiveness and reliability (see Chapter 4).

b. Physical access. Additional space must be provided for access from the main compart-

ment entrance to and between the various work stations. For one operator, this can be reduced to a minimum (e.g., an airplane cockpit). For accesses through which several personnel must sometimes hurry, additional clearances should be provided.

c. Illumination. Illumination requirements become more complex for a large crew, especially where these requirements vary among operators. General lighting must be provided for the overall area, aisles, exits, etc., and individual illumination, filters, partitions, etc., often must be provided for specific personnel (see Chapter 2).

d. Acoustics. When several operators are in a compartment, special equipment might be needed to permit internal voice communication while filtering out interfering and extraneous sounds (see Chapters 3 and 4).

e. Environment. When several persons are gathered into a compartment together with the equipment that they operate, the problems of providing ventilation and air conditioning increase (see Chapter 10).

f. Space and equipment. With two or more men in the same compartment, many savings are possible both in space and in equipment because they often can be shared. Although problems can arise from one man's impeding the other or there being competition to use a certain facility, thoughtful layout can greatly reduce such interference.

Transient Personnel

In some systems, transient personnel concerned with messages, maintenance, and liaison will vary the size of the crew from time to time. Unless adequate provisions are made for such personnel, they are likely to hamper the operation of the system. The following should be considered:

a. Access space for (and adequate visual clearance to) important displays should be provided.

b. Space should be provided next to those persons who must receive and dispatch written or printed messages.

c. Aisle space to "operating" positions should allow for continuous traffic.

§ 8.2.1

Crew Mobility

The nature of the operator's job determines to a large extent whether he must be free to move around his work station. Provision for such freedom affects the layout of the compartment; the layout must provide for uncluttered access to various spaces to accommodate personnel who must move around to accomplish their jobs.

For jobs that require mobility, the operator will generally stand or alternate between sitting and standing (see Chapter 7). The effects of these positions on compartment layout are small but important. For instance, the standing position is characterized by the following compartment-layout considerations:

a. The standing operator requires less front-to-rear operating room but more vertical room than the seated operator.

b. The standing operator does not require a seat.

c. The standing operator is more mobile, even when confined to a small operating position, and can move out of another person's way to allow him to pass.

Thus, if traffic is not too heavy, the standing operator can be stationed in a traffic space or aisle. For example, aboard ship, controls and displays are mounted on the deck and bulkheads of the bridge. Thus, the space between the bridge guard rail and pilot house is used both as a passageway and as an operating station (see Fig. 8-5, above, right).

The factors listed above permit the designer latitude in compartment layout as well as savings in total floor or deck space as compared with designs for seated crew members. Standing operators, however, find some pedal operations awkward, and, in moving vehicles, they have to expend considerable effort in just maintaining their footing.

Operators should not be forced to stand if the job does not specifically require it. Preferably, the designer should allow the operator to stand or sit at will, especially where the job is prolonged and fairly continuous. But the seated position has the following drawbacks as far as compartment layout is concerned:

a. The control area is limited, and movement from one position to another is hindered.

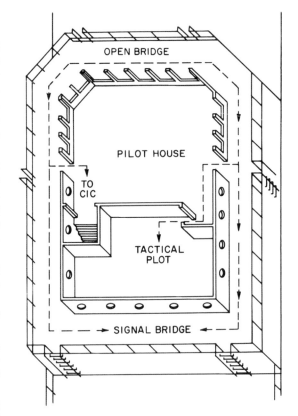

b. Open space (not a part of the useful operating area) generally is required for access to the seat, although rotary seats give good access with minimum space requirements.

c. Space is required behind the seat for fore-and-aft seat adjustment.

d. If seats are in a row, additional space is required for access to the inside seats.

Where operators are seated in close proximity, however, space will be saved by running an aisle directly in back of the seats. This aisle space can be used jointly for general traffic, individual access to operating stations, seat adjustments, and maintenance purposes (see Fig. 8-6).

EQUIPMENT SIZE AND OPERATION

The gross dimensions of an equipment, together with the clearances necessary for its operation, should be considered as an integral

326

§ 8.2.1

space requirement. Additional equipment space requirements, such as clearance for maintenance (see article 8.2.3), cables, and ventilation, should be considered separately.

Equipment Size

The height of the equipment partly determines compartment layout, especially where clearances are needed for viewing the same display by more than one operator and for verbal communication between operators. The maximum height of equipment over which something can be viewed will vary according to the location of the object to be viewed and the position of the viewer. Before locating any equipment over 55 in. high, however, it should be determined that the extra height will not interfere with any operator's line of sight. Generally, equipment taller than this should be located against a wall or bulkhead or in an open space where it acts as a wall (see Fig. 8-7). Of course, this requirement can highly restrict the number of possible compartment shapes and arrangements (see Fig. 8-8).

Where operators attending tall units of equipment must view major displays, it might be necessary to provide additional compartment height for adequate visual clearance. Communication by voice or visual signal between operators who are not seated side by side imposes similar requirements.

The gross physical dimensions of the equipment, augmented by approximate requirements for operating areas, aisle space, etc., will yield an initial estimate of compartment size. In general, space can be saved when small rather than large equipments are used

because small equipments are more versatile with respect to arrangement in the following ways:

a. They can be ideally located relative to the operator.

b. They can be stacked or mounted overhead or on bulkheads.

c. When used infrequently, they can be mounted in low-priority areas.

d. They can be put through small hatches or doors.

e. They can be carried or moved with less effort or mechanical assistance.

Equipment Operation

As stated above, the volume required for operating the equipment can be added directly to that occupied by the equipment itself. The design of the equipment will determine, within close limits, the method of operation and, consequently, the required operating room, regardless of the location of the equipment with respect to other equipments within the compartment.

VISUAL REQUIREMENTS

Clearances for adequate vision to major displays or to other personnel with respect to the *arrangement* of equipment are discussed in section 8.3, but visual requirements are also important factors in determining compartment *size and shape*. When a main display must be viewed by a number of operators within a compartment, these should be stationed so that they get a direct view and so that their line of sight to the display surface forms an

8-6

AISLE SPACE

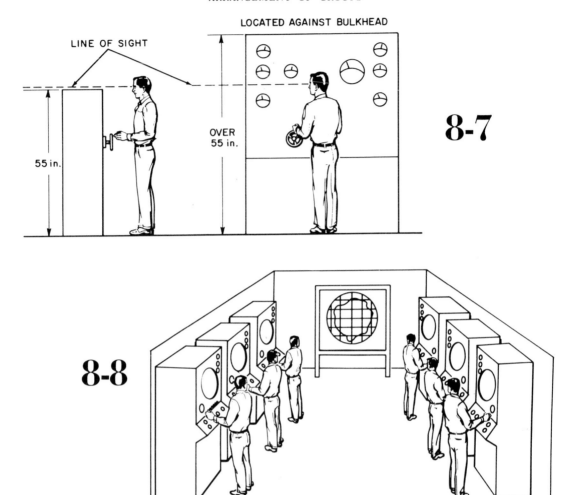

LOCATED AGAINST BULKHEAD

LINE OF SIGHT

55 in.

OVER 55 in.

8-7

8-8

angle between 60 and 90 deg (never less than 45 deg). If the majority of the operators must view the display, the area containing the display and the operators will be wedge-shaped or an elongated rectangle, which situation will set at least one minimum dimension for the compartment (see Fig. 8-9).

COMMUNICATION REQUIREMENTS

Communication facilities require special space planning both for the equipment itself and for operating room and access to the equipment. Provisions for adequate communications imposes important conditions on compartment layout.

Communication Within the Compartment

Visual methods. The distance between the viewer and visual displays (e.g., closed-circuit television) determines the required size and brightness of the display for effective visibility. In general, visual information should be arranged within 30 deg of the viewer's normal line of sight. (See Chapter 2 for a detailed discussion.)

Auditory methods. As with visual clearance, there should be clear space between personnel who will communicate directly by voice to insure adequate audibility (without shouting) and intelligibilty—the latter is enhanced when the listener can see the talker (see Chapter 4). In addition, all personnel requiring

§ 8.2.1

direct voice communication should be within normal voice range of the speaker. Acceptable voice range depends on the prevailing noise level, compartment size, etc. (see Chapter 4).

Communication Between Compartments

Visual methods. The recommendation given above with respect to visual displays such as television receivers should be observed. The effect of intercompartmental communication by visual displays such as plotting and status boards is discussed in article 8.2.4.

Auditory methods. Intercom units, handsets, voice tubes, plug-in headsets, etc., might not require additional space where the communication equipment can be located within the normal reach of the operator. The individual equipments by themselves generally require little space and often can be fitted be-

tween larger equipments or mounted overhead or on bulkheads within the convenient reach of the operator. Communication equipment should be placed outside normal passageway and operating spaces so that it does not cause, nor is subject to, accidents. Where communication equipment is shared (such as an intercom unit), the designer must provide operating room as well as access space to the equipment.

If messengers or runners are to be used, they will require an access space to key personnel from main aisles. This space should be large enough to prevent interference with the movements of operating personnel when messages are delivered or received.

The location of loudspeakers and their effect on compartment size and shape presents problems in acoustical design and speech communication that are beyond the scope of this chapter (see Chapters 3 and 4), but the lay-

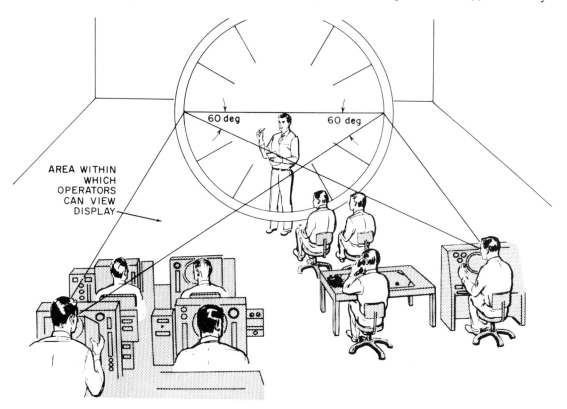

8-9

out problems include determining the desirable area to be covered by any one loudspeaker in competition with another and stationing personnel in groups that can share information provided by the loudspeaker.

8.2.2 *The layout of traffic spaces*

Though access spaces, passageways, and stairs generally must be provided, they are not, strictly speaking, part of the working area. Therefore, the arrangement of working groups (see section 8.3) and the arrangement of equipment and operators must be given first priority. If a choice is required, adequate operating room at the expense of space for traffic usually can be justified.

An architect designs space for traffic in terms of the type, amount, and weight of the traffic, with consideration of the frequency of use, routing, speed, etc. Discussion of such factors can be found in standard sources; the present discussion is limited to the human-engineering aspects of such design.

AISLES AND CORRIDORS

Aisles are spaces designed to provide for the passage of men and equipment *within* a compartment; corridors provide for passage *between* compartments, i.e., between areas separated by a wall or partition. In hangars or depots where large areas are enclosed to form a single compartment, no distinction need be made between aisles and corridors.

It is advisable to provide an aisle when it is expected that there will be an appreciable amount of traffic within a compartment during normal operations. When there is slight traffic, such as an orderly change of personnel at the end of a shift, the traffic can make its way through whatever path is available (assuming there are no special requirements for safety). In any case, it is clear that the arrangement of operators, displays, and equipment and the establishment of clear lines of sight should be given prime consideration.

Design Recommendations

Figures 8-10, 8-11, and 8-12 show recommended widths for aisles and corridors. An aisle can be narrower than a corridor because it should take less traffic and because it usually is convenient for one person to wait or stand aside while another passes; in corridors, there should be free passage for all personnel. Figure 8-13 (page 334) shows the recommended location of aisles with respect to exits.

The following additional recommendations should be observed in the design of aisles and corridors:

1. Make them straight; put in as few corners as possible; avoid blind corners.

2. Locate paths for minimum distances; use flow charts, diagrams, movement analyses, etc., to indicate where the most traffic will be.

3. Mark traffic guides (aisle limits, arrows, etc.) on floors, walls, or ceilings.

4. Make intersections converge at 90 deg; this arrangement will minimize lost floor space.

5. Keep aisles clear; do not allow equipment or structural-support columns to protrude into any aisle.

6. Avoid locating an aisle against a blank wall because this will permit access from only one side.

7. Avoid providing for one-way traffic in aisles (because it will not be followed); one-way traffic is possible, but not desirable, in corridors.

CATWALKS AND TUNNELS

Catwalks and tunnels should be considered as special facilities for handling traffic. As such, they can be recommended only where space or environmental conditions preclude normal aisles or corridors.

The floor of a catwalk should have a non-skid surface. Wherever possible, the stairway to the catwalk should approach the catwalk at right angles. Guard rails should be provided, fastened to the lower half of which should be wire mesh or other screening.

Fully enclosed walkways (or tunnels) that allow the user to walk erect, or almost erect, may be shaped, roughly, according to the

COMPARTMENT LAYOUT

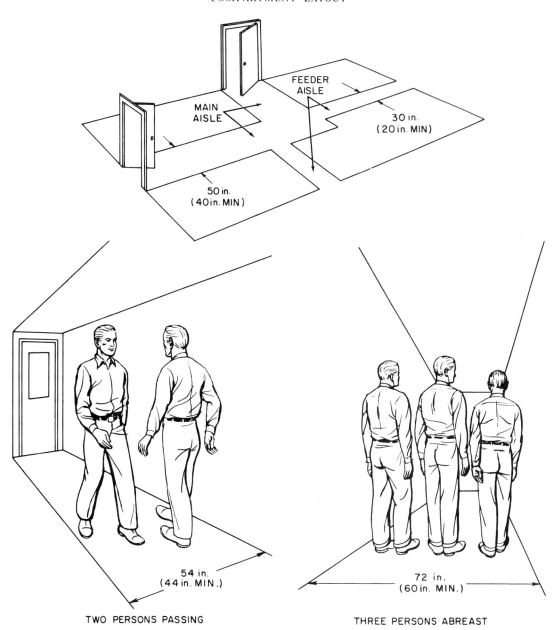

MAIN AISLE

FEEDER AISLE

30 in. (20 in. MIN)

50 in. (40 in. MIN)

54 in. (44 in. MIN.)

TWO PERSONS PASSING

72 in. (60 in. MIN.)

THREE PERSONS ABREAST

8-10

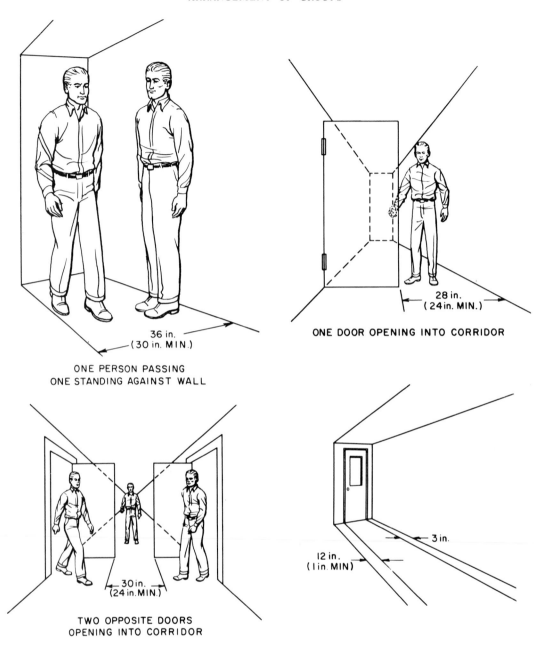

36 in.
(30 in. MIN.)

ONE PERSON PASSING
ONE STANDING AGAINST WALL

28 in.
(24 in. MIN.)

ONE DOOR OPENING INTO CORRIDOR

30 in.
(24 in. MIN.)

TWO OPPOSITE DOORS
OPENING INTO CORRIDOR

3 in.

12 in.
(1 in. MIN)

8-11

§ 8.2.2

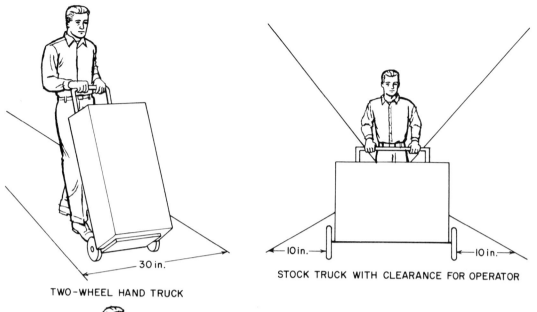

30 in.

TWO-WHEEL HAND TRUCK

10 in. — 10 in.

STOCK TRUCK WITH CLEARANCE FOR OPERATOR

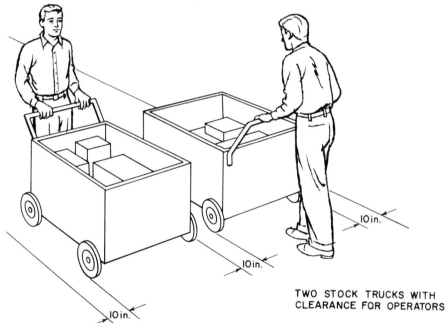

10 in.

10 in.

10 in.

10 in.

TWO STOCK TRUCKS WITH
CLEARANCE FOR OPERATORS

8-12

§ 8.2.2

THEORETICALLY IDEAL
FOR ONE EXIT

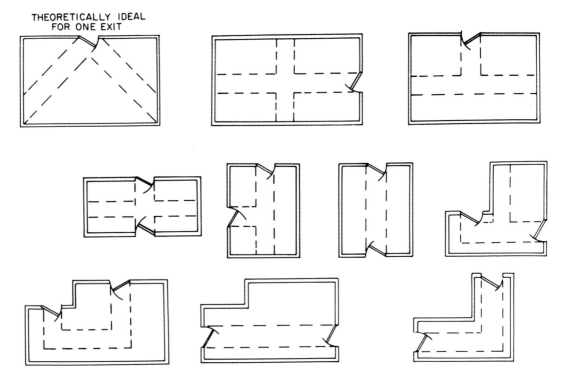

human contour to minimize space and weight requirements. The lateral measurements of such a passageway, shown in Fig. 8-14, will have to be increased for personnel wearing or carrying bulky equipment. If the enclosed walkway is in a moving vehicle, however, extra space should be provided for a handrail (see Fig. 8-15).

Sometimes the only feasible type of passageway is one in which the user must stoop, crawl, slide, or ride (on a trolley). Dimensions for crawlways are shown in Fig. 8-16. The dimensions for clearance in tunnels, such as those shown in Fig. 8-17, are 25 in. for shoulder clearance in either case, 16 in. for body clearance in the first case (top), and 22 in. for body plus "elbow room" in the second case (bottom). Both of these two latter dimensions are measured from the top surface of the trolley. All of these dimensions are based on the 95th-percentile man, and any allowance required for equipment or heavy clothing should be added to them. (See Chapter 11 for the appropriate increments to be added to the dimensions given here to allow for certain kinds of bulky clothing.)

DOORWAYS AND HATCHES

The dimensions recommended in the following paragraphs for various kinds of doorways and hatches will accommodate over 99% of the population wearing light to medium clothing, viz., shoes, trousers, jacket, and hat. These dimensions may be decreased if less than 99% of the population is to be provided for, or if the users can stoop, bend, or otherwise adapt to inadequate openings. These dimensions might have to be increased, on the other hand, to allow for bulkier or specialized clothing or equipment. (See Chapter 11 for the appropriate increments.) For most purposes, these dimensions should be considered minimum, with additional space to be supplied whenever possible.

Hinged Doors

The dimensions shown in Fig. 8-18 are adequate for access to and from a compartment for one person at a time; larger dimensions will be required for moving bulky equipment.

§ 8.2.2

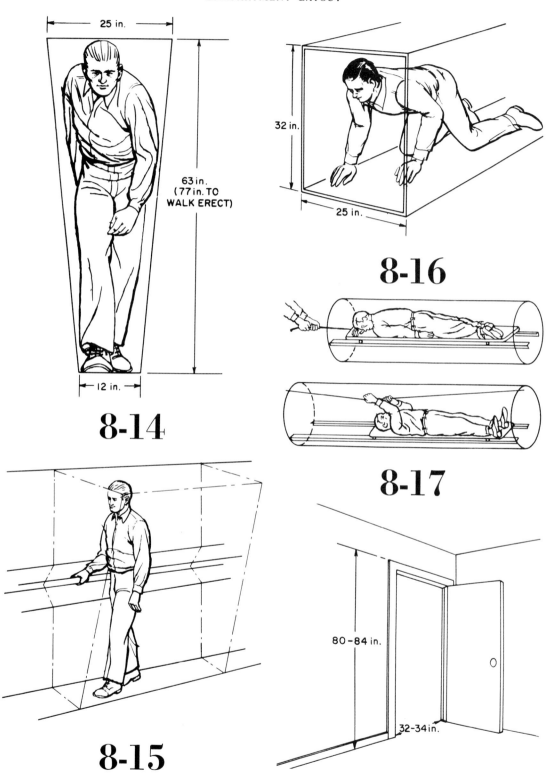

25 in.

63 in.
(77 in. TO
WALK ERECT)

12 in.

8-14

32 in.

25 in.

8-16

8-17

8-15

80-84 in.

32-34 in.

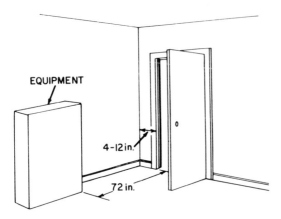

EQUIPMENT

4-12 in.

72 in.

Doorsills are not recommended except where weather protection or special ventilation control is required. Clearance of at least 4 in., and preferably 12 in., between the door and wall is recommended, and equipment should be located no closer than 6 ft (72 in.) from the doorway (see Fig. 8-19, above).

Sliding Doors

Vertical and horizontal sliding doors are useful for cramped spaces, but they are easily jammed when subject to blast, collision, etc. and, therefore, should never be installed in the only exit. Where large vehicles or pieces of equipment have to be moved into and out of compartments, a sliding door is recommended. A separate hinged door in the sliding door should be provided for personnel use.

Open Doorways

The dimensions given in Fig. 8-20 apply to any unobstructed opening between compartments. If space and structural strength permit, open doorways should be wide enough to allow two men to pass through simultaneously.

Escape Hatches

The proper dimensions for escape hatches will depend on the compartment to be es-

caped from, the equipment and clothing worn by the man, and the environment he will enter. In general, it is advisable to study the particular conditions of escape before deciding on the size of the hatch.

Figure 8-21 shows escape-hatch sizes for aircraft other than certain types of high-speed aircraft, which have special ejection requirements (White, et al., 1952). Side hatches should be flush with the floor if structural considerations will permit this arrangement. It should be possible to open the hatch with a single motion of the hand or foot, and, when a handle is used, the force required should not exceed 30 lb.

Watertight Doors and Armored Hatches

Heavy, metal hatches must be as small as possible to reduce the weight and to preserve the structural strength of the bulkhead or deck in which they are to be mounted. Figure 8-22

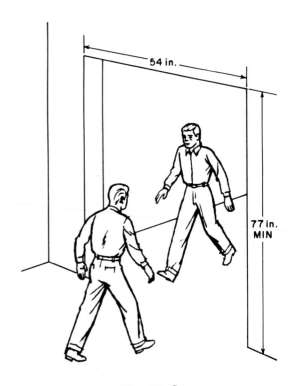

54 in.

77 in. MIN

8-20

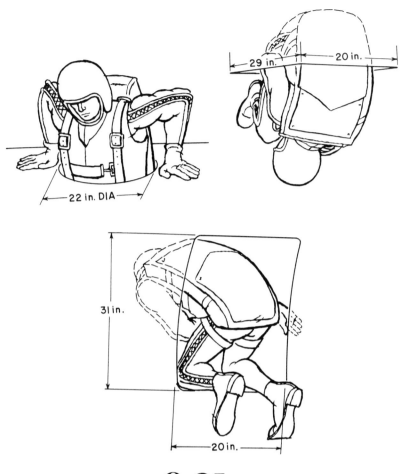

8-21

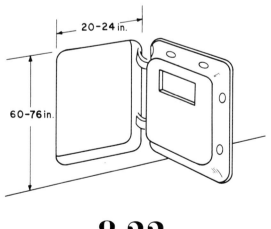

8-22

shows minimum and recommended dimensions for bulkhead-mounted (vertical) hatches. The 76-in. dimension permits the 95th percentile man to walk through erect.

If men must go through a bulkhead-mounted hatch carrying heavy loads, less muscular strain is produced in stepping over a high coaming than in stooping excessively. For such situations, 68 in. is recommended for the top of the hatch, with the height of the coaming above the deck being 10 in. (see Fig. 8-23). In no case, however, should a coaming be as high as the crotch height of the small, 5th-percentile man (30.4 in.). For regular traffic through bulkhead-mounted hatches, design for the range of the popula-

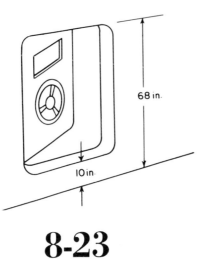

8-23

tion that will use the hatch and not just for
the average man (see Chapter 11).

Figure 8-24 shows minimum and recommended dimensions for deck-mounted (horizontal) hatches. The actual depth of the hatch
depends on the angle (X) of the ladder leading up to the hatch, i.e., the larger the angle,
the greater must be the depth of the hatch
(with a minimum of 24 in. in any case). The
recommended depth is 30 secant X. Thus, for
vertical ladders, the depth should be 24–30 in.
(see Fig. 8-25). For angled ladders, the minimum and recommended vertical distances between the lower front edge of the hatch and
the ladder tread immediately below this point
are shown in Fig. 8-26.

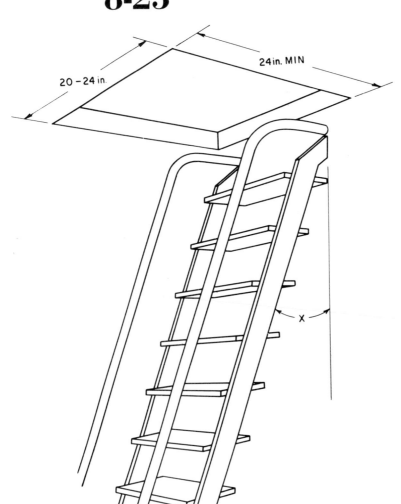

8-24

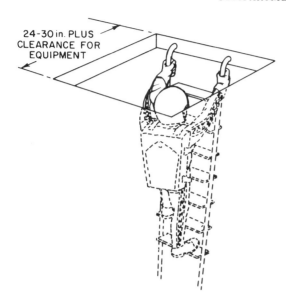

24-30 in. PLUS CLEARANCE FOR EQUIPMENT

8-25

LADDERS, STAIRS, AND RAMPS

These all have the same function, viz., to provide for traffic flow between levels within a compartment or between compartments. They are treated here more or less in the order of the degree of complexity of their construction.

Ladders

Ladders should be used where the desired rise from the horizontal is at an angle of 50 deg and more, or where stairways are not practicable. Some ladders have flat horizontal treads (as opposed to round rungs) and hand-

8-26

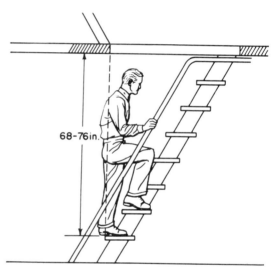

68-76 in.

8-27

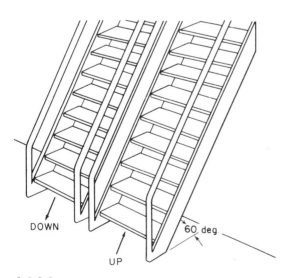

DOWN

UP

60 deg.

rails. The most familiar example of this type is the ship's ladder, which usually rises at an angle of 68 deg but probably should be closer to 60 deg. This type of ladder generally has clearance for one person only. If simultaneous two-way traffic is desired, separate up and down ladders are provided. If these are located side by side, a double handrail in the center should be provided (see Fig. 8-27).

Figure 8-28 shows recommended dimensions for this type of ladder. The optimum height between treads is 8½–9 in. Treads should be open (without risers) and should be provided with nonskid surfacing. Metal screening should be fastened to the under-

§ 8.2.2

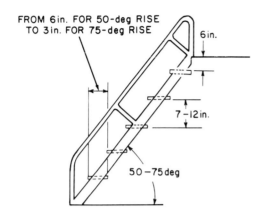

FROM 6 in. FOR 50-deg RISE
TO 3 in. FOR 75-deg RISE

6 in.

7 – 12 in.

50 – 75 deg

8-28

8-29

8-30

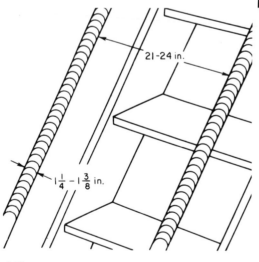

21-24 in.

$1\frac{1}{4} - 1\frac{3}{8}$ in.

side of the ladder to prevent the foot from slipping through (see Fig. 8-29). Where ladders are located one above the other, solid metal sheeting instead of screening may be used to protect those on the lower ladder from dirt from the feet of those on the ladder above. The handrails on both sides of the ladder, should be covered with braided line or other nonslip surfacing and should have the dimensions shown in Fig. 8-30.

For some other ladders, round rungs are used to provide both hand grips and foot

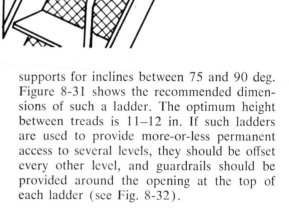

HEAVY WIRE
SCREEN OR
SHEET METAL
BACKING

supports for inclines between 75 and 90 deg. Figure 8-31 shows the recommended dimensions of such a ladder. The optimum height between treads is 11–12 in. If such ladders are used to provide more-or-less permanent access to several levels, they should be offset every other level, and guardrails should be provided around the opening at the top of each ladder (see Fig. 8-32).

Stairs

Stairs should rise from the horizontal at an angle of between 20 and 50 deg, with the op-

§ 8.2.2

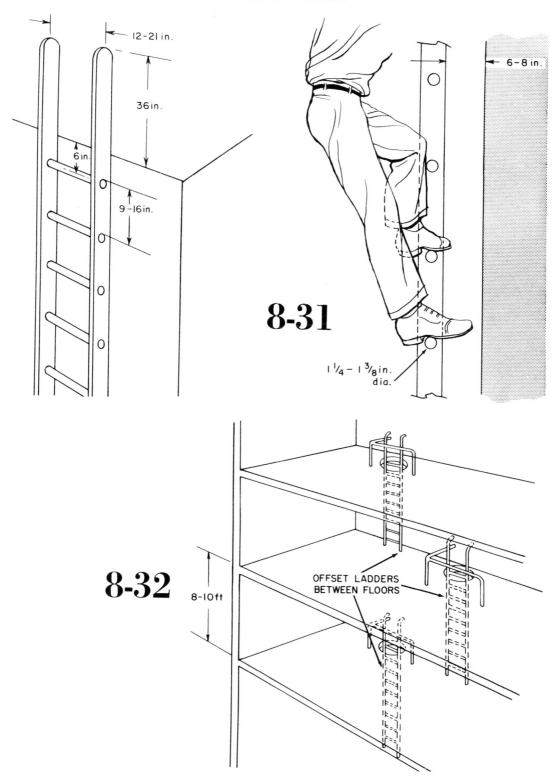

8-31

12-21 in.

36 in.

6 in.

9-16 in.

1¼ - 1⅜ in. dia.

6-8 in.

8-32

8-10 ft

OFFSET LADDERS
BETWEEN FLOORS

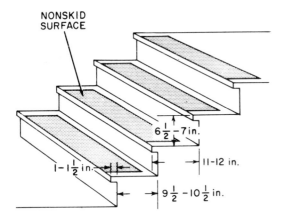

NONSKID
SURFACE

$6\frac{1}{2}$–7 in.

11–12 in.

1–1$\frac{1}{2}$ in.

$9\frac{1}{2}$–10$\frac{1}{2}$ in.

timum range being between 30 and 35 deg. The ratio of riser height to tread depth will depend on the stair angle, but the minimum riser height should be 5 in. and the maximum 8 in., and the optimum tread depth is $9\frac{1}{2}$–$10\frac{1}{2}$ in. plus a 1–1$\frac{1}{2}$ in. overhang (see Fig. 8-33, above). These dimensions provide depth such that, in descending the stairs, the ball of the foot does not extend beyond the front edge of the tread, and the heel comfortably clears the overhang of the step above.

Long flights of stairs should be avoided, and, where space permits, landings should be provided every 10–12 treads. In addition,

stairs should have a handrail, on one side at least, which should have the recommended heights shown in Fig. 8-34. The width of stairs (between handrails or between wall and handrail) should be as shown in Fig. 8-35 (top of next page).

For open stairways and landings, guardrails should be provided halfway between the handrails and treads. In addition, screen guards should be provided between the guardrail and the landing for landings between flights of stairs that are at right angles.

Ramps

Ramps or inclines should be used for grades under 20 deg, but, in general ramps are of value only when rolling stock must be moved between different levels. For pedestrian traffic only, a stairway is more efficient from the standpoint of space, safety, and speed. For ramps that are to be used for pedestrian traffic, however, cleats should be provided on the ramp surface that are spaced about 14 in. apart and extend from handrail to handrail at right angles to the line of traffic. Where a smooth (but nonskid) surface or runway for wheeled vehicles is needed,

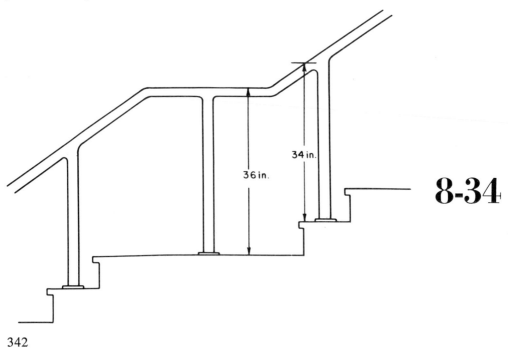

34 in.

36 in.

8-34

it should be located in the center of the ramp, with the cleated portions on the outside next to the handrails. A combination ramp and stairway, however, is preferred for this situation. For vehicle traffic only, the entire surface of the ramp should be smooth (see Fig. 8-36).

ESCALATORS AND ELEVATORS

Escalators have a disadvantage, as do elevators, from the standpoint of the possibility of their being incapacitated because of a mechanical failure, power loss, etc. They have advantages, however, in that they can transport rapidly large numbers of personnel between levels, especially where these levels are

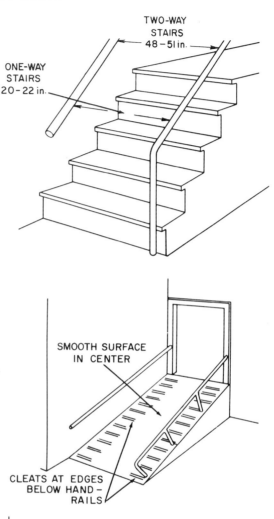

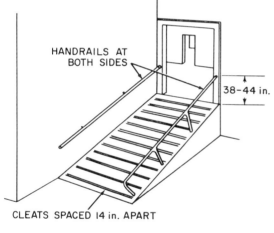

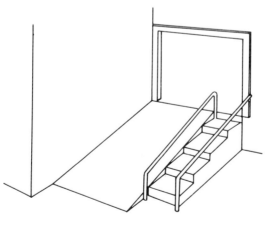

8-36

higher than one story. For heights of one story or less, however, a stairway is more efficient; physically sound men can run up (or down) stairs at a rate exceeding that which is safe to run an escalator.

The recommended rate of travel for an escalator is 120–138 ft/min, although rates from 90 to 180 ft/min can be found. When entering an escalator running at speeds over 120 ft/min, even experienced users will pause to judge their footing. This pause slows up traffic to an extent that more than offsets the travel time gained by advancing the escalator rate of travel. Moreover, when personnel are heavily loaded with equipment, too high a travel rate will tend to upset their balance when entering the escalator.

The preferred angle of ascent for escalators is 30 deg, but 45 deg is satisfactory, provided that the angles at the entrance and exit are more gradual. In addition, the moving hand-rail tends to coordinate the user's entering speed with that of the escalator so that it should move at exactly the same speed as the steps, and, at the entrance to the escalator, the moving handrail should extend 5–6 ft beyond the point where the moving treads begin (see Fig. 8-37).

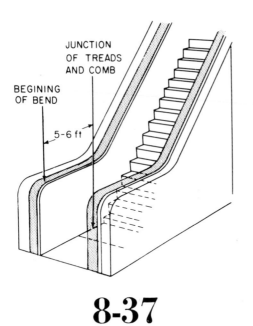

JUNCTION
OF TREADS
AND COMB

BEGINNING
OF BEND

5-6 ft

8-37

Elevators should be used only for transporting heavy equipment and/or a limited number of personnel between levels where the distance exceeds two stories. In a military situation, however, elevators should not be relied upon for critical movements because they might become nonfunctioning just when they are needed most. Escalators still can be used as ordinary stairs in such an emergency, whereas elevators become useless until they have been repaired. Moreover, elevators are space consuming, and, though their speeds are relatively high, their capacities are limited.

CEILINGS AND OVERHEADS

Overhead-space design is concerned mainly with the following problems:

a. Locating equipment overhead that can be operated by short operators, that is out of regular aisles or places where it will be bumped into, and that does not interfere with fixed lines of sight.

b. Establishing clear lines of sight over equipment and/or heads of personnel.

If equipment is located above an aisle, it is restricted to a fairly limited range. Vertical clearance for a tall man (plus shoes and helmet) is 76–77 in., but the height that can be comfortably reached by short men is about 76–78 in., depending on the type of grasp and the strength required. Thus, the vertical clearance for overhead controls is limited to only 1–2 in. for most cases (see Fig. 8-38). If the equipment to be mounted overhead does not have to be operated or requires only periodic adjustment or maintenance, it can be located anywhere between the ceiling and 76–77 in. above the floor (head clearance for the tall operator).

In the seated position, the difference in height between the 95th- and 5th-percentile operator is only 4.2 in. (38 vs. 33.8 in.). The seated operator can actuate controls that are 10–12 in. above his head momentarily (for longer periods, controls should be no more than 6 in. above his head). Thus, the vertical clearance for overhead controls is limited to 6–8 in. for the seated position (see Fig. 8-39).

§ 8.2.2

8.2.3 *The layout of maintenance spaces*

The space provided for maintenance is not primarily a convenience; it is a requirement to insure an acceptable level of operating efficiency. In laying out a workplace, consideration must be given to the methods by which the equipment in it will be maintained, especially if more than a normal amount of space will be required to perform maintenance (see Chapter 9).

WORKING SPACE AND CLEARANCE

Figures 8-40 and 8-41 show the normal space and clearance that must be provided for various body positions assumed by the maintenance man while making adjustments and conducting repairs. The dimensions given are the minimum recommended clearances. In addition, at least 30 in. lateral clearance is required to provide the operator with "elbow room."

The minimum recommended clearances shown in Figs. 8-40 and 8-41 should be unobstructed spaces measured from the maintenance surface to the nearest opposing surface. Additional clearance should be given when these opposing surfaces contain the following:

a. Controls, such as toggle switches and levers, that could be inadvertently bumped or kicked.

b. Indicator faces, glass panels, or other objects that are breakable.

c. Protruding objects against which the body or clothing could be snagged.

Maintenance spaces should also include space for the temporary storage or operation of special equipment, such as test meters, large wrenches or other tools, work stands, stepladders or dollies, and electrical patch cords, where these might be required.

AISLE SPACE

In most compartment layouts, the aisle serves double duty for both traffic and maintenance. In general, because maintenance is performed only occasionally, the regular aisle

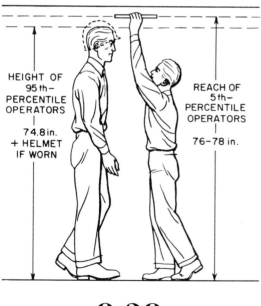

8-38

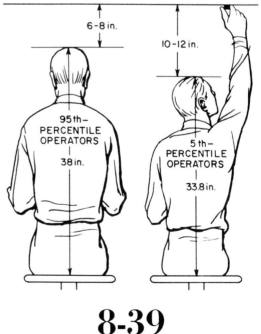

8-39

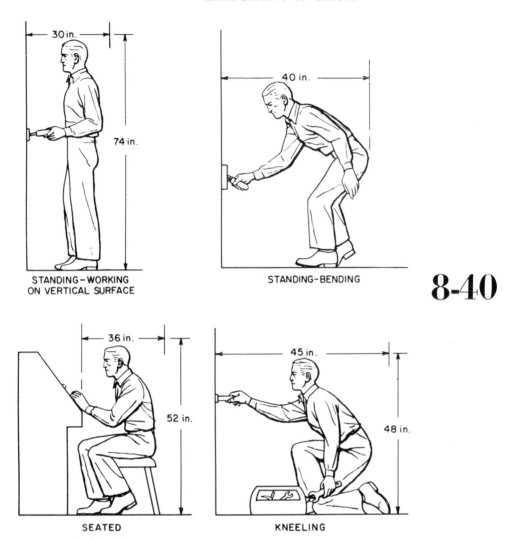

STANDING—WORKING
ON VERTICAL SURFACE

STANDING—BENDING

8-40

SEATED

KNEELING

dimensions provide only for traffic flow, with the result shown in Fig. 8-42. If possible, where maintenance operations encroach on frequently used aisle space and no alternate space for rerouting traffic is available, additional space should be provided in that area, i.e., furnish aisle space plus maintenance space.

INTERACTION BETWEEN EQUIPMENTS

Maintenance access requirements are of primary importance in the location of equip-

ment. In laying out compartments, full advantage should be taken of the possibility of combining or "pooling" the various necessary clearances. For instance, an item of equipment might require clearance for ventilation at the sides if it is located against a bulkhead. If it is located beside another heat-producing item of equipment, additional side clearance might be required. By adding a few more inches, sufficient space could be gained to allow maintenance at the sides of each piece of equipment.

Another obvious combination occurs in the situation in which two items of equipment each require side clearance for maintenance

§ 8.2.3

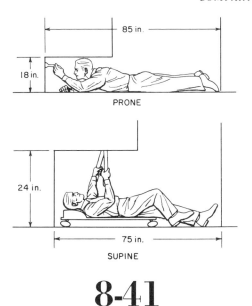

PRONE

SUPINE

8-41

8-42

access. A single space will suffice for both units if they are located side by side. In addition, aisle space is almost always available for maintenance space, provided clearance is available for at least one-way traffic.

Layout for maintenance access also should take into account the position of the operators of adjacent equipment. Thus, the man repairing console A is stationed correctly if the area in which he is kneeling is aisle or exclusively maintenance space. If another console is in position B, however, with an operator stationed in front of it, there will be interference between the two men (see Fig. 8-43). When two or more equipments operate interdependently (e.g., console A receives inputs from console B or otherwise depends on B for its proper functioning) so that both are out of operation simultaneously, then the layout can take advantage of this situation by placing them together.

With equipment complexity constantly on the increase, maintenance scheduling is certain to become of equal importance with operation scheduling. A complex system will demand that preventive maintenance take place according to a strict schedule. The mathematics and techniques necessary to determine this scheduling are beyond the scope of this chapter, but it should be pointed out that the

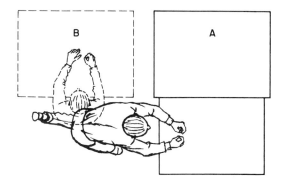

8-43

§ 8.2.3

schedule might have an important bearing on the location of equipment. For instance, it might be undesirable to place two equipments together if both of them will require frequent maintenance checking.

8.2.4 *The layout of plotting spaces*

This article deals with plotting boards and status boards from the point of view of placing information on them. Information is placed on status and plotting boards by operator-plotters and the location of these facilities importantly influences compartment layout.

The operator-plotters have certain space requirements and minimum limits within which they can operate effectively. These limits are determined by the following considerations:

a. The limits of reach of the operator-plotter.

b. Whether or not structural aids are provided.

c. The required rate and density of plotting.

THE LIMITS OF REACH

Plotting-space requirements will depend on the size and location of the plotting area that the operator is required to cover. The optimum vertical dimension of the area the standing operator can cover, without stooping, is from about 30–80 in. above floor level; stooping will extend the lower limit to within 12–15 in. of the floor (see Fig. 8-44). Although most plotters can reach higher than 80 in., it is not recommended that they be required to do so because the short operator will have to stand on tiptoe or with his body against the plotting surface. Either of these positions would make writing movements awkward and give the plotter a distorted perspective of the plotting surface (see Fig. 8-45).

The optimum horizontal dimension of the area the standing operator can cover depends on the lateral movement the operator is al-

lowed. The right-handed, stationary operator can comfortably plot (within the vertical dimensions given above) within an area from 18 in. left of the centerline of his body to 30 in. to the right of this line (see Fig. 8-46).

The standing plotter should have a minimum of 30 in. of space in front of the plotting or status board in which to move. In addition, he should have something he can use for a backrest or he should have a guardrail against which he can lean. To allow the plotter to bend from the waist or to kneel, additional space must be provided (see Fig. 8-47).

STRUCTURAL AIDS

To increase the normal vertical coverage of the plotter, various structural devices, such as platforms and elevators, can be used. Ladders are generally unsatisfactory because they are inherently unsafe and are cumbersome to move and position.

Mobile and Stationary Platforms

When a single operator must cover a large plot that extends above his normal reach, a movable platform with attached steps is recommended. The platform should be narrow

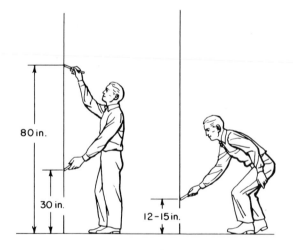

8-44

DISTORTED PERSPECTIVE BECAUSE OF POOR VISUAL ANGLE

(not over 24 in. wide) and at least 36 in. deep, with guardrails at the sides. It should be light but of rigid construction and should move on tracks. One recommended design is illustrated in Fig. 8-48 (top of next page).

A stationary platform is satisfactory where one or more operators must remain stationed above floor level. If used, the following design features should be included in such a structure:

1. Two-level guardrails should be provided at the rear and sides with wire mesh between the platform and bottom guardrail.

2. The front edge of the platform should be provided with a guard strip at least 3 in. high

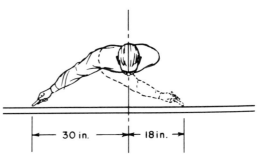

← 30 in. → ← 18 in. →

8-45

8-46

├─ 30 in. ─┤
MIN

├─ 40 in. ─┤

├─ 45 in. ─┤

8-47

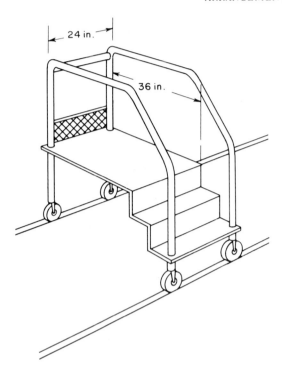

should be the safety of the operator. If possible, the device used should position the operator within the limits of reach of the standing operator (see above). In addition, the operator should not be required to move more than a step from the platform controls on a moving platform, and the platform should have two-level guardrails on all four sides (the operator enters through a gate).

PLOTTING RATE AND DENSITY

The operator rapidly loses efficiency when he is required to plot above a certain rate (see

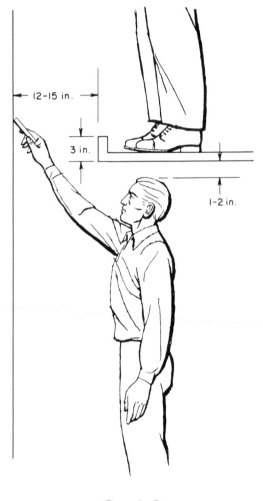

8-49

to prevent the operator's foot from slipping off the platform and to prevent articles on the platform from slipping off.

3. Platforms should be located so that the plotter on the level below can cover the plotting sector up to 12 in. above the level of the platform above to relieve the operator on the next level from covering this hard-to-reach area. The distance between the plotting surface and the front edge of the platform should be between 12 and 15 in. (see Fig. 8-49). This allows a plotter adequate room to plot on surfaces up to 12 in. above the next level.

4. The vertical distance between levels ideally should not exceed the standing height of the plotter (see Chapter 11) by more than 2 or 3 in.

Elevators

Elevators that move both vertically and horizontally and other elaborate mechanisms have been used where a single operator is responsible for covering the plot on a very large surface. Here the primary consideration

Matheny, 1955). If the information comes in at a high rate and in a constricted plotting sector, the plotter can cover only a small area. In such a situation, the dimensions of the sector assigned to the plotter should be governed by the anticipated peak load rather than by anthropometric considerations.

8.2.5 Conference rooms and auditoriums

Conference rooms, classrooms, and auditoriums are frequently useful in military and business installations. Conference rooms, as described in this article, include compartments that will seat up to 30 persons; rooms that hold 30–100 persons are called classrooms; compartments that hold 100 or more persons are defined as auditoriums.

CONFERENCE ROOMS

Ideally, a conference grouping in which all present are to participate actively probably should not include more than 8–10 persons. With larger numbers, it becomes difficult for the group to function as a unit. Seating in a conference room should be an around-the-table arrangement. This arrangement is more satisfactory for encouraging discussion than the speaker-audience arrangement found in classrooms and auditoriums. The table also provides a large work surface for material to be examined at close range by all participants.

Equipment Arrangement

A properly equipped conference room should have one or more optical projectors (for slides and moving pictures), a screen, a blackboard, and a display board. The viewing angle between the line of sight and information on a screen or wall should be at least 60 deg, if possible, but never less than 45 deg; for moving pictures, the larger value should be used. Recommendations on the design of

visual details to ensure adequate legibility and visibility are discussed in Chapter 2.

Although a microphone and loudspeaker should be available for such circumstances as an unusually large number of personnel in the conference room or a lecturer who will make a long briefing, the room size and acoustical design should make voice amplification unnecessary. The table seating arrangement will aid in this respect if each person partially faces the other people in the room.

Seating Arrangement

The distance recommended as the minimum lateral allowance for men seated at a table is some 30 in. per person. This clearance permits using armchairs with 2-in.-wide armrests (see Fig. 8-50). When several persons are seated at a table in a row roughly perpendicular to a visual presentation, the lateral distance between personnel becomes critical. Visual clearance depends on the following:

a. The width of the display in relation to the width of the table.

b. The lateral distance between each person (see Fig. 8-51). Although the people nearest the display can shift backward to get out of the way, this might interfere with taking notes.

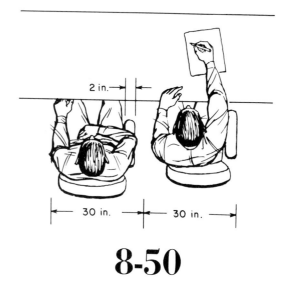

8-50

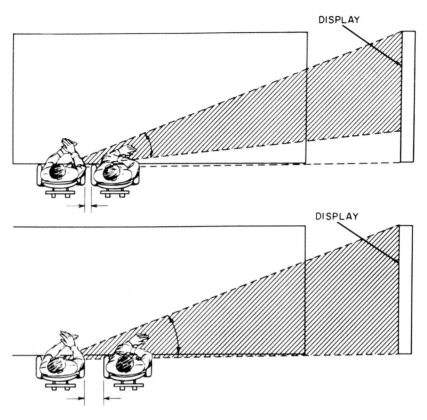

8-51

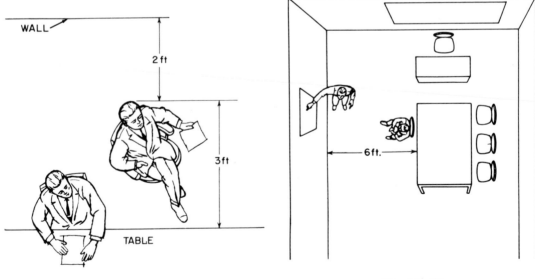

8-52

8-53

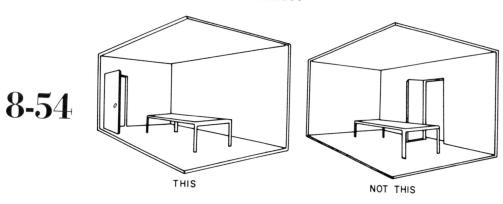

8-54

THIS

NOT THIS

Aisles and Entrances

A minimum clearance of 4 ft between the table edge and the nearest wall will provide a 2-ft aisle along the wall when people are seated at the table. An additional clearance of 12 in. will provide more freedom of movement for the seated people (see Fig. 8-52). With 6 ft or more clearance between table and side wall, this wall can be used for displays that can be seen by everyone at the table (see Fig. 8-53).

Doorways or other entrances should be located in a corner of the conference room (see Fig. 8-54). This location will provide maximum wall space for large displays and minimize the clearances needed for entrance space. In cramped areas, a folding or sliding door should be considered.

AUDITORIUMS

The design of an auditorium generally involves a series of compromises that make space convenient for most, but not all, of the audience. For the purpose of viewing a display such as a chart or movie screen, the ideal shape of an auditorium is a fan or a truncated wedge (see Fig. 8-55). Acceptable viewing angles are those that are not less than 60 deg in the horizontal plane and 10 deg from the horizontal, either up or down, in the vertical plane (see Fig. 8-56). If the vertical angle exceeds 10 deg, either up or down, the viewers will have to slump or lean forward in their seats. Ideally, the screen should be normal (90 deg) from the line of sight of all observers. In practice, this ideal cannot always be realized, and an effective compromise is shown in Fig. 8-57.

Seat Type and Arrangement

Auditorium seats should have a narrow silhouette and be of the "spring-up" type. Where the seats are divided by a single armrest, a seat 24–26 in. wide is recommended (see Fig. 8-58). A 28-in.-wide seat is recommended where two armrests are provided for each individual seat.

A practical rule-of-thumb is that no seat should be closer than double the maximum dimension of the visual display (see Fig. 8-59). The recommended separation between seats in adjacent rows is 40 in., but adherence to this dimension will depend on the desired auditorium seating capacity and the space available for the auditorium. To save some ceiling height, the floor elevation can be specially structured, with a reverse incline for the first few rows (see Fig. 8-60). It should be noted, however, that being able to use a reverse incline depends on the number of rows involved; with fewer than 22 rows, it is impractical.

It is seldom necessary, except where the available space is very narrow, to arrange seating so that a person must see over the *head* of another person seated in front. Few installations can provide the required ceiling height necessary for such an arrangement. In practice, seats usually can be staggered or offset so that a person can look over the *shoulder* of the person directly in front.

§ 8.2.5

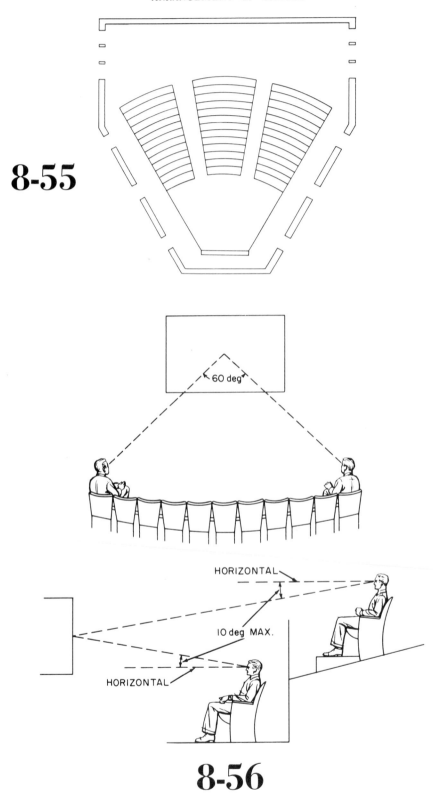

8-55

8-56

8-57

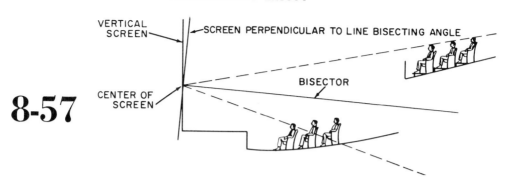

The principle for arranging rows of seats to insure proper visual clearance is that each person should be offset by about a head's width (8–10 in.) to obtain a full view of the display. The result of staggering the seating, in effect, is to halve the between-row distance that would be required if the seats were directly behind one another in a column.

A staggered seating arrangement for maximum visual clearance should permit a short man (sitting *eye* height of 29.4 in. plus seat-pan height) to see the bottom of the display over the shoulder of a tall man in front of him (sitting *shoulder* height of 27 in. plus seat-pan height). The horizontal angle of the field of view is a function of both the lateral separation between seats and the separation between rows (see Fig. 8-61). For further details on optimizing the horizontal field of view, see Ramsey and Sleeper (1956).

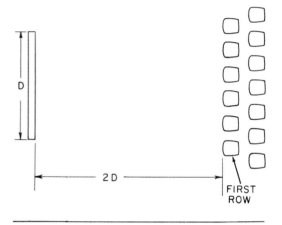

8-59

8-58

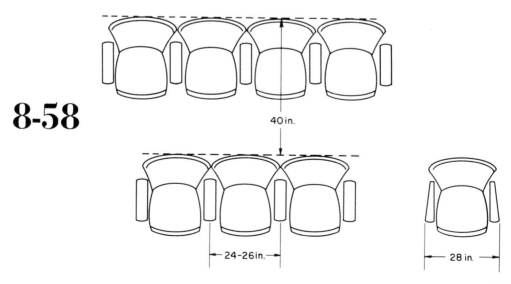

355

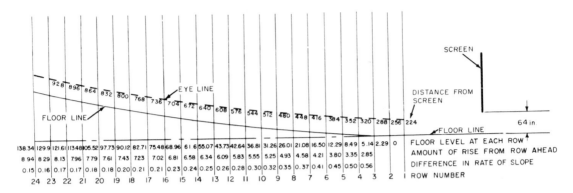

INCLINED FLOOR

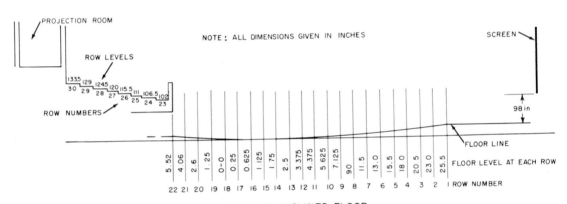

NOTE: ALL DIMENSIONS GIVEN IN INCHES

REVERSE-INCLINED FLOOR

8-60

On a level floor, the eye height of the seated short man is about 2½ in. above the shoulder height of the seated tall man (see above). Thus, when the bottom of the display is *above* eye level, e.g., on the main floor of an auditorium, the short man has no difficulty in seeing the bottom of the display. But, when the bottom of the screen or other viewed object is *below* the level of the eye, as in a balcony, the angle between the eye of the viewer, the lower part of the display, and the floor should not be less than 4 deg (see Fig. 8-62). For the short man to see over the head instead of the shoulder of any person two rows in front, the angle between the eye of the viewer, the lower part of the display, and the floor would have to be at least 9 deg.

Aisles and Exits

The following general recommendations will help provide maximum safety and speed under emergency conditions:

1. Allow adequate clearance (40 in.) between rows, and use spring-up seats.

2. Provide main aisles along either side of the auditorium, and place exit doors along these aisles. For large auditoriums, a center aisle also should be provided.

3. Provide exit doors that will push open from the inside.

4. Avoid having aisles run into narrow corridors so that the two form a "T," and, especially, avoid right angle turns where people can get jammed into a corner (see Fig. 8-63).

356

§ 8.2.5

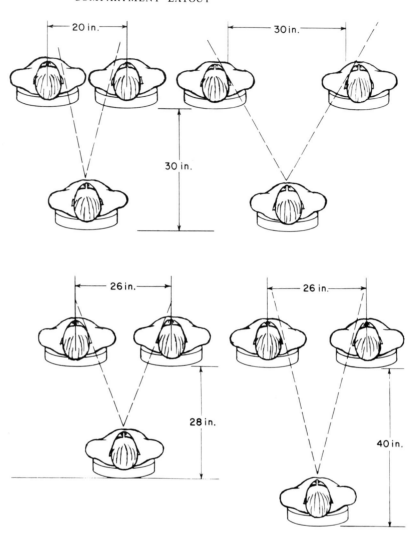

8-61

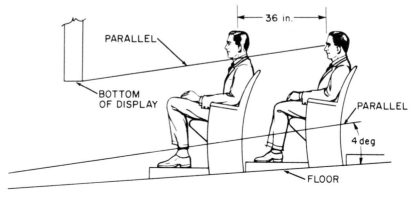

8-62

357

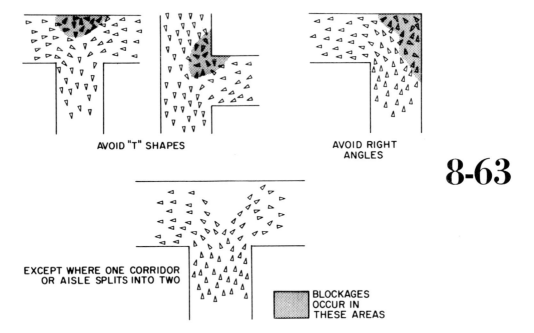

AVOID "T" SHAPES

AVOID RIGHT
ANGLES

8-63

EXCEPT WHERE ONE CORRIDOR
OR AISLE SPLITS INTO TWO

BLOCKAGES
OCCUR IN
THESE AREAS

Balconies

The design of balconies is largely dependent on what is being viewed. When the presentation is on a large central screen, such as that in a land-based combat information center (see article 8.3.2), the desirable viewer's distance from the screen is a function of image size (and sound qualities). To keep the vertical viewing angle close to 90 deg, the floor pitch should remain fairly small. When an auditorium is to be used predominantly for small presentations (especially when "live," such as a lecturer, panel of speakers, or cast of actors), it is important to minimize the distance from the audience to the stage. This can be accomplished by bringing the front of the balcony close to the object being viewed and by increasing the pitch of the balcony.

8.3 Arrangement of Groups of Men

Industrial engineers have built up a considerable body of knowledge concerning the location of equipment, desks, workbenches, and surrounding workspaces. No attempt is made in this section to duplicate or summarize the literature of industrial engineering. Rather, this section provides information concerning the characteristics of the human operator that should be taken into consideration when arranging equipment within compartments. Generally, this type of information has not been stressed in the literature.

358

8.3.1 *The formation of groups*

Men can be arranged in groups when one or more of the following requirements exists:

a. More than one person must see the same equipment or display, either to avoid duplicate equipment or for other reasons.

b. Face-to-face communication is desirable (it is, generally, the most effective), either to reduce the number of communication networks or for other reasons.

c. A single equipment requires several operators.

d. Two or more equipments have to be operated in close proximity to each other (because of cross shafting, mechanical linkages, wave guides, etc.).

8.3.2 *The location of groups*

The physical location and arrangement of groups should be planned to satisfy one of more of the following requirements:

a. The flow or sharing of material, information, equipment, or personnel.

b. The direction of several groups by a single supervisor.

c. The coordination of the activities of their groups by several supervisors.

d. The sharing of certain facilities by several groups.

GENERAL PRINCIPLES

To meet the above requirements, plans for the physical location and arrangement of groups should be drawn up according to the following general principles:

1. Locate closely related groups in a single building and on a single floor, if possible.

2. Juxtapose groups according to a plan of work flow.

3. Integrate related activities (such as mechanical and nonmechanical, professional and nonprofessional) in accordance with actual requirements for contact (i.e., don't separate them simply because their work is different).

4. If noise between related activities is a problem, use partitions.

5. Where noise is not a problem, separate related activities with space rather than partitions.

6. Provide privacy for supervisors.

7. Locate supervisors so that they can readily contact their subordinates.

8. Integrate supervisory locations of closely related subgroups.

9. Provide face-to-face access for related groups.

10. Integrate working areas that are closely related; do not separate arbitrarily by storage space, equipment, etc.

11. Give a central location to a group that has many contacts with other groups.

EXAMPLES OF ARRANGEMENTS

Illustrated here are some examples of desirable group arrangements that are applicable to a variety of situations. It is hoped that these will serve as a source of ideas for the designer of man-machine systems. Each example is based on actual cases, and its principal features are described.

Electronics Development Laboratory

The arrangement shown in Fig. 8-64 (not drawn to exact scale) has the following principal features:

a. Central locations for people or areas having relatively equal contact with, or use by, most groups (chief project engineer, secretarial pool, first aid, building superintendent, and lavatories).

b. Relatively central locations for facilities used by a high percentage of the staff (dining and recreation areas, library, and conference room).

c. Interaction is facilitated by face-to-face accesses to group areas.

d. Supervisory locations are compartmented but integrated with those of subordinates.

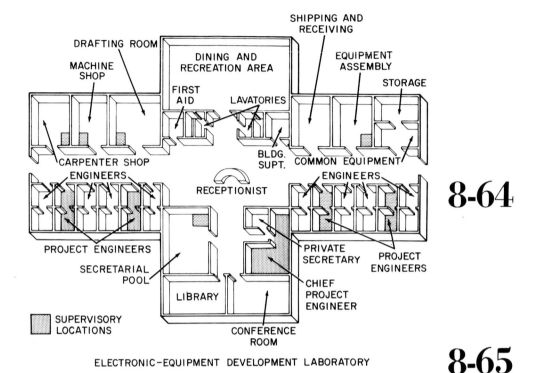

8-64

ELECTRONIC–EQUIPMENT DEVELOPMENT LABORATORY

8-65

e. The development staff has privacy with ease of access to shop facilities, to superiors, and to each other.

f. Isolation is minimized and counteracted by the location of entrances.

g. A large central area accommodates traffic peaks.

Large Data-Processing System

The arrangement shown in Fig. 8-65 (not drawn to exact scale) has the following principal features:

a. Supervisory personnel are accessible to their own groups as well as to each other.

b. The juxtaposition of areas facilitates the flow of work and results in relatively short intergroup distances.

c. Input-output and control groups are shielded from noise.

d. System supervisor is centrally located.

e. A conference room for intra- and inter-system meetings is located near the personnel most likely to use it—the system supervisor and the program group.

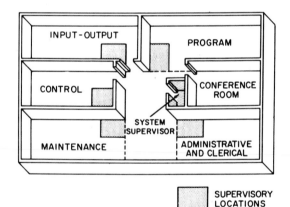

Land-Based Combat Information Center

The arrangement shown in Fig. 8-66 (not drawn to exact scale) has the following principal features:

a. Central cluster of key personnel.

b. Location plus transparent partitions permit personnel in areas of the battle staff, commanding general, and combat-operations staff to have both privacy and a clear view of information displayed in the operations room.

$\S$ 8.3.2

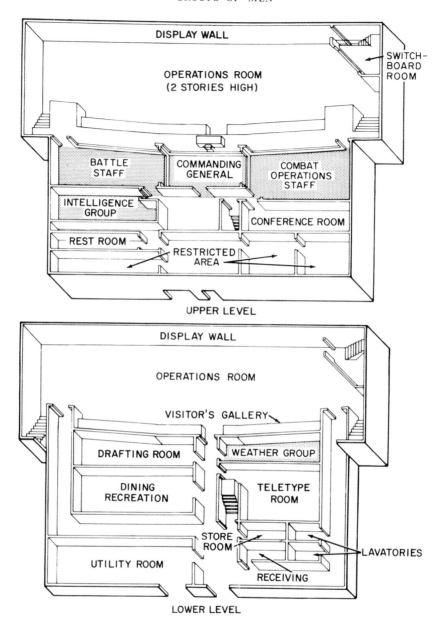

COMBAT INFORMATION CENTER (LAND BASED)

8-66

§ 8.3.2

c. The conference-room location facilitates accessibility by the three primary user groups: battle staff, commanding general, and combat-operations staff.

d. Location plus transparent partitions permit the switchboard operator to search visually for personnel who are not at their stations.

e. The location of the visitor's gallery permits both ease of access and excellent viewing without disturbing CIC activities.

f. The juxtaposition of drafting room, weather group, and operations room facilitates the delivery of materials and information.

Aircraft Combat Information Center

The arrangement shown in Fig. 8-67 (not drawn to exact scale) has the following principal features:

a. The central supervisory location makes it readily accessible to all other groups.

b. The location of the communications area permits visual and verbal contact with the officer in charge.

c. The standby and monitoring facility is convenient to either the search-track group or the officer in charge.

d. Equipment required in the work area is placed to one side so as not to break up the working groups.

e. The maintenance and storage area is readily accessible to the working area.

f. The dining-recreation area and the lavatory are physically separated from, but convenient to, the work area.

g. The rest area is isolated from the principal work areas.

8.3.3 *Rows and columns of operators*

When space is available, two-man operator teams are usually seated in a row for the following reasons:

a. The physical separation between operators is small enough so that displays close to them (29½ in. or less) can be seen by both.

b. Side-by-side seating makes for better communication (by voice, writing, or manual signal) than a tandem arrangement, and each operator is located within the peripheral vision of the other.

c. A single set of controls and displays is operable and visible by both, which permits standby operation by either of the two operators (see Chapter 7).

A row arrangement for more than two operators is relatively inefficient, however, for the following reasons:

a. Considerable space is necessary between the first row and major displays.

b. The width of a row is restricted by the visual angle.

c. Any equipment between the first row and the display must be located so as not to interfere with the operators' line of sight (see article 8.2.1).

Columns provide a near-optimum viewing angle for each operator in the column. Columns must be limited in size, however, because increasing the length of the column increases the distance from the display. Rows, on the other hand, provide approximately equal distances from all observers to the dis-

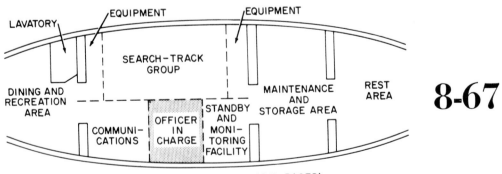

COMBAT INFORMATION CENTER (AIR BASED)

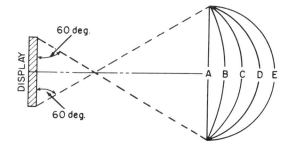

play, but, row arrangements usually give less satisfactory viewing angles. A column arrangement is most useful where console operators must share a single display and the width of the consoles would preclude an adequate viewing angle if a row arrangement were used.

ROWS OF OPERATORS

For a single stationary display, a row of operators should be seated no closer than the width of the display and preferably not closer than 1½ times the width. For single; moving displays, operators should not be seated closer than twice the width of the display.

It is most desirable to be able to look "head-on" at a display. An oblique viewing angle introduces distortion of perspective and parallax error. Where a row of operators is viewing a single display, observing this principle means that the length of the row must be limited and that it also might be necessary

to angle some of the displays a few degrees.

A row of operators may be seated in a straight line or in an arc. The greater the arc (in degrees), the more operators it will hold. For instance, in Fig. 8-68, in which lines *A* through *E* represent row arrangements, row *E* (a semicircle) will hold about 50% more people than row *A*.

For a row of operators, the standard dimensions for all equipment locations can be determined by the operators at each end of the row. If the viewing angles for these operators are within the acceptable range, the operators in the middle automatically will be taken care of. For all displays, a viewing angle of 90–60 deg is recommended and, although 60–45 deg is acceptable, the viewing angle should never be less than 45 deg (see Fig. 8-69).

Rather than optimize vision for any particular individual or group, the designer should insure, first, that the visual demands on all personnel are above the minimum recommended standards, i.e., that none of these angles is less than 45 deg. If the displays extend beyond either end of the row of operators, there is no problem along these lines. If, on the other hand, the ends of the row extend beyond the displays, then a real problem exists. For instance in Fig. 8-70, line *EM* to display No. 1 is a most difficult visual task for operator *E*. To make this task easier for *E*, the display can be rotated toward him (*M* to *M'*). This alteration makes line *AN* (to the same display) a more difficult visual task for operator *A*.

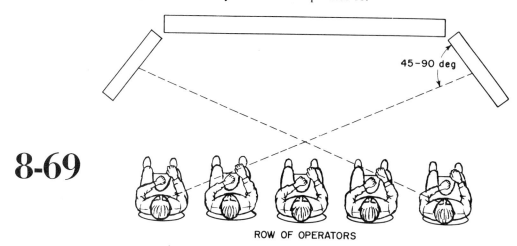

8-69

45–90 deg

ROW OF OPERATORS

There are at least three possible solutions to this dilemma. These are as follows (see Fig. 8-71):

1. Equate angles $M'NA$ and $NM'E$ if both angles are greater than 45 deg.

2. Provide a supplementary display for operators seated at opposite ends of the row.

3. Form a second row of operators.

COLUMNS OF OPERATORS

By offsetting displays, special column arrangements (such as staggering) can be avoided. The amount of offset should be determined by the viewing angle of the last operator in the column (but not less than 45 deg). If this operator has a full view beyond the head and shoulders of the person directly in front of him, the view for the others automatically will be clear. In addition, it might be desirable to angle the display a few degrees to give the front operator a better viewing angle. A good general rule is to equate the viewing angles for the front and rear operators; then those in between also will have an acceptable visual angle (see Fig. 8-72, top of next page).

Seated Operators

An arrangement to accommodate standing operators in a column often requires excessive headroom. A seating arrangement will save headroom (and still permit the operators to see) for the following reasons:

a. The differential in height among operators that is due to leg length is eliminated, leaving only the differential due to the torso; this circumstance saves nearly 4 in. of headroom allowance for each operator.

b. By providing adjustable seats, the tall

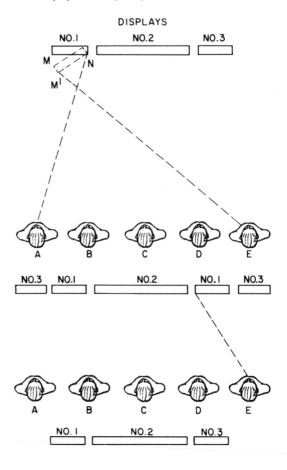

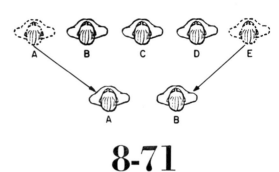

DISPLAYS

8-70

8-71

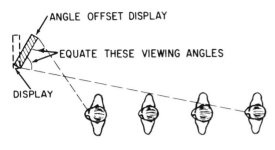

ANGLE OFFSET DISPLAY

EQUATE THESE VIEWING ANGLES

DISPLAY

operator can sit in a lowered seat, while the short operator can sit in a raised seat.

c. The seated operator's eye and head heights are lower than those of the standing operator (about 15 in., on the average, for most seats).

Seated and Standing Operators

When a column of only a few operators is involved, a further reduction in overall head-room can be made by having both seated and standing operators. This arrangement can be provided in the following manner:

a. The front operator can sit in a seat with a low seat pan.

b. The next operator can sit in a standard seat.

c. The next operator can stand (or sit on an elevated stool).

Of course, with adjustable seats and raised platforms, any number of variations to this arrangement can be made.

Standing Operators

Where a standing operator must see over the head of a standing operator in front of him, the following dimensions are involved (see Fig. 8-73):

a. The height of the bottom edge of the display above the floor (A).

b. The distance of the front operator from the display. (B).

c. The distance between operators (C).

d. Head height of the front operator above the floor whether he is standing or seated (D).

e. Eye height of the second operator (E). With these dimensions, the column seating arrangement can be determined successively for each operator. For example, suppose these dimensions were as shown in Fig. 8-74. By subtracting measurement E from D (74.2 − 61.9) it is evident that the second row must be elevated 12.3 in. At this elevation, the second operator would be able to see horizontally, but, when the bottom of the display is lower than the front operator's head, an additional increment must be added. The following formula closely approximates this increment:

$$\frac{(D-A)C}{B}. \qquad (8\text{-}1)$$

In the above example, this increment would be (74.2 − 60)(48)/96 or 7.1 in. Thus, the

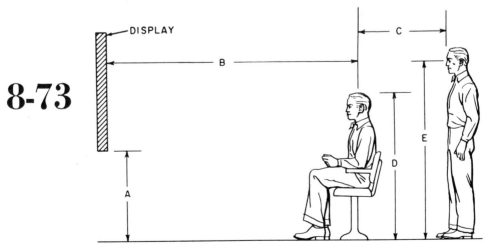

8-73

DISPLAY

B

C

E

D

A

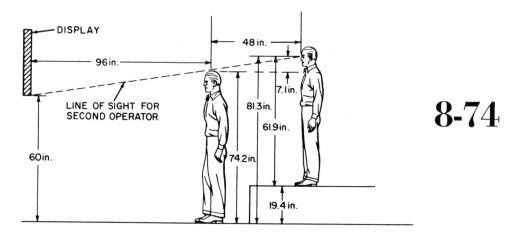

8-74

second row should be elevated 19.4 in. (12.3 + 7.1) above the floor level. Note that, when the bottom of the display is higher than the head of the front-row operator, the quantity $(D - A)$ is negative, and the increment is subtracted rather than added. The identical process can be used for computing the platform elevation for each succeeding operator by calculating the required height with reference to the operator in the row in front.

9

design for ease of maintenance

TEN YEARS AGO, the "reliability" of machines and systems was a vague, qualitative attribute. Today, it is a quantitative property that increasingly is included in military and commercial specifications with explicitly stated acceptance criteria and test conditions.

Today, maintainability is—as reliability was ten years ago—a somewhat vague qualitative attribute, and, where attempts have been made to define the concept quantitatively, no agreement among governmental and industrial groups is at all evident. The divergence of views on how maintainability should be defined is widespread, but it is not the purpose of this chapter to resolve this semantic argument. Rather, the purpose of this chapter is to guide those designing new equipment toward the improvement of maintainability. Thus, it will suffice if we employ a broad dictionary-like definition such as the following:

"Maintainability is the degree of facility with which an equipment or system is capable of being retained in, or restored to, serviceable operation. It is a function of parts accessibility; internal configuration; use and repair environment; and the time, tools, and training required to effect maintenance."

The discussion of specific concepts entering into maintainability, however, will be most meaningful when it is related to the broad objectives of the maintainability effort. The broad objectives behind the present emphasis on improved maintainability can best be summed up as follows:

a. To increase the *availability* of equipment (or systems) for the performance of their intended function.

b. To reduce the *costs* of operational support within the planned service life of the equipment.

It is clear that these two factors (availability and support cost) must be balanced at some reasonable level. We cannot go all the

This chapter, drafted by Alphonse Chapanis and Jesse S. Cook III, is based, in part, on material prepared by J. D. Folley and J. W. Altman of American Institute for Research, Inc.

way in either direction; it is likely that absolute availability would be achieved only with prohibitive support cost and zero support cost with unacceptable availability.

9.1 *Reliability and Maintainability*

In addition to the progress made in specifying reliability in a meaningful way, real progress also has been made in reliability improvement. The improvement is particularly evident in the reliability of component parts for which failure-rate reductions, in the early hours of part life, have been reduced, in many cases, by factors of 10 to 20. Nevertheless, these gains have failed to keep pace with the concurrent increase in system complexity.

When the major effort to improve reliability was first initiated, it was hoped by many that the improvement would be so substantial that the need for maintenance activity would be practically obviated. The growth in complexity, however, reduced this hope, and, although the search for further reliability improvement goes on, it seems unwise to predicate future system planning on this basis.

Faced with this problem, it is little wonder that military and industrial organizations are paying increased attention to the relatively new art of design for maintainability. Although design for ease of maintenance has always been a part of effective design engineering, it has only been relatively recently that systematic and formal attention has been given to this area of technology.

Maintainability has four characteristics that make it very useful as a partial solution to the problem of current system complexity. These characteristics can be listed as follows:

a. Within rather broad limits, maintainability can be traded off against hard-to-achieve reliability in obtaining the required system availability.

b. Impressive gains in maintainability often can be achieved at little or no additional system-development cost.

c. Maintainability built into the system during development can drastically reduce operating costs.

d. The payoff from maintainability can be expected to be large, initially, because it is a relatively new technological development.

To the system designer, emphasis on minimizing repair time is one of the most important aspects of designing for maintainability. An outstanding difference between reliability and repairability that will undoubtedly complicate design improvement appears in the degree of dependence on human factors, particularly as related to the system user.

Reliability, or what happens before (or until) failure, is more nearly an inherent system property. Certainly, it can be degraded by malpractices or abuses in the field, but, when used in the manner and for the purpose intended, an equipment's reliability is predominantly dependent on the merits (or demerits) of its design. Repairability, on the other hand, seems, by its very nature, to be dependent on the user. The characteristics of repairability, however excellent from the designer's viewpoint, are intimately bound to the existing knowledge, practices, skills, facilities, and supplies of the user-maintainer.

In reliability measurement, stress is placed on defining the system under measurement, the criteria of failure, and the conditions under which the measurements are taken. No less emphasis on these factors is permissible

368

in the case of repairability. As a matter of fact, the added importance of the human factors involved in repairability makes it far more important that the capabilities of maintenance personnel be considered.

Although it is recognized that all of the physical and human conditions that might conceivably effect repairability cannot be covered, there are important known factors that have been shown to have a sizeable effect. This chapter of the Guide will outline these important factors and will present design recommendations to specify these factors adequately.

9.2 A Design Schedule for Maintainability

Maintainability must be designed into the equipment in the early stages of development if costly maintenance or costly redesign is to be avoided. Once the developmental model is fairly well along, it is always difficult, and often impossible, to backtrack and revise design decisions to improve maintainability. Thus, a design schedule for maintainability should include the following steps: a) planning for maintainability, b) designing for maintainability, c) testing and revising the design.

9.2.1 Planning for maintainability

In this preliminary stage, the following should be accomplished (see Fig. 9-1):

1. Study operational equipment resembling the one to be designed. In particular, list the maintenance features built into the operational equipment, and, from a study of the maintenance experience and history of this equipment, list the maintenance features that should have been designed into the equipment but were not.

2. Become familiar with the entire system into which the new equipment will be installed. Find out exactly where the equipment will be installed in the system and the measurements of access spaces, crawlways, passageways, and/or doors the maintenance man will have to go through to get to the equipment.

3. Find out what test equipment and tools are already in use on related equipment and might be adapted to the one to be designed.

4. Find out what kind of maintenance men will be available to service the equipment. List the kinds of skills they will have.

5. Find out what work and storage facilities are already available and might be used for the new equipment.

6. Determine what kinds of and how many manuals maintenance personnel will need to maintain the equipment properly.

7. Discover what supply facilities are available to provide spare parts for the equipment.

9.2.2 Designing for maintainability

This is the critical step, and it must be well under way by the time functional diagrams, unit specifications, and schematics are being prepared. (Failure to do this usually means poor maintainability.) Designing for maintainability involves everything that follows in

§ 9.2.1

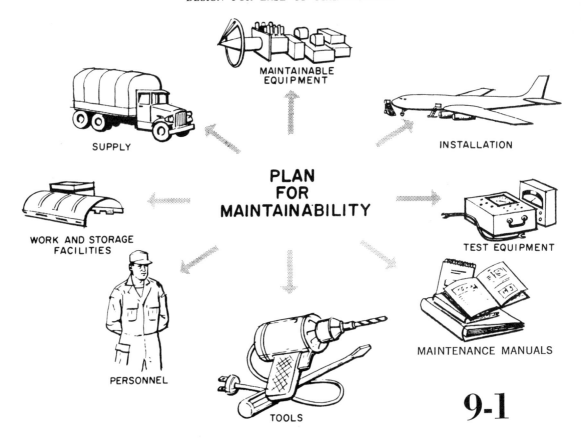

PLAN
FOR
MAINTAINABILITY

MAINTAINABLE
EQUIPMENT

SUPPLY

INSTALLATION

WORK AND STORAGE
FACILITIES

TEST EQUIPMENT

PERSONNEL

MAINTENANCE MANUALS

TOOLS

9-1

this chapter, but there are five general areas that should be considered by the designer at the time the equipment is being planned and developed. These areas include the prime equipment, installation, test equipment, maintenance manuals, and tools.

For ease of maintenance, the most important features to be designed into prime equipment are the following:

a. Modular or unit packaging, and, when warranted, "throw-away" units.

b. Replaceable modules or units that are independent and interchangeable. Some equipment is so designed that the replacement of a single unit requires the extensive adjustment and realignment of a number of other units with which it is associated in the system. This increases the load placed on maintenance. For example, replacing the spark plugs in certain modern automobiles requires the deactivation, disassembly, reassembly, recharging, and readjustment of the air conditioning system.

c. Ease of access to test points and the internal parts of the equipment.

d. Self-checking features or test points for checking by auxiliary equipments.

All of these features should be carefully evaluated from the overall system point of view. For example, guided missiles with modular components and uncrowded, easily accessible packaging are highly desirable from the maintenance man's point of view, but such a design might add so much of a space and weight penalty that the missile cannot be built to meet other specifications. On the other hand, operational missiles without any of these features require highly motivated and skilled technical personnel to maintain them, which considerably reduces their strategic value. (See also article 9.4.1.)

Equipment that is easy to service in the shop might be hard to service or check when it is installed in a larger system (for example, in a tank, submarine, or aircraft). Design

§ 9.2.2

equipment so that it can be serviced where it is to be finally installed. (See also article 9.4.2.)

Functions of the prime equipment that are not self-checking must be checked by auxiliary test equipment. Design prime equipment so that it can be checked with readily available, standard test equipment. If this cannot be done, design and build special test equipment so that it will be available when the prime equipment is ready for use. (See also article 9.4.3.)

The designer of a piece of equipment is the man best qualified to help in the preparation of the maintenance manual. Maintenance manuals should be ready to go with the equipment when it is released for use. The manuals should list all of the steps necessary to maintain the equipment. They should contain illustrations, descriptive material, diagrams, and check lists that are correct, up to date, readable, and easy to follow. (See also articles 9.4.4 and 9.4.5.)

Equipment should be designed to be repaired and serviced with standard tools and with as few different tools as possible. If special tools are required, however, design them early enough so that they can go out with the equipment. (See also article 9.4.6.)

9.2.3 *Testing and revising the design*

In testing the developmental and production models of the equipment, maintainability tests should duplicate, as nearly as possible, the conditions under which the equipment will be maintained. In particular, the tests should do the following:

1. Use only those procedures, tools, test equipments, and manuals that will be available to the maintenance man.

2. Use maintenance men no more highly trained than the maintenance personnel who will likely be assigned to the job in the field.

3. Run through *all* of the procedures.

4. Include trouble shooting a variety of malfunctions.

These tests should be conducted under environmental conditions simulating those in the field. The emphasis of the tests should be on finding ways to improve the prime equipment, test equipment, maintenance procedures and instructions, and tools for the maintenance man.

9.3 *Planning for Maintainability*

The following will be discussed in this section:

a. An overall plan for maintenance.

b. Personnel capabilities and limitations.

c. Conditions under which maintenance is performed.

Each of these topics is discussed separately in the following articles.

§ 9.3.1

9.3.1 *An overall plan for maintenance*

An effective overall plan for maintenance should include the following general steps to insure that the design for maintainability will proceed in an orderly and efficient manner:

1. Specify maintenance levels and their general requirements, and decide how much maintenance will be done at each level. These levels will generally break down into the following:

a. Operator maintenance—servicing and minor repairs made by the operator.

b. Line maintenance—more extensive repairs made by maintenance men on the equipment where it is installed.

c. Field or shop maintenance—repairs made at an operational base or site on equipment that is removed from its installation.

d. Factory or depot maintenance—repair and overhaul performed on equipment that is returned to the factory or a depot.

Decisions about maintenance levels should be made carefully because they interact with the operational use of the equipment and with almost every other aspect of the maintenance picture. For example, if an excessive amount of equipment is designed for factory maintenance, this will quickly overload supply channels. On the other hand, putting most of the burden on line maintenance presupposes that there will be an adequate number of trained technicians, test equipments, tools, and spare parts available locally to do the work. In short, economics, personnel, training, supply, and engineering feasibility all must enter into these decisions.

2. Divide equipment into units for maintenance at each level. This step should begin when layouts and schematics become available for the developmental model. Divide the entire equipment into units according to the four levels at which they can be replaced or repaired most efficiently and effectively. In making these decisions, keep in mind the overall plan and the requirements for maintenance levels reached in Step 1.

3. Prepare maintenance procedures. Make a list of maintenance procedures for the system as a whole and for each unit at each maintenance level. Do this first for operator-maintenance units and then for line-maintenance, shop-maintenance, and, finally, depot-maintenance units. At each level, be sure that the maintenance procedures cover all aspects of checking, trouble shooting, adjusting, replacing, repairing, and servicing the units.

4. Extract design requirements from the procedures. Go through each procedure step by step, and write down for each step the design features that are required to make the procedure work. In preparing this list, answer each of the following questions:

a. What controls and displays are needed to adjust, check, or service the equipment?

b. What test points should be provided?

c. What connections are needed?

d. What construction features will simplify maintenance?

e. What installation features will make the equipment easy to maintain?

f. What standard test equipment can be used for maintenance?

g. What special test equipment is required?

h. What bench mockups are needed to maintain or check the equipment?

i. What standard tools can be used by the maintenance man?

j. What special tools are required?

5. Review the maintainability requirements. Check every item in the list for consistency with other items and for reasonableness. Ask the following questions about every item:

a. Can it be developed or obtained within the budget and time limits of the project? Developing special test equipment or special tools, or specifying elaborate maintenance tests might be unreasonably time consuming or costly.

b. Can the item be supplied and used under typical maintenance conditions? For example, specifying delicate or sensitive laboratory test equipment for field conditions is unreasonable.

c. Is there any reasonable expectation that technicians will be available with the proper skills to perform the maintenance? If not, can they reasonably be trained to do the job?

d. Do the advantages of each item outweigh the cost of developing and procuring (and maintaining) it?

e. Is it possible to redesign any aspect of the prime equipment to eliminate special tools or test equipment, to eliminate certain maintenance tests, or to combine test functions?

6. Translate the requirements into equipment and instructions. Construct items of test

equipment, tools, and bench mockups, and prepare maintenance instructions in a form suitable for use by the technicians that will be available. This final step should be timed so that it is completed at about the same time that the developmental model is completed.

9.3.2 *Personnel capabilities and limitations*

The effectiveness of maintenance is determined, in the final analysis, by the extent to which prime equipment, test equipment, and work environments fall within the capabilities and limitations of the available personnel. These capabilities and limitations are of two principal kinds: physical limitations and maintenance skills.

PHYSICAL LIMITATIONS

People come in various sizes, but there are certain minimum and maximum dimensions that must not be exceeded if a man is to work at all (see Chapters 8 and 11). People are also limited in the amounts of force they can exert (see Chapter 11) and in the weights they can lift and carry. These limits, in turn, determine the maximum allowable weights for test equipments, modules, and replaceable units. The following paragraphs provide anthropometric data on lifting and carrying.

Weight-Lifting Capacity

The most important determinant of lifting force is the distance of the grasping axis from the feet. Lifting force is greatest when the weight lifted is in the same vertical plane as the body and decreases sharply as the weight moves away from the body plane (Whitney, 1958).

In general, "leg lift" (back vertical and legs bent) affords a stronger vertical pull than "back lift" (legs straight and back bent), although at lifting heights from 5–20 in., there is no appreciable difference between the two methods (Bedford and Warner, 1937; Clarke, 1945; and Whitney, 1958). There is so much less risk of back injury with the leg lift, however, that it is the preferable method of lifting heavy objects.

Figure 9-2 shows the heaviest weights that can be lifted to various heights by men of the 5th percentile in lifting strength. The data were derived from tests of 19 healthy young men (Emanuel, Chaffee, and Wing, 1956). The weight was an aircraft ammunition case roughly 25 in. long, 11 in. high, and 6 in. wide with handles at either end. The leg lift was used, and the tests were not carried to the point of fatigue.

The weights shown in Fig. 9-2 can be used as maximums for lifting an object of any convenient size and shape with unlimited space available in which to maneuver. The designer should try for much smaller weights to take into consideration realistic work conditions, but 95% of technicians should be able to lift these weights under the conditions specified.

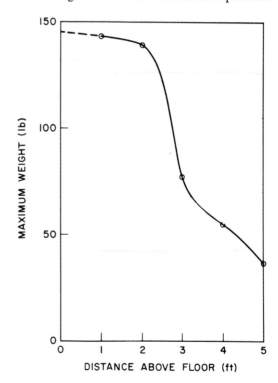

DISTANCE ABOVE FLOOR (ft)

Weight-Carrying Capacity

Any carrying method that requires an alteration of the erect posture or normal gait will be inefficient and physiologically costly. One study (Bedale, 1924), measured the oxygen consumed in several methods for carrying loads of 20–60 lb and rated them from most to least efficient as follows: 1) yoke (often impractical), 2) bundles (one in each hand), 3) shoulder, 4) tray, 5) rucksack (low rating possibly because of poor placement), and 6) hip. In any case, the more compact the container, the more easily it can be carried. For bulky equipment, the center of gravity should be not more than 20 in. from the carrier's body.

The best individual loads, if carried in either hand by means of handgrips, are about 60 lb for short distances and 35 lb for longer distances. The weight of bulky articles (around 30 in. to a side) should not exceed 20 lb. In general, a weight is "heavy" when it reaches 35% or more of human-body weight (Bedale, 1924).

MAINTENANCE SKILLS

Usually, the least-skilled men, from the maintenance point of view, are those associated most closely with the operation of the equipment—the men in the organization to which the equipment is assigned. Maintenance at this level, therefore, normally is restricted to periodic checks of equipment performance, cleaning the equipment, "front panel" adjustments, and removal and replacement of some components. Personnel at this level usually do not repair the removed components but forward them to the next higher level.

Usually, the most-skilled men, from the maintenance point of view, are those associated least closely with the operation of the equipment—the maintenance men at the factory or depot, which may be far removed, geographically, from the organization to which the equipment is assigned and may perform services for several such organizations. At the factory or depot, facilities are usually available for completely overhauling the equipment and for rebuilding it if necessary.

Reasons for Stratification

Stratification by level of maintenance in the military is made essential by the demands for tactical deployment of the equipment, but, as in industry, it also is a solution to the problem of efficiently using maintenance men of varying skills. Periodic checkouts of electronic equipment, for instance, require a major portion of maintenance time. This type of work, however, normally does not require a high level of skill and can be assigned effectively to the less skilled men, thus releasing the more highly skilled men to perform the more difficult repair jobs.

Effect of Skill Levels on Design

One of the factors that must have a large influence on design considerations is the skill level of available maintenance personnel. Equipment that requires skill levels higher than those that can be made available cannot be maintained successfully. In fact, if the maintenance-skill level required is much in excess of that available, the equipment can be a liability instead of an asset. This is not only because it will be unavailable much of the time, but also because a considerable amount of maintenance-manpower and supply-channel effort will be expended uselessly on it. It thus is apparent that equipment design must take into account the actual skills available at each maintenance level.

Despite vigorous efforts by the military, it so far has proven impossible, in our political and economic system, to obtain and retain a sufficient number of skilled maintenance personnel. It cannot be assumed that present-day military technicians have much interest or proficiency in maintenance. In general, all that can be expected of these service personnel is some in-service training and some high-school education (but not necessarily graduation). Such technicians are able to perform only simple maintenance tasks after they complete their in-service training.

Although on-the-job training might prove effective if service personnel participated in this over a long enough period of time, the short average length of enlistments and the low re-enlistment rate leaves little time for achievement of high on-the-job proficiency. As long as this situation exists, everything possible must be done by the designer of equipment to "build in" maintenance features that he himself would find unnecessary and, even, that would be unnecessary for effective maintenance by highly skilled technicians.

9.3.3 *Maintenance conditions*

The conditions under which maintenance is performed frequently include the following:

a. Extremes of lighting. Technicians sometimes work in almost total darkness with only the illumination of a flashlight; at other times they work in bright sunlight that is reflected from the equipment. Even in bright sunlight some equipment might be located in dark corners or areas that make it especially difficult for the technician to see details because his eyes take time to become adapted to the darkness. See Chapter 2 for detailed information on visual acuity, illumination, etc.

b. Lack of working space. There usually is little room for technicians to work in—let alone spread out diagrams, instructions, and tools—because only a certain amount of space can be allotted to the performance of maintenance (see Chapter 8).

c. Temperatures ranging from arctic cold to tropic heat. Working in a position that might be only mildly uncomfortable in moderate temperatures can become almost intolerable in a few minutes of extreme heat or cold. Perspiration makes the technician's hands slippery so that objects tend to slip from his grasp; low temperatures make his fingers stiff so that it is extremely difficult to make fine movements or hold tools and equipment. In addition, weather changes often delay maintenance on equipment because the equipment is not protected from the weather. See Chapter 10 for detailed information on the effects of environmental conditions on human performance.

d. High psychological stress. Line maintenance is frequently performed under the stress of combat or a shortage of time.

Of course, conditions for line maintenance in the military are much more severe than those for comparable civilian maintenance and require special efforts to make equipment maintainable. Thus, the designer should determine the working conditions under which equipment most likely will have to be maintained and design the equipment accordingly.

9.4 *Designing for Maintainability*

9.4.1 *Prime equipment*

Large or heavy pieces of equipment ordinarily should be designed with small remov-

able or replaceable units. This makes it easier to do the following:

a. Divide maintenance responsibility among the various maintenance levels.

b. Locate and isolate malfunctions.

c. Get at malfunctioning parts. (It is usually easier to remove an assembly from a major component and work on it than it is to work on the same part while it is still mounted within a big piece of equipment.)

UNIT DESIGN

The way units are designed depends on where and how the unit is to be maintained. For example, if the maintenance procedures specify that a unit should be brought into a service shop if it contains *any* malfunction, there is no point in designing the unit with subassemblies that are removable by the operator or line maintenance man. Thus, the designer should follow the design schedule in article 9.3.1 and divide the equipment into reasonable units for each level of maintenance. Ideally, each unit should be small and light enough (under about 25 lb) for one man to carry.

The Location of Components

The following recommendations should be observed when planning the location of components within units:

1. Mount parts in an orderly way on a flat surface; do not stack them on top of each other.

2. Mount parts on one side of a board, and put all wiring (including printed or soldered circuits) on the other side.

3. Position components so that there is sufficient space to use test probes, soldering irons, and other tools without difficulty.

4. Provide for subassemblies and other parts to be replaced without removing other subassemblies and without interference from them.

5. Locate all fuses so that they can be seen and replaced without removing any other parts or subassemblies. (Tools should not be required for replacing fuses.)

6. Locate delicate components where they will not be damaged while the unit is being worked on.

7. Internal controls, such as switches and adjustment screws, should not be located close to dangerous voltages.

8. Components that retain heat or electrical potential after the equipment is turned off should not be located where the technician is likely to touch them when he first opens up the equipment.

9. Orient all tube sockets with gaps facing in one direction so that tubes can be replaced easily (see Fig. 9-3).

Mounting and Assembling Features

The following recommendations should be observed when designing unit mounting and assembling features:

1. Use plug-in assemblies and subassemblies rather than solder-connected ones.

2. Use as few mounting screws as is consistent with stresses and vibration requirements.

3. Assemblies and subassemblies should be replaceable with common hand tools.

4. Units that must frequently be pulled out of their normally installed position for checking should be mounted on roll-out racks, slides, or hinges (see Fig. 9-4).

5. Always provide limit stops on roll-out racks and drawers to prevent their being dropped. These should be positive stops, and manual unlatching should be required to remove the rack or drawer.

6. Provide guide pins on units and subassemblies for alignment during mounting (see Fig. 9-5).

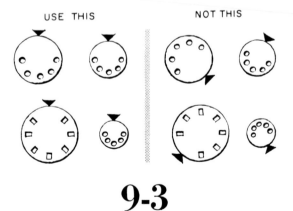

USE THIS   NOT THIS

9-3

USE ROTATABLE
HARDWARE

USE ROLL-OUT
HARDWARE

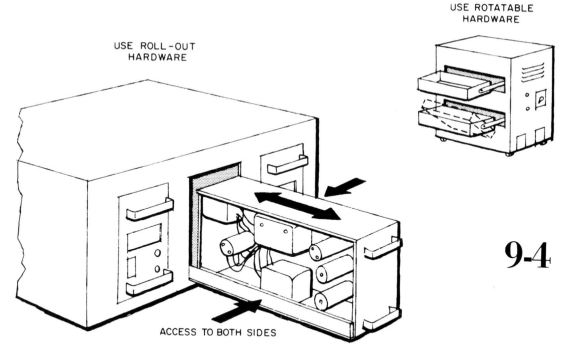

ACCESS TO BOTH SIDES

9-4

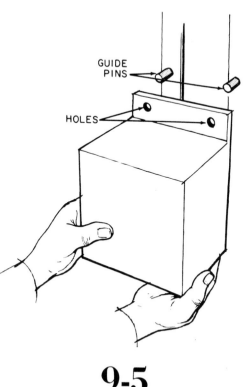

GUIDE
PINS

HOLES

9-5

7. Mount units in the equipment so that replacing one unit does not require the removal of other units.

8. Covers or shields through which mounting screws must pass for attachment to the chassis should have holes large enough for the screw to pass through without the covers or shields being perfectly aligned.

Mounting bolts and fasteners. The following design recommendations should be observed when providing for mounting bolts and fasteners in units:

1. Fasteners for assemblies and subassemblies should fasten or unfasten with no more than one complete turn. If bolts are used, they should require only a few turns to tighten or loosen them.

2. Use hand-operated fasteners (see Fig. 9-6) if at all possible. As a second choice, use fasteners that can be manipulated with standard tools. Do not use fasteners requiring special tools.

3. If hand-operated fasteners cannot be used, use mounting bolts with deep internal-slots and hex heads. This type of fastener can be turned with a standard screwdriver or

377

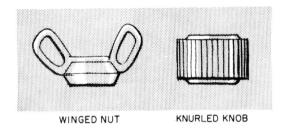

WINGED NUT   KNURLED KNOB

wrench if it is jammed (see Fig. 9-7).

4. Make mounting bolts semipermanently captive. Snap-on collars are good for this purpose because they allow damaged bolts to be replaced easily (see Fig. 9-8). Avoid loose washers and loose nuts whenever possible.

5. Provide mounting bolts and fasteners with an "M" embossed on the top of the head, or specify that they be painted a distinctive color code (red, for example) to make them easy to locate.

6. Use mounting bolts and fasteners made of rust- and corrosion-resistant material.

7. Mounting screws should be interchangeable. Use as few different sizes as practicable.

8. If screws with different thread pitches are used, they should be of different nominal sizes, otherwise screws of the wrong size might be forced into the wrong holes and the threads stripped.

9. Space the heads of mounting bolts and fasteners far enough from other surfaces so that technicians can get at them (see Fig. 9-9).

Wire connections. The following design recommendations should be observed when providing for wire connections in units:

1. For easy maintenance, plug-in contacts are better than screw terminals and screw terminals are better than solder connections.

2. The end of a wire soldered to a terminal should be left out of the solder so that it will be easy to remove (see Fig. 9-10).

3. Use U-lugs rather than O-lugs whenever practicable (see Fig. 9-11).

4. Separate terminals to which wires are to be soldered far enough apart so that work on one terminal does not damage neighboring ones (see Fig. 9-12).

5. Terminals or other connections to which

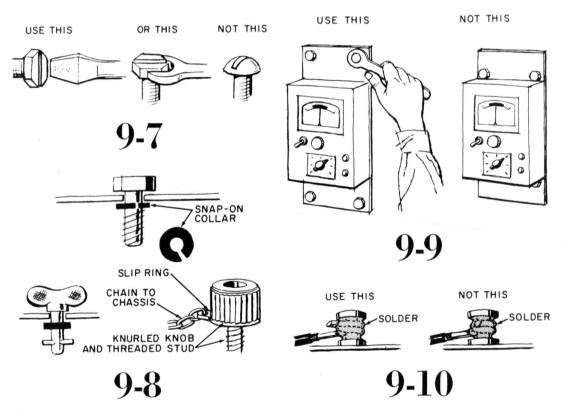

USE THIS   OR THIS   NOT THIS

9-7

SNAP-ON COLLAR

SLIP RING
CHAIN TO CHASSIS
KNURLED KNOB
AND THREADED STUD

9-8

USE THIS   NOT THIS

9-9

USE THIS   NOT THIS
SOLDER   SOLDER

9-10

USE THIS   NOT THIS

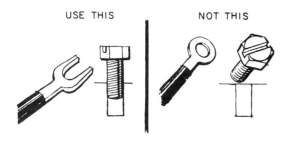

wires are to be soldered should be long enough so that insulation and other materials are not burned by the hot soldering iron (see Fig. 9-13).

Identifying Units and Parts

Labeling. The following design recommendations should be observed when providing labeling on and in units:

1. Label every unit and part with full identifying information.

2. The electrical characteristics of resistors, condensers, and tubes should be provided on the outside cover of the part. This practice is better than using color coding.

3. Label each terminal with the same code symbol as the wire to be attached to it.

4. Use labels that are etched or embossed on the component or chassis rather than labels that are merely painted or stamped on the surface. If surface labels have to be used, however, decals or stamped labels are better than stenciled labels because the latter are harder to read.

5. Do not put labels where they will be hidden by other units or parts. For example, do not put labels on a chassis *under* the parts the labels identify.

Color coding. The following design recommendations should be observed when using color coding for identifying parts in units (see Chapter 2 for design recommendations concerning color coding in general and, in particular, what colors to use):

1. Use color coding as an alternative to labeling but only when the coding is unambiguous.

2. State the meaning of the colors clearly in the manual that accompanies the equipment and on a panel of the equipment itself, if possible.

3. Use the same color code throughout the prime equipment and all of the equipment associated with it.

4. Use coloring matter that will not wear off or fade.

Other Design Recommendations

The following general recommendations should be observed in the design of units:

1. Keep the number of inputs to and outputs from each unit as small as possible. Do this by grouping circuits so that there is a minimum of crisscrossing of signals between units.

2. No unit should have more than about 30v applied to it (for heater or standby) when the main power switch is turned off.

USE THIS   NOT THIS

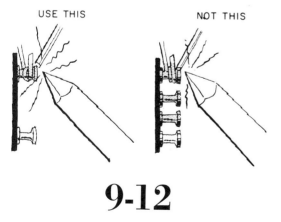

9-12

USE THIS   NOT THIS

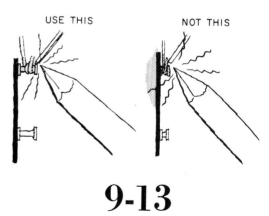

9-13

3. Do not "marry" units to each other. It should be possible to check and adjust each unit separately and then connect the units together into a total functioning system with little or no additional adjustment.

4. Provide overload indicators on each major circuit even if it sometimes might be desirable to keep overloaded circuits in operation.

5. Use regularly stocked, standard parts whenever possible.

6. Design as many assemblies, subassemblies, and parts as possible to be interchangeable within and between equipments.

7. Units having mechanical components, such as gear trains, should have provisions for lubrication without disassembly or should not require lubrication (by being sealed in a lubricant or by being self-lubricating).

8. Irregular extensions, such as cables, wave guides, and hoses, should be easily removable. Such protrusions, if not removable, can be damaged during maintenance and make handling the unit awkward.

9. Provide a brace to hold hinged assemblies in position while they are being worked on.

10. Provide rests or stands on which units can be set to prevent damage to delicate parts during repair. The rests or stands should be part of the basic chassis (see Fig. 9-14).

11. Provide fold-out construction for units whenever feasible (see Fig. 9-15), and arrange the parts and wiring so that they are not damaged when the assembly is opened or closed.

UNIT COVERS AND CASES

From the maintenance standpoint, the most important characteristic of unit covers is that they should be easy to put on and take off. In general, this means that they should not fit so tightly that they have to be put on with painstaking care. It also should be possible to open or remove a unit cover to gain access to interior components without removing the unit from its installed position.

Structural Characteristics

The following recommendations should be observed when designing unit covers and cases:

1. Covers and cases should be designed so that they can be lifted off of the units rather than the units lifted out of them (see Fig. 9-16).

2. Make covers and cases sufficiently larger than the units they enclose so that wires and other components are not likely to be damaged when the cases are taken off or put on.

USE THIS   NOT THIS

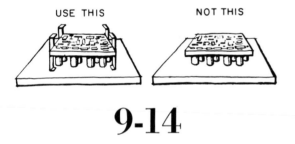

9-14

CLOSED   OPEN

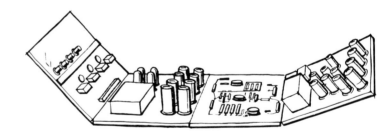

9-15

§ 9.4.1

3. When the edges of a case must be slid over sealing material such as rubber stripping, the sealing material should adhere tightly enough to prevent it from buckling or tearing.

4. Use hinged covers whenever possible to reduce the number of fasteners that must be removed. (Nonpressurized units might need only one fastener with a hinged cover.) One disadvantage of a hinged cover, however, is that it needs a space equal to its own size in which to open.

5. The method of opening a cover should be obvious from the construction of the cover itself. If it is not, instructions should be permanently affixed to the outside of the cover.

6. It should be made obvious when a cover is in place but not secured. Otherwise, a unit might be picked up by its loose cover and dropped.

7. Covers and cases should have rounded corners and edges for safety.

8. Ventilation holes in covers should be small enough so as to make it unlikely that anything will be inserted, inadvertently, and touch high-voltage sources or moving parts.

Fasteners for Covers and Cases

The following design recommendations should be observed when providing fasteners for unit covers and cases:

1. Use captive fasteners whenever feasible.

USE THIS **NOT THIS**

9-16

2. Make maximum use of tongue-and-slot features to minimize the number of fasteners required.

3. Use as few fasteners as are necessary to maintain the required strength and integrity. In many designs, one fastener at each corner of a rectangular cover, or three on a round cover, will be adequate. In some designs, one fastener at each end of a diagonal will do.

4. Fasteners for one-piece cases should be located so that they can be reached easily from convenient working positions when the units are in their normal, installed positions.

5. Fasteners on covers should be operable either by hand or by standard hand tools.

6. Fasteners should be quick acting and require only part of a turn or a snap action to fasten or unfasten.

7. If bolts are needed, only a small number of turns should be required to tighten them.

8. Use the same size and type of fasteners for all covers and cases on a given piece of equipment, with the following exception: if a system has one or two pressurized units that require large, fine-threaded screws to hold the pressure, do not use this type of screw on other units having only dust covers.

Handles

The following design recommendations should be observed when providing handles for units:

1. Locate handles above the center of gravity so that the unit will not tip when it is lifted and carried.

2. Handles that technicians must grasp firmly should be at least 4.5 in. in height and 2 in. in depth (see Fig. 9-17, next page).

3. Provide handles even on small, light units that otherwise would be difficult to grasp, remove, or hold without using components as grips.

4. Units weighing more than 10 lb should have convenient handles to assist in removing, replacing, and carrying the unit.

5. Units weighing more than about 25–40 lb (depending on the size and bulkiness of the unit) should be provided with handles for two-man carrying.

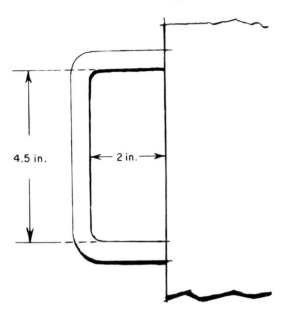

4.5 in.   2 in.

6. Units weighing more than 100–150 lb (depending on the size and bulkiness of the unit) should be provided with suitably labeled lifting eyes.

7. Handles should be shaped so that they do not cut into the hand of the man using them.

CABLES AND CONNECTORS

Because the primary purpose of interconnecting conductors is to transmit power and

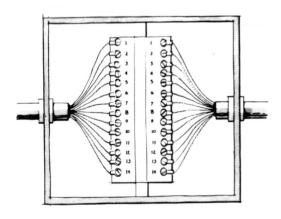

9-18

signals reliably to and from the various parts of the equipment, end connections are usually soldered, tightly screwed, or made permanent or semipermanent in some way. Such design practices make it more difficult for the technician to connect and disconnect the units when this becomes necessary. But reliability need not be sacrificed for ease of maintenance; the recommendations that follow can be used to improve maintainability without affecting reliability.

Cable Design

The following recommendations should be observed when designing cables:

1. Cables should be long enough for the following:

a. So that each unit can be checked in a convenient place (extension cables should be provided when necessary).

b. So that units in drawers and slide-out racks can be pulled out to be worked on without breaking electrical connections.

c. So that connectors can be reached easily for replacement or repair.

d. So that units that are difficult to connect where they are mounted can be moved to a more convenient position for connecting and disconnecting.

2. The length of cables should be the same for each installation of a given type of electronic equipment if the circuit might be affected by differences in the length of the cable. (Even if a unit can be adjusted to compensate for differences in the length of the cable, using different lengths of cable means that adjustments made on the bench might be out of tolerance when the unit is installed.)

3. Cable harnesses should be designed so that they can be built in a shop or factory and installed as a package.

4. Cables should "fan out" in junction boxes for easy checking (see Fig. 9-18), especially if there are no other test points in the circuits. Each terminal in the junction box should be clearly labeled and easy to reach with test probes.

Cable Routing

The following design recommendations should be observed:

1. Route cables so that they cannot be pinched by doors, lids, or slides; will not be walked on or used for handholds; are accessible to the technician (i.e., are not under floorboards and behind panels or components that are difficult to remove); and need not be bent or unbent sharply when connected or disconnected (see Fig. 9-19).

2. Provide guards or other protection for easily damaged conductors such as waveguides, high-frequency cables, or insulated high-voltage cables.

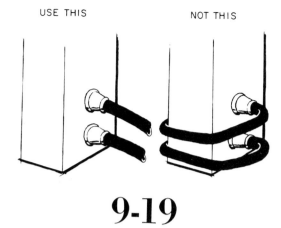

USE THIS   NOT THIS

9-19

Connecting and Disconnecting Features

The following recommendations should be observed when providing for the connecting and disconnecting of cables:

1. Use plugs and matching receptacles that make it impossible to connect the two incorrectly. For example, use different sizes of plugs for nearby connections, use different keys or alignment pins, and/or color code each plug and the receptacle to which it belongs (see Fig. 9-20).

2. Plugs and receptacles should have painted stripes, arrows, or other indications to show the proper position of keys and aligning pins for proper insertion (see Fig. 9-21).

3. Each pin on each plug should be clearly identified.

4. Use quick-disconnect plugs or plugs that can be disconnected with no more than one turn rather than plugs with fine threads that require many turns.

5. Plugs with a self-locking safety catch are preferable to plugs that must be safety wired.

6. Use plugs in which the aligning pins or keys extend beyond the electrical pins. This arrangement protects the electrical pins from damage through poor alignment or twisting of the plug when it is partially inserted (see Fig. 9-22).

7. Avoid symmetrical arrangements of aligning pins or keys so that plugs cannot be

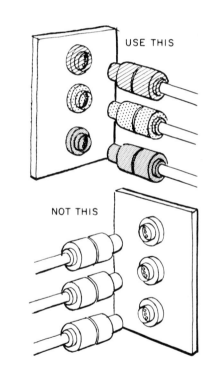

USE THIS

NOT THIS

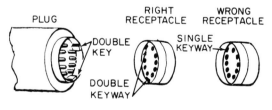

PLUG   RIGHT RECEPTACLE   WRONG RECEPTACLE

DOUBLE KEY   SINGLE KEYWAY

DOUBLE KEYWAY

9-20

§ 9.4.1

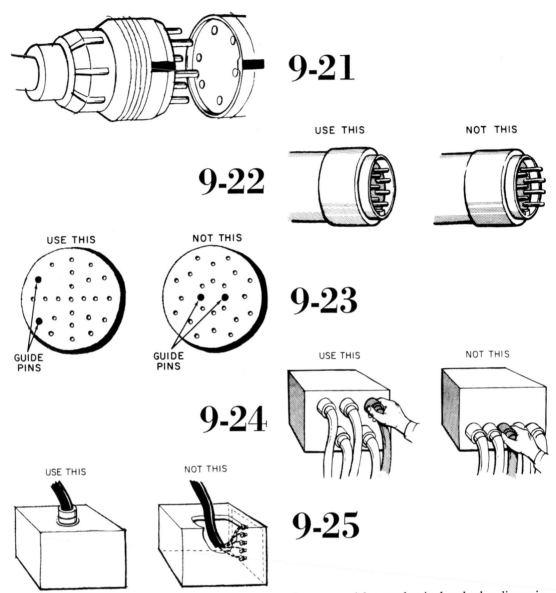

9-21

9-22

USE THIS   NOT THIS

USE THIS   NOT THIS

GUIDE
PINS   GUIDE
PINS

9-23

9-24

USE THIS   NOT THIS

USE THIS   NOT THIS

9-25

inserted 180 deg from the correct position (see Fig. 9-23).

8. Locate connectors far enough apart so that they can be gripped firmly for connecting and disconnecting. The space needed will depend on the size of the plug, with 2.5 in. between plugs being a minimum separation (see Fig. 9-24).

9. When a part of a machine or system (for example, the tail section of an aircraft) can be removed for mechanical or hydraulic maintenance, cables connecting the removable part with the rest of the machine or system should have plugs and receptacles that will disconnect before the cables will break, particularly if nonelectronics personnel do the removing. (A jerk-open plug will separate before any damage is done; a screw plug will not.)

10. Use plugs and receptacles for connecting cables to equipment units rather than "pig-tailing" them; "pig-tailed" connections are harder to replace (see Fig. 9-25).

§ 9.4.1

Other Design Recommendations

The following general design recommendations should be observed when providing connectors for cables:

1. Use plugs with integral test points for each input and output that cannot be easily checked otherwise. If dust or moisture is a problem, provide an integral, sliding cover for the test points on the plug (see Fig. 9-26). As an alternative, provide a test-point adapter for insertion between plugs and receptacles (see Fig. 9-27).

2. Use fewer plugs with many pins rather than more plugs with fewer pins (see Fig. 9-28); it takes about the same amount of time to connect a plug with many pins as it does one with a few pins.

3. Use connectors in which electrical contacts cannot be shorted by external objects.

4. Receptacles should be "hot" and plugs "cold."

EQUIPMENT ACCESSES

Well-designed equipment accesses are essential for ease of maintenance, and should be provided whenever a maintenance procedure would otherwise require removing a case or covering, opening a fitting, or dismantling a unit. Before designing equipment accesses, the engineer should list the parts of the equipment that have to be reached and the operations that are likely to have to be performed on each part; the access then should be designed to make those operations as convenient as possible.

The designer should include, not only accesses for repairs but, also, accesses to electrical connectors, lubrication fittings, pneumatic fittings, hydraulic fittings, etc., and provide inspection windows wherever necessary. See Table 9-1 for what kind of accesses to use for various operations.

The Shape and Size of Accesses

The following recommendations should be observed when designing accesses:

§ 9.4.1

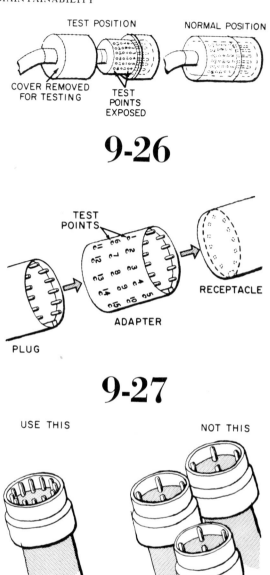

9-26

9-27

1. Make accesses whatever shape is necessary to let the technician do his job; accesses do not have to be any conventional shape.

2. Accesses must be big enough to take the components that have to go through them plus the technician's hands, arms, or body plus whatever clothes he might be wearing (for example, arctic gloves or flight clothing).

Table 9-1 Recommended Equipment Accesses

Desirability	For physical access	For visual inspection only	For test and service equipment
Most desirable	Pullout shelves or drawers (see article 9.4.2)	Opening with no cover	Opening with no cover
Desirable	Hinged door (if dirt, moisture, or other foreign materials must be kept out) *	Plastic window (if dirt, moisture, or other foreign materials must be kept out)	Spring-loaded sliding cap (if dirt, moisture, or other foreign materials must be kept out)
Less desirable	Removable panel with captive, quick-opening fasteners (if there is not enough room for hinged door)	Break-resistant glass (if plastic will not stand up under physical wear or contact with solvents)	
Least desirable	Removable panel with smallest number of largest screws that will meet requirements (if needed for stress, pressure, or safety reasons)	Cover plate with smallest number of largest screws that will meet requirements (if needed for stress, pressure, or safety reasons)	Cover plate with smallest number of largest screws that will meet requirements (if needed for stress, pressure, or safety reasons)

* The hinges on hinged access doors should be at the bottom so that they will stay open without being held (see Fig. 9-29).

3. If the technician has to see what he is doing, make the access big enough for his hands or arms and then add some space for him to see, or design both an access door and a window (see Fig. 9-30).

4. Following are the minimum sizes of accesses that will accommodate about 95% of technicians performing various tasks (make the accesses bigger if possible):

a. For inserting an empty hand held flat, make the access $2\frac{1}{4} \times 4$ in. (see Fig. 9-31).

b. The smallest square hole through which an empty hand can be inserted requires an access of $3\frac{1}{2} \times 3\frac{1}{2}$ in.

c. Inserting a miniature vacuum tube (held with the thumb and first two fingers) up to the center knuckle of the middle finger requires an access of 2×2 in. (see Fig. 9-32).

d. Inserting a large vacuum tube with a base diameter of $1\frac{3}{8}$ in. and a height of $4\frac{1}{2}$ in. (excluding pins and grid cap) requires an access of 4×4 in.

USE THIS   NOT THIS

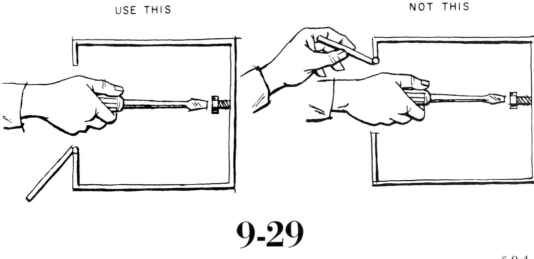

9-29

§ 9.4.1

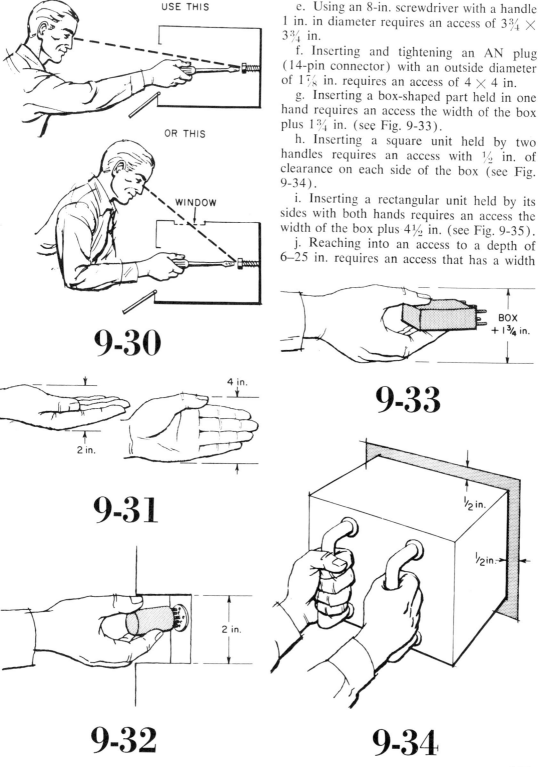

e. Using an 8-in. screwdriver with a handle 1 in. in diameter requires an access of $3\frac{3}{4} \times 3\frac{3}{4}$ in.

f. Inserting and tightening an AN plug (14-pin connector) with an outside diameter of $1\frac{7}{8}$ in. requires an access of 4×4 in.

g. Inserting a box-shaped part held in one hand requires an access the width of the box plus $1\frac{3}{4}$ in. (see Fig. 9-33).

h. Inserting a square unit held by two handles requires an access with $\frac{1}{2}$ in. of clearance on each side of the box (see Fig. 9-34).

i. Inserting a rectangular unit held by its sides with both hands requires an access the width of the box plus $4\frac{1}{2}$ in. (see Fig. 9-35).

j. Reaching into an access to a depth of 6–25 in. requires an access that has a width

USE THIS

OR THIS

WINDOW

9-30

4 in.

2 in.

9-31

2 in.

9-32

BOX + $1\frac{3}{4}$ in.

9-33

$\frac{1}{2}$ in.

$\frac{1}{2}$ in.

9-34

of three fourths the depth of reach and a height of 4 in. (see Fig. 9-36).

k. Reaching straight into an access a full-arm length (up to the shoulders) requires an access that has a width of 19½ in. and a height of 4 in.

Safety Features

The following safety features should be provided when designing accesses:

1. Provide internal fillets or rubber, fiber, or plastic protection on the edges of accesses that might otherwise injure the technician's hands or arms.

2. Provide safety interlocks on accesses that lead to equipment with high voltages. If the technician might need to work on the equipment with circuits energized, provide a "cheater" switch that automatically resets.

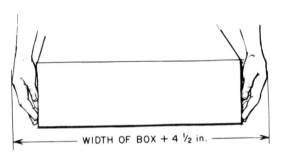

WIDTH OF BOX + 4 ½ in.

9-35

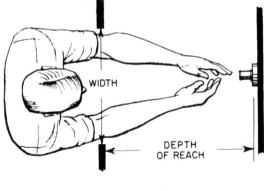

WIDTH

DEPTH
OF REACH

9-36

3. Provide warning labels on all accesses leading to high voltages or rotating machinery.

Labeling and Coding Accesses

The following access labeling and coding should be provided where appropriate:

1. When a tube or plug has to be put through a small hole, show, by a label adjacent to the access, how the pins on the tube or plug will line up with the holes in the socket.

2. Label each access with a number, letter, or other symbol that identifies it in the maintenance instructions.

3. Label each access, if possible, with the items that can be reached through it and with the service equipment to be used there, if any.

EQUIPMENT TEST POINTS

To be most useful, test points must be in the proper functional location, i.e., tied into circuits where the technician needs to sample signals, and in the proper physical location, i.e., placed where the technician can get at them easily.

Functionally Locating Test Points

Test points should be planned so that they systematically trace signals and power-supply voltages through the equipment. They should make it possible for the technician to follow signals and determine at precisely what point the signals go out of tolerance. For line maintenance, to take an example, a test point should be provided for each input and output of each line-replaceable unit.

Maintenance procedures (see article 9.4.4) and specifications for test points should be prepared at the same time that test points are planned because it is usually necessary to make compromises between technical limitations and good design. In preparing specifications for test points, the designer should be sure to consider the physical location of the test points along with the functional location;

§ 9.4.1

sometimes the functional location of a test point depends on a certain physical location, and vice versa. For example, it might be possible to design a test point for a certain spot in a circuit only if the lead is no more than 1 or 2 in. in length to prevent losing the signal in transmission. If the only possible physical locations of such a test point are in places that the technician could not reach, it would be necessary to devise a substitute check procedure, a new functional location for the test point, or both.

An important point to note in connection with the above is that the technician does not necessarily need to know what the true signal is as it appears in the circuit. All that he needs is an indication that the true signal, whatever its nature, is or is not out of tolerance. Even if the wave shape of a signal is changed in being transmitted from the circuit to a test point, it still might be useful if the signal at the test point could be used to predict an out-of-tolerance condition in the circuit.

Physically Locating Test Points

Generally speaking, test points should be concentrated in one place. Practically speaking, however, it is not always possible to do this. Following are five possible arrangements:

a. A built-in test unit. The best way to provide test points is to put all of them into one built-in test unit. If voltages and wave shapes must be checked, for example, the test unit might consist of a meter, an oscilloscope, and a rotary switch for selecting circuits (see Fig. 9-37). The meter and oscilloscope should have fixed, preset circuits so that the meter always reads center scale and the oscilloscope needs no adjustment. Either an in-tolerance meter reading or an in-tolerance waveform on the oscilloscope should be coded for each position of the rotary switch. If more test points are needed than can be handled by a single switch, multiple switches could be used, of course.

b. A partially built-in test unit. Because some oscilloscopes are large, heavy, and expensive, it might not be practical to design a

test unit such as that recommended above for each major component of a system. An acceptable compromise is to mount a center-reading meter on each major component that can be checked by meter and then provide a set of test jacks as an outlet for signals requiring an oscilloscope (see Fig. 9-38). The selector switch and circuits for this arrangement should be designed as before.

c. A portable test unit. If neither of the two arrangements recommended above is practicable because of space or weight limitations, design an integrated portable test unit resembling the built-in unit (see Fig. 9-39). A single multi-prong contact on the end of a cable can be used to attach the test unit.

d. A built-in test panel. If, for some reason, none of the alternatives described above is practicable, a test panel should be provided on the equipment (see Fig. 9-40). With this arrangement, the outputs of each test point should be designed for checking with standard test equipment, and the points should be planned to provide a miniature block diagram of the system, with each block representing a line-replaceable unit. Overlays for the test panel should direct the technician to the test points he should check and the order in which he should check them. In-tolerance signals should be shown on the overlays, and test points should be coded on the panel with full instructions provided in the maintenance manual in the event the overlay is lost.

e. Test points on replaceable units. If none of the above arrangements is practicable, provide test points for the inputs and outputs on each replaceable unit. If possible, mount components on one side of the board or chassis and wiring on the other side (see Fig. 9-41). Even if the wiring is mounted on the same side as the parts, test leads should be brought through to the back. An advantage in having test points on the back is that full identifying information for each test point can be marked on the back without being obscured by parts.

Labeling Test Points

The following design recommendations should be observed when labeling test points:

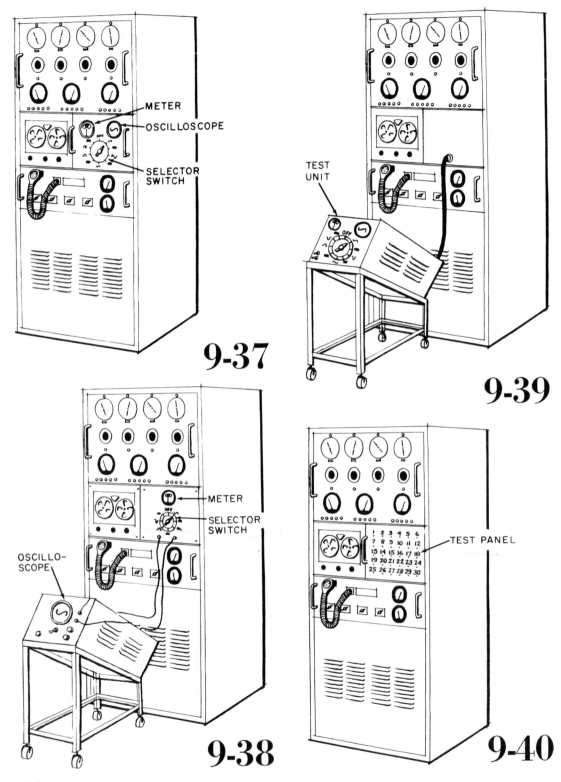

METER
OSCILLOSCOPE
SELECTOR SWITCH

9-37

TEST UNIT

9-39

OSCILLO-SCOPE

METER
SELECTOR SWITCH

9-38

TEST PANEL

9-40

1. Label each test point with a number, letter, or other symbol that identifies it in the maintenance instructions.

2. Label each test point with the in-tolerance signal and the tolerance limits of the signal that should be measured there, if possible.

3. Include the name of the unit in the label, if possible.

4. Consider color coding test points so that they can be located easily.

5. Use phosphorescent markings on test points, selector switches, and meters that might have to be read in very low ambient illumination.

Other Design Recommendations

The following general design recommendations should be observed when providing test points for equipment:

1. All test points should be placed or guarded so that the technician cannot contact high voltages while using them.

2. If a test probe must be connected to a test point without being held by the technician, the test point should have a quick-disconnect fastener.

3. Test points used in checking should be located close to the controls or displays that are used in the checking procedure.

4. Each test point used for adjusting should have one—and only one—adjustment control associated with it. The control should be near the test point, and the signal at the test point should indicate clearly when the adjustment control has been moved to the correct position.

DISPLAYS FOR MAINTENANCE

Displays tell the operator and maintenance man whether the system, or parts of it, are performing normally. Because most of the principles that apply to the design of displays for the operator also apply to the design of displays for maintenance, see Chapter 2 for complete design recommendations for displays; the following paragraphs contain rec-

ommendations peculiar to displays for maintenance.

The Type of Display

The following design recommendations should be considered when choosing the type of maintenance display:

1. Go-no-go displays should be used whenever possible.

2. Use auditory signals in addition to lights for displays that are not watched all the time, especially if it is important that changes be noted immediately. (For example, maintenance men might not notice that a signal light is energized, but a horn or bell would get the maintenance men's attention immediately, and the light would tell them what was wrong.)

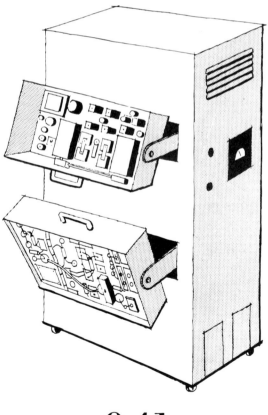

9-41

3. Use moving-pointer fixed-scale indicators (see Chapter 2) for most maintenance indications. This is the best all-around indicator for setting, checking, and reading exact numerical information.

4. When center-null meters are used, design the circuit so that the needle will not stop in the in-tolerance position if power fails.

5. Displays should be provided with illumination (see Chapter 2) so that they can be read by the technician wherever they will be installed.

The Location of Displays

The following design recommendations should be observed when planning the location of maintenance displays:

1. Put displays where they can be read most easily by the maintenance man in his normal working position.

2. Displays used in checking a system should be located so that they all can be seen from one position.

3. On equipments that have separate displays for operation and maintenance, put displays for maintenance behind an access door on the operator's panel. Usually, the maintenance man must be able to see both the displays for maintenance and those for operation, but the former should be out of sight during normal use of the equipment so that they will not confuse the operator.

4. Sometimes maintenance can be carried on during the operation of the equipment. If this is likely to happen often, do not put displays for the maintenance man where they are likely to interfere with the operator.

5. Locate displays for maintenance near (preferably above) the controls the technician will need to use in checking or adjusting the equipment.

Scale Markings

The following recommendations should be observed when providing scale markings:

1. Displays should contain only as much information as will be needed by the tech-

nician to make a decision or take some action. For example, a meter with a green strip to show the in-tolerance reading is better than one on which the technician must read an exact value and then interpret the value to decide if the equipment is or is not in-tolerance (see Fig. 9-42).

2. If a display must provide numerical information for some operations and only in- or out-of-tolerance information for others, markings for both types of information should be used (see Fig. 9-43).

3. If more than one reading must be taken from a single meter, use coded scale areas that correspond to coded switch settings to indicate in-tolerance ranges. Color coding can be used but only if there will be adequate illumination and only if the illumination itself will not be colored. Each position on the switch also should be labeled with the condition it measures (see Fig. 9-44).

4. Numerical scales should be only as fine as will be needed to make settings or take readings accurately. Interpolation should not be required, nor should unneeded scale markings be included (see Fig. 9-45).

5. Displays should present exact indications, that is, the technician should not have to multiply the values on the indicator by a constant or otherwise transform them.

6. If there is no way to avoid scale-reading transformations, provide a conversion table beside the indicator, and, to simplify the arithmetic, use decimal transformations only.

7. If multi-scale indicators must be used, design the display so that only one scale will be visible at a time. If there is no way to avoid having more than one scale visible at a time, the scales should be clearly labeled and, possibly, color coded to their respective control positions.

Labeling Displays

The following design recommendations should be observed when labeling displays for maintenance:

1. Labels should tell what function is being measured, not the electrical characteristic. For

example, use TRANSMITTER OUTPUT, not POWER; use +300V SUPPLY, not VOLTAGE; use MAGNETRON CURRENT, not MILLIAMPS.

2. Labels should tell where the display fits into the system circuitry. For example, use TURRET DRIVE VOLTAGE, not 115V.

3. Labels should not include obscure or highly technical abbreviations. For example, use NS RATE SERVO OUTPUT, not Rn; use TAS TRANSMITTER OUTPUT, not Rt.

4. Labels on displays should be similar to the labels on their corresponding controls. For example, if the control label is TRANSMITTER OUTPUT ADJUST, the display label should be TRANSMITTER OUTPUT.

CONTROLS FOR MAINTENANCE

Controls should be provided for the maintenance man whenever the operator's controls cannot put into the system information called for by the maintenance procedures. Specifications for maintenance controls should be prepared at the same time as the equipment itself is being developed; only in this way can the designer make reasonable compromises among the requirements for good circuit design, test points, maintenance procedures, and locations for maintenance controls.

Many controls designed for the operator of a piece of equipment are also used by the maintenance man. Some controls, however, are built into equipment strictly for maintenance purposes. Because the design of both kinds of controls have much in common, see Chapter 6 for a fuller discussion of design recommendations for controls; the following paragraphs contain only recommendations peculiar to controls for maintenance purposes.

The Type of Control

The following design recommendations should be observed when deciding what type of maintenance control to use:

1. Use hand-operated knobs instead of tool-operated devices when frequent adjustments must be made.

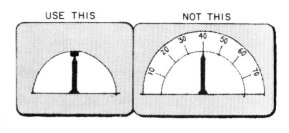

9-42

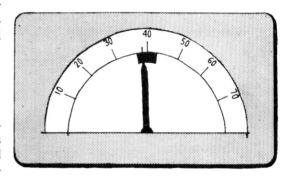

9-43

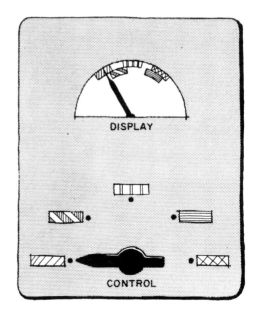

9-44

IF READINGS MUST BE MADE ONLY TO NEAREST 5 UNITS

USE THIS

NOT THIS

9-45

BAR-
SHAPED
POINTER

KNOB WITH
ORIENTING
DOT

KNOB
WITH
CRANK

9-46

USE THIS — OR THIS — NOT THIS

RADAR
TRACK

WARM
UP — MANUAL
TRACK

OFF — EMERGENCY
OPERATE

115 VAC

250
VDC

9-47

USE THIS — NOT THIS

MAIN POWER
ON

OFF

ON

OFF

2. For other purposes, use the following controls (see also Fig. 9-46):

a. For selector switches, use bar-shaped pointers.

b. For continuous rotation for a few turns, use a round knob with an orienting dot, triangle, bar, etc.

c. For continuous rotation for many turns, use a round knob with a crank that is hinged and can be folded into a recess.

The Location of Controls

The following design recommendations should be observed when planning the location of controls for maintenance:

1. For equipments that have controls for operation, put the controls for maintenance on the front panel behind an access door in such a way that the operator's front panel also is accessible to the maintenance man.

2. For equipments that do not have controls for operation, locate all maintenance controls together on the outside of one side of the equipment (a side that will be accessible when the equipment is installed).

3. Ideally, all adjustment controls should be located on a single adjustment panel.

4. Keep controls away from high voltages, hot tubes, rotating machinery, etc. Use extension shafts for screwdriver adjustments if necessary.

5. Arrange controls in the order in which they normally will be used by the maintenance man. (Caution: do not follow this recommendation if the same controls are used by the operator in a different order; the operator's order of usage takes precedence over the maintenance man's.)

Labeling and Coding Controls

The following design recommendations should be observed when labeling and coding maintenance controls:

1. Make control-position markings descriptive rather than coded. The markings should describe a condition, an action, or an indication (see Fig. 9-47).

2. Every control should have a functional name and should be labeled with that name (see Fig. 9-48, left).

3. Controls should be numbered in the order of their operation whenever they are used in a fixed sequence, and this sequence number should be included in the label.

§ 9.4.1

9.4.2 *Installation in prime equipment*

A piece of equipment that is otherwise easy to maintain can be impossible to service where it is installed. The most important requirement for a good installation is accessibility. Requirements for accessibility are determined, in part, by maintenance procedures. For example, if trouble-shooting checks must be made in a junction box, the box should be easy to get to. On the other hand, there is no need for a line technician to have access to the inside of units that will be worked on only in a shop or depot.

Requirements for accessibility are determined also by technical limitations. For example, if the space available for a piece of equipment will allow only one face of the unit to be accessible, all maintenance controls, displays, cables, and test points must be accessible from that face.

EQUIPMENT SPACE

Equipment can, and should, be designed to facilitate effective maintenance with a minimum of space being required for access to the equipment. A great deal of progress has been made along this line, notably with large and complex electronic equipment. Techniques include making the chassis an integral part of the structure of the equipment, as is the case with pullout shelves or drawers (see Fig. 9-4), which replace such standard techniques as hinged doors and removable panels.

The principal advantage inherent in the integral-chassis techniques lies in the fact that all of the components of the equipment are made readily accessible, including those at the rear of the chassis, with a minimum of space being required for access. Removable-panel accesses are satisfactory only for servicing or replacing components that lie in a plane parallel to, and within 6 in. of, the access opening. This is also true for hinged access doors, and

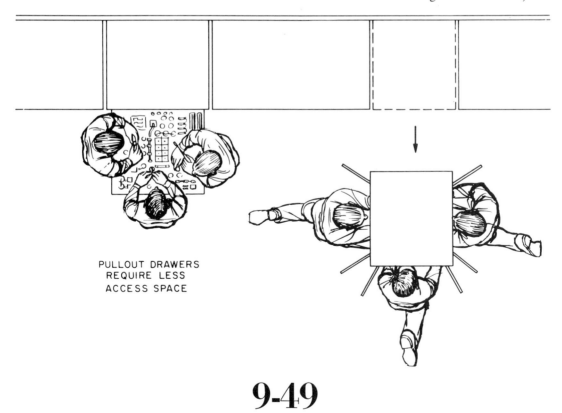

PULLOUT DRAWERS
REQUIRE LESS
ACCESS SPACE

9-49

these doors require additional space for opening. Thus, in most arrangements, for the maintenance man to get inside equipment with only hinged access doors or removable panels, the equipment must be pulled out of its normally installed position, and accesses must be provided on at least three sides (see Fig. 9-49).

In the pullout-drawer design, the maintenance man has access from three sides. In addition, this design allows one, two, or three maintenance men to work on the same shelf or drawer simultaneously, which is often difficult or impossible when technicians must work inside the equipment. Note, also, that it generally requires less room to work on equipment with pullout shelves or drawers than on equipment with hinged access doors or removable panels.

DESIGNING FOR ACCESSIBILITY

The following steps in planning the installation of units in the prime equipment should be carried out:
1. Find out what the technical limitations of the installation are. For instance:
   a. How much space is available and what is its shape?
   b. How must the weight be distributed?
   c. How big will the equipment be and how much will it weigh?
   d. What restrictions will there be on the lengths of cables?
   e. What accesses will be available?
2. List the operations the maintenance man must do on the equipment when it is installed. For instance:
   a. Which units will he have to get to?
   b. Which sides of the units must he get to?
   c. Which units will need frequent servicing or replacing?
3. Design the installation of units so as to meet both the limitations in Step 1 above and the needs for access in Step 2 above.

Unit Weight and Height Limitations

Remember that technicians are limited in the weights they can lift (see article 9.3.2).

In any event, technicians should not have to reach out for and lift units weighing more than about 25 lb. Although almost any man can lift 100 lb or more if it is of convenient size and if it is close to him, hardly anyone can handle more than 25 lb at arm's length.

Study the position the technician will have to assume in maintaining the equipment, and design the installation accordingly. What might look like good accessibility from casual observation might require the technician to hold a very awkward position. Install maintenance displays, controls, and test points 3–5 ft above the floor.

Installation for Ease of Replacement

The following design recommendations should be observed when planning the installation of units:
1. Locate each unit in the equipment in such a way that no other unit or equipment has to be removed to get to the unit.
2. If it is necessary to put one unit behind another, the unit requiring less frequent attention should be in back of the one requiring more frequent attention.
3. Do not put a unit in a recess, or behind or under structural members, floor boards, operator's seats, hoses, pipes, or other parts of the equipment that are difficult to remove unless this serves some necessary purpose (for example, protecting the unit).
4. Removing any given line-replaceable unit should require the technician to open only one access.
5. Units generally should be designed for removal through the front rather than through the back of the equipment.
6. Units should be removable from the installation along a straight or moderately curved line; they should not have to be juggled around corners (see Fig. 9-50).

Other Design Recommendations

The following general design recommendations should be observed when planning the installation of units:

1. If the technician must have access to the back of a hinge-mounted unit, install the unit so that it will open to its full distance and remain open without being held (see Fig. 9-51).

2. Locate units so that their covers can be opened without interference from bulkheads, brackets, or other equipment.

3. Locate units so that check points, adjustment points, connectors, and labels face the technician and are not hidden by other units.

4. Units that require frequent visual inspection, e.g., desiccators or fuses, should be located where they can be seen easily without having to remove panels, covers, or other units.

5. Units that must be checked out in successive steps should be located together so that technicians will not have to do a lot of moving around to check them.

6. Do not locate units where oil, other fluids, or dirt is likely to drop on the technician.

9.4.3 *Test equipment and bench mockups*

Test equipment and bench mockups are, basically, just pieces of equipment, and, like any other equipment, such test units must themselves be checked, calibrated and maintained. For this reason recommendations about the design of units, covers and cases, cables and connectors, test points, displays, and controls apply just as much to test equipment and bench mockups as to prime equipment. Consult all of the prior articles of this section for recommendations about these aspects of the design of test equipment and bench mockups.

TEST EQUIPMENT

There are four general types of test equipment used in maintenance work, and these can be listed as follows:

a. Built-in test equipment, which is an integral part of the prime equipment. This type can be a complex automatic checker or a simple voltmeter with external leads (see article 9.4.1).

b. Go-no-go test equipment, which provides only one of two possible answers to the question: Is the given signal in or out of tolerance?

c. Automatic test equipment, which checks two or more signals in sequence without help from the technician. (The test usually stops when the first out-of-tolerance signal is detected.)

d. Collating test equipment, which presents the results of two or more checks as a single display, e.g., a light might come on only if a number of different signals are in tolerance.

These four types of test equipment are not mutually exclusive, however, and a given test unit might have all or some of the features of any of them in any combination. There seems to be no good general rules for specifying how much of each type should be built into a given item of test equipment. The relative advan-

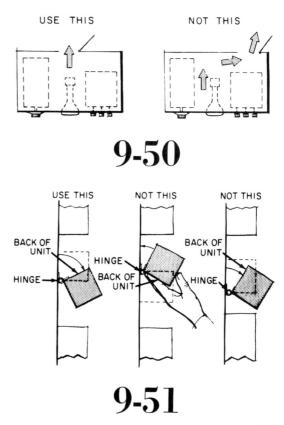

USE THIS   NOT THIS

9-50

USE THIS   NOT THIS   NOT THIS

BACK OF UNIT

HINGE   HINGE   BACK OF UNIT   HINGE   BACK OF UNIT

9-51

Table 9-2 Advantages and Disadvantages of Four Types of Test Equipment

Type	Advantages	Disadvantages
Built-in	Cannot be lost or damaged independently of prime equipment Requires no special storage facilities Does not need to be transported to prime equipment	Might add appreciably to size and weight of prime equipment Will require greater total number of test units because there must be one for each prime equipment Calibration of each test unit might be difficult or inconvenient Might increase complexity of, and amount of maintenance needed on, prime equipment
Go-no-go	Presents information that is clear and easy to read Simplifies decisions and tasks for maintenance man	Unique circuitry usually required for each signal value to be tested The additional number and complexity of circuits often adds to cost of test unit and to time required for its development and, later, maintenance Usually of little help in checking common voltages or simple waveshapes except in long sequences that must be checked quickly
Automatic	Can make rapid series of checks with little or no chance of omitting any steps	Usually large, heavy, and expensive Usually highly specialized with little versatility Almost essential that it have self-checking features to detect its own malfunctioning, which adds to cost and difficulty of maintaining it
Collating	Reduces number of indicators technician must read and so reduces checking time and errors Simplifies trouble shooting if it provides indication of which signal, if any, is out of tolerance	Disadvantages are similar to those for go-no-go and automatic test equipments If it merely indicates that all signals are, or are not, in tolerance, it will not aid in troubleshooting

Table 9-3   Number of Obstacles Encountered by Maintenance Men Carrying Test Equipment Aboard U. S. Navy Vessels

Weight of instrument (lb)	Relative size of ship	Number of obstacles encountered					Number of times instrument bumped on steel
		Doors [1]	Coamings [2]	68-deg ladders [3]	90-deg ladders [4]	Misc. [5]	
4	Small	52	43	21	13	16	2
	Large	97	84	63	3	91	5
8	Small	46	40	19	3	19	6
	Large	92	83	59	3	88	19
16	Small	38	32	17	0	16	21
	Large	88	78	43	1	70	30
>16	Small	21	27	5	0	9	29
	Large	33	21	23	0	32	36

[1] Most doors are 26 in. wide (a man walking comfortably is 21 in. wide).

[2] Watertight doors have a 7–12 in. coaming over which the man must step (see Fig. 9-52).

[3] Ladders are usually at a 68-deg angle with 25-in.-wide steps. Handrails of chain or rope (which give 4–8 in.) are used although solid railings are more common (see Fig. 9-53).

[4] Watertight hatches are generally 18 in. in diameter and always have a vertical (90-deg) ladder leading to them.

[5] Most passageways are 32 in. wide, allowing a man only about 6 in. on each side of him when *not* carrying an instrument.

tages and disadvantages (see Table 9-2) of each feature must be judged in terms of the demands that will be placed on the equipment and on maintenance technicians in the field.

One general point to keep in mind, however, is that very elaborate test equipment can simplify the job of the line technician and reduce preparation time, or turn-around time, for systems like interceptor aircraft and missiles. This situation does not necessarily reduce the total maintenance load, however, because complex test equipments sometimes require so much maintenance that they increase, rather than reduce, the total amount of maintenance required. Above all, test equipment should be designed so that it is easy, fast, and safe to use.

Another general point to keep in mind is that the weight of portable test units interacts with the amount of rough treatment they receive. Table 9-3 shows the number of obstacles encountered by Navy electronic technicians in making fifteen regular service trips

with instruments of various weights. Note the direct correlation between the weight of the instruments and the number of times they bumped against steel.

Design Recommendations

The following recommendations should be observed when designing test equipment:

1. To simplify test equipment, do the following:

a. Minimize the number of controls and displays.

b. Reduce the number and complexity of the steps required to operate the set (e.g., by "ganging" certain controls or by making certain operations automatic).

c. Prepare clear operating and maintenance instructions.

2. Provide "reverse interlocks" that turn off the set when the cover is closed, and/or

use both warning lights and written warnings on the test equipment to remind the technician to turn off the equipment when he is through with it.

3. Use selector switches on test equipment rather than plug-in connections (see Fig. 9-54); selector switches are quicker to use and they reduce the likelihood of faulty connections.

4. Provide a signal to show when the set is warmed up and ready to use. If such a signal cannot be provided, a label near the warmup switch should state clearly how much warmup time is required.

5. Provide a simple check to show when the set is out of calibration or is not working properly.

6. The outer case and all removable parts should be clearly labeled.

7. A label on the cover or case of the set should state its purpose and the precautions that should be observed in using it.

8. Full instructions for using the set should be stored in it, and/or a checklist for operating the equipment should be printed on a metal plate and attached to it.

9. Label every item that the technician must recognize, read, or use.

10. Provide circuit-protection devices, such as circuit breakers and fuses, to protect the set against damage if the wrong switch or jack position is used.

11. Provide adequate, integral storage space for such removable items as test leads.

9-52

9-53

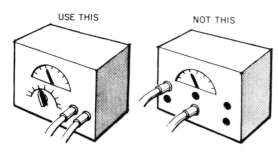

USE THIS   NOT THIS

12. Provide fasteners or holders so that accessories will be held securely and safely in the storage compartment.

13. Label what goes into the storage compartment and show how it should be stored.

14. Test leads should require no more than a fraction of a turn for attachment to the prime equipment.

15. Portable test equipment should be rectangular in shape for convenient storage.

16. Handles on the cover and/or case should be recessed or hinged for convenient storage.

BENCH MOCKUPS

As used here, the term "bench mockup" refers to prime-equipment units set up in a maintenance shop or depot to check or locate faults in units brought in from the field. Such mockups might consist of an entire system or only part of a system, and they might be provided with signal generators and dummy loads to simulate inputs and outputs.

A unit of the mockup is replaced with a unit from the field that is suspected of a malfunction. The bench mockup feeds signals into and receives signals from the suspected component. If an out-of-tolerance signal appears when the suspected unit is installed, but not when the regular unit is installed, the technician knows there is something wrong with the suspected unit.

Although bench mockups are usually put together from production units of the prime equipment, they should be designed as items of test equipment because they often require additional maintenance aids such as signal generators, dummy loads, and extra junction boxes, terminal strips, test points, controls, and displays. Moreover, the man who designed the prime equipment is in the best position to design the mockup and to fit it into the total maintenance picture.

Design Recommendations

The following recommendations should be observed when designing bench mockups:

USE THIS

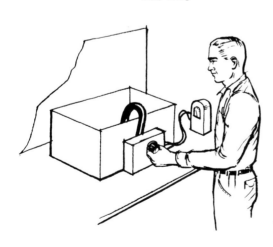

NOT THIS

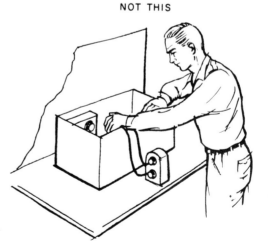

9-55

1. Provide extension cables for all units so that they can be removed from the mockup for checking (see Fig. 9-55).

2. End connectors on all mockup cables should be of the quick-disconnect type that require only a strong push or pull to connect or disconnect them. (Mockup cables need not withstand strong vibration or shock, but, because of the way mockups are used, they do need to be connected and disconnected frequently.)

3. Provide extra heavy coverings on mockup cables (for example, vinyl tubing) to protect them from wear resulting from frequent connection and disconnection.

4. Mockup cables, including extension cables for units, should be provided with test points to check the signal flow through each

wire. One satisfactory design is to provide test points at the connector (see Fig. 9-56). Another is to provide test points on junction boxes or terminal strips.

5. Operating instructions for the mockup should give correct signal values and tolerances for each test point.

6. Use transparent plastic covers on mockup units that contain parts the operation of which may be checked visually. (Caution: Do not follow this recommendation if a metal cover is needed for electrical shielding.)

7. Mockup units should be installed so that every unit is accessible without removing any other unit.

8. The layout of the mockup should provide enough space so that the technician can get at the units.

9. Provide a pullout shelf or some other method of supporting the test equipment while it is being used (see Fig. 9-57).

9.4.4 Maintenance procedures

Maintenance procedures should state in words exactly what steps a technician must go through to perform a given maintenance task.

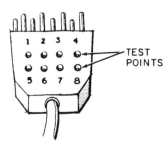

TEST POINTS

9-56

USE THIS

NOT THIS

9-57

Ideally, every maintenance operation should have a set of written procedures prepared and tested during the development of the system. Such procedures are needed for each task in inspecting, checking, trouble shooting, adjusting, replacing, repairing, and servicing at each maintenance level (see article 9.3.1). Of these, checking and trouble-shooting procedures should be given the most attention because these two functions take up the major part of the technician's time.

GENERAL RECOMMENDATIONS

The following general recommendations should be observed when preparing maintenance procedures:

1. Keep maintenance procedures as brief as possible without sacrificing necessary information.

2. Prepare procedures that give results that are not ambiguous.

3. Make tolerances realistic for the level at which maintenance will be performed, i.e., line, field or shop, factory or depot maintenance.

4. Procedures should not be too difficult for technicians to follow. Keep the ideas and words as simple as is practicable. Procedures sometimes can be simplified by designing the test equipment to do some or all of the programming (see Table 9-2).

5. Keep the number of decisions the technician must make as few as is reasonable. In general, the greater the number of decisions, the harder the technician's job. On the other hand, reducing the number of decisions to as few as possible might be achieved only at the expense of a very long and tedious series of steps. Obviously, the designer should look for the best compromise from the standpoint of the technician.

6. Keep decisions as simple as practicable by reducing the number of alternatives and prior conditions the technician has to keep in mind in arriving at any decision.

7. Use exact step-by-step procedures, and use the same ones as often as possible. (This will make it easy for inexperienced technicians to learn the procedure.)

8. Be sure each procedure states how to start up the equipment and how to shut it down.

9. Do not require the technician to work near dangerous voltages or delicate components unless absolutely necessary.

10. Always provide *systematic* trouble-shooting procedures for the technician to follow. Failure to do this often results in the technician following inefficient and even dangerous procedures.

TROUBLE-SHOOTING PROCEDURES

Systematic trouble shooting should proceed in the following three phases:

1. Routine check of the equipment or system to identify or verify malfunction symptoms.

2. Analysis of symptom patterns to narrow the area of malfunction.

3. Special checks to isolate the malfunction to a replaceable or repairable unit.

Routine Checks

Routine checks are those that are regularly used to determine if an equipment or a prescribed portion of an equipment is operating properly, needs adjustment, or is malfunctioning. Trouble shooting will usually begin with a routine check. The routine check will tell the technician that a malfunction is present within the equipment or system and will provide information as to where the malfunction is located. This information is in the form of a pattern of malfunction symptoms. The analysis of these symptoms is the next phase. Table 9-4 is an example of an outline of the steps in a routine check, and Table 9-5 is an example of a portion of the actual step-by-step check procedure.

The Analysis of Symptom Patterns

One way to help the technician analyze symptom patterns is to provide him with special diagrams that indicate which components

Table 9-4   Outline of Preflight Check, B-7 Fire-Control System

1. Radar-set check
   1.1 Power-supply check
      1.1.1 +300v d-c regulated
      1.1.2 +150v d-c regulated
      1.1.3 −150v d-c regulated
      1.1.4 Repeller voltage
      1.1.5 Power bus (a-c)
      1.1.6 Relay supply voltage (d-c)
   1.2 Transmitter-output checks
      1.2.1 Frequency check
      1.2.2 Inspect frequency spectrum
      1.2.3 PRF check
      1.2.4 Inspect modulation envelope
          shape
      1.2.5 Power-output check
   1.3 Receiver test
      1.3.1 Sensitivity check
      1.3.2 Receiver-output check
      1.3.3 AFC check

2. Search-mode operational check
   2.1 Antenna search-pattern check
      2.1.1 Narrow-pattern check (right
          and left)
      2.1.2 Wide-pattern check (center)
      2.1.3 Antenna spin-pattern check
   2.2 Display calibration
   2.3 Artificial-horizon check
3. Manual-track operational check
   3.1 Antenna-control check
   3.2 Manual-track test
   3.3 Lock-on check
      3.3.1 Check sensitivity of lock on
      3.3.2 Check display function
4. Auto-track operational check
   4.1 Attack-phase operational check
   4.2 Rocket-fire check
   4.3 Pull-out-warning check
5. Miscellaneous checks
   5.1 Check antenna-table dither
   5.2 Check radar anti-jam control
      operation
   5.3 Check pilot's scope controls

Table 9-5   Antenna Search-Pattern Check, B-7 Fire-Control System

Step	Component	Action	Indication	Remarks
2.1	Antenna	Mount azimuth and elevation protractors		See dwg P
2.1.1	Pilot's control box:	Set to:	Antenna travel on protractors should be:	
	Operation Sw.	Auto-Search		
	Antenna-Az. Sw.	Center-Narrow	Az: ±23½ deg	Adjust pot. P2371
	Antenna-El. Con.	Center	El: ±2½ deg	Adjust pot. P2346
	Pulse length Sw.	Long		
2.1.2	Pilot's control box:	Set to:	Antenna travel on protractors should be:	Same as for 2.1.1
	Antenna-Az. Sw.	Center-broad	Az: ±67 deg	
	Antenna-El. Con.	Full clockwise	El: +30 deg −25 deg	

affect each system output for each step of the routine-check procedure. With these diagrams the technician can "figure out" which components could be causing a certain pattern of symptoms. It is probably more useful, however, to provide a diagram for each symptom pattern that shows the data flow among possible malfunctioning components.

Where the number of different symptoms that can be observed from a particular routine check is n, the number of possible patterns is $2^n - 1$. Thus, even when the number of different symptoms observable from a routine check is relatively small, the number of patterns might be too large to provide analyses for all of them. For example, 10 different symptoms can yield 1023 patterns.

There are two major ways of reducing the number of different patterns that must be analyzed; both involve working with groups of symptoms. The first way is to combine a number of individual symptoms into a single group symptom. The group symptom is considered to have occurred if any of the individual symptoms in the group occurs. A diagram is then prepared for each pattern of group symptoms showing the data flow among all of the components in which a malfunction could cause the observed pattern of group symptoms.

The second, and probably more useful, way to reduce the number of symptom patterns is to divide the individual symptoms into groups and then prepare a diagram only for each within-group symptom pattern. Thus, if nine symptoms were divided into three equal groups, the designer would prepare $2^3 + 2^3 + 2^3 - 3$ or 21 different diagrams instead of the 2^9 or 511 diagrams for all possible patterns for individual symptoms. An example of this method is shown in Table 9-6 and Fig. 9-58.

Special Checks

The designer now should provide the technician with aid in choosing the best sequence of special checks to use after the symptom pattern has been analyzed. This aid should be included with the data-flow diagram.

§ 9.4.4

Table 9-6   Symptom Patterns Obtainable from Preflight Check, B-7 Fire Control System [1]

Test pattern [2]			Directions
1.1	1.2	1.3	
X	O	O	Do not run test 1.2 and 1.3 until power supply is adjusted correctly or replaced
O	X	O	Use data flow diagram 1.a for trouble shooting
O	O	X	Use data flow diagram 1.b for trouble shooting
O	X	X	Use data flow diagram 1.c for trouble shooting
2.1	2.2	2.3	
X	O	O	Use data flow diagram 2.a for trouble shooting
O	X	O	Use data flow diagram 2.b for trouble shooting
O	O	X	Use data flow diagram 2.c for trouble shooting
X	X	O	Replace master controller (LRU 7)
O	X	X	Use data flow diagram 2.d for trouble shooting
X	O	X	Replace master controller (LRU 7)
X	X	X	Replace master controller (LRU 7)
3.1	3.2	3.3	
X	O	O	Use data flow diagram 3.a for trouble shooting
O	O	X	Use data flow diagram 3.b for trouble shooting
X	X	O	Replace master controller (LRU 7)
O	X	X	Use data flow diagram 3.c for trouble shooting
X	O	X	Use data flow diagram 3.d for trouble shooting
X	X	X	Use data flow diagram 3.e for trouble shooting
4.1	4.2	4.3	
X	O	O	Use data flow diagram 4.a for trouble shooting
O	X	O	Use data flow diagram 4.b for trouble shooting
O	O	X	Use data flow diagram 4.c for trouble shooting
X	O	X	Use data flow diagram 4.d for trouble shooting
O	X	X	Replace master computer "B" (LRU 13)
X	X	X	Use data flow diagram 4.e for trouble shooting
5.1	5.2	5.3	
X	O	O	Use data flow diagram 5.a for trouble shooting
O	X	O	Use data flow diagram 5.b for trouble shooting
O	O	X	Use data flow diagram 5.c for trouble shooting
X	X	X	Check for voltage at main power bus. If this checks OK, replace pilot's control box (LRU 3)

[1] Patterns not shown in this table probably never will occur.

[2] X = malfunction symptom observed, O = in-tolerance indication obtained.

The sequence of checks usually should be flexible, with the exact sequence depending on where malfunction symptoms are observed. An inflexible order of checks can be specified if the time required for a particular sequence is likely to be small. This is usually the case only in trouble shooting to parts after a malfunction has been isolated to a particular unit of the equipment.

DATA FLOW DIAGRAM (LINE MAINTENANCE), B-7 FIRE CONTROL SYSTEM
SYMPTOM PATTERNS 2.A (2.1:X, 2.2:0, 2.3:0, AZIMUTH TRAVERSE OK)

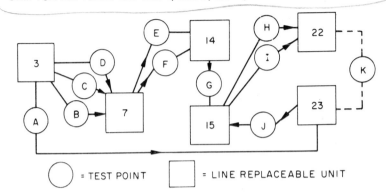

◯ = TEST POINT   ▢ = LINE REPLACEABLE UNIT

TEST POINT	CORRECT READING
A	+200 VDC
B–F	CONTINUITY
G	⎍ ±130V
H TO I	+250 VDC
J	+150 VDC
K	MOTOR 22 OPERATES

CHECK INFORMATION

VOLTAGE AND CONTINUITY CHECKS
1 USE VM 811
2 TOLERANCE ±5V

WAVE SHAPE CHECKS
1 USE KS 339 SCOPE
2 SIGNALS THRU DC AMPLIFIER
3 INTERNAL SWEEP 3 CPS
4 WAVE SHAPE NOT CRITICAL
5 ABSENCE OF SIGNAL OR SPURIOUS OSCILLATIONS INDICATE MALFUNCTION
6 ASYMMETRY ABOUT ZERO AXIS REQUIRES ADJUSTMENT. SEE TASK INSTRUCTION FORM 2.1

CHECKS

1 MAKE CHECKS ON TOP LINE FIRST.
2 IF ALL ARE IN TOLERANCE, MAKE CHECKS IN BOX IMMEDIATELY BELOW AND TO THE RIGHT.
   IF ANY CHECK IS OUT OF TOLERANCE, MAKE CHECKS IN BOX IMMEDIATELY BELOW AND TO THE LEFT.
3 CONTINUE WORKING DOWN TABLE UNTIL YOU COME TO A NUMBER.
4 REPLACE THE UNIT WHOSE NUMBER YOU COME TO.

SEQUENCE OF CHECKS

OUT OF TOLERANCE ←   → IN TOLERANCE

G						
B,C and D			K*			
3	E and F		J			23
	7	14	A		H to I	
			3	23**	15	22

* PRIOR TO CHECK K REMOVE MOTOR FROM MOUNT BUT DO NOT OPEN ELECTRICAL CONNECTIONS. MOVE ANTENNA PLATFORM MANUALLY TO POSITIVE ELEVATION ANGLE STOP.

** ONLY THE FOLLOW-UP POTS IN THIS UNIT NEED TO BE REPLACED AT THIS POINT.

9-58

A sequence of checks should be prescribed such that the malfunction is first isolated to a single chain. The best check to make first in isolating the trouble to a particular chain is at the terminal output of the chain where the probability of observing the malfunction in that check, divided by the time required to make the check, is a maximum. The probability of the malfunction being in a given chain may be determined from data on the frequency of malfunctions or may be based simply on the number of components in the chain. The time required to perform certain checks might have to be estimated.

Once a malfunction has been isolated to a single chain, the best check is at the point in the chain where the probability of observing a malfunction is closest to one half (Miller, et al., 1953). This method is known as the half-split method of trouble shooting (see Fig. 9-59). In this method, the order is affected by the time required to make the various checks. It might be desirable to make the least time-consuming checks first, even though this would not be adhering to the principle of one-half probability. It also might be desirable to delay checks of components in feedback loops if the time required to break the loop for checking is appreciable.

USING THESE PROCEDURES

The following have been included to illustrate checking and trouble-shooting aids:

a. An outline of a routine check (see Table 9-4).

b. A symptom-pattern table that indicates what action to take for each symptom pattern (see Table 9-6).

c. A data-flow diagram (line maintenance) that shows the functional interconnections of line-replaceable units and trouble-shooting steps for one symptom pattern (see Fig. 9-58).

d. A data-flow diagram (shop maintenance) that shows the functional interconnections of shop-replaceable units and trouble-shooting steps for one line-replaceable unit (see Fig. 9-60).

e. A data-flow diagram (shop or depot) that shows the functional interconnections of electronic parts for one shop- or depot-replaceable unit (see Fig. 9-61).

An attempt has been made in preparing these samples to make them only complete enough to illustrate their characteristics and interrelationships. A complete set for a weapon system would, of course, be much more comprehensive. The steps to be followed in using these samples for checking and trouble shooting are as follows:

1. Perform all steps in Section 1 of the routine check.

2. If no malfunctions are noted, perform the steps in Section 2, etc.

3. If malfunction symptoms are observed, refer to the symptom-pattern table.

4. Locate on the symptom-pattern table the pattern that was observed in the routine check. From the table, determine which unit to replace or which line-maintenance data-flow diagram to use in making further checks.

5. Refer to the appropriate data-flow diagram. From this diagram, determine what special checks will isolate the malfunction.

6. Replace the malfunctioning unit as identified through the special checks.

7. Refer to the shop-maintenance data-flow diagram for the replaced unit, and perform the standard check-out procedure for that unit.

HALF-SPLIT METHOD

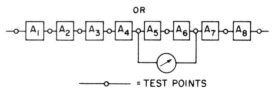

STEP I

STEP 2

OR

——o—— = TEST POINTS

9-59

DATA FLOW DIAGRAM (SHOP MAINTENANCE), B-7 FIRE CONTROL SYSTEM
ANTENNA SERVO AMPLIFIER UNIT – LINE REPLACEABLE UNIT 15

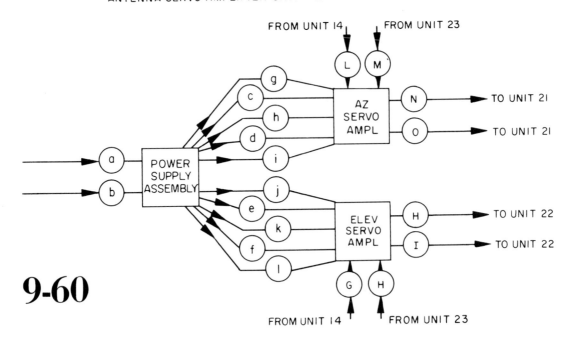

9-60

DATA FLOW DIAGRAM (SHOP OR DEPOT), B-7 FIRE CONTROL SYSTEM
ELEVATION SERVO AMPLIFIER ASSEMBLY OF LINE REPLACEABLE UNIT 15

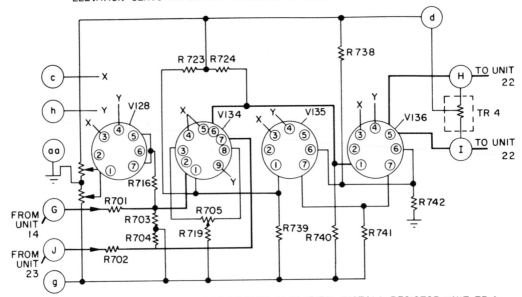

NOTE: BEFORE BENCH CHECKS ARE MADE ON THIS AMPLIFIER, INSTALL RESISTOR UNIT TR 4.

9-61

§ 9.4.4

8. If necessary, follow a trouble-shooting procedure similar to that in Steps 3–5 above, using the appropriate diagrams for the unit.

9.4.5 *Maintenance manuals*

One of the most important considerations in designing for maintainability has to do with maintenance manuals. If instructions are not clear and readable, technicians will not understand them, and this might undo all the good work that has gone into the design of the equipment for maintainability. The following paragraphs give recommendations for preparing maintenance manuals. See Chapter 2 for recommendations concerning the presentation of information through printed materials in general.

THE FORM OF PRESENTATION

The following recommendations should be observed when deciding on the form of presentation of maintenance instructions:

1. Be sure that the form of presentation is appropriate for its purpose.

2. Use step-by-step instructions for all maintenance tasks.

3. Use drawings or photographs to clarify written instructions or to provide extra information the technician needs for his job. Good quality drawings are at least as effective as photographs because photographs frequently show too much detail and thus obscure the point they are supposed to illustrate. On the other hand, photographs with irrelevant details blanked out and relevant details highlighted can be very effective.

4. Use tables for presenting data, and be sure the instructions state when and how each table should be used.

5. Provide tabular data that can be used by the technician without having to make conversions or transformations.

6. Use diagrams to describe processes and interrelationships.

7. Show components in data-flow diagrams in the same relative position that they are in the equipment, if practicable.

8. Show only the electrical characteristics of the signal in data-flow diagrams, not the electrical characteristics of the component.

INSTRUCTIONAL CONTENT

The following recommendations should be observed when considering the instructional content of maintenance manuals:

1. Provide the technician only with the information he needs to do his job; avoid excessive detail, unnecessary theory, and too many words.

2. Instructions should be geared to the task. Line maintenance is a different task from shop maintenance and both of these are different from depot maintenance. Don't try to make one set of instructions cover all three tasks; prepare separate instructions for each kind of maintenance task.

3. Make the symbols and names in the instructions agree with those actually used on the equipment.

4. Give the in-tolerance signal characteristics and the acceptable tolerances for each test point.

5. Index the job instructions thoroughly, and be sure that the index contains the words a technician is likely to look for in locating a particular item.

6. Be sure that the information in the instructions is accurate. This seems almost too obvious to mention, yet instruction manuals often contain errors and/or text and illustrations that are out of date because they refer to earlier models of the equipment. Even a single error in the instructions can cause great confusion and waste much time. Instructions prepared by technical writers should be carefully reviewed by the designers.

9.4.6 *Maintenance tools*

The requirements for tools are determined, in part, by the operations the maintenance man must perform and, in part, by the way equipment is designed. Each equipment or system should come with a complete list of the tools needed to maintain it, and all tools on the list should be tried out early in the development of the equipment or system to discover the following:

a. Duplications and omissions.

b. Inefficient designs that require more tools than necessary (see Bilinski, 1959).

c. Unnecessary design features that require the use of special tools.

d. Tools that are not suitable for the conditions under which they will be used.

DESIGN RECOMMENDATIONS

The following design recommendations should be observed when considering tools:

1. Design equipment and systems so that they can be maintained with standard tools. The design should require the use of special tools only when absolutely necessary.

2. Design equipment so that maintenance tasks can be carried out with as few different kinds of tools as possible.

3. Do not require tools with metal handles if they must be used in extreme cold or in proximity to electrical voltages.

4. Provide *guides* in the equipment for tools when an adjustment control would otherwise be *difficult* to locate.

5. Provide *guards* in the equipment for tools when an adjustment control would otherwise be *dangerous* to locate.

6. Design equipment so that a given tool can be used for as many different tasks as possible if it can be used efficiently in all of the tasks.

10

effects of environment on human performance

THE ENVIRONMENT in which a man operates a machine must be included as a consideration in the design of the man-machine system because the environmental conditions can seriously affect his performance. Indeed, ma-chines often have failed to fulfill their missions, not because they were poorly designed or badly constructed, but because they demanded more of the operator than was humanly possible considering the environment.

10.1 *External and Internal Environments*

When referring to environment, it is helpful to distinguish two kinds: the external environ-ment and the internal environment. The external environment is the environment outside the man and includes such influences as air pressure, humidity, temperature, odors, vibration, noise, and acceleration. The internal environment consists of the conditions within the body that affect the activities of cells, tissues,

This chapter was drafted, for the most part, by Ross A. McFarland of Harvard University and Warren H. Teichner of the University of Massachusetts.

and organs. These internal environmental conditions include such influences as body temperature, blood oxygen, carbon dioxide in the blood, and blood chemistry in general.

Human beings can withstand moderate changes in the external environment without any deterioration in performance primarily because their internal environments are kept reasonably constant by regulatory mechanisms controlled by the central nervous system. These mechanisms provide for exchanges with the external environment, which exchanges maintain body temperature, blood chemistry, etc. within rather narrow limits. Only in this way can the nervous system and body muscles and certain glands perform normally.

Changes in the external environment, however, can prove too extreme for the regulatory mechanisms. In such cases, these mechanisms are unable to maintain a constant internal environment, and there results a deterioration in the performance of the sense organs, central nervous system, and/or muscles and glands. When the human being is part of a man-machine system, the performance of the system deteriorates as well.

10.1.1 *Special considerations for biophysical systems*

This chapter will consider the environmental conditions that must be maintained so as not to exceed the capabilities of the body's regulatory mechanisms for maintaining a constant internal environment and, hence, relatively normal performance. The designer should be aware, however, that the environmental considerations of biophysical systems differ from those of physical systems in certain critical ways, which operate sometimes for and sometimes against the advantage of the designer. These special considerations are discussed in the following paragraphs.

ADAPTATION

The *physiological* characteristics of man change with continued exposure to unusual environments. In general, tolerances are *increased* (positive adaptation) with exposure, within limits, to altitude, low-level illumination, accelerative forces, thermal loads, and some toxic agents; they are *decreased* (negative adaptation) with exposure to high-intensity sound, high-intensity illumination, and certain toxic agents. The width of the tolerance limit at any time depends on the level and duration of exposure, the time since last exposure, and the effort required of the task.

Some negative adaptations are cumulative and do not dissipate with time, as, for example, permanent hearing losses associated with certain kinds of sound exposure or the effects of certain toxic agents. Other negative adaptations do dissipate with time, as, for example, temporary hearing losses associated with some acoustic environments. Positive adaptations also are cumulative sometimes and, in addition, can include, not only adaptation to a specific environmental stress, but, also, adaptation to other, less severe stresses. Thus, adaptation of some sort will be involved in every situation, but, unless the specific nature and degree of the adaptation can be assumed, the system should be designed for the unadapted man.

HABITUATION

The *psychological* characteristics of man also change with repeated exposure and with repeated practice. The result is a decrease in the fear of exposure, an increase in tolerance to discomfort, and an increase in intellectual and coordinative skill. Habituation depends only partly on adaptation, and it is suspected that habituation tends to be fairly specific to the conditions in which the man has had extensive practice. Again, habituation will be a factor in every situation, but, if it cannot be assumed that the man is habituated to the expected conditions, the system should be designed for those conditions to which he is habituated.

PREPARATION

Tolerance limits sometimes can be manipulated by specially preparing the man. Some of the forms that this preparation can take are physical conditioning, indoctrination and emotional conditioning, and diet and drugs. In situations in which the specific preparation of the man is not known, the system should be designed with the assumption that preparation is minimum.

VARIATION

The variation of human tolerance limits from person to person is large compared to that of machine systems. In addition to factors already mentioned that affect these limits, they can vary for reasons of age; sex; geographical, cultural, and educational background; motivation; and other factors. Although no one has ever accounted for all of these factors at one time, it is likely that the probability distribution of a given tolerance limit would be Gaussian if all of the factors were accounted for. Thus, in design situations involving risks, the system should be designed for the more probable human limits only if these limits can be determined in such a way as to identify and exclude from exposure people who fall beyond them. If this cannot be done, the system should be designed for the entire range of human limits.

OPTIMIZATION

Optimum environmental conditions are those that make minimum demands of the body's self-regulatory mechanisms. Ideal engineering design for environmental conditions is that which accommodates these optima. In many cases it is possible to state permissible deviations from ideal conditions, but the amount of permissible deviation will depend on criteria of health, safety, required level of skill, the amount of effort and endurance demanded, and the level of discomfort that the individual can accept or control. Where self-regulating mechanisms are not available for

the protection of the personnel, ideal design calls for zero exposure. Permissible deviations can be stated for some of these conditions too, but, in general, the engineer should attempt to achieve the ideal to prevent costly redesign later.

10.1.2 *Variation in the pattern of effects*

A further consideration is that the effects of environmental stresses do not follow a consistent pattern from one type of exposure to another. Thus, the first effects of some exposure conditions include discomfort whereas other environments are never associated with discomfort or even an awareness of undesirable conditions. In some cases, skills show early deterioration and are more sensitive indications than measurable physiological effects; in other cases, performance might be maintained, in spite of serious physiological symptoms, until near collapse. For these reasons, it is not possible to present a list of symptoms of increasing order of seriousness that can be standard for all environments. Similarly, because the order of occurrence of effects is not standard, a warning symptom under one set of conditions might not be such for another set of conditions.

In every case, only the major effects will be presented in this chapter, and these will be related to the major engineering variables of the given environmental condition. In using these relationships, however, the designer should exercise caution because many situations involve, not just one environmental stress factor, but include a number of them. The effects of combined or multiple environmental stresses are not clearly understood, but it cannot be assumed that these effects are equal to that of the most serious single factor nor, on the other hand, can it be assumed that the effects are merely additive.

Data and recommendations presented in this chapter are all qualified by the preceding considerations, but, to reduce the uncertainty associated with any specific recommendation,

unless otherwise indicated, all recommendations are intended for male human beings,
18–30 yr of age, in good health, and with
good physical and psychological conditioning.

In spite of this, the reader is warned that specific recommendations in an area as complex,
and, in part, as little explored as this one,
must be treated as attempts to "best-guess."

10.2 *The Atmospheric Environment*

As man ascends from the earth to higher
and higher altitudes, and eventually into
"space," he encounters a number of changes
in the external environment that are primarily
a function of altitude, although some also
vary with latitude. Article 10.2.2 describes the
effect of most of these changes on human
comfort, health, and performance. Other articles cover the effects of temperature and humidity (article 10.2.3) and of toxicity and
contaminants (article 10.2.4) in the atmosphere.

10.2.1 *The physical characteristics of the atmosphere*

Because the physical characteristics of the
earth's atmosphere vary significantly with altitude, it is often convenient to differentiate
one region from another on the basis of these
varying characteristics and to designate these
regions by unique names. Various geophysi-
cists have proposed systems of nomenclature,
some of which conflict with others on one or
more points. The International Union of
Geodesy and Geophysics (IUGG) considered
the problem and published its recommendations as to nomenclature in 1953. Unfortunately, no nomenclature as yet has been

adopted as standard by all those working in
the field.

In all of the systems of nomenclature that
have been advanced for characterizing the
vertical structure of the atmosphere, the atmosphere is considered as consisting of nearly
concentric, approximately spherical, contigu-
ous shells. The various shells are distinguished
from one another by differences in definable
and potentially measurable parameters such
as temperature, ionization, and chemical reactions. Names assigned to each of the shells
are composed of a root somewhat indicative
of the defining characteristic, as envisioned by
the originator of the name, and the suffix
"sphere." The corresponding upper boundary
of each shell has a name containing the same
root but having the suffix "pause."

In deriving a specific nomenclature, one
may define all the shells in terms of variations
of a single parameter, or one may choose to
define shells in terms of the most predominant
or well known characteristic of each of the
various regions. The system that has received
the official sanction of the IUGG defines the
shells in terms of variations of a single parameter (Chapman, 1950), but two other often-
used systems define these shells in terms of
the most predominant or well known characteristic of each region (Gerson and Kaplan,
1951 and Goody, 1954). All three systems
are shown in Fig. 10-1 (Wares, 1957) for
comparison. Note that defining the regions in

ALTITUDE (km)	IUGG RECOMMENDED SYSTEM					GERSON'S SYSTEM	GOODY'S SYSTEM	ALTITUDE (mi)
	CHAPMAN'S SYSTEM				SPITZER'S SYSTEM			
	TEMPER-ATURE	COMPO-SITION	CHEMICAL REACT-IONS	IONIZATION	MOLEC-ULAR REACTIONS			
1000	THERMO-SPHERE	HETERO-SPHERE			EXO-SPHERE	EXO-SPHERE	EXO-SPHERE	600
						MESO-SPHERE		500
500								400
400			CHEMO-SPHERE	IONO-SPHERE		IONO-SPHERE	IONO-SPHERE	300
300								200
200								100
100	MESO-PAUSE	HOMO-PAUSE				CHEMO-SPHERE	STRATO-SPHERE	50
50	MESO-SPHERE	HOMO-SPHERE				STRATO-SPHERE		30
30	STRATO-PAUSE STRATO-SPHERE							20
20	TROPO-PAUSE					TROPO-SPHERE	TROPO-SPHERE	10
10	TROPO-SPHERE							5
5								1
1								

10-1

terms of a single variable necessitates a separate subsystem for each variable and that defining the regions in terms of the predominant or best known characteristic involves a certain amount of arbitrariness.

With the exception of "mesosphere," the general meaning of each name is more or less consistent among the systems. Following is a brief description of each shell in the system recommended by IUGG:

a. The *troposphere* is characterized by a more or less uniform decrease in temperature

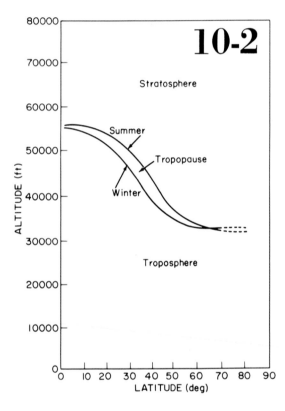

Table 10-1   Ozone Concentration *

Altitude (ft)	Ozone concentration (cm/km)	Relative air density	Ozone concentration (ppm)
0	0.005	1.000	0.05
30,000	0.010	0.375	0.3
50,000	0.030	0.153	2.0
70,000	0.040	0.059	7
90,000	0.024	0.022	11
110,000	0.009	0.0084	11
130,000	0.002	0.0034	6
150,000	0.0005	0.0015	4

* DiTaranto and Lamb, 1958.

about 25 km (82,025 ft) in the middle latitudes. (In some systems of nomenclature, the region between about 56,000 and 100,000 ft is called the ozonosphere.)

c. The *mesosphere* is the region of the first temperature maximum (see Fig. 10-3) and lies above the stratosphere and below the major temperature minimum, which is found at altitudes of from 70 to 85 km and constitutes the *mesopause*.

d. The thermosphere is the region of increasing temperature above the major temperature minimum and has no upper boundary.

e. The *homosphere* is the region of substantially uniform composition (see Table 10-2). The *homopause* is found at altitudes

Table 10-2   Composition of the Atmosphere *

Constituent	Molecular fraction (%)	Molecular weight
Nitrogen	78.09	28.016
Oxygen	20.95	32.0000
Argon	0.93	39.944
Carbon dioxide	0.03	44.010
Neon	1.8×10^{-3}	20.183
Helium	5.24×10^{-4}	4.003
Krypton	1.0×10^{-4}	83.7
Hydrogen	5.0×10^{-5}	2.0160
Xenon	8.0×10^{-6}	131.3
Ozone	1.0×10^{-6}	48.0000
Radon	6.0×10^{-18}	222.0

* Minzner, et al., 1959.

and is the domain of weather (wind, precipitation, clouds, etc.). The *tropopause* varies with latitude and seasons of the year (see Fig. 10-2) and is the domain of high winds (e.g., the jet streams).

b. The *stratosphere* has a nominally constant temperature on the order of arctic-winter temperatures (about −67° F). Maximum ozone concentration (see Table 10-1) is found near the *stratopause*, which is at

10-3

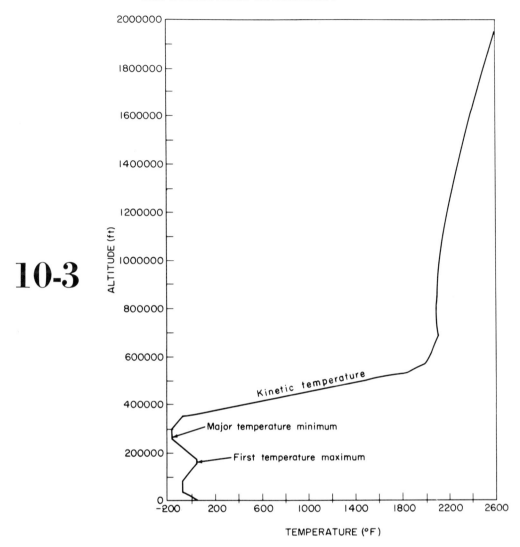

ALTITUDE (ft)

Kinetic temperature

Major temperature minimum

First temperature maximum

TEMPERATURE (°F)

between 80 and 100 km. The composition of the atmosphere changes here primarily because of the disassociation of oxygen, and mean molecular weight of the air decreases accordingly.

f. The heterosphere is the region of significantly varying composition and extends upward indefinitely.

g. The chemosphere is the region in which chemical (primarily photochemical) activity is predominant.

h. The ionosphere is the region of sufficiently large electron density so that it affects radio communication.

i. The exosphere is the region in which

molecular escape from the earth's atmosphere is significant.

Nothing as yet has been said about atmospheric pressure and density. Atmospheric pressure, like temperature, decreases with altitude. Unlike temperature, however, pressure continues to decrease until it disappears altogether in space. According to the gas laws, the pressure of air, like any gas, is inversely related to its volume and varies directly with its temperature. The density of air also is inversely related to its volume and varies directly with its mass. But mass decreases with altitude, and each layer of air is weighted down by the air above it.

§ 10.2.1

Hence, atmospheric pressure at any given altitude is a function of the temperature and density of the air above it. Because the pressure at any altitude varies with atmospheric conditions, a set of values called the Standard Atmosphere have been established for calibrating instruments such as altimeters and barometers (see Table 10-3).

Not only does the total pressure of air decrease with altitude, so does the partial pressure of each of the atmosphere's components. For example, the total air pressure (p_B) at sea level is 760 mmHg, and the partial pressure of oxygen (pO_2) is 159 mmHg; at 10,000 ft, the p_B drops to 522 mmHg, and the pO_2 drops to 109 mmHg; and so on.

Knowing the total pressure at a given altitude and the percentage composition of air, one can calculate the partial pressure of atmospheric gases by multiplying the total pressure by that percentage. In making such a calculation, however, the water vapor in the air (humidity) must be considered. Water vapor acts like any of the atmospheric components except that temperature limits the amount required to saturate the air. At 20° C, for example, the vapor pressure of saturated air (100% humidity) is 17.5 mmHg. In calculating the partial pressure of other components, 17.5 mmHg must first be subtracted from the total pressure, which, at sea level, would be $760 - 17.5 = 742.5$ mmHg. The net result

Table 10-3 Some Properties of the U. S. Standard Atmosphere

Altitude		Pressure			Temperature		Density
ft	m	mmHg	mbar	psi	° C	° F	ratio
0	.0	760.0	1,013.2	14.696	15.0	59.0	1.000
2,000	609.6	706.65	942.1	13.665	11.0	51.9	0.9428
4,000	1,219.2	656.41	875.0	12.692	7.1	44.7	0.8881
6,000	1,828.8	609.09	811.9	11.778	3.1	37.6	0.8358
8,000	2,438.4	564.59	752.5	10.917	−0.8	30.5	0.7859
10,000	3,048.0	522.76	696.7	10.108	−4.8	23.3	0.7384
12,000	3,657.6	483.46	644.3	9.349	−8.8	16.2	0.6931
14,000	4,267.2	446.63	595.1	8.636	−12.7	9.1	0.6499
16,000	4,876.8	412.09	549.0	7.969	−16.7	1.9	0.6088
18,000	5,486.4	379.78	505.8	7.344	−20.7	−5.3	0.5698
20,000	6,096.0	349.53	465.4	6.759	−24.6	−12.3	0.5327
22,000	6,705.6	321.28	427.7	6.212	−28.6	−19.5	0.4947
24,000	7,315.2	294.89	392.5	5.702	−32.5	−26.6	0.4640
26,000	7,924.8	270.33	359.7	5.227	−36.5	−33.7	0.4323
28,000	8,534.4	247.43	329.2	4.784	−40.5	−40.9	0.4023
30,000	9,144.0	226.13	300.8	4.373	−44.4	−48.0	0.3740
32,000	9,753.6	206.35	274.4	3.990	−48.4	−55.1	0.3472
34,000	10,363	188.00	249.8	3.635	−52.4	−62.3	0.3218
35,332	10,565	176.63	234.5	3.415	−55.0	−67.0	0.3058
36,000	10,973	170.99	227.2	3.306	"	"	0.2962
38,000	11,582	155.37	206.5	3.004	"	"	0.2692
40,000	12,192	141.18	187.6	2.730	"	"	0.2447
42,000	12,802	128.29	170.5	2.481	"	"	0.2224
44,000	13,411	116.58	155.1	2.254	"	"	0.2021
46,000	14,021	105.94	140.9	2.049	"	"	0.1838
48,000	14,630	96.27	128.1	1.862	"	"	0.1670
50,000	15,240	87.49	116.4	1.692	"	"	0.1518
52,000	15,850	79.51	105.8	1.537	"	"	0.1379
54,000	16,459	72.26	96.15	1.397	"	"	0.1254
56,000	17,069	65.66	87.39	1.270	"	"	0.1140
58,000	17,678	59.68	79.43	1.154	"	"	0.1036
60,000	18,288	54.24	72.19	1.049	"	"	0.0941

§ 10.2.1

is that, at any given temperature and altitude, the partial pressure is lower in saturated air than it is in dry air.

10.2.2 The effects of altitude

The supply of oxygen for tissue metabolism is one of the most critical requirements of human survival. Total lack of oxygen results in unconsciousness within about 1 min and death within about 10 min. A partial reduction of the oxygen supply results in a wide variety of physiological and psychological effects that depend on the amount of reduction and its duration.

BODY FUNCTIONS

Oxygen is supplied to the body by *external* respiration, which involves the exchange of gases between the blood in the lung capillaries and the external atmosphere, and by *internal* respiration, which is an exchange of gases between body-tissue cells and the blood. As illustrated in Fig. 10-4, the lungs may be represented as an open-loop exchanger-diffuser system, the volume of which is governed by the mechanics of respiration. In this illustration, the composition of air at sea level is shown

in terms of the partial pressures of those atmospheric components of major importance. Note that gases of higher partial pressure are transferred in the direction of those of lower partial pressures.

Because tissue metabolism is constantly consuming oxygen, the pO_2 in the tissue cells is less than that in the hemoglobin in which it is carried by the blood to the tissue cells. Similarly, the pO_2 is greater in the alveoli of the lungs and still greater in air. Thus, oxygen is transferred from the air to the lungs and then to the bloodstream for transport and transfer to the tissue cells. Conversely, water vapor produced by evaporation in the lungs and CO_2 produced in the tissue cells are transferred to the atmosphere. Nitrogen is physiologically inert, and this situation is shown as a symmetrical exchange at each point in Fig. 10-4. The major biological parameters of this process are the alveolar-oxygen pressure and the arterial-oxygen saturation.

The proportionate decrease in pO_2 in the atmosphere with increase in altitude results in a reduced rate of oxygen transfer between the atmosphere and the lungs and between the lungs and the bloodstream. The pressure of alveolar CO_2, however, decreases only slightly with altitude, and water vapor, which depends only on body temperature, maintains a constant pressure. Thus, as the total pressure in the lungs decreases, the volume of CO_2 and water vapor become proportionately larger at the expense of oxygen (and nitrogen). As alti-

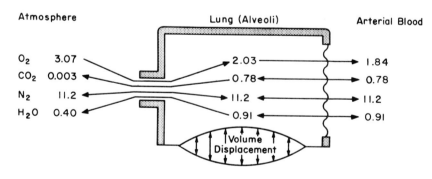

Atmosphere		Lung (Alveoli)	Arterial Blood
O_2	3.07	2.03	1.84
CO_2	0.003	0.78	0.78
N_2	11.2	11.2	11.2
H_2O	0.40	0.91	0.91

Volume Displacement

10-4 Lungs as exchanger-diffuser system. Values are partial pressures in psi. Volume displacement is indicated as fraction of total lung volume in resting state. pN_2 for each point is approximately equal. Alveolar pH_2O is saturated at lung temperature. Body temperature is 98.6° F (Taylor, 1951)

419

tude increases, pO_2 becomes increasingly reduced so that an altitude is eventually reached at which it is not possible, even by breathing 100% oxygen, to sustain life. This critical pressure altitude is about 44,800 ft.

Lung volume depends on the mechanics of respiration. As altitude is increased, the rate and volume of breathing increases. This is a positive adaptation (see article 10.1.1) that displaces the alveolar CO_2 and results in an increase in alveolar-oxygen pressure. This adaptation, however, is of negligible benefit above 10,000 ft; continued exposure to altitudes of up to 18,000 ft produce other adaptations that can permit living without supplemental oxygen at this altitude and, even, working a normal day at 19,000 ft. This type of adaptation is associated with an increase in the ability of the blood to carry oxygen, increased respiration rate, decreased blood pressure, and increased heart size and cardiac output, among other things.

OXYGEN DEFICIENCY (HYPOXIA)

Most altitude design problems arise because people are adapted to sea-level atmospheric pressure. The effects of gradual increases in altitude on arterial-oxygen saturation for such persons are shown in Fig. 10-5. This graph shows the tremendous gain made in tolerance while breathing oxygen, but, as indicated, the

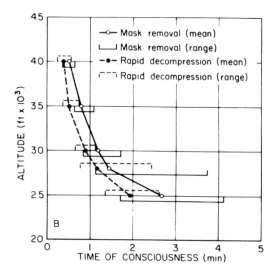

absolute upper limit, even with supplemental oxygen, is under 44,800 ft.

Hypoxia can be produced by gradual ascent or by sudden exposure, as might happen in the sudden loss of cabin pressure in a pressurized aircraft or the removal of an oxygen mask at high altitude. Figure 10-6 (Comfort and Wilson, 1950) shows the effect of sudden exposure on the duration of useful consciousness for an inactive person. With activity, the duration of consciousness decreases. Exercise sufficient to double pulmonary ventilation reduces consciousness time about 50%; tripling pulmonary ventilation reduces duration of consciousness about 67%.

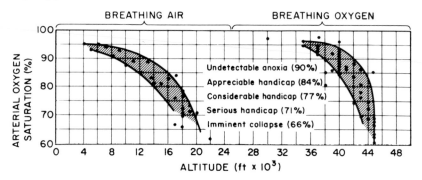

10-5 Effect of lack of oxygen at various altitudes. Lack of oxygen is represented in terms of oxygen saturation of arterial blood. Indifferent stage of 90% or more saturation extends to 12,500 ft while breathing air, and to 42,000 ft while breathing 100% oxygen. Critical stage of 66% or less saturation, in which person collapses after short exposure, begins at about 20,000 ft while breathing air and about 44,000 ft while breathing 100% oxygen (USAF, 1953a)

As someone approaches unconsciousness, he passes through a short phase of dizziness and disorientation, during which his efficiency is severely limited. Useful consciousness refers to that stage of the process that precedes this phase. The actual length of the useful period, aside from the upper limits shown in Fig. 10-6, are importantly determined by the physical and psychological condition of the person. Tasks for which the operator is highly trained or that require little effort or emotional response permit a longer useful consciousness.

decreased concentration of oxygen in the inspired air. Note that light sensitivity is impaired significantly at altitudes as low as about 5,000 ft, and, at 15,000 ft, more than twice as much light is required for minimum visibility.

Auditory sensitivity and speech reception also are affected by increases in altitude (see Chapters 3 and 4). Although a major portion of these effects is due to changes in the sound transmission properties of the air, there is some indication that both processes also are slightly affected during short exposures and

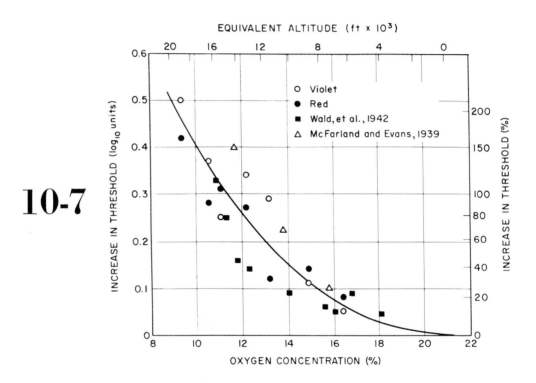

10-7

Major Sensory Effects

The most sensitive indicator of the effects of oxygen deficiency is loss of visual function. This is a general effect that manifests itself early as a loss in absolute sensitivity for light and in contrast sensitivity, both in central and peripheral vision (see Chapter 2). Figure 10-7 (Hecht, et al., 1946) shows how much the threshold of vision—the intensity of light just barely visible in total darkness—is increased as a function of increased altitude and

slightly more seriously affected as a result of long-term adaptation (Smith, 1946; Smith and Seitz, 1946; and Tonndorf, 1953).

Effects on Coordinative Skills

Tasks of complex coordination, such as handwriting, begin to deteriorate in quality above 10,000 ft (Kennedy, 1952). With greater altitudes, performance deteriorates progressively. Less complex tasks, such as pursuit and compensatory tracking (see Chapter 5), and reaction times begin to deteriorate importantly above 15,000–20,000 ft, depending on their complexity (Kennedy, 1952). Similar effects occur with sudden exposures as well, but, in addition, tremors of the eyelids, fingers, and other body parts occur at altitudes of 16,000 ft, and, with sudden exposure at still higher altitudes, muscular rigidity and cramping are frequent.

Effects on Intellectual Functions

Memory in its various forms and other intellectual functions, such as reading and arithmetical skills, might show deterioration at altitudes as low as 10,000 ft. With adaptation to this altitude, intellectual impairments might be prevented up to about 15,000 ft (Finan, et al., 1949).

A detailed review, in terms of the specific intellectual functions affected by altitude, can be found in McFarland (1932). As might be expected, the more complex memory tasks or problem-solving tasks tend to be the most sensitive to altitude.

Subjective and Emotional Effects

The physiological and psychological impairments described above might go completely unnoticed by the operator until he approaches collapse. This is true even though his performance is characterized by an inability to write legibly or to make even an approximate dial setting. In fact, all the time that he is deteriorating, he might experience a feeling of well-being and competence.

With increased oxygen deficiency, however, the person behaves in a manner similar to that of a man under the influence of alcohol: the hostile person becomes angry or irritable or sullen or indifferent, and the nonhostile person becomes exhilarated and boisterous, and, in both types, the capacity for self-criticism is strikingly absent. These emotional symptoms first begin to appear in most unadapted persons at 16,000–18,000 ft, and they are accentuated as the altitude increases (McFarland, 1932).

Biophysical Relationships

The partial pressure of alveolar oxygen is described by the following formula:

$$pO_2 = fO_2(P - pH_2O)$$
$$- pCO_2\left(fO_2 + \frac{1 - fO_2}{RQ}\right), \quad (10\text{-}1)$$

where fO_2 is the volumetric fraction of oxygen in dry inspired air (vol %), P is the barometric pressure (psi), pH_2O and pCO_2 are the partial pressures of water vapor and CO_2 in alveolar air (psi), and RQ is the respiratory quotient, qCO_2/qO_2, in which q is the volume rate.

Figure 10-8 shows pO_2, fO_2 and pCO_2 as a function of barometric pressure. This graph illustrates that, up to the value of P at which RQ, fO_2, and pCO_2 remain constant, pO_2 is related to P by Equation 10-1. Below a barometric pressure of 10.10 psi (10,000 ft), the increased volume and rate of respiration increases pO_2 and decreases pCO_2 so that the three measures depart from what would be expected from Equation 10-1.

By increasing the oxygen fraction in the inspired air, the decrease in pO_2 can be overcome so that all the properties of alveolar air

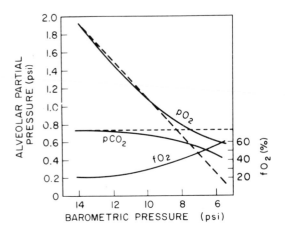

10-8 Alveolar partial pressures. Dotted curves are theoretical; solid curves are from experimental data. The fO_2 is that calculated to preserve sea-level alveolar pO_2 (Carpenter, 1948)

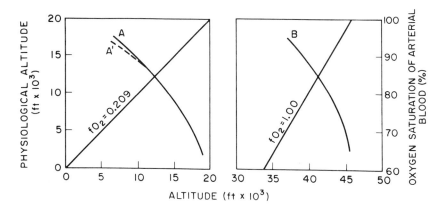

10-9 Relationship between alveolar composition and arterial oxygen saturation. Physiological altitude, based on alveolar pO_2 and pCO_2, is related to true altitude by two fO_2 parameters—air ($fO_2 = 0.209$) and 100% oxygen ($fO_2 = 1.00$). Curves A and B are means of oxygen saturation of arterial blood (like those of Fig. 10-5). Curve A' was obtained from oxyhemoglobin dissociation curve (Taylor, 1951)

are maintained at any desired level. This can be achieved by solving Equation 10-1 for fO_2, using appropriate constants, as follows:

$$fO_2 = \frac{pO_2 + pCO_2/RQ}{P - pH_2O - pCO_2 + pCO_2/RQ}.$$

$$(10\text{-}2)$$

Relationships and values for alveolar pressures and arterial saturations are given in Fig. 10-9. Values for fO_2 and pO_2 are given in Fig. 10-8.

Using Equation 10-2 permits setting the desired alveolar condition, which is expressed as equivalent altitude pressure, called physiological altitude. Table 10-4 presents examples of how oxygen supplementation computed with the aid of Equation 10-2 can be used to obtain specific physiological altitudes, i.e., combinations of pO_2 and pCO_2. As shown in Fig. 10-9, either pO_2 or arterial oxygen saturation can be used as the basis for determining the oxygen supplementation required for any given physiological altitude. In a similar way, the equivalent physiological altitude desired to offset any specific effect can be obtained by using the minimum altitude at which the effect occurs and relating it to the required alveolar condition.

Table 10-4   Interrelationships Among Oxygen Supply, Alveolar Conditions, and True and Physiological Altitudes *

True altitude (ft)	Atmospheric pressure (psi)	fO_2	Alveolar pressure (psi)			Arterial saturation (%)	Physiological altitude (ft)
			pO_2	pH_2O	pCO_2		
0	14.7	0.21	1.99	0.91	0.77	95	0
8,000	10.9	0.21	1.29	0.91	0.70	91	8,000
33,000	3.8	1.00	1.99	0.91	0.77	95	0
38,000	3.0	1.00	1.29	0.91	0.70	91	8,000

* Taylor, 1951.

§ 10.2.2

BAROMETRIC-PRESSURE PAIN

In addition to producing an alveolar-oxygen deficiency with increases in altitude, other effects associated with changes in barometric pressure are important. These effects, called barometric-pressure pains or dysbarism, are associated with the expansion of gases trapped in body cavities (trapped-gas syndromes) and with the liberation of gas bubbles (primarily nitrogen) from the blood (evolved-gas syndromes) and the resultant formation of free gas bubbles in the blood and cell tissues.

Trapped-Gas Syndromes

Figure 10-10 (Lovelace and Hinshaw, 1942) illustrates the expansion of gases in body cavities at different altitudes. The most sensitive body areas that experience this effect are the middle ear, the sinuses, and the abdominal cavity. The pain from any of these areas can be very intense.

Abdominal pain results from a reduction in total pressure with altitude that permits expansion of abdominal gases. This effect is rarely experienced below 25,000 ft, and can be relieved by the oral and anal emission of gases. Middle ear and sinus discomfort, on the other hand, occur during descent and are the result of gas escapes during ascent that cannot be recovered easily during descent. Thus, these pains are associated with external pressures rather than internal ones.

Evolved-Gas Syndromes

Evolved-gas syndromes, also called decompression sickness or aeroembolism, are generally more serious conditions than trapped-gas syndromes and include such maladies as the "bends," "chokes," central-nervous-system collapse, and circulatory-system collapse. These effects are the result of nitrogen bubbles that come out of solution in the body fluids when atmospheric pressure is decreased.

At sea-level pressure, it has been estimated that the body fluids hold 800–1200 cm³ of nitrogen in solution; at 34,000 ft, where the barometric pressure is 25% of that at sea level, the body must lose 600–900 cm³. If the ascent has been slow enough, the gas might escape via the lungs. If the ascent is too rapid, however, the gas is liberated too quickly and forms bubbles in the tissues and blood. The critical rate of ascent depends on the altitude—the greater the altitude, the slower the rate required—and it varies among different people (values as low as 78 ft/min have been reported as dangerous).

PROTECTION AGAINST ALTITUDE

Denitrogenation up to practical limits can be achieved for most people by breathing 100% oxygen prior to or during the ascent. It is standard practice for military high-altitude flight to breathe pure oxygen from the ground up.

The longer 100% oxygen is breathed prior to the flight, however, the greater the protection obtained. In one USAF experiment involving 251 cadets, breathing 100% oxygen for 45 min prior to a 2-hr flight at 38,000 ft

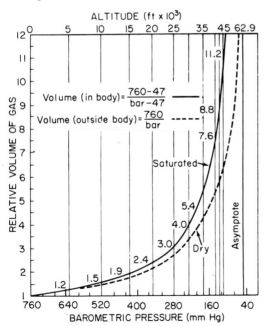

10-10

Table 10-5 Approximate Amount of Nitrogen Eliminated from the Body of a Resting Subject Breathing Pure Oxygen

Time (min)	Nitrogen eliminated (cc)
15	250
30	350
45	480
60	550
75	650
90	700
120	850
150	950
180	1050
210	1150
240	1200

dents had occurred at altitudes above 30,000 ft, and if the pilots had flown the same flight paths, it is apparent that the situation would have been very serious.

Engineering requirements are often expressed in terms of supplemental oxygen and cabin pressurization. The supplemental oxygen required to maintain the desired alveolar conditions can be determined theoretically with Equation 10-2. Actually, in practice, a richer oxygen supply than is indicated by this equation is usual. Thus, 100% oxygen is supplied at 30,000 ft, rather than at 33,000 ft, as would be demanded by the above-mentioned equation.

The type of supply used up to 30,000 ft is a demand system that supplies oxygen periodically in response to a valve controlled by

reduced severe symptoms from 30.3% to 5.8%. It is now recommended that a period of denitrogenation precede all high altitude flights (Scarpelli, 1958).

Table 10-5 shows the approximate amount of nitrogen that is eliminated from the body while breathing pure oxygen. Complete elimination of nitrogen from the body is not necessary to achieve adequate protection from the "bends" and other evolved-gas syndromes. After 60 min, about 46% of the nitrogen is eliminated, and, for all practical purposes, this 1-hr "prebreathing" period has been found to provide adequate protection for personnel undergoing altitude-chamber flights at simulated altitudes of up to 75,000 ft while wearing pressure suits.

In high-altitude and space flight in small, pressurized cockpits or satellite capsules, pressure suits are worn to provide protection against the inadvertent loss of cabin pressure. The inadvertent loss of cabin pressure at high altitudes without pressure suits requires the immediate return to a safe physiological altitude because the time of useful consciousness is so short (see Fig. 10-6). Figure 10-11 (McFarland, 1953) shows the actual flight paths taken by three commercial aircraft following accidents in which cabin pressure was lost during flight. If these same three acci-

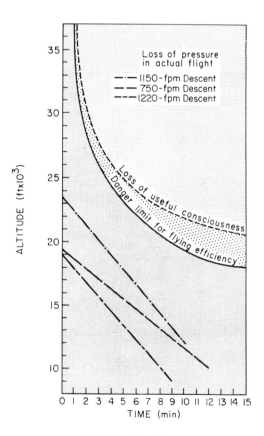

10-11

the breathing. Table 10-4 shows that, for zero physiological altitude, compensatory oxygen supplied by demand is effective up to 33,000 ft, and, for a physiological altitude of 8,000 ft, it is effective only up to 38,000 ft. Thus, at some altitude above 30,000 ft, it is necessary to supplement demand flow with positive-pressure flow. Recommended limits for the use of the two systems are indicated in Table 10-6.

The pressurized cabin represents the ideal solution to all altitude problems, but it is offset by disadvantages of weight, power requirements, and risks of explosive decompression. For very high altitudes, complete pressurization is a necessity. In other situations it is possible to compromise between physiological requirements and engineering penalties. For example, Fig. 10-12 shows cabin pressure expressed as the differential (d) between cabin and flight pressures used for different types of aircraft. Variations from one aircraft to another depend on cabin size, which affects the risk of explosive decompression, and flight routines. Table 10-7 shows actual pressure differentials for major U. S. passenger aircraft.

Table 10-6 Major Effects of Altitude Without Supplemental Oxygen or Pressurization, Approximate Time of Consciousness, and Recommended Altitude Limits for Various Situations *

Altitude (ft)	Major effects	Approx. time of consciousness (sec)	Recommended limits
5,000	Loss of central night vision initiated	—	
8,000		—	Begin supplemental oxygen for routine flights
10,000	Loss of peripheral night vision, complex coordination, orientation, hearing, memory, and intellectual skills initiated	—	Maximum without supplemental oxygen in routine situation
15,000	Loss of tracking skills and reaction (decision) time initiated	—	
16,000	Loss of emotional control initiated	—	
17,000	Loss of simple coordination and vision initiated	—	
18,000		—	Maximum without supplemental oxygen in emergency
20,000		—	Begin cabin pressurization for routine flights
23,000	Decompression sickness initiated	—	
25,000		116	
28,000		69	Maximum without cabin pressurization
30,000		54	Begin positive-pressure breathing for routine flights
35,000		32	Maximum for demand oxygen in routine situation
40,000		23	
42,000			Maximum for positive-pressure breathing in routine situation Maximum for cabin pressurization
43,000			Maximum for demand oxygen in emergency
45,000			Maximum for positive-pressure breathing in emergency Begin use of pressure suit

* Cornell, 1958.

§ 10.2.2

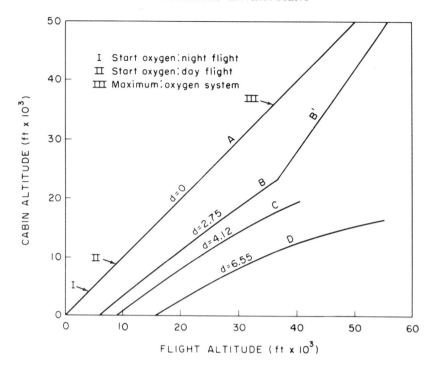

10-12 Oxygen and pressurization standards for aircraft. Curve A is for unpressurized aircraft; curves B and B' are for fighter aircraft (d = 2.75 to 37,000 ft, then changes to 2.3 to avoid dangerous explosive decompression); curve C is for commercial aircraft; and curve D is for bomber aircraft (Taylor, 1951)

Table 10-7 Differential Between Cabin and Flight Pressure in Major U. S. Passenger Aircraft [1]

Aircraft	Operating altitude (ft)			Cabin altitude[2] (ft)	Differential pressure (psi)
	Cruising	Ceiling	Maximum		
Boeing 377		25,000		5,500	6.55
Boeing 707	35,000	40,000	45,000	5,000–8,000	8.6
Boeing 720	25,000	40,000	45,000	4,000–7,000	8.6
Convair 240	8,000		16,000	0–6,000	3.75
Convair 340	9,000	16,000	17,000	0–6,000	4.16
Convair 440	9,000	14,000	20,000	0–8,000	4.16
Convair 880	21,000	35,000	40,000	0–8,000	8.2
Douglas DC-6	18,000	20,000	25,000	6,000–11,300	4.16
Douglas DC-7	22,000			6,000	5.4
Douglas DC-8	35,000	40,000	45,000	5,000–8,000	8.6
Lockheed Constellation		20,000		8,000	4.07
Lockheed Super G		20,000		5,000	5.36
Lockheed Electra		25,000	30,000	5,000–8,000	6.55

[1] American College of Chest Physicians, 1960.
[2] Range indicates cabin altitude at lowest to highest operating altitude shown.

10.2.3 *The effects of temperature and humidity*

Man's internal heat regulatory mechanisms tend to keep his body at a constant temperature of about 98.6° F. Normally, the body is losing heat constantly through the lungs and skin, but, if the person needs to lose more heat to maintain constant body temperature, either because he is producing too much heat or because his environment gets too hot, his regulatory mechanisms come into play to increase the heat loss.

The regulatory mechanisms include dilation of the blood vessels of the skin (bringing more blood near the surface of the skin) and perspiration, which increases heat loss through vaporization. Conversely, if the person's environment cools, and he needs to conserve heat, perspiration stops, and the blood vessels constrict. In addition, if the cold becomes extreme, reflex shivering causes more heat to be produced.

This, briefly, is the way in which regulatory mechanisms maintain body temperature. It explains in part some of the reactions of man to heat and humidity in his environment as well as to exposure to extreme cold. Before we discuss this subject more thoroughly, however, a few of the terms to be used should be explained. These terms and their explanations are as follows:

a. Temperature. The terms temperature, air temperature, ambient air temperature, and *dry-bulb* temperature are all synonymous.

b. *Wet-bulb* temperature. This is the temperature obtained when the thermometer bulb is cooled by the rapid evaporation of water by air moving at a velocity of 900 ft/min (fpm). Wet-bulb temperature varies with humidity and is the same as dry-bulb temperature when the humidity is 100%.

c. Humidity. The terms humidity, *absolute humidity,* and moisture content are synonymous and refer to the amount of water vapor in a given quantity of air.

d. *Relative humidity* (RH). This is the ratio between absolute humidity and the saturation value at a given temperature expressed in percent (%). When a quantity of air holds all the water vapor it can, it is said to be saturated and the humidity is 100%. The amount required for saturation increases with dry-bulb temperature.

BODY FUNCTIONS

The body exchanges heat with the external environment by radiation, convection, conduction, and evaporation. With these four methods, sedentary people who are conventionally dressed for the season of the year can maintain thermal balance if the temperature is 70–80° F at 45% relative humidity. These are the conditions under which most people report the most comfort.

Below about 75° F for the normally clothed person and below about 85° F for the lightly clothed one, evaporative losses are slight, and those that occur are due to evaporation from the relatively dry skin and to respiration. Above these temperatures, thermal balance is maintained by the evaporation of perspiration. At 95–100° F, radiation and convection exchanges change direction; at slightly higher temperatures, evaporative heat losses fail to take care of the rate of heat production, and body temperature begins to rise.

The internal temperature of the body is a summation of the external heat exchanges and internal heat production. A dual mechanism, triggered by the temperature sensors of the skin and controlled in the brain by the hypothalamus, regulates body temperature. This dual mechanism is the regulation of internal heat-producing metabolic activities and the regulation of external heat loss through automatic variation in the rate of blood flow to the skin and the operation of the sweat glands. The major elements in the process are shown in Fig. 10-13 (Du Bois, 1941).

Under resting (basal) conditions, only slight thermoregulatory activity is required to maintain the heat balance. If the load on either side of the balance is increased by, for example, moderate exercise, which increases heat production, or by exposure to a cooler environment, which increases heat loss, an adjustment is made automatically on the other side of the balance.

The summation of heat exchanges shown in Fig. 10-13 can be expressed in terms of a basic heat-balance equation as follows:

$$M + S = H_r + H_d + H_c + H_v, \quad (10\text{-}3)$$

where: M = energy metabolism or body-heat production,
S = body-heat storage,
H_r = radiative heat exchange,
H_d = conductive heat exchange,
H_c = convective heat exchange, and
H_v = evaporative heat exchange.

Terms on the right are positive when heat flow is toward the environment and negative when it is away from the environment. The equation shows that thermal balance is obtained when the total heat production and storage of the body is equal to the total exchange of heat of the body with the environment.

Biological Response to Cold

The immediate thermoregulatory activities of the body depend on whether the body is being heated or cooled. The first response on being cooled is a constriction of the blood vessels (vasoconstriction), which keeps the warm blood away from the surface of the body. The result is a progressive cooling of

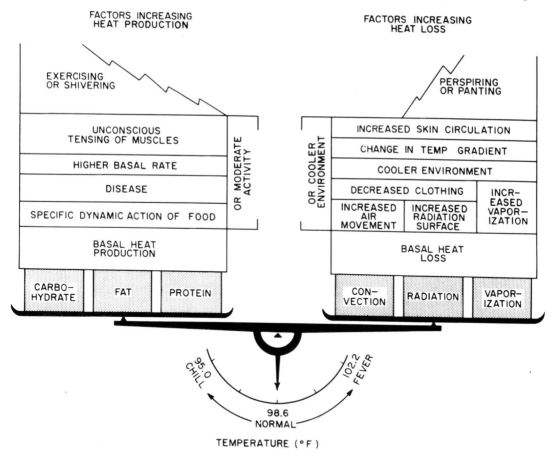

10-13

the body surface and, therefore, a decrease in the amount of heat lost to the air.

The relative blood flow to the extremities accompanying vasoconstriction is reduced to a much greater extent than to other body areas. As a mechanism for reducing heat loss, this is efficient because normal blood flow is high relative to the volumes of the extremities. Once the extremities have been cooled, however, the mechanism for reducing heat loss is a handicap because then it is very difficult to resume blood flow to the extremities without rewarming the body completely.

The second response on being cooled is shivering, first insensibly, then sensibly, and, later, violently. Shivering is an involuntary muscular action that adds enough to the metabolic heat production to prevent or reduce further heat loss, but it is never sufficient to replace heat already lost nor is it as effective as voluntary exercise.

Biological Response to Heat

As the body is heated, the skin blood vessels expand (vasodilation) and the output of the heart decreases. As a result, there is an increase in blood flow to the skin, a convective process which carries heat from the internal parts to the outside of the body where it is lost by radiation and convection. When the temperature of the environment becomes higher than that of the skin, the direction of the radiation and convection is reversed, and the body would begin to gain heat if it were not that, at this point, the perspiration rate increases.

Heat, in the form of water vapor is lost by the body at all times through the skin and by breathing. Usually, these vapors are not visible (insensible water loss) although expired vapor can be seen in cold weather, and, in very cold weather, the hands "steam."

In the cold, insensible water loss is non-adaptive because its effect is a loss of body heat. On the other hand, in the heat, or, at least, when the body is not being cooled, insensible water loss is an important part of the maintenance of the thermal balance; the total normal loss is almost one liter of water a day, which is about one-fourth of the resting (basal) heat production. In very hot environments and with exercise, as much as three liters can be lost in an hour (Buskirk and Bass, 1957). Only perspiration that evaporates, however, reduces body heat; perspiration that is held by clothing or that drips off the body without evaporating does not contribute to the heat loss.

Biologial Response to Change

The self-regulating characteristics of the body's thermal control are similar to the general characteristics of any feedback control system. Changed inputs do not result in immediate, errorless, corrective actions. Instead, the thermal output of the body resembles an initially underdamped oscillation or "hunting reaction" followed by a second critically damped response. This is illustrated in Fig. 10-14 (Hutchinson, 1942) in terms of the feeling of warmth and cold of a person exposed to a changed environment following adaptation to a previous one.

Initially, in Fig. 10-14, the person's body is in heat balance (A), and his thermal experience is slightly warmer than would be indicated by the ambient conditions. He then is exposed to a warmer environment, and there is an initial overreaction (B) during which he feels excessively warm. This feeling dissipates rapidly as the body cools in the direction of balance with the new conditions. This period is followed by one of adjustment (C) that ends in equilibrium (D), as a result of which he feels slightly cooler than the ambient temperature would indicate. If the air temperature is lowered, he overcompensates

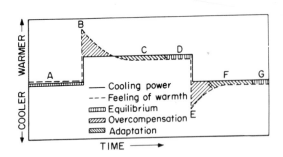

§ 10.2.3

again (E) and feels excessively cool, and then, gradually, he comes into balance with the new conditions (F and G).

HEAT STRESS

As thermoregulation fails and body-heat storage increases, a person can become disabled. In order of increasing severity, the disability might take the form of heat cramps, heat exhaustion, or heat stroke. These forms of disability might follow each other or they might overlap. The stress imposed is mainly the result of the body's inability to achieve a sufficiently high rate of evaporation by perspiration.

If conductive heat exchanges are ignored, the heat-balance equation (Equation 10-3) may be expressed in terms of the amount of perspiration theoretically required to maintain balance in any environment, as follows:

$$M + H_r + H_c = E_{req}, \qquad (10\text{-}4)$$

where E_{req} is the evaporation rate required to maintain thermal balance. For the purpose of this equation, M can be obtained from the table of estimates of energy metabolism of various types of activity in the Heating, Ventilating, and Air Conditioning Guide (ASHAE, 1960). Both H_r and H_c can be estimated with heat-exchange equations using appropriate constants given in the ASHAE Guide.

In relatively dry air, water losses through perspiring will be equal to E_{req}; in relatively humid air, when evaporation is limited, perspiration exceeds E_{req} and does not evaporate. The body then becomes completely wet, and a maximum rate of cooling is established that is not increased regardless of how much more perspiring occurs.

The maximum conditions under which heat balance can be maintained can be estimated, in terms of M, skin temperature, and the thermal properties of the environment, which determine H_r and H_c, by the following equation:

$$M + 22(t_w - t_s) + 2\sqrt{V}(t_w - t_s)$$
$$= 10 V^{0.4}(P_s - P_a), \quad (10\text{-}5)$$

where: t_w = mean radiant temperature or black-body equivalent (°F),

t_s = mean body-area-weighted skin temperature,

V = effective air velocity (ft/min),

P_s = vapor pressure of H_2O at skin temperature (mmHg), and

P_a = partial pressure of H_2O in air (mmHg).

The Heat-Stress Index

Equation 10-5 is used as the basis for developing the heat-stress index (HSI). This index is defined as the ratio of E_{req} to E_{max}, where any set of environmental conditions that produces E_{max} is arbitrarily given an HSI of 100, i.e.:

$$\text{HSI} = 100 \, \frac{E_{req}}{E_{max} < 2400}. \quad (10\text{-}6)$$

If a globe thermometer is used, both air temperature and mean radiant temperature can be expressed as a single value. If this value is known, and if M, wet- and dry-bulb temperatures, and air velocity are known, the HSI can be determined quickly by means of the flow charts for determining heat-stress-index values in the Heating, Ventilating, and Air Conditioning Guide (ASHAE, 1960).

The HSI is based on two criteria selected to represent the limit of safe, prolonged heat stress: body-heat storage is not to exceed a limit represented by an average skin temperature of 95° F, and perspiration rate is not to exceed 1 liter/hr (E_{max}), a rate that is equivalent to an evaporative heat loss of 2,400 Btu/hr. These criteria may be used as the maximum perspiration rate required to maintain thermal balance that can be tolerated by young, adapted men for a normal 8-hr work day.

The environmental control required to achieve any desired HSI requires a consideration of the human heat loads imposed on the environment by radiation, convection, and evaporation for a variety of activities and en-

§ 10.2.3

431

vironmental conditions. These requirements can be established for working and resting conditions over an 8-hr period from data presented in the Heating, Ventilating, and Air Conditioning Guide (ASHAE, 1960). Tolerance limits for shorter exposures are not well-developed, but they can be estimated, roughly, from Fig. 10-15 (Blockley, et al., 1954).

The Effective-Temperature Index

The data in the ASHAE Guide are expressed in terms of effective temperature (ET). This is an empirical thermal index in wide use that expresses the combined effect of air temperature, humidity, and air movement in terms of the subjective feeling of warmth. In an environment where the air is completely saturated (RH = 100%) and the air velocity is zero, the ET is defined as the value of the air temperature. Combinations of temperature, humidity, and air velocity that produce the same subjective feelings of warmth are assigned the same ET value. This index, therefore, provides a simple method of expressing a variety of environmental conditions along a single dimension and includes the human factor in the expression.

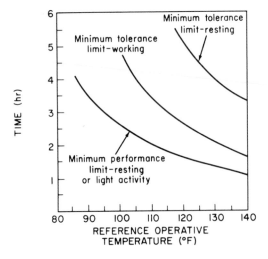

10-15

Figure 10-15 shows that human performances requiring only light physical activity are more susceptible to heat stress than are other performances. In general, losses in these performances tend to be initiated at 84° ET for exposures of ½–1 hr. There is some reason to believe that, at least at the level of these small losses, performance might be maintained through the introduction of artificial alerting signals, variation of task requirements, or other techniques that tend to maintain the alertness level of the operator (Mackworth, 1950; Pepler, 1958; and Teichner, 1959).

Adaptation and Habituation to Heat

Heat adaptation begins immediately upon exposure, progresses with continued exposure, and is highly developed in 4–7 days. Heat adaptation depends importantly on activity and, for active people, can be induced by short exercise periods in the heat; inactive people show only slight adaptation, regardless of exposure. Heat adaptation to severe conditions facilitates effort at less severe conditions as well as to other kinds of equally severe environments. For example, adaptation to a hot-dry environment increases the ability to work in a hot-wet environment (Buskirk and Bass, 1957).

Adaptation can be maintained at a high level for about two weeks after the person is removed from the heat. Beyond this period, adaptation decreases so that, after about two months, most of it is gone (Buskirk and Bass, 1957). Thus, if it is necessary to remain adapted to heat, re-exposure at two-week intervals is necessary.

Air Conditioning

Ideal air conditioning is represented by conditions in which thermal comfort is obtained, and environments in which thermal balance is maintained with minimum physiological regulation correspond approximately to those in which comfort is greatest. Because thermal balance depends on such factors as previous exposure conditions, clothing, and activity, no universally fixed comfort range can be stated. The comfort charts in the Heating, Ventilating, and Air Conditioning Guide (ASHAE, 1960) present values for ideal comfort in terms of air-conditioning variables and in terms of the expected proportion of people (in the United States) wearing indoor clothing and engaged in sedentary work during summer and winter seasons. These charts show that, in general, people are comfortable when the air temperature is between 73 and 77° F, relative humidity is between 25 and 60%, and air velocity is uniform around 25 ft/min, regardless of the season.

COLD STRESS

Maintaining thermal balance under cold conditions involves an optimum balance of clothing insulation and activity (heat production). Figure 10-16 can be used to estimate optimum combinations. The unit of insulation

used, the clo, is defined as the insulation necessary to maintain comfort in a motionless, sitting man whose skin temperature is 33° C and whose total rate of heat loss is 38 cal/m²/hr for ambient conditions of 21° C, 50% relative humidity, and air movement of 20 ft/min. More specifically, 1 clo = 0.18° C/cal/m²/hr.

Because, under extreme conditions, clothing does not prevent the loss of body heat but merely reduces the rate of heat loss, the duration of exposure for various conditions of clothing, activity, air movement, and air temperature must be taken into account. Table 10-8 provides data on a variety of such conditions for prolonged exposures, and Table 10-9 provides similar data for 1-hr exposures.

The Windchill Index

No general index, such as effective temperature (ET), is available for expressing all of

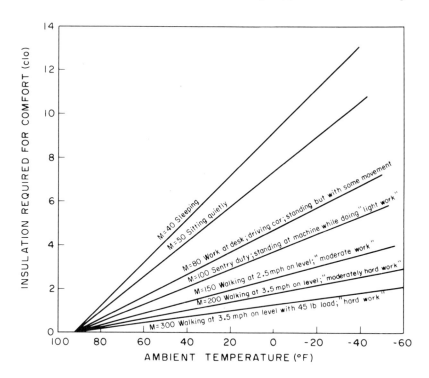

10-16 Prediction of total insulation required for prolonged comfort at various activities in the shade as a function of ambient temperature. M is heat production in cal/m²/hr (Belding, 1949)

Table 10-8 Estimates of Time for Maximum Safe Loss of Stored Body Heat in Cold Environments at Various Rates of Motion [1,2]

		Time for max. safe loss of stored body heat (hr)					
		Environment at 0° C			Environment at −40° C		
Effective insulation (clo[3])	Air movement (ft/min)	Body at rest	Walking 3 mi/hr	Walking 4 mi/hr	Body at rest	Walking 3 mi/hr	Walking 4 mi/hr
1	4,000	0.58	1.10	11.20	0.22	0.27	0.34
1	100	0.73	1.90	indef.	0.27	0.34	0.44
2	4,000	1.15	indef.[4]	indef.[5]	0.48	0.78	1.60
2	100	1.17	indef.	indef.	0.53	0.90	2.10
3	4,000	3.30	indef.	indef.	0.80	2.20	indef.[6]
3	100	3.80	indef.	indef.	0.85	2.50	indef.
4	4,000	8.80	indef.	indef.	1.20	21.0	indef.
4	100	10.80	indef.	indef.	1.30	57.0	indef.

[1] Spector, 1956.
[2] Estimated safe loss of stored body heat by an adult is 80 cal/m^2 of body surface.
[3] See definition of this unit in text.
[4] Complete protection given by 1.2–1.7 clo of effective insulation.
[5] Complete protection given by 0.6–1.1 clo of effective insulation.
[6] Complete protection given by 2.6–2.7 clo of effective insulation.

Table 10-9 Predicted Lowest Ambient Temperatures for 1-hr Exposure and for Prolonged Thermal Equilibrium in Various Stages of Attire [1,2]

	Environment			Predicted lowest ambient temperatures (° C)					
				Exposure of 1 hr			Thermal equilibrium		
Activity	Wind (mph)	Sun or shade	Altitude (ft)	Nude	Normal attire[3]	Heavy attire[4]	Nude	Normal attire[3]	Heavy attire[4]
Sitting[5]	0	Shade	0	17	−4	−67	27	21	0
Running[6]	5	Shade	0	10	−27	−138	14	−15	−104
Sitting[5]	5	Sun[7]	0	19	−1	−48	23	17	−7
Walking[8]	5	Shade	0	20	−3	−72	25	10	−34
Standing[9]	5	Shade	0	25	4	−56	29	20	−6
Sitting[5]	5	Shade	0	26	4	−55	30	24	4
Sitting[5]	25	Shade	0	28	12	−36	31	26	10
Sitting[5]	5	Sun[7]	20,000[10]	8	−19	−111	13	4	−32

[1] Spector, 1956.
[2] Values are approximations for young, adult males.
[3] Business suit; effective insulation is 1 clo.
[4] Arctic clothing; effective insulation is 4 clo.
[5] Body at rest; $M = 50$.
[6] At 6.2 mph; $M = 440$.
[7] Absorbed solar heat (S) becomes part of H in basic formula; $S = 130$ for nude, $S = 13.75$ for normal attire, $S = 16$ for heavy attire.
[8] At 3.7 mph; $M = 180$.
[9] Performing light work; $M = 80$.
[10] Because of the greater intensity of solar radiation at the higher altitude, the value of S increases 70%.

the factors involved in cold exposure, but the Windchill Index is a commonly used scale for expressing the severity of cold environments. This index is an empirical expression for the total cooling power of the environment, and, although it is not based on human cooling and is probably not even very accurate as an expression of physical cooling, it has come into use as a single-value, practical guide to the severity of temperature-wind combinations.

dexterity, can be expected to deteriorate when men are exposed to air temperatures below 60° F, especially if the airspeed exceeds 5 mph (Teichner, 1957 and Teichner, 1958). Such deterioration can be expected even if the operators are appropriately dressed and in approximate thermal balance. For unhabituated men, the loss in performance is dependent on the physiological effects of the environment, on the distractions provided by the sounds of moving air, and on other events that

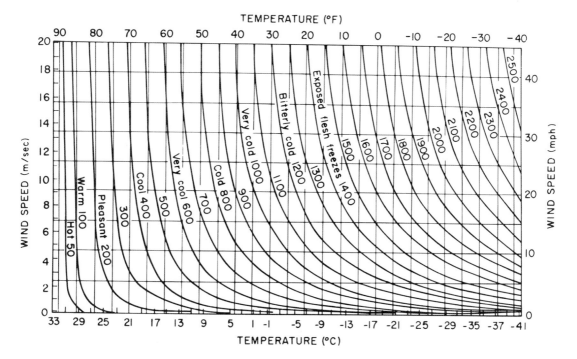

10-17 Windchill chart. Numbers on curves represent windchill in kg-cal/m²/hr (Falkowski and Hastings, 1958)

Figure 10-17 is a Windchill chart. It may be used as a guide to the severity of exposure conditions for men who are appropriately dressed and not wearing heated garments. Under bright, sunny conditions, the values on the chart should be reduced about 200 kg-cal.

The Numbness Index

Reaction time and skilled motor performances, such as tracking and tasks of manual

indicate to them that they are in the cold (Teichner, 1957).

The direct effects of cooling on the temperature of the skin and the viscosity of fluids in the joints reduces manual dexterity and the sensitivity of the skin to stimulation (Le Blanc, 1956). Figure 10-18 (Teichner, 1959) shows tactile sensitivity, simple visual reaction time, and manual skill as they are affected by cold exposure for unadapted, unhabituated, but appropriately dressed men. Figure 10-19 (Mackworth, 1953) presents

§ 10.2.3

the Numbness Index, a measure of tactile sensitivity in terms of the size of gap that is detectable when the skin is stimulated at two points that are close together. The Numbness Index of Fig. 10-19 is for 3-min exposures of the skin to varying air temperatures and

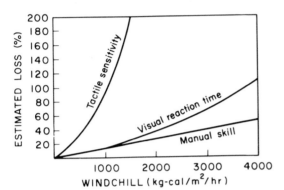

10-18

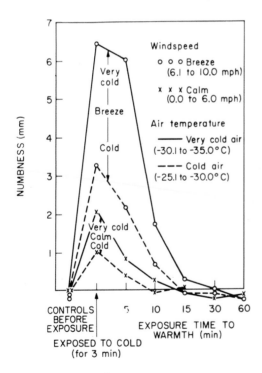

10-19

velocities. This graph shows the tremendous loss in sensitivity accompanying exposure and the slow recovery following it.

10.2.4 The effects of contaminants and toxicity

All atmospheric contaminants are toxic if introduced into the body in amounts greater than some threshold value, but, even for amounts that might be subthreshold, contaminants are toxic if present in the body in abnormal concentrations or states. Thus, any substance can be a poison under appropriate conditions, including substances that are normally present in the body. For this reason, it is not possible to select any particular biological parameter for relation to engineering variables. Each substance must be treated in terms of its own threshold value and its bodily effects. In all cases, both concentration and time of exposure are the critical conditions.

CARBON DIOXIDE

Most atmospheric contaminants result from industrial or automotive processes and are, therefore, subject to engineering control. An exception is carbon dioxide (CO_2), which might be an industrial residue but which also is introduced into the air as a product of body metabolism.

The relationships of alveolar and arterial CO_2 to respiration and oxygen supply were discussed in article 10.2.2. It was seen there that the physiological function of CO_2 is as a respiratory stimulant and circulatory regulator of the oxygen supply to the brain. Because this is so, CO_2 has been used as a stimulant for emergency medical purposes. The short-term physiological effects of CO_2 exposure are expressed in the time-concentration curve shown in Fig. 10-20 (Aero Medical Assoc., 1953), which uses unconsciousness as a criterion.

§ 10.2.4

Chronic or long-term exposure to even small quantities of CO_2, on the other hand, produces alterations in these physiological functions and slightly larger quantities produce performance decrements (Schaefer, 1961). Using the acid-base balance of the blood (compensation for respiratory acidosis) as a criterion for physiological adaptation to CO_2 exposure, a time-concentration curve has been developed on which tolerance criteria for long-term exposure are expressed. This curve is shown in Fig. 10-21, from which it can be seen that 1.5% is a lower limit of safety against long-term physiological effects even though performance decrements do not begin until a concentration of 3% is maintained for about six days. On this basis, for prolonged, continuous exposure, a maximum concentration of about 1% is recommended (Schaefer, 1960).

Engineering control of CO_2 by ventilation depends on the size of the space to be ventilated, the number of occupants in the space, the rate of production of CO_2 (which depends on exercise level), time, and the volumetric concentration of CO_2 in the ventilating air. At sea level, air usually contains 0.03% CO_2. The oxygen consumption of a normal adult male is 0.74 ft^3/hr, and his CO_2 production with light activity is 0.61 ft^3/hr. Ideal engineering control is one that achieves a steady-state ventilating rate that maintains the CO_2 concentration below the maximum allowable.

Figure 10-22 presents the effect of ventilation rates on CO_2 removal and oxygen replenishment. This graph shows that very low ventilating rates are adequate to maintain CO_2 within the maximum allowable concentration. Thus, under ideal conditions, ventilation for CO_2 removal is a minor problem at best. If other sources of CO_2 are present, and if body odors and the like are to be removed, the required rate of ventilation is 2.5 times that shown in Fig. 10-22.

CARBON MONOXIDE

Carbon monoxide (CO) is odorless and, therefore, cannot be detected by the human sense of smell. It is present in the atmosphere

§ 10.2.4

as a result of incomplete combustion almost everywhere that people are found but especially in industrialized areas. Further, it is easily taken up by the body, which loses it very slowly. Of all atmospheric contaminants, CO is considered, normally, the most important because of the universality of its presence

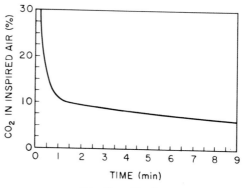

10-20

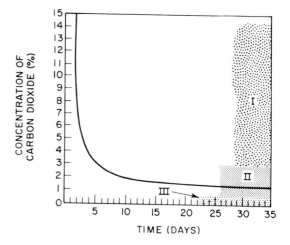

10-21 Time-concentration curve for adaptation to CO_2. Curve is based on human and animal experiments. Tolerance limits for chronic CO_2 toxicity for three levels of activity are as follows: I (3% CO_2 and above) performance deterioration, alterations in physiological functions, but (finally) adaptation; II (1.5–3% CO_2) no change in performance, basic physiological functions, or long-range adaptation processes; III (0–1.5% CO_2) no adaptation (Schaefer, 1961)

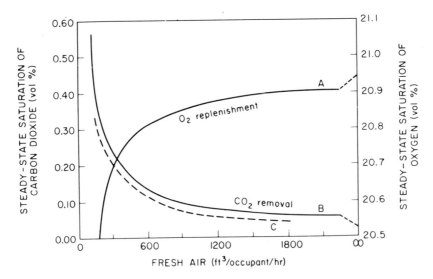

10-22 Steady-state concentrations of oxygen and CO2 per occupant as function of fresh-air ventilation. Curves A and B determined by calculation; curve C experimentally determined by Yaglou, Riley, and Coggins (Taylor, 1951)

and the seriousness of its effects. Major sources of CO are water gas (40%), industrial blast furnaces (30%), artificial illumination gas (25%), gasoline-engine exhaust and incomplete combustions in the home (7%), and coal gas (5%). Tobacco smoke also is an important source; about 1.0–2.5% of the total volume of the smoke of a cigarette is CO; with cigar smoke, the concentration might be as high as 5.0–8.0%. (The blood of heavy smokers often contains critical amounts of CO that can lower their efficiency and tolerance for even moderate altitudes.)

The chief physiological effect of CO is to produce a reduction in arterial-oxygen saturation, thus reducing the availability of oxygen for metabolic processes. In addition, CO affects the blood in two ways: it combines with some of the oxygen-carrying pigment in the blood (hemoglobin) in such a way that it prevents the hemoglobin (Hb) from transporting oxygen to the tissue cells, and it affects the remaining hemoglobin in such a way that the hemoglobin gives up oxygen to the tissues less readily. These effects are additive, and the combined effect is a reduction in pO_2 in the blood and tissue—the same effect as produced by increases in altitude.

The likelihood of contamination by CO is high because the affinity of the hemoglobin for CO is approximately 210 times that for oxygen. Thus, small amounts of CO readily replace large amounts of oxygen. In addition,

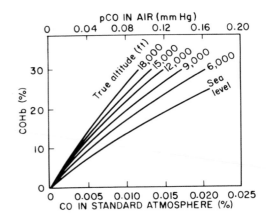

10-23 Effect of altitude on uptake of carbon monoxide. Each curve is maximum amount of carbon monoxide taken up by blood on prolonged exposure. More carbon monoxide is taken up at high altitude because there is less oxygen to compete with it (McFarland, 1946)

438

§ 10.2.4

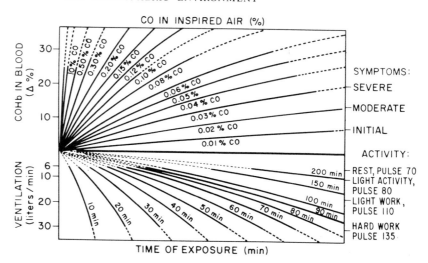

CO IN INSPIRED AIR (%)

TIME OF EXPOSURE (min)

because the density of CO referred to air is 0.967, it is readily maintained in air and thus remains available for inspiration unless deliberately removed.

Because pO_2 decreases with altitude, the uptake of CO by the blood increases with altitude for a given percentage of CO (fCO). Figure 10-23 illustrates the intake of CO in hemoglobin (Hb) at different altitudes and at different values of fCO, assuming oxygen and CO combine with nearly all the hemoglobin in the blood. This graph is for equilibrium saturation resulting from prolonged exposure.

The rate of uptake of CO depends on the time-concentration function, lung ventilation, and body-activity level. Figure 10-24 (Forbes, et al., 1945) shows the inter-relationships among these variables in their effects on fCOHb. The upper half of the illustration shows the fCOHb as a function of fCO in the inspired air with exposure time; the lower half relates exposure time, activity, and ventilation.

To determine the fCOHb in a man whose ventilation rate is 25 liters/min after 80 min of exposure to an atmosphere whose fCO is 0.05%, for example, draw a horizontal line from 25 liters/min on the lower left-hand scale of Fig. 10-24 to the 80-min line, then go up vertically to the 0.05% line in the upper half of the figure, and then horizontally to the left on the %COHb scale. If this is done, it can be seen that, in this case, the saturation of blood by CO is approximately 28%.

§ 10.2.4

In solving design problems, the engineer can calculate permissible time-concentration data by setting a given fCOHb for a given activity as constant and reading off the set of values that would produce it. Table 10-10 presents a summary of the gross effects of fCOHb that can be used to establish these criteria. In addition, Fig. 10-25 (McFarland, et al., 1944) shows the effects of time and CO (from cigarette smoking) on the visual threshold. Because vision is very sensitive to oxygen

Table 10-10 Symptoms of Carbon Monoxide Poisoning

COHb in blood (%)	Resulting symptoms
0–10	None subjectively noticeable, but initial visual impairment is revealed in objective tests.
10–20	Tightness across forehead, slight headache, flushed complexion.
20–30	Headache with throbbing in temples, breathlessness from any exertion.
30–40	Severe headache, weakness, dizziness, dimness of vision, nausea, and vomiting with possibility of collapse.
40–50	All preceding symptoms with increased pulse rate and respiration and greater possibility of collapse.
50–60	Loss of consciousness, with increased or irregular respiration, rapid pulse, and possibility of coma with convulsions.
60–80	Coma, convulsions, depressed heart action, respiratory failure and possibility of death.

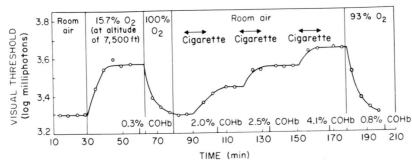

10-25

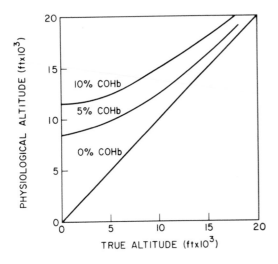

10-26

deficiency, this graph may be used to establish more refined criteria than those indicated in Table 10-10.

Because the presence of CO in the atmosphere reduces the pO_2 in air, and because oxygen in the blood is reduced by CO, the effects of CO can be expressed in terms of physiological altitude (see article 10.2.2), even at sea level. Thus, it would not be unreasonable in solving design problems to use Figs. 10-23, 10-24, and Table 10-10 or to establish the physiological altitude for given CO blood saturations and apply altitude criteria. Figure 10-26 (McFarland, et al., 1944) shows the relationship between physiological and true altitudes for 0, 5, and 10% COHb.

In establishing any CO time-concentration value, it is clear that the criterion is the oxygen requirement of the blood. Because noticeable effects of oxygen deficiency occur when the oxygen capacity of the blood is reduced about 10%, any CO concentration values or altitudes that would produce such a drop in a given period of exposure should be treated as dangerous. A standard of 12% COHb for long flights under noncombat conditions has been adopted as a critical level. This limit corresponds to blood in equilibrium for 1 hr before reaching the critical 12% value.

In general, it is recommended that 0.003% CO (30 ppm) be used as the standard permissible limit for long-term exposure. This standard provides a maximum COHb of 4% at sea level or a physiological altitude of approximately 8,000 ft. For shorter exposures where there is not enough time for equilibrium to be established between the blood and air, higher concentrations are permissible. For example, approximately the same blood concentration and physiological effect can be obtained from a 4-hr exposure to 0.005% CO as exposure for a longer period to 0.003%.

OTHER CONTAMINANTS

Carbon monoxide is a *chemical* asphyxiant in that its effects are produced through chemical action in the blood. The discussion of CO above may be taken as representative of the action of some other chemical asphyxiants. Carbon dioxide is a *simple* asphyxiant in that its effects are produced simply by displacing oxygen in inspired air. Other simple asphyxiants, e.g., helium, hydrogen, nitrogen, methane, ethylene, and nitrous oxide, act in the same manner and for these the discussion of CO_2 may be taken as representative.

§ 10.2.4

Using nitrogen as an example, the oxygen deficiency produced by simple asphyxiants can be estimated from the following equation:

$$fO_2 = \frac{qO_2}{Qi - qN_2 - qC}, \quad (10\text{-}7)$$

where Qi is the volume of air inspired (ft^3/min); qO_2, qN_2, and qC are the volumes of inspired oxygen, nitrogen, and contaminating gas (ft^3/min); and fO_2 is the oxygen fraction by volume. The value of fO_2 obtained can be entered into Equation 10-1 along with other appropriate quantities, and limiting conditions can be selected according to those discussed in article 10.2.2.

Agents other than asphyxiants differ in their manner of action on the body; irritants are inspired and act upon the upper respiratory tract and the lungs; narcotics are carried by the blood to the brain; various types of poisons are transported by the bloodstream to tissue or to the nervous system. The following paragraphs briefly discuss some agents encountered in industrial and military environments, and Table 10-11 presents a brief list of common toxic agents and their maximum allowable concentrations (as established by the American Conference of Governmental Industrial Hygienists in 1961).

Alcohols

Alcohols are anesthetic, somewhat irritating to the eyes and upper respiratory tract, and possess other toxic properties as well. These effects generally increase with molecular weight, but, because volatility correspondingly decreases, poisoning by alcohols of low volatility (above amyl alcohol in the saturated-aliphatic series) is unlikely. Methyl alcohol (CH_3OH) is an exception; although it has the lowest molecular weight, it is nearly five times as toxic as ethyl alcohol (C_2H_5OH), the next higher in the series. Methyl alcohol also causes a rather specific disability—blindness or impairment of vision—not typically caused by other alcohols. It is an exception here because the human body is less able to rid itself of methyl alcohol than of heavier compounds,

§ 10.2.4

Table 10-11 Common Sources and Maximum Allowable Concentrations of Some Toxic Agents

Common source	Toxic agent	Maximum allowable concentration (ppm)
Fuels and propellants	Ammonia	100
	Aniline	5
	Ethyl alcohol	1,000
	Gasoline	250
	Kerosene	500
	Methyl alcohol	200
	Nitrogen tetroxide	5
Engine exhausts (including rocket engines)	Aldehydes:	
	Acetaldehyde	200
	Acrolein	0.5
	Formaldehyde	5
	Furfural	5
	Carbon dioxide	5,000
	Carbon monoxide	100
	Bromine	1
	Nitrogen dioxide	5
	Sulfur dioxide	5
Hydraulic fluids	Butyl cellosolve	50
	Diacetone	50
	Aryl phosphates	0.06
	Dioxane alcohol	100
Fire extinguishants	Carbon dioxide	5,000
	Carbon tetrachloride	25
	Chlorobromethane	400
	Methyl bromide	20
Oil sprays and fumes	Aldehydes: (see above)	
Refrigerants	Carbon dioxide	5,000
	Freon	1,000
	Methyl bromide	20
	Sulfur dioxide	5
Smoke	Phosgene (plus same as for engine exhausts)	1

and, hence, methyl-alcohol poisoning lasts longer and is more serious.

Aldehydes and Ketones

The common aldehydes and ketones are volatile; generally soluble in water, alcohol,

441

and ether; and are quite active chemically. They have narcotic effects and irritate the mucous membranes and the lungs as well. The aldehydes are predominantly irritants, and some of them (e.g., acrolein) are among the most highly irritant substances known, and they are also somewhat anesthetic. Aldehydes from hot oil fumes have been suspected of causing symptoms similar to those of carbon-monoxide poisoning. Ketones are, generally, less irritant than their corresponding aldehydes and are hazardous mainly because of their narcotic properties.

The more commonly encountered aldehydes are: formaldehyde, acrolein, acetaldehyde, croton aldehyde, paraldehyde, and furfural. The more common ketones include: acetone, methyl ethyl ketone, and diacetone. Toxic concentrations of aldehydes and ketones usually can be detected quickly by their odor.

Aromatic Hydrocarbons

The aromatic hydrocarbons of interest here are benzene, aniline, xylidine, xylene, toluene, and cumene. Aromatic hydrocarbons are rapidly absorbed through the skin as well as by the lungs and intestines.

Next to tetrachlorethane, benzene, the parent compound of the series, is one of the most toxic industrial solvents known. In acute exposure, it is strongly narcotic, but it is most dangerous in chronic exposure. It causes progressive anemia, weakness, internal hemorrhage, bleeding gums and nose, chills, delirium, and death due to decreased oxygen-carrying capacity of the blood.

The effects of chronic exposure to xylene, toluene, or cumene in pure form have not been determined, but, because commercial xylene and toluene might contain significant amounts of benzene, they must be regarded with suspicion. Unfortunately, one cannot depend on odor for detecting toxic concentrations of the vapors of these substances.

Carbon Tetrachloride

Carbon tetrachloride has been used in fire extinguishers and as a solvent, especially in dry cleaning. It is an irritant and a narcotic. The usual symptoms of acute exposure are nausea, vomiting, abdominal pains, diarrhea, headache, and dizziness. High concentrations can cause rapid loss of consciousness. Severe exposure over long periods might be followed by liver damage and jaundice.

Cellosolves

The members of the series of cellosolves vary widely in toxicity. One of the least toxic is monoethyl ether, commonly known as "cellosolve." Butyl cellosolve, however, is irritating to the eyes and respiratory tract and causes headache, dizziness (vertigo), and impairment of judgment. Methyl cellosolve, in chronic exposure, causes abnormal blood pressures and neurological symptoms. The cellosolves in general are injurious to the kidneys.

Chlorobromomethane

This compound has been used as a fire extinguishant in airplanes. It is strongly narcotic, and its thermal decomposition products (hydrobromic acid, hydrochloric acid, phosgene, etc.) are markedly irritant and toxic. In acute exposure it is probably more toxic than carbon tetrachloride, but in chronic exposure, somewhat less. The maximum allowable concentration has been established at 400 ppm.

Glycols

The glycols are colorless, nearly odorless, water-soluble compounds. Because they are relatively nonvolatile, their vapors ordinarily are not dangerous, but they are readily absorbed through the skin. Although they are slightly irritant to the lungs and anesthetic, the major hazard from exposure to them is kidney damage. This is especially true of diethylene dioxide (dioxane), for which the maximum allowable concentration has been established at 100 ppm. No comparable figures, however, have been determined for the other common glycols or their derivatives.

Methyl Bromide

Methyl bromide is colorless and odorless, but it volatilizes at ordinary temperatures and pressures. Because its vapor is three times heavier than air, it tends to pool where it is released. It is primarily absorbed in the body through the lungs rather than through the skin.

The immediate symptom of exposure to methyl bromide is difficulty in breathing. In more chronic exposures, no real symptoms might appear for several days, but then the victim develops muscular twitchings and cramps, increasing to convulsions with disturbance of sight, fever, delirium, and, possibly, coma and death. One warning symptom of methyl bromide poisoning is the complaint that food is tainted or tastes bitter, "like burned rubber." For long term exposure, the suggested maximum allowable concentration is 20 ppm.

Oxides of Nitrogen

Nitrogen dioxide is the most toxic of the oxides of nitrogen. It gives little warning, and enough can be breathed without serious discomfort to cause death some hours later. Inhaled at body temperatures, 70% of it is quickly altered to nitrogen tetraoxide, which reacts with body water to form nitric and nitrous acids. These acids probably account for the irritation of the eyes and respiratory tract that follows.

Acute exposure to the fumes of oxides of nitrogen is followed by headache, dizziness, cough, restlessness, and insomnia. In chronic exposures, the symptoms are loss of appetite and weight, dyspepsia, constipation, and ulcers of the mucous membranes. The recommended maximum allowable concentration for nitrogen dioxide and tetroxide is 5 ppm.

Sulfur Dioxide

Sulfur dioxide, though extremely toxic, is so irritating that it is difficult to breathe lethal concentrations of it. Those, however, who are acclimatized to breathing air heavily contaminated with sulfur dioxide can develop severe poisoning from it. If endured, chronic breathing of it causes chemical pneumonia or bronchitis, and more severe exposure causes death by swelling of tissues in the respiratory system (glottis and lungs) and consequent suffocation. The recommended maximum allowable concentration for long-term exposure to sulfur dioxide is 5 ppm.

PROTECTION AGAINST TOXICITY

Personal hygiene, routine inspection of workplaces and personnel, and indoctrination of personnel in precautions in the presence of toxic agents can never be overemphasized, but environmental control and design for adequate protection are indispensable. The environmental-control techniques to use depend on the nature of the contaminant, the time-concentration functions, whether the equipment must be portable or fixed, etc. Toxic agents that cannot be eliminated at the source can be reduced in intensity by ventilation and personal protective equipment.

Ventilation

The amount of ventilating air required to reduce concentrations to minimum allowable levels in rooms or compartments usually is so large, however, as to make this procedure very inefficient. A more effective procedure is to use local exhaust ventilation systems (e.g., fume hoods in chemical labs). The ideal, of course, is the complete enclosure of the process generating the contaminant, but this arrangement often is not possible because of visual requirements.

Adequate ventilation rates for the removal of contaminants, whether produced by human occupants or by other processes, are not generally agreed on, but minimum rates can be estimated from Equations 10-8 and 10-9 below. The rate of air supply or exhaust (Q) required as a minimum can be determined from a knowledge of the rate of contaminant production (G) and the maximum allowable concentration (MAC) as follows:

$$Q = \frac{G}{\text{MAC}} \times 10^6 \qquad (10\text{-}8)$$

And the concentration (C) of a contaminant at any given time (t) in a room of given volume (R) can be calculated from the following formula:

$$C = G/R(1 - e^{-Q/Rt})10^6. \qquad (10\text{-}9)$$

Although odors might induce nausea and might have a slight effect on voluntary food consumption in some people and thus are undesirable atmospheric contaminants, they are not known to affect health and are not classed as poisons. Generally, however, it is desirable to eliminate unwanted odors. Often, the production of body odors in an enclosed space requires ventilation. These requirements are illustrated in Fig. 10-27. The index used is based on the intensity of smell sensations, which are assumed to vary with the logarithm of the concentration.

Personal Protective Equipment

Personal protective equipment supplements ventilation systems or is required for emer-

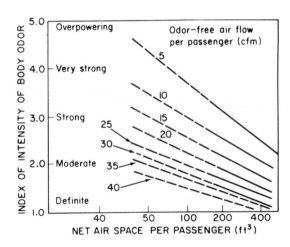

10-27 Ventilation requirements related to net air space and body odor. Solid parts of curves are based on experimental data; dashed portions are extrapolations of conditions found in aircraft (Yaglou, et al., 1936)

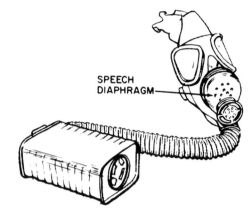

SPEECH DIAPHRAGM

10-28

Table 10-12 Purifying Materials for Canister Gas Masks

Contaminants	Filter color	Filtering material
Acid gases and vapors	White	Soda lime (sodium hydroxide and calcium oxide)
Ammonia	Green	Silica gel
Ammonia and smoke	Brown	Copper sulfate, activated charcoal, and filter
Carbon monoxide	Gray	Hopcalite, calcium chloride, and caustic soda
Mixed gases, vapors, and fumes	Red	Charcoal, copper sulfate, calcium chloride, Hopcalite, and filter
Hydrocyanic acid	Blue	Caustic soda (sodium hydroxide)
Mixture of organic vapor and acids	Yellow	Activated charcoal and soda lime
Mixture of organic vapor, acid, and smoke	Yellow (striped)	Activated charcoal, soda lime, and filter
Organic vapors and fumes	Black	Activated charcoal

§ 10.2.4

gency conditions or is required for normal operating conditions when men must be in the presence of toxic substances.

The following are various types and kinds of personal protective equipment:

a. Dust respirators are simple breathing apparatus that use filters to remove large-size dust particles.

b. Canister gas masks (see Fig. 10-28) use chemical and/or mechanical filters against gaseous materials and suspended particles (see Table 10-12).

c. Hose masks are connected by flexible hoses to some source of uncontaminated air.

d. Completely self-contained masks provide portable air sources and CO_2 absorbents.

e. Special protective clothing is designed to protect the skin against damage from agents that produce their effects by contact.

10.3 The Mechanical Environment

The mechanical stresses to which the body might be exposed are caused by accelerations and vibrations that arise from natural physical forces or machines. Exposure to these stresses might be continuous over a period of time or might occur only in a given situation; they might affect only certain specialized organs of the body, or they might produce general impairment and damage to structures and processes in the body. The mechanical forces encountered by man in the modern environment are produced largely by the machines that the engineer has created. For this reason, the engineer should know the effects of these forces on the body and how those that are detrimental can be avoided or minimized by proper design.

10.3.1 The effects of acceleration

Acceleration, the second derivative of motion with respect to time, is expressed in

This article was drafted, in part, by Albert Damon and Howard W. Stoudt of Harvard University.

terms of "g," the force of gravity, which is 32 ft/sec^2. The selection of terms used to describe the direction of accelerative-force vectors acting on the man in a man-machine system depends on what displacements are used as directional references. Four nomenclatures are in use. Two of these use vehicular displacements for reference, and two use the human body as reference. Of the latter two, one uses the displacement of the heart within the chest for reference; the other uses the longitudinal axis of the body as reference.

This last system of nomenclature appears to be the most useful for the present treatment because it is in the widest use in the human-engineering literature and because the response of the human body to accelerative motion is determined by reactive forces resulting from the inertia of the body. For these reasons, and because the use of this system permits the easiest reference to the article on vibration (10.3.2), the last system will be used as our basic system.

The nomenclature in this basic system is illustrated in Fig. 10-29 for various positions of the body. As shown in Fig. 10-29, the acceleration vector in a plane parallel to the body's longitudinal axis is called *positive* acceleration, if it is in the head-to-foot direc-

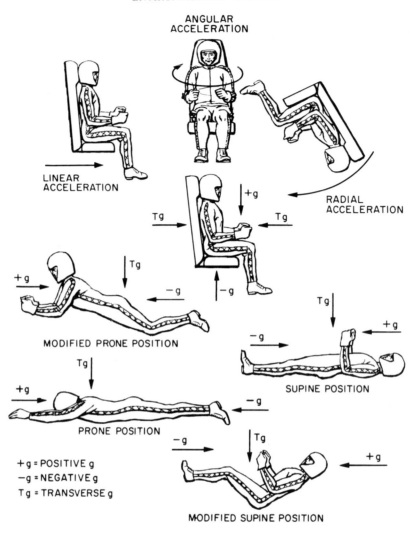

ANGULAR
ACCELERATION

LINEAR
ACCELERATION

RADIAL
ACCELERATION

+g

Tg

Tg

−g

−g

MODIFIED PRONE POSITION

+g

Tg

Tg

−g

SUPINE POSITION

−g

+g

Tg

+g

PRONE POSITION

−g

Tg

+g

+g = POSITIVE g
−g = NEGATIVE g
Tg = TRANSVERSE g

MODIFIED SUPINE POSITION

10-29

§ 10.3.1

tion, and *negative* acceleration, if it is in the foot-to-head direction. The acceleration vector in a plane perpendicular to the longitudinal axis of the body is called *transverse* acceleration. The forward- or backward-facing positions are equivalent in transverse-g tolerance as long as comparable body restraint is provided. This means that data on transverse-g tolerance are equally applicable to acceleration and to deceleration.

For purposes of comparing human and animal data, as well as human data obtained in a variety of postures, the designations of "positive" and "negative" of the basic system will be replaced sometimes by "headward" and "tailward" (or "footward") acceleration. These new terms represent equivalent vehicle displacements; they are equal in force but opposite in direction to those inertial forces (positive and negative) that act directly on the body. The equivalent vehicle displacements of transverse forces will be designated as vehicle displacements in a "sternumward" direction or in a "spineward" direction.

The direction of accelerative motion of the entire body can also be described with reference to the longitudinal axis. *Linear* acceleration is acceleration in which the position of the longitudinal axis, and so the whole body, changes in a straight line. *Radial* or centrifugal acceleration is produced when the longitudinal axis is rotated around a central point so that its velocity vector is constantly changing *direction*. *Angular* acceleration is produced for the same condition when the velocity vector changes *magnitude and direction*.

Two or all three of these kinds of acceleration are usually present at one time, but one usually predominates to such an extent as to permit neglecting the other two. It is convenient, therefore, to study the response of the body to one kind at a time.

LINEAR ACCELERATION

For physiological reasons, the duration of linear accelerative force is divided into the following periods:

a. "Abrupt" acceleration is that lasting less than 2 sec.

b. "Brief" acceleration is that lasting 2–10 sec.

c. "Prolonged" acceleration is that lasting longer than 10 sec.

Examples of acceleration situations of various durations are shown in Table 10-13. In general, duration and force are inversely related, i.e., the shorter the time, the more acceleration that can be tolerated, and vice versa (Gauer and Zuidema, 1961).

Abrupt Acceleration

In this time period, tissues react by structural damage or failure. Tissue damage is determined by such physical properties as tissue

Table 10-13 Approximate Duration and Magnitude of Some Accelerations *

Vehicle	Activity	Acceleration Duration (sec)	Acceleration Magnitude (g)
Elevator	Average acceleration in "fast service"	1–5	0.1–0.2
	Comfort limit for acceleration		0.3
	Emergency deceleration		2.5
Train	Normal acceleration and deceleration	5	0.1–0.2
	Emergency stop (braking from 70 mph)	2.5	0.4
Automobile	Normal stop	5–8	0.25
	Quick stop	3–5	0.45
	Emergency stop	3	0.7
	Crash (potentially survivable)	<0.1	20–100
Aircraft	Normal takeoff	>10	0.5
	Catapult takeoff	1.5	2.5–6
	Crash landing (potentially survivable)		20–100
	Seat ejection	0.25	10–15
	Parachute opening at 40,000 ft	0.2–0.5	33
	Parachute opening at 6,000 ft	0.5	8.5
	Parachute landing	0.1–0.2	3–4

* Goldman and von Gierke, 1960.

§ 10.3.1

elasticity, viscosity, frequency of response, tensile and shearing strength, and compressibility. Stress on solid tissues (e.g., bone) produces little or no displacement until the yield point is reached, when fracture results. In visco-elastic tissues (muscle, skin, internal organs), unit stress produces logarithmic displacement; in body fluids, displacement is linear.

The limits of human tolerance to abrupt acceleration are summarized in Figs. 10-30 through 10-33, inclusive (Eiband, 1959). The limits indicated are based on situations involving healthy, young subjects that were expecting the force and were provided with maximum body support or restraint.

Human tolerance to abrupt acceleration involves the following five mechanical factors:

a. The type of body support or restraint.

b. The orientation of the body with respect to the direction of force.

c. The rate and duration of application of the force.

d. The magnitude of the force.

Of these factors, the type of restraint is probably the most important in view of the fact that experimental data are good only for the conditions specified for harness, helmet, molded form, or other protective gear, and that adequate restraint is the primary variable in tolerance to rapidly applied accelerations. Table 10-14 shows the maximum body support necessary to survive the maximum tolerance limits shown in Figs. 10-30 through 10-33.

With the harness arrangements indicated in Table 10-14, shoulder straps should be looser than lap, thigh, and chest straps so that most of the force is transmitted to the pelvis. Lap straps should be as tight as comfort will permit because loose straps result in higher g forces for a given impact than do tightly fitting straps. Moreover, the low hysteresis of nylon (as compared with rayon, for example) means that the harness should be snug so as to prevent a "sling-shot" or "whiplash" effect that is capable of breaking a man's neck (Odelgard and Weman, 1957). The best harness material for routine (nonexperimental) use is double-thickness, No. 9, drawn nylon 3 in. wide.

It should be pointed out that survival in abrupt-acceleration situations depends, not only on resistance to the impact forces themselves but, also, on the ability of the person to recover rapidly enough to release body restraints and leave the vehicle within seconds or, at most, minutes. Fire and water hazards, vibratory shock (as in helicopters), and the enemy in combat situations all make immediate exit imperative. Thus, even temporary disability can be disastrous.

Biologically, the limiting factor in human tolerance to headward g in the normal, seated posture is spine fracture, particularly in the upper lumbar portion, just above the "small of the back" concavity. With optimum alignment, up to 35g can be tolerated at less than 500g/sec rate of onset, but, with the back bent forward to the limit of motion, this limit diminishes to below 15g. Animals with spines optimally aligned have withstood 75g (hogs) and 65g (chimpanzees) without fracture at higher than 5,000g/sec onset. Human limits are presumably in this area, but data are lacking. With optimum support, as in immersion baths or form-fitting couches, the limit might be about 1,000g in "zero" time (0.001 sec).

Tailward g has not been tested to tolerance limits, but 10–12g is tolerable at the rate of 10–82g/sec onset lasting 0.003–0.2 sec. With transverse g, the subject reacts like a boxer to a blow; at a threshold of 30g with a jolt of 1,000g/sec, there is a brief period of shock, lowered blood pressure, and weakness, and, at 40g for 1,500g/sec, he loses consciousness.

Figure 10-34, which shows the relationship between magnitude and duration of force, is based on experiments on Air Force personnel who were seated facing forward and were exposed to spineward g (Stapp, 1957). Spine pain at 700–900g/sec onset for 0.002–0.2 sec marks the human limit of reversible incapacitation to transverse acceleration at 23–27g when restrained only by a lap strap.

Brief Acceleration

At about 0.2 sec duration, hydraulic effects begin. These consist of the displacement

§ 10.3.1

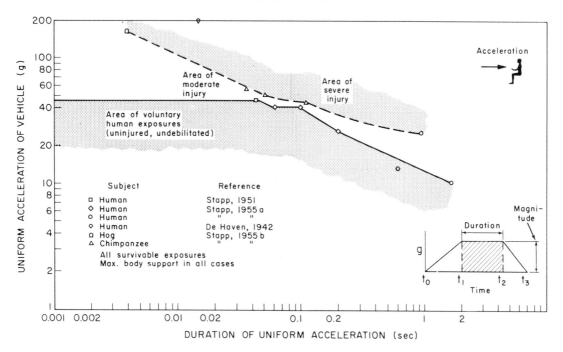

10-30

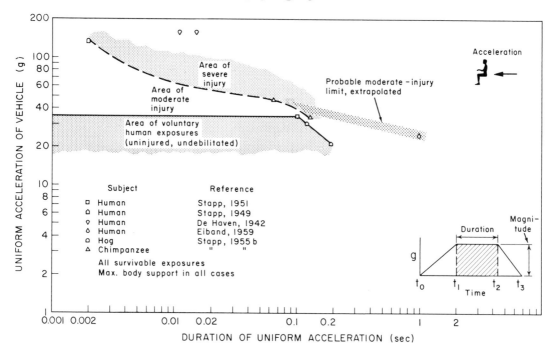

10-31

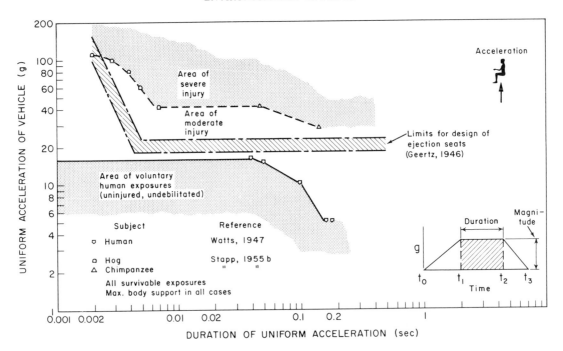

10-32

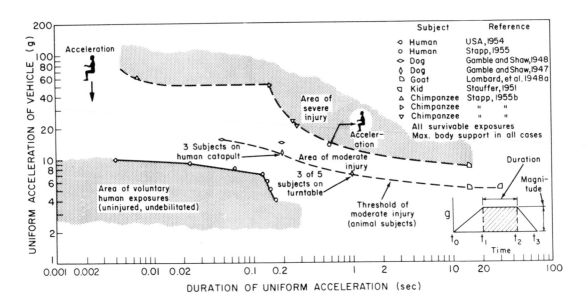

10-33

Table 10-14 Conventional and Additional Restraint for Maximum Body Support [1]

Direction of acceleration	Vehicle occupant	Body position	Conventional restraint	Additional restraint for maximum body support
Spineward	Operator	Seated facing forward	Lap strap Shoulder straps	Thigh straps
	Passenger or crew-member	Seated facing forward	Lap strap	Shoulder straps Thigh straps Armrests and hand-holds Toe straps
Sternum-ward	Passenger or crew-member	Seated facing backward	Lap strap	Backrest [2] Headrest [3] Chest strap [4] Leg and foot supports Armrests and hand-holds
Headward	Operator	Seated facing forward	Lap strap Shoulder straps	Thigh straps Chest strap [4] Headrest [3]
	Passenger or crew-member	Seated facing forward	Lap strap	Shoulder straps Thigh straps Chest strap [4] Headrest [3] Armrests and hand-holds
		Seated facing backward	Lap strap	Chest strap [4] Headrest [3] Armrests and hand-holds
Footward	Operator	Seated facing forward	Lap strap Shoulder straps	None
	Passenger or crew-member	Seated facing forward	Lap strap	Shoulder straps Handholds Toe straps
		Seated facing backward	Lap strap	Chest strap [4] Handholds Toe straps
		Supine	Lap strap	Webbed netting [5]

[1] Eiband, 1959.
[2] Rigid with padded "wings."
[3] Full height, integral with backrest.
[4] Arm-pit level.
[5] Full support.

§ 10.3.1

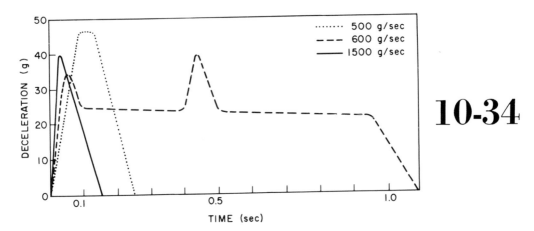

of fluids in the body cells, changes in the hydrostatic equilibrium between small blood vessels and their surrounding body fluids, changes in permeability and structural failure of blood vessels, and the mechanical displacement or deformation of body structures. Body orientation determines the physiological effect of the hydraulic displacements.

With headward g, fluids and organs are displaced downward, *away from* the head and eyes. Functional time limits for tolerance are set by visual blackout and loss of consciousness—the hypoxic effects of Fig. 10-35 (Stapp, 1957). The oxygen-carrying blood does not reach the brain; it pools instead in the lower portions of the body. Vision fails before consciousness because arterial blood pressure must overcome a normal pressure of about 28 mm Hg in the eyeball, whereas the opposing pressure inside the skull is negligible. Total cessation of blood flow to the brain causes unconsciousness in about 7 sec (Rossen, et al., 1943) and irreversible damage in 2–3 min.

With tailward g, fluid is displaced *into* the head and eyes, and the increased pressure causes confusion, pain, and hemorrhage. In addition, tears fail to drain and thus impair vision. About 3–5g of tailward g can be tolerated for periods up to 30 sec.

For transverse g in the seated position, tolerance limits are set by hemorrhage into the eyes, retinal detachment, chest pain, and difficulty in breathing. The following forces are tolerable: 3g for 900 sec, 10g for 120 sec,

15g from 5–50 sec, and 25g for 1 sec. In the well supported prone and supine positions, transverse-g tolerance will probably be limited only by the strength of the heart or lungs.

Parachute opening shock is a special case of total body deceleration acting over a 1–2 sec period with the body in various positions. Peak forces, acting for about 0.05 sec, will vary from 8–33g, depending on altitude and on the 4th power of parachute-opening velocity (Webster, 1953).

Both operating experience and experiments (Hallenbeck, et al., 1945) indicate that opening shock is greatest at high altitudes. Forces below 20g are considered to be safe, forces of 20–30g are borderline, and forces of over 30g are dangerous for man, parachute, and harness.

Prolonged Acceleration

The body attempts to compensate for the hydraulic effects of acceleration by physiological reflexes, chiefly by increasing the heart's rate and force to help circulate the blood that would otherwise pool peripherally and by constricting blood vessels to reduce peripheral flow and the escape of blood through vessel walls. Compensatory reflexes begin at about 5 sec, are fully active in 15–20 sec, and might persist for many minutes or even hours if the g forces are not too great. If the g forces are excessive, the reflexes will fail, marking the person's time limit for tolerating that particular level of acceleration.

With prolonged acceleration, both posture and type of restraint are major variables. Even such a slight change as inclining the head and torso 20 deg will increase tolerance to sternumward g in the seated position from 5–6g to 9–10g (Ballinger and Dempsey, 1952). Figures 10-36 and 10-37 (Bondurant, et al., 1958) summarize several Air Force experiments with prolonged acceleration.

Weightlessness is a special case of prolonged acceleration at 0g. With 0g, rest and motion lose their customary meanings. The system conserves momentum, and every action produces an obvious reaction that is equal and opposite. Movement of a body member results in a corresponding countermovement of the entire body. The body, therefore, must be restrained for any operation; otherwise, for example, in trying to turn a crank, the body would rotate about the axis of the crank, with the relative angular velocities of body and crank depending on the ratio of their respective moments of inertia. The same would hold for the effect of human movements on a stationary vehicle, i.e., if a man tried to stand up

in a hovering space capsule, the capsule would be as likely to be pushed down as the man to push up.

The purely mechanical aspects of weightlessness, however, present no major difficulties, provided that efficient voluntary motion can be initiated and sustained. Although the effects of weightlessness on performance are largely unknown, they are potentially more serious than the mechanical effects because of the basic role of gravity in human motor and autonomic nervous reflexes. In the control of voluntary movements, gravity is so essential that we are unaware of it until muscular strength or equilibrium become impaired.

Orientation depends, predominantly, on the vertical coordinate, gravity. Without gravity, the pressure receptors in the labyrinth of the inner ear (see Chapter 3) and the spine, arm, and leg joints will lose their value in establishing equilibrium, leaving only vision to perform this function. The discrepancy between visual impressions and those received from the labyrinth and other pressure receptors might give rise to a sensation of falling in free space. The effects of such sensations on the auto-

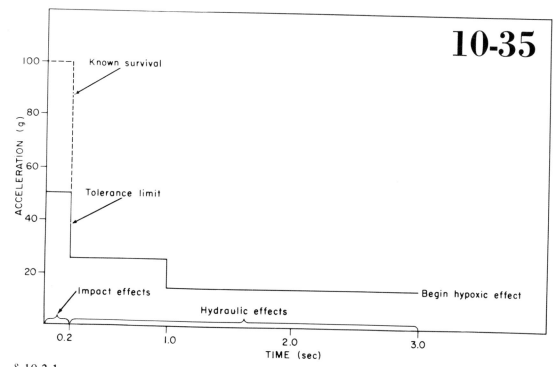

nomic nervous system (nausea, vomiting, apathy, and functional impairment, as in motion sickness) will vary with individual persons, as will the time needed to compensate for these effects.

Without gravity, the labyrinthine receptors will respond to any acceleration of the body to a much greater extent than the same stimulus would produce at 1g. Tilting the head, for example, or moving it vertically in a rotating vehicle, might produce incapacitating dizziness, and this effect might impose an insuperable obstacle to providing artificial acceleration by rotating the vehicle.

Muscle tone, which depends on activity, is largely determined by body weight—considerable energy is expended simply in maintaining upright posture. Our neuromuscular coordination is based on interpreting sensations de-

rived from joints and muscles and responding appropriately. This process is predominantly automatic through our autonomic reflexes, with gravity providing the major sensory input. Without gravity, neuromuscular coordination will have to be relearned. At first, posture might be seriously impaired, and an arm or leg movement might be much too exaggerated because the customary cues for stopping it will be missing.

Without doubt, the appropriate adjustments can be learned, but the relative ease of relearning, the time necessary, and the residual functional handicap have yet to be studied. Experiments on relearning visual interpretation— presenting stimuli by special lenses as the retina receives them rather than as they are interpreted as perceptions—indicates that several weeks might be required. And, once relearning

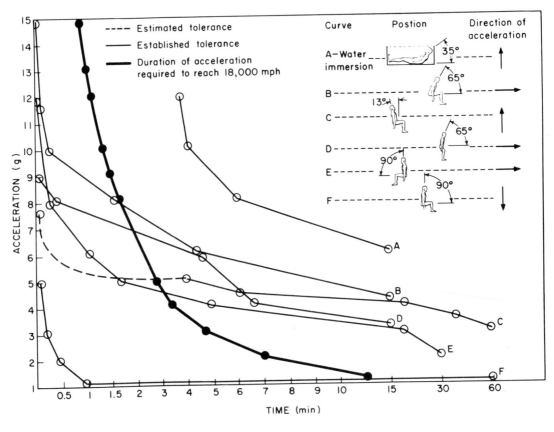

10-36

§ 10.3.1

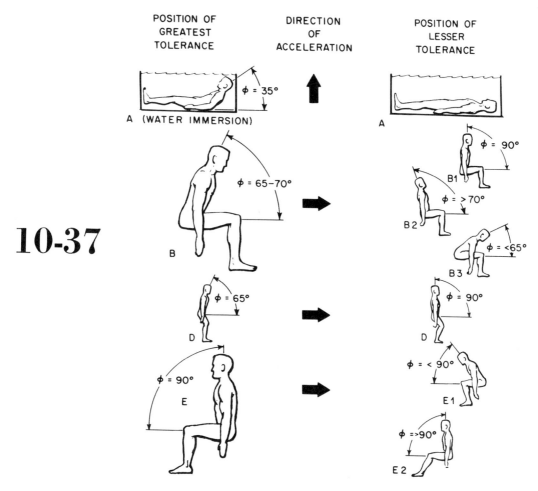

POSITION OF GREATEST TOLERANCE

DIRECTION OF ACCELERATION

POSITION OF LESSER TOLERANCE

10-37

A (WATER IMMERSION) $\phi = 35°$

$\phi = 65-70°$ B

$\phi = 65°$ D

$\phi = 90°$ E

A

$\phi = 90°$ B1

$\phi = >70°$ B2

$\phi = <65°$ B3

$\phi = 90°$ D

$\phi = <90°$ E1

$\phi = >90°$ E2

has been effected at 0g, the same problems in reverse will be encountered on re-entering a gravitational field.

Mention of muscle tone above introduces the topic of metabolic alterations anticipated in space flight. These become important only for periods of weeks to months, as in planetary flight, rather than days, as for moon flight. The chief problem is that exertion, whether against gravity or, when prone, against an external object, is necessary for the proper function of muscles and bones. "Disuse atrophy" is the structural consequence of inactivity, as in the muscle wasting and osteoporosis of paralyzed or bedridden patients. To replace gravity as a constant stimulus to bone and muscle maintenance, the space traveler must keep active. Passive exercise might have to be provided, together with less calcium and more water in the diet.

Once again, after the new equilibrium has been reached in space transit, the process will have to be reversed on re-entry into a gravitational field. Weakened bones will certainly not be able to withstand the g forces previously tolerable, and human strength and biomechanical capabilities will certainly be less, for a few weeks, than when the trip began.

RADIAL ACCELERATION

Simple tumbling creates centrifugal forces that are directed headward and footward from the axis of rotation. These forces at any given point increase with the square of the rotational

§ 10.3.1

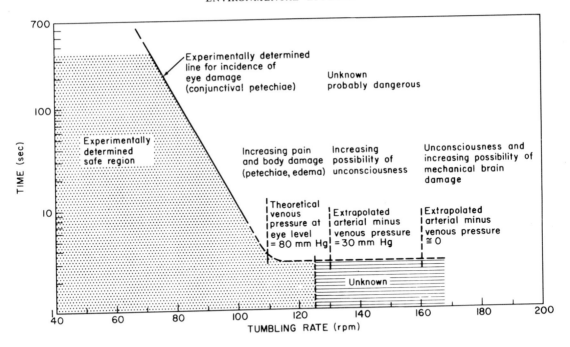

10-38

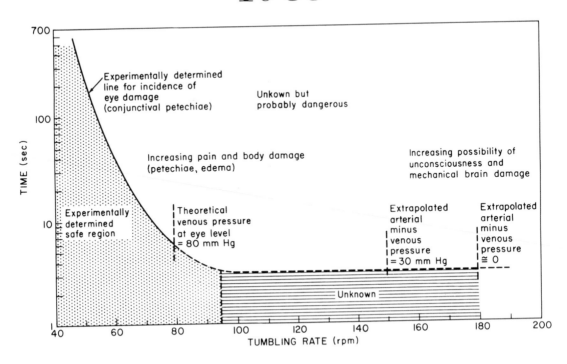

10-39

§ 10.3.1

velocity and might produce extensive damage. The most serious effect is a pooling and increase in the hydrostatic pressure of the blood in the head and legs. Although this effect might rupture small blood vessels in these areas, the most serious effect would be the reduction in blood supply to the heart.

With the center of rotation at heart level, the resulting net pressure to the carotid sinus (a blood-pressure-regulating sensor located in a large artery in the neck) is less than at resting levels, which results in an increase in heart rate. When the center of rotation is at eye level, the net pressure is greater, and a satisfactory pressure gradient is maintained. When the center of rotation is at the hips, the hydrostatic column to head level is considerably larger and results in a net increase in pressure at the carotid sinus in spite of a fall in the output of the heart. The effect of this last is to reduce the decrease in blood volume in the heart and lungs with more severe symptoms in the head region—an effect similar to that of negative g for this type of rotation whereas, for rotations at higher pivot points, the effect more nearly resembles that of positive g.

Experimental studies concerned with this problem have been forced to stop short of blackout when using human subjects because of the extreme pain involved. Tolerance data, therefore, are extrapolated from these studies and from studies using animals. Figures 10-38 and 10-39 present a summary of data available and extrapolated for rotation at the hip and heart levels, respectively, as a function of rotation rate (Weiss, et al., 1954).

The phenomenon of epicyclic tumbling occurs primarily after emergency ejection from high-speed aircraft. Rates of tumbling as high as 200 rpm can be expected, and the wind-drag superimposes a decelerative g field. An idea of the magnitude of the decelerative forces involved can be had by looking at Figs. 10-40 and 10-41 (Goodrich, 1956). These decelerative forces are dangerous if encountered alone, but, when superimposed on head-over-heels tumbling, the type of damage that results is qualitatively different from either the effects of deceleration alone or of tumbling alone or of a mere summation of these effects. For example, at 60 rpm in a 30g field, the

force exerted on the body is 30g, the vector of this force changes direction by 180 deg every $\frac{1}{2}$ sec, and the result is a severe, low-frequency vibration (see article 10.3.2).

Under 50,000 ft in altitude, deceleration should decay to less than 10g within 5 sec, but, at higher altitudes, where air density is lower, a longer time will be required for it to decay to an insignificant level (see Fig. 10-41) —as much as 30 sec might be required, which is a period of time sufficient to produce the circulatory effects described above. At moderate altitudes, circulatory interruption will not be a problem unless tumbling is prolonged. In this case, the violent shaking is the more

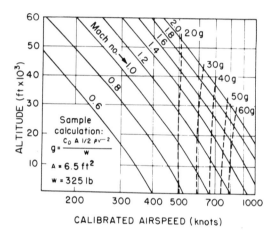

CALIBRATED AIRSPEED (knots)

10-40

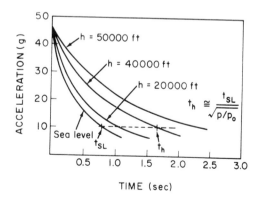

TIME (sec)

10-41

dangerous aspect of the situation.

The primary result of epicyclic tumbling, like that of vibration (see article 10.3.2), is mechanical damage to loosely suspended organs resulting from compression by the changing force vectors. Rigidly held organs are damaged less, and, for this reason, some amount of protection is obtained with abdominal compression produced by pressure suits.

Animal data and the results of actual ejections indicate that moderate tumbling in a field of less than 15g is not dangerous. This phenomenon is thought to be due to the low-frequency response of the vascular (blood) column, which might suggest that tumbling is beneficial when deceleration occurs. It should be remembered, however, that the mechanical damage associated with tumbling is a more serious result. Thus, except for special instances, when high levels of deceleration are anticipated, stabilized ejection seats are recommended.

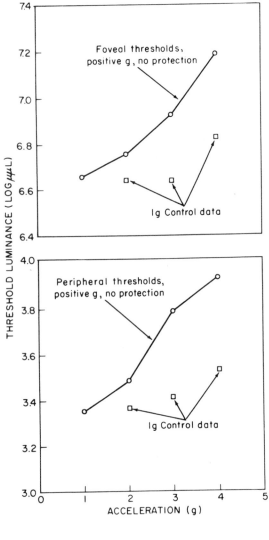

ANGULAR ACCELERATION

Accelerative forces acting on the fluids of the inner ear and on the motion of the eyeballs produce disturbances in the sense of equilibrium. *Oculogyral* illusion is associated with the effects of angular *accelerations* on the semicircular canals of the ears. With the onset of rotation, an object that is fixed with respect to a person will appear to move in the direction of rotation. If rotation continues at a uniform velocity, the apparent motion of the object slows and then comes to rest. If rotation stops suddenly, the object appears to move rapidly in a direction opposite to the previous rotation.

If the person is rotated in the dark, the illusion will be transferred to his body. With the onset of rotation, he might believe that he is turning in the actual direction of rotation. With continued rotation at constant speed, the feeling of rotating will slow down until he does not believe that he is rotating. Following this, the person occasionally will experience a feeling of rotating in the opposite direction. When rotation is stopped, a series of illusions follow that are all in the direction opposite to that of the actual previous rotation.

Also associated with the semicircular canals of the ear is *audiogyral* illusion, which occurs during angular *deceleration*. After rotation has stopped, sounds appear displaced in space in the direction of the previous rotation so that, after rotation to the left, a sound coming from in front appears to be emitted from a position left of center. Average displacements of 17 deg have been reported. Note that this effect is opposite that of the oculogyral illu-

10-42

§ 10.3.1

sion in which, following rotation to the left, the displacement is toward the right.

When rotational, centrifugal, and gravitational effects are combined, the *oculogravic* illusion occurs. It occurs when the person is seated facing the center of rotation. In this position he is subjected to both transverse and gravitational g forces, with the effect that, as rotation begins, he feels that he is being tilted backwards. As centripetal forces reach 1.5g, he has the sensation of being on his back in a horizontal seat fixed to a vertical platform with the walls of the room rotating around him. When the rotation stops, the opposite sensations are experienced. The illusion develops progressively over a period of 5–50 sec while rotation continues at constant speed. If the person faces away from the center of rotation, a similar illusion occurs, but in the opposite direction.

PERFORMANCE IN ACCELERATION

The major effects on performance of physiologically tolerable accelerative forces are those associated with visual and motor performances, which can be expected to be affected adversely at forces of 2–4g. The evidence available regarding effects on thought processes, decision-making, and the like are not sufficient so far to conclude anything one way or the other.

Visual Performance

The effect of accelerative forces on the blood supply to the head and eyes has already been described. At levels less than grayout, however, important losses in both central and peripheral visual functions are observed. These effects are shown in Fig. 10-42 (White, 1958) in terms of the brightness just detectable by the human eye at various accelerations. Compared with the control data shown in this graph, it can be seen that the loss in peripheral brightness sensitivity is slightly greater than the loss in central brightness sensitivity and that, in both cases, the loss is appreciable by 2g and becomes relatively greater

with increased acceleration.

To some degree, this visual loss can be counteracted by increasing the brightness of the signal light. This fact is illustrated in Fig. 10-43 (Brown and Burke, 1958), which also illustrates the effects of g forces on visual reaction time. This graph shows that the normal increase in speed of reaction that is associated with increased signal intensity is not reduced even though the sensitivity of the eye is reduced.

Figure 10-43 also shows the reduction in visual reaction time with acceleration. The same kind of reduction also has been observed for auditory signals. A word of caution, however, regarding reaction times in the use of both kinds of signals: the loss in speed of response in both cases presumably depends partly on the impairments in motor performance associated with reacting. In the case of the visual reaction time, loss of visual function also would seem to be involved; whether the loss in response to acoustic signals involves a loss in hearing acuity is not known.

Visual acuity, i.e., the ability of the eyes to

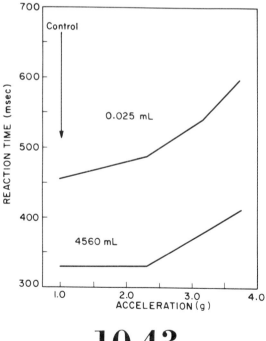

10-43

resolve detail (see Chapter 2), is also affected by moderate g forces, as is shown in Fig. 10-44 (White and Jorve, 1956). The loss in visual acuity can be seen to be essentially linear and not importantly affected by the two body positions shown. The graph shows that, at 7g, target size must be twice that at 1g to be seen.

Because both brightness sensitivity and visual acuity decrease with increasing acceleration, it would be expected that an operator subjected to these forces would commit errors in instrument reading. That this does indeed happen is shown in Fig. 10-45 (White and Riley, 1956), which also shows again that, at least up to 3g, the loss of visual function can be importantly counteracted by increases in brightness above 0.1 ft-L. The use of relatively high brightnesses at all levels, however, is clearly indicated.

Motor Performance

Normal body weight is defined as weight at 1g. As the accelerative force exceeds this value, weight is increased; as 0g is approached, weight decreases. As body weight increases with increased g force, the power demands on the muscle system become greater. The result is a loss in speed of limb displacement and applied force. The effect varies, however, according to whether the acceleration is directed along the longitudinal axis of the body or perpendicular to it.

Figure 10-46 (Chambers and Brown, 1959) shows the vehicle accelerations (rather than those of the body) at which movement of various body parts is barely possible. It can be seen that, although transverse g has much less effect on circulatory, visual, and other similar functions, it has a much greater effect on movements; a man under high transverse g might retain vision and consciousness but might not be able to move his body.

Post-Acceleration Performance

It should be a matter of concern in most situations involving significant g forces that the operator not only sustain these forces with-

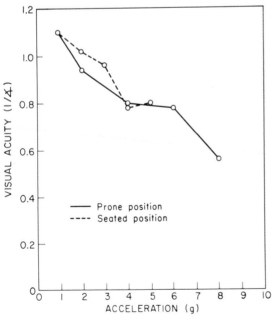

10-44

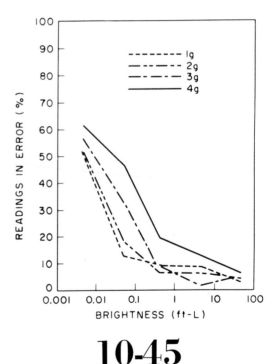

10-45

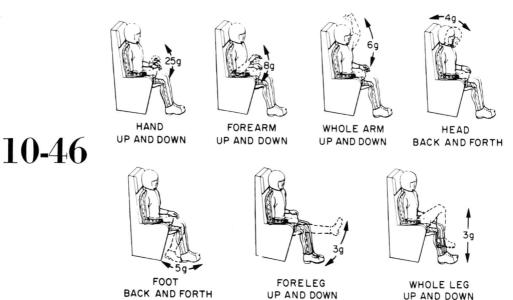

10-46

HAND
UP AND DOWN

FOREARM
UP AND DOWN

WHOLE ARM
UP AND DOWN

HEAD
BACK AND FORTH

FOOT
BACK AND FORTH

FORELEG
UP AND DOWN

WHOLE LEG
UP AND DOWN

out damage or signficant loss in performance but that he also be able to perform at required levels following exposure. Unfortunately, information of general value for this problem is not available. As a working principle, however, it should be assumed that, if the operator's ability to perform (see, move, etc.) is affected during increased acceleration, there will be a short time lag following recovery to normal conditions before the operator's abilities recover. Some of the factors involved here have been described with regard to illusions of equilibrium; it is reasonable to expect a time lag in the resumption of normal circulatory action and other physiological phenomena as well.

SETTING TOLERANCE LIMITS

As do all biological data, the limits of human tolerance to acceleration vary widely

Table 10-15   Examples of Variation in Human Tolerance to Headward Acceleration for 10 sec *

Symptom	Acceleration at which symptom occurred (g)			Range at which symptoms occurred in different subjects (g)		
	Min.	Avg.	Max.	Able	Baker	Charlie
None	2.5	3.5	5.0	—	—	—
Early grayout (peripheral lights dim)	2.6	3.8	7.0	3.0–4.3	2.8–3.8	2.1–6.7
Late grayout (peripheral lights lost)	3.3	4.7	7.7	4.9–6.0	3.7–4.7	5.4–7.2
Blackout (central lights lost)	3.3	5.2	7.8	4.9–6.0	4.6–6.5	5.5–7.6
Confusion	3.6	5.4	8.3	6.0–6.2	4.9–6.9	5.6–7.7
Unconsciousness	3.5	5.6	8.6	6.1–6.5	5.2–7.5	5.6–7.9

* Stauffer, 1953.

§ 10.3.1

from one person to another and from time to time with the same person. This error introduced by human variation is likely to be a factor close to two or three as shown in Table 10-15.

In addition to factors such as human variation and the nature of the task, it is clear that setting tolerance limits for accelerative forces depends on which of several possible end criteria is selected. The most sensitive effect of positive accelerations is loss of visual function. Some vision is possible even with grayout; thus, grayout could be used as a tolerance limit with initial losses in peripheral visual acuity as a sign of the impending approach to this limit.

For experienced operators, on the other hand, disabling confusion (barring the necessity for vision) might not appear until shortly after blackout. This fact is illustrated in Fig. 10-47 (Stoll, 1956), which presents an acceleration-tolerance curve relating dependent limiting values of grayout, blackout, confusion, and unconsciousness to maximum accelera-

tion, exposure time, and rate of application of the g force. Thus, blackout could be used as a tolerance limit.

Tolerance to positive acceleration is greater than that to negative acceleration, and tolerance to transverse g is greater yet. Figure 10-48 (Mayo, 1957) shows theoretical limits for all three for various durations using unconsciousness as the criterion. For many situations, on the other hand, the onset of losses in visual acuity or other performance criteria might provide much more significant limits.

PROTECTION AGAINST G FORCES

Basically, three methods of protection against the effects of acceleration are in routine use: body restraint, manipulation of body posture and position by means of seat or couch design, and compensating pressure suits and helmets. The use of vasoconstricting drugs has also been considered but, at this time, these do not appear very promising.

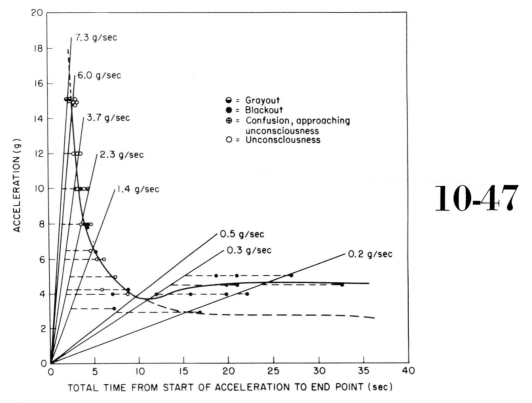

ACCELERATION TOLERANCE

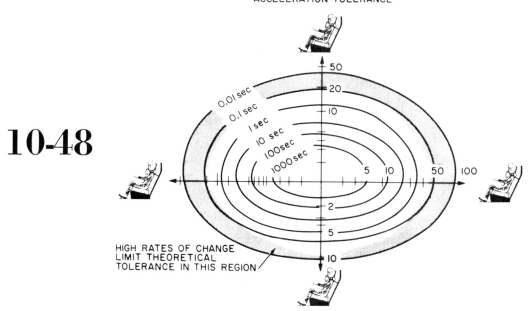

10-48

Body Restraint

Maximum protection against crashes and other abrupt accelerations can be achieved by providing complete body support and restraint (see Table 10-14). Certain other basic principles can be stated as follows:

1. Provide for the distribution of the decelerative load over as wide an area of the body as possible.

2. Prevent the transmission of forces along the spine.

3. Provide for the transmission of forces directly to the skeleton (most preferably, directly to the pelvic area).

4. Moderate the forces as much as possible by providing for the deformation or collapsing of intermediate structures.

5. Avoid bringing the operator into contact with the interior surfaces of the vehicle.

6. For protection against head injury, distribute the impact energy over as wide an area of the skull as possible. This can be achieved by using a helmet with a hard outer shell suspended by webbing at a distance of $\frac{5}{8}$–$\frac{3}{4}$ in. from the head.

7. Interpose energy-absorbing materials between the head and the outer shell of the

helmet. Padding, used in combination with the webbed supports indicated above, can be used to incorporate this principle. In general, foam plastics appear to be the most useful for this purpose.

Manipulating Posture and Position

Anything that reduces the heart-to-head distance reduces hydrostatic effects and favors a higher g tolerance. With transverse g, in either the prone or supine position, the heart-to-head distance is very short. Consequently, much higher acceleration levels are tolerable. Positive and negative accelerations applied to the standing or normally sitting person represent the longest heart-to-head distances and the lowest tolerances. If the operator is permitted to crouch or hunch forward, which shortens this critical distance by almost a half, g tolerance can be measurably increased.

Considerable attention has been given to the engineering design of couches for the high accelerative forces to be encountered in space flight. Figure 10-49 (Chambers and Brown, 1959) shows three couch designs that have been studied. With Couch B tipped to an

§ 10.3.1

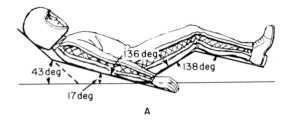

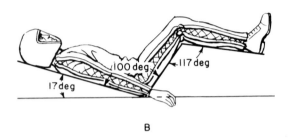

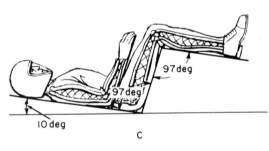

10-49

8-deg back angle, a subject was able to tolerate as high as 25 g in a record run. Figure 10-50 (Chambers and Brown, 1959) shows the data obtained with this record run. The baseline data indicate the reaction of the subject to a signal light. It can be seen that he was able to react throughout the entire buildup and decay of acceleration, a total time of 40 sec.

Thus, by combining the crouching-hunching effect with total body position so as to permit the resultant force to act in the transverse direction, maximum tolerance by variation of posture and position can be achieved. Figure 10-51 (Gagge, 1946) illustrates this fact with the results of several studies of the effects of body position. It can be seen that as body position varies from supine, through seated upright, to prone, tolerance is varied in the manner expected.

Pressure Suits and Helmets

Pressure methods of protection operate by applying a back pressure to critical body areas so as to reduce the flow of blood to or from these areas to maintain blood pressure. Table 10-16 shows the results of a study in which a comparison was made between no protection and full positive pressure applied to the head with a helmet from an Air Force partial pressure suit. It is clear that the g tolerance

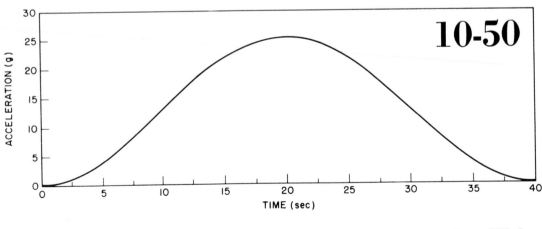

10-50

§ 10.3.1

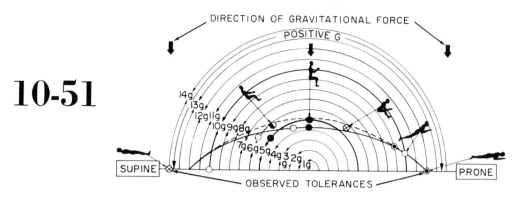

10-51

was raised and that, at any level, the occurrence of undesirable symptoms was reduced to less serious ones.

Current anti-g suits consist of five bladders. These protect the calves, thighs and abdomen. With the onset of acceleration, the bladders are inflated by compressed air. As g forces are increased, this pneumatic counter-pressure is regulated accordingly. The effect is to limit peripheral pooling of the blood and aid the return flow of blood to the heart, thereby maintaining heart output and arterial pressure.

If the onset of acceleration is gradual (i.e., acceleration builds up to a peak slowly)

tolerance is considerably increased (see Fig. 10-52). Although slow onset rates might not be achievable, the tolerance of the individual person under these hypothetical conditions may be used as a standard against which to compare the effectiveness of anti-g measures. Such a comparison is made in Fig. 10-53 (next page). The conditions represented in this graph are a constant rate of 0.07g/sec for the gradual-onset condition with no protection and 1g/sec to peak followed by 15 sec at plateau value for the rapid-onset condition with the protection of a standard pressure suit.

Table 10-16   Effects of Negative g on Protected [1] and Unprotected Subjects Seated Upright [2]

| | Percent of subjects experiencing symptoms | | | | | | | |
| | Without protection | | | With protection | | | | |
Symptoms	1g	2g	3g	1g	2g	3g	4g	5g
Uncomfortable fullness and pressure in head and neck	40	90	100	0	10	40	50	80
Abnormally slow heartbeat	30	90	100	60	50	50	40	30
Headache	0	0	50	0	0	0	0	30
Ear pain	0	0	20	0	10	30	50	50
Cardiac insufficiency and dilation	0	0	50	0	0	0	0	0
Conjunctival hemorrhage	0	0	40	0	0	0	0	0
Difficulty in breathing	0	0	40	0	0	0	0	30
Diminished vision	0	0	40	0	0	10	20	30
Sinus pain	0	0	30	0	0	0	0	0

[1] Pressure helmet only.
[2] Sieker, 1952.

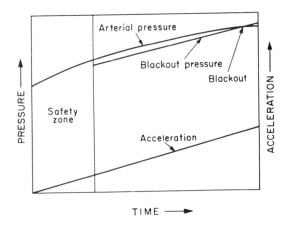

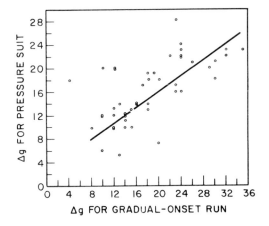

10-52

Arterial pressure and blackout pressure as function of time during gradual onset of acceleration. If rate of onset is slow enough, arterial pressure stays above blackout pressure (Edelberg, et al., 1956)

10-53

Increment in tolerance produced by anti-g suit compared with that produced by making onset of acceleration more gradual. Criterion is relaxed blackout threshold for rapid onset (Edelberg, et al., 1956)

10.3.2 *The effects of vibration*

The biological problems of vibration are concerned with the effects on human performance of periodic mechanical forces impinging on body tissue. Of interest are vibratory forces the effects of which displace or damage bodily organs or tissue other than those involved in ordinary hearing and/or those that produce perceptible feelings of pain, annoyance, or fatigue. In general, these are high-amplitude, low-frequency vibrations generated by machines of some sort.

The most common sources of these vibrations are automobiles and aircraft; a representative spectrum for each of which is shown in Fig. 10-54 (Janeway, 1948 and Critchlow, 1944). Vibration amplitudes in these vehicles depend, for the most part, on the power of the propulsion system and aerodynamic forces; natural frequencies depend on the mass of the vehicle. Thus, in Fig. 10-54, the aircraft is seen to have a wider range of frequencies than the automobile. High-performance aircraft and manned space vehicles present higher-order problems associated with their larger

masses and very-high-power propulsion systems.

The effect of vibrations on the body depends on the physical parameters of the impinging energy, its direction of application with respect to the longitudinal axis of the body, and the mechanical impedance and absorption coefficient of body tissue, organs, and the body as a whole. In addition, because the matching of applied frequencies to the natural frequency of the body and/or its parts will produce resonances, resonant frequencies of the body and its parts assume special importance.

BIOPHYSICAL RELATIONSHIPS

The parameters of vibration are frequency, amplitude (displacement), velocity, acceleration, and jolt. For a fixed frequency, the last three terms are successive derivatives of amplitude with respect to time. This fact is illustrated in Fig. 10-55 (right).

Figure 10-56 (SAE, 1950) shows the interrelation among maximum velocity, maximum acceleration, amplitude, and frequency of simple harmonic motion. For an object with an amplitude of 1 in. and a maximum velocity

466

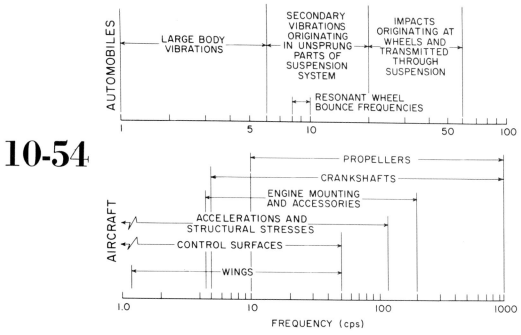

AUTOMOBILES

LARGE BODY VIBRATIONS

SECONDARY VIBRATIONS ORIGINATING IN UNSPRUNG PARTS OF SUSPENSION SYSTEM

IMPACTS ORIGINATING AT WHEELS AND TRANSMITTED THROUGH SUSPENSION

RESONANT WHEEL BOUNCE FREQUENCIES

AIRCRAFT

PROPELLERS

CRANKSHAFTS

ENGINE MOUNTING AND ACCESSORIES

ACCELERATIONS AND STRUCTURAL STRESSES

CONTROL SURFACES

WINGS

FREQUENCY (cps)

10-54

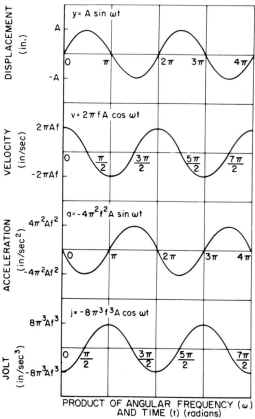

DISPLACEMENT (in.)

$y = A \sin \omega t$

VELOCITY (in./sec)

$v = 2\pi f A \cos \omega t$

ACCELERATION (in./sec^2)

$a = -4\pi^2 f^2 A \sin \omega t$

JOLT (in./sec^3)

$j = -8\pi^3 f^3 A \cos \omega t$

PRODUCT OF ANGULAR FREQUENCY (ω) AND TIME (t) (radians)

of 10 in./sec, for example, the frequency and maximum acceleration can be obtained by finding the intersection of the horizontal maximum-velocity line at 10 in./sec and the diagonal line of amplitude at 1 in. Reading vertically down from this point, the frequency turns out to be about 6.0 cps; reading along the acceleration diagonal, the acceleration turns out to be about 0.26g.

Although a general model covering the body's response to a wide range of frequencies is available, a simplified, lumped-parameter model has been found satisfactory within the range of 1–70 cps. It is in this range that the energies of vibrations from vehicle sources are likely to be most important to man. A simplified mechanical circuit analogue of a man standing or sitting on a vertically vibrating platform is shown in Fig. 10-57 (Coermann, 1959). This analogue, which is applicable to low-frequency vibration, describes transmission along the longitudinal axis in terms of the series impedances offered by various parts of the body.

The total impedance of the body for the situation of Fig. 10-57 is shown in Fig. 10-58 (Goldman and von Gierke, 1960), which also shows the effects on mechanical impedance

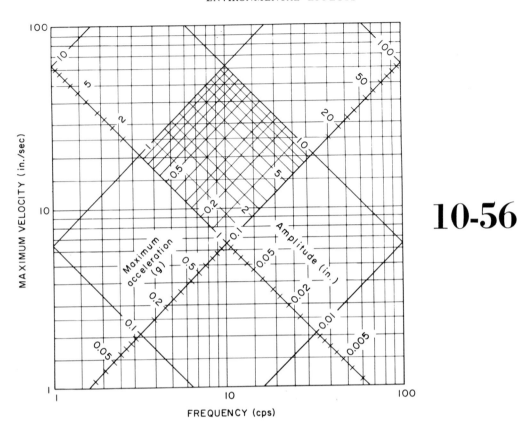

10-56

of muscular tension and of a semirigid pressure envelope around the abdomen. It can be seen that a decrease in impedance is brought about when the musculature is relaxed, either by sitting (as compared to standing) or by sitting relaxed. Figure 10-58 shows that impedance is also lowered when the pelvis is stiffened by being enclosed in a semirigid envelope. Of considerable importance in Fig. 10-58 are the prominent resonance peaks at 4–6 cps.

The actual amplitude and direction of motion of various parts of the body for the situation represented in Fig. 10-57 will depend, not only on the impedances shown in Fig. 10-58, but also on changes in the center of gravity of the upper torso and of the head with changes in body posture. Actually, because, for the man standing erect, the center of gravity of the upper torso is forward of the spine, nonvertical motions will occur even for forces applied in a direction parallel to the

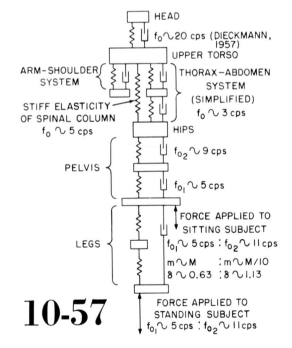

10-57

468

10-58

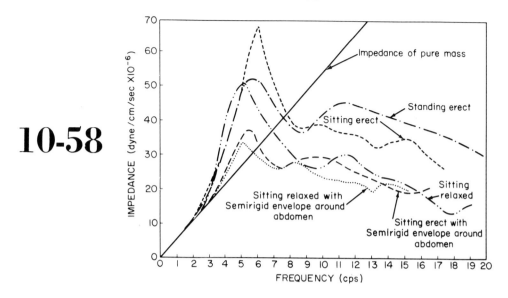

With the above understanding, the relative axis of the spine. Similarly, forward-backward rotation of the head results from displacement of the center of gravity of the head. Thus, even for the situation depicted in Fig. 10-57, the motion of the torso and of the head is not pure vertical motion, but includes rotational components.

With the above understanding, the relative amplitude of vibration of different parts of the body for the situation of Fig. 10-57 is shown in Fig. 10-59 (Dieckmann, 1957) for the standing man and in Fig. 10-60 (Dieckmann, 1957) for the sitting man. The measure used

is the ratio of acceleration of the body member to that of the vibrating table (Fig. 10-60 also shows the amplitude of the head relative to that of the shoulder). The effect of the resonances indicated in Fig. 10-58 is seen clearly in these two graphs. Also clearly indicated is the effect of the increasing impedance

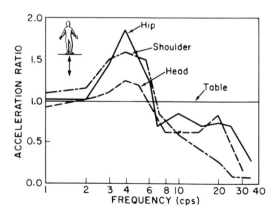

10-59

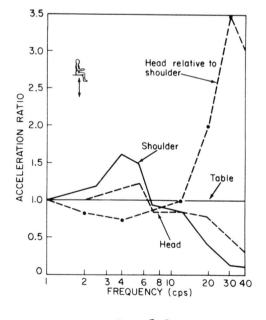

10-60

along the series circuit of Fig. 10-57.

The impedance and transmission factors shown in Figs. 10-58 through 10-60 vary with the various factors already mentioned, but they also are modified by seat and back supports. As a consequence, the transmission factor varies widely, especially at resonant frequencies. The resonant frequencies, however, are fairly constant.

Figures 10-58 through 10-60 also show that vibrations are increasingly attenuated as frequency increases. Above 8–10 cps, the amplitude of body vibration is less than that of the vibrating platform. At 100 cps the attenuation of the head is about 40 db. It also can be seen, however, that the head has additional resonant frequencies at 20–30 cps, and, between 60–90 cps, there is another range of disturbances, presumably associated with the resonance of the eyeball. These phenomena are important factors in situations requiring sensitive visual performance.

One of the most important factors in human tolerance to vibration is the thorax-abdomen system. Vibrations within this system are in both longitudinal and transverse directions. Vibrations in the latter direction result in displacement of the abdominal contents and abdominal wall and of the diaphragm and chest wall. Natural frequencies of this system have been determined by measuring the acceleration of the abdominal wall, the alternating expansion of the thorax, and the velocity of air exchange at the mouth. In this way, it has been determined that the major resonance of the thorax-abdomen system is around 3–4 cps.

Transverse forces (horizontal forces acting at right angles to the longitudinal axis of the body) depend importantly for their effect on the distribution of body masses rather than on the line of gravitational force. These effects for the standing and sitting man are presented in Fig. 10-61 (Dieckmann, 1958), which shows that all important resonant frequencies lie between 1 and 3 cps and, above 2–3 cps, all vibrations of the body are less than that of the vibrating table. It should be kept in mind, however, that the application of transverse energies excites longitudinal as well as transverse components at the head, an effect that is seen as a nodding movement of the head.

Above about 5 cps with horizontal table motion, most of the motion of the head is vertical.

MAJOR EFFECTS OF VIBRATION

The human body appears to respond selectively to one of three differential quantities over each of three portions of the range of 1–250 cps: between 1–6 cps the body responds primarily to the jolt component of the vibration, between 6–9 cps the body responds primarily to the maximum acceleration, and between 9–250 cps the body responds primarily to the maximum velocity imparted by the vibration.

Very-low-frequency, high-amplitude vibrations are the primary cause of motion sickness in automobiles, ships, and aircraft. The highest percentage of illness occurs when the vibrational acceleration changes act *perpendicular* to a horizontal plane passing through the ear openings and external corners of the eyes. Forces acting *within* this plane are much less effective. The degree to which the individual person is affected is quite dependent on physical, psychological, and environmental factors. Symptoms include loss of appetite, loss of interest, perspiring, salivation, nausea, headache, and vomiting.

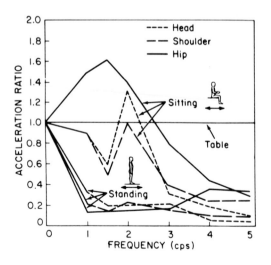

10-61

470

Vibrations in the range 1–250 cps can produce headaches and fatigue when at the intolerable level. If the exposure at this level is of sufficiently long duration, permanent physical damage can occur. This is an important problem in the trucking industry where such vibrations are often found at intolerable levels. Prolonged exposure to vibrations of less than intolerable levels, though they might not produce physical damage, commonly produce annoyance and fatigue—factors that can be expected to reduce the general performance and effectiveness of the operator.

It already has been suggested that visual functions are impaired by vibration of the head. This effect can be expected even when the amplitude of head vibration is less than that of the platform. It also has been shown that exposure to vibration increases the energy expended in working and affects the general emotional response of the operator. These various effects, however, are very little understood, and only general statements can be made about them.

By far the best established human responses to low-frequency vibrations are subjective feelings and perceptions, including the ability of the individual to detect the presence of the vibration, discomfort, and pain. Tolerance limits, therefore, are expressed in terms of these subjective reactions and in terms of the limits of vibration that individual people have indicated they would tolerate voluntarily. Figure 10-62 is a human-tolerance curve for very-low-frequency vibration that shows the duration of tolerable, peak, vertical acceleration at very-low frequencies.

The most widely used method for classifying the severity of vibrations is based on the data shown in Fig. 10-63 (Goldman and von

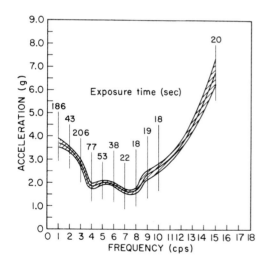

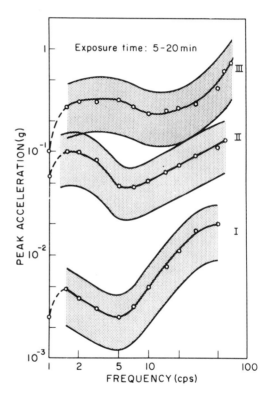

10-62 Human vibration tolerance. Average peak acceleration at various frequencies at which subjects (restrained with standard USAF lap and shoulder straps) refused to tolerate further short exposure to vertical vibration. Shaded area is about one standard deviation on either side of mean (Ziegenruecker and Magid, 1959)

10-63 Vibration tolerance criteria. Average peak accelerations at various frequencies at which subjects perceive vibration (curve I), find it unpleasant (curve II), or refuse to tolerate it further (curve III). Subjects were without body restraint. Shaded areas are about one standard deviation on either side of mean (Goldman, 1948)

Gierke, 1960). This graph presents three classifications of effect: perception of the presence of vibration (I), the unpleasantness of the vibration (II), and refusal to tolerate the vibration (III). The curves shown represent averages for the standing, sitting, and prone positions. For multidirectional vibrations, it has been suggested that the vector sum of the components represent the composite acceleration. Accelerations larger than Class III can be tolerated for very short periods of time without harmful effects only by young adult males (see Fig. 10-62).

PROTECTION AGAINST VIBRATION

Figure 10-64 (Goldman and von Gierke, 1960) describes the vibration levels associated with various types of ground and air vehicles. This figure also indicates vibrations that, for long-term exposure, are intolerable and those that are tolerable. Areas indicated for ground vehicles are maxima rather than spectra. In general, rubber-tired farm tractors and trucks have maximum vertical vibrations of 2–6 cps; for earth-moving equipment the range of maximum vibration is 1.5–3.5 cps; for crawler-type tractors it is about 5 cps. Figure 10-64 also shows the effects of various powered hand tools; most of these are within the range at which chronic hand injuries can be expected. Tool design and operation, therefore, are critical for these devices.

Protection against vibration is achieved by reducing the applied forces or by manipulating body posture and body supports. Cushions are ineffectual in the human resonance range and might even amplify vibrations at human resonance frequencies, although they are generally effective in damping higher frequency vibrations. Figure 9-65 (Goldman and von Gierke, 1960) shows this effect in terms of the mechanical impedance of a man on a seat. Resonance can be seen at about 6 cps; the addition of the cushion dampens the system at higher frequencies but results in a resonance at a lower frequency.

For the innerspring cushion, the man-spring system not only has a new resonance frequency, but it also is amplified at that point.

To produce an effective isolation of the man in this system would require a large static deflection of the man into the spring. This situation is shown in Fig. 10-66 (Goldman and von Gierke, 1960), which relates deflection of a seat spring by the mass of the man to the resonance of the man-seat system. As stated previously, the range of human resonance is 2–5 cps, and to reduce the resonance of the system below this would require static deflections of 10 in. Thus, cushions are used for static comfort and are effective in damping above the human resonance range but are of no help at or below this range.

Seat suspension systems are usually hydraulic shock absorbers, coil and leaf springs, torsion bars, or some combination of these. When designed to move only in a linear direction, all of these systems have been successful and appear about equal in effectiveness. When designed to permit the seat to pivot around a center of rotation, these systems produce undesirable pitching motions and fatigue the rider. Of all of these suspension systems, hydraulic shock absorbers appear to be most acceptable when measured in terms of fatigue effects.

In general, the most effective attenuator of vibration is the man's legs. This fact has al-

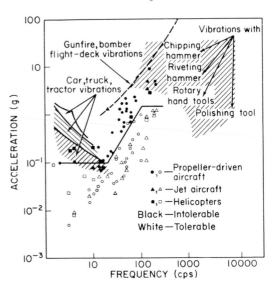

10-64

472

ready been shown in terms of differences between vibration transmitted in the seated and standing positions. For situations near intolerable levels, it is possible to develop seats and harnesses that provide the maximum advantage of position and body support. Semirigid or rigid pressure envelopes appear to be very promising, although they have been used, so far, only in laboratory tests.

10.3.3 *Effects of noise*

Noise is defined as any undesirable sound, even though it might be a meaningful one. The criterion of undesirability is based on the capacity of sound to disrupt communications,

This article was drafted, in part, by Robert S. Gales of the U. S. Navy Electronics Laboratory.

cause injury to hearing (hearing loss), produce annoyance or discomfort, or reduce skilled performance. In this discussion, consideration will be given to noise environments for all criteria except that of speech communication, which has been considered in Chapter 4. Chapters 3 and 4 should be consulted for definitions of units and background information.

HEARING LOSS

Temporary hearing losses resulting from noise exposures are greater the higher the noise level, the longer the duration of exposure, and, within limits, the shorter the bandwidth within which the energy is concentrated. The effect is seen as a loss in auditory acuity, especially between 1,000 and 6,000 cps, and as a reduction in the loudness of sound. For example, a 15-db loss in sensitivity to octave-bandwidth sounds can follow exposure to steady-state octave-band pressure levels of 100 db. The loss in sensitivity to pure tones at and above 1,000 cps following the same conditions might be of the order of 35 db. The loss is greatest for people with normal hearing.

Temporary hearing losses are produced rapidly and are maximum within about 7 min

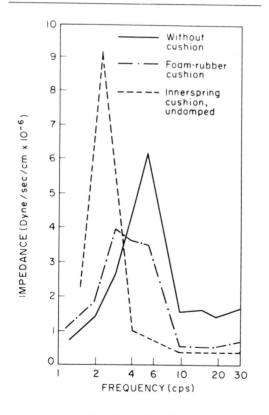

10-65

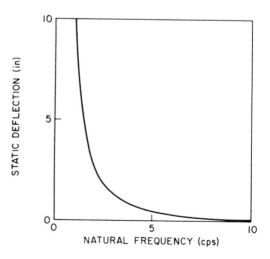

10-66

for exposure to pure tones. Maximum loss from wide-band noise is longer and depends on whether or not it is steady-state noise. For steady-state noise in an industrial setting containing octave-band pressure levels of 90–100 db, an average loss in auditory acuity of 15 db for tones above 1,000 cps can be expected following a 4-hr exposure. Exposure to non-steady and intermittent noise of the same level has a lesser effect; a full working day of exposure to this kind of environment is required to produce an average temporary hearing loss of 5 db at frequencies above 1,000 cps.

Recovery from temporary hearing loss depends on the duration of exposure, the nature of the sound, and the age of the person so incapacitated. Recovery from nonimpulsive sounds might require two to five times the duration of the exposure, depending on the nature of the sound. For example, normal workday exposure to octave-band levels of 95 db might require 2–5 days for complete recovery of normal auditory acuity, particularly in the 1,000–6,000 cps region, and a 30-min exposure to a pure tone of 105 db might require 2–3 hr for complete recovery. The fact that the major losses are primarily within the region of speech sounds has serious implications for speech-communication systems (see Chapter 4).

ANNOYANCE OR DISCOMFORT

Because noise is any undesirable sound, it may be thought of as related to a negative reaction or feeling of annoyance in the listener. The extent of his reaction will depend on the nature of his activity and the nature of the noise. Intermittent or other nonsteady noise and high-frequency components appear to be somewhat more annoying than other sounds. The annoyance value of the noise, however, does not seem to be a property of sound as such, but rather of the distracting power of the sound as a competitive stimulus. Thus, habituation to a steady-state noise is more rapid than habituation to other sounds. Similarly, temporary hearing loss resulting from steady-state noise is more rapid than loss from intermittent noise because the inter-

mittent periods of relative quiet permit some recovery.

Annoyance increases with loudness and also with pitch. These relationships have been quantified in terms of thresholds of annoyance and equal-annoyance contours for relatively simple sounds such as pure tones and bands of noise. Figure 10-67 shows annoyance thresholds for bands of noise and for several conditions of listening attitude and noise experience.

Working criteria have been established for evaluating the reaction of a residential community to noise. The noise rating of the criteria is based on surveys of complaints and legal actions taken by residents located near airfields, industrial noise sources, and street traffic. The information required for developing a noise rating is provided in Figs. 10-68 and 10-69 (Rosenblith and Stevens, 1953) and Table 10-17.

To establish working criteria, proceed as follows:

1. Obtain the octave-band noise spectrum that describes the noise in the listener's area.

2. Superimpose the spectrum on Fig. 10-68, and determine the highest level-rank zone into which the spectrum extends. The level rank is identified by alphabetic letters.

3. Consulting Table 10-17, obtain the algebraic sum of the correction factors indicated for those conditions that characterize the noise.

4. Correct the level rank obtained in Step 2 by the correction factor obtained in Step 3. For example, if the level rank were H and the correction factor were −1, the corrected level rank would be G.

5. Use the corrected rank as the noise rating shown on the abscissa of Fig. 10-69 to obtain the expected response.

REDUCED PERFORMANCE

There is little to indicate that nonauditory human performance suffers in noisy environments except as the noise provides a source of distraction. The intensity of the distraction can be evaluated in terms of the annoyance produced. Thus, motivation, adaptation, and habituation can be expected to play large parts in any noise/performance situation. Those performances most likely to be most susceptible to noise will be those most susceptible to distraction in general, i.e., tasks involving sustained attention over relatively long periods of time (such as are involved in many dial- or signal-monitoring situations), complex rather than simple tasks, and tasks in which the operator is paced by the system (particularly if the pacing is irregular).

PROTECTION AGAINST NOISE

The engineering solution to the noise problem requires one or more of the following procedures:

a. Reduction of the noise output at the source. This procedure might involve design and material considerations, damping by suit-

able mounting, sound-power reduction, etc.

b. Changes in system requirements or operation. For example, street or airstrip traffic might be scheduled at more opportune times of the day or over different routes to reduce resident reactions, remote or automatic control devices might be feasible, etc.

c. Attenuation or deflection of the sound from the source. This procedure might involve insulation of the source, baffles, insulation of the operator, or ear-protective devices.

Predicting Hearing-Damage Risk

The prediction of hearing-damage risk is difficult because it depends on the individual person, on the spectral composition of the sound, and on the duration of exposure. The following general recommendations, however,

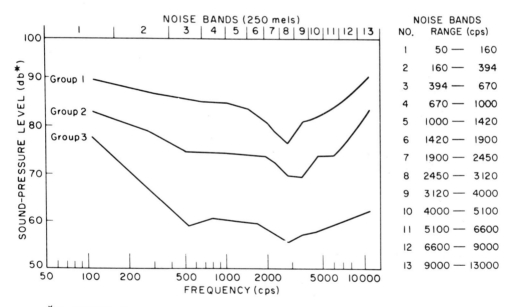

*Re 0.0002 μbar

10-67 Threshold of annoyance for bands of noise. Annoyance-threshold judgments of 20 observers on 13 noise bands. Observers were divided into three subgroups. Upper curve represents mean judgments of six observers who had once worked at noisy jobs and who imagined some definite work situation while making judgments. Middle curve represents mean judgments of seven observers who had only worked at quiet jobs and who imagined some definite work situation while making judgments. Lower curve represents mean judgments of seven observers who had only worked at quiet jobs and who attended to the noise as such, or otherwise did not imagine any definite work situation while making judgments (Spieth, 1956)

475

should be observed whenever possible:

1. Make necessary exposures to intense sounds as brief as possible. The human ear can stand extremely intense sounds for a few seconds without lasting effects, but prolonged exposure to intensities of 85–95 db or above can cause damage to the ear and an accompanying hearing loss. Figure 3-23 (Chapter 3) shows recommended upper limits for noise exposure.

2. Provide for measuring the hearing of individual persons exposed to intense sounds, especially after several hours of continuous exposure. This is important because individual persons differ markedly in their susceptibility to noise-induced hearing loss, although the following are reliable guidelines:

a. Hearing losses usually appear first in the region of 4,000–6,000 cps and then spread with continued exposure to higher and lower frequencies.

b. Sounds capable of producing hearing damage generally produce a temporary hearing loss. If the person is removed from the sound when the loss is first detected, his hearing will return within a few hours or days.

c. The effects of exposure are cumulative, and a small, but permanent, hearing loss becomes more serious with continued exposure. Whereas about 95 db is the limit for an 8-hr day, 130 db can be tolerated for only 10 sec, as shown in Fig. 3-24 (Chapter 3).

d. A useful rule is that, if hearing is lost and then recovered overnight, cumulative permanent loss is unlikely.

3. When significant hearing losses are measured, avoid further damage by providing for one of the following:

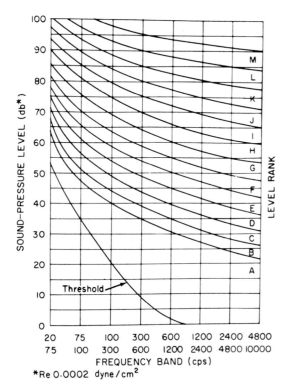

10-68

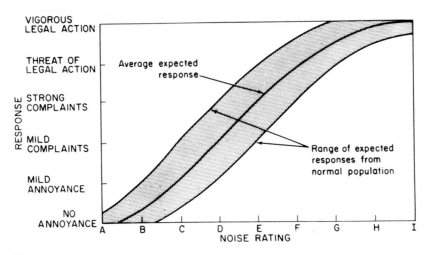

10-69

Table 10-17 Correction Factors to be Applied to Level Rank to Find Noise Rating *

Influencing factor	Possible conditions	Correction factor
Noise-spectrum character	Pure-tone components	1
	Wide-band noise	0
Peak factor	Impulsive	1
	Not impulsive	0
Repetitive character (about ½-min noise duration assumed)	Continuous to one exposure per minute	0
	10–60 exposures per hour	−1
	1–10 exposures per hour	−2
	4–20 exposures per day	−3
	1–4 exposures per day	−4
	One exposure per day	−5
Background noise	Residential suburban	1
	Suburban	0
	Residential urban	−1
	Urban	−2
	Industrial	−3
Time of day	Nightime	0
	Daytime	−1
Previous conditioning	No previous conditioning	0
	Some previous conditioning	−1
	Considerable previous conditioning	−2

* Rosenblith and Stevens, 1953.

a. Removing the person from the high-noise environment.

b. Supplying the person with protective devices that reduce effective sound levels in the ear to more moderate values.

c. Reducing the noise in the environment.

4. Pay special attention to the reduction of high-frequency environmental noise. Low-frequency noises (500 cps and below) are much less damaging than higher ones.

5. Establish criteria for the risk of damage to hearing for different noise levels, frequencies, and durations of exposure by consulting Figs. 3-23 and 3-24 (Chapter 3).

§ 10.3.3

Ear-Protective Devices

Where noise masks signals, or causes discomfort and annoyance, or threatens hearing damage, attempts should be made to reduce noise at its source or in the neighborhood of the operator. Such attempts, however, often fall far short of providing a noise-free environment for carrying out auditory tasks. In such cases, ear-protective devices should be used, some of which will effectively improve the detection and identification of signals.

Ear-protective devices fall into the following four categories (see Fig. 10-70):

a. Earplugs (inserts) that fit into the ear canal. These are of two types: pre-formed (e.g., molded rubber, plastic, etc.) and unpreformed (e.g., waxed cotton).

b. Semi-inserts that fit into the ear canal but are supported by headset-type bands.

c. Ear muffs or sockets or cushions that fit over the external ear. These are of three types: foam-rubber cushions that press against the ear as well as against the head, fiber- or rubber-filled "doughnuts" that fit around the ear and press against the head rather than against the ear, and fluid-filled doughnuts similar in size and shape to the fiber- or rubber-filled doughnuts.

d. Rigid helmets that fit over the entire head.

To achieve high attenuation of ambient noise, it is necessary to have a good acoustic seal between the ear protective device and the surfaces against which it bears. With anything short of an airtight seal, attenuation is markedly reduced. Moreover, attenuation is limited to about 50 db by the fact that noise can "out-

FOUR TYPES OF EAR PROTECTORS

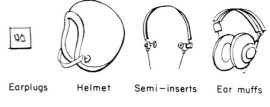

Earplugs   Helmet   Semi-inserts   Ear muffs

10-70

flank" the ear-protective device through the bone of the head (see Chapter 3).

Used by themselves, earplugs are more effective in attenuating noise, especially at low frequencies, than are ear muffs, as can be seen from Fig. 10-71 (Zwislocki, 1957), which compares the attenuation characteristics of all types of ear-protective devices. Earplugs and ear muffs can be worn at the same time, however, to provide greater attenuation than either alone can provide, but the attenuation afforded by the combination is not the sum of the two separate attenuations; it is usually less than that sum. Another combination is a rigid helmet with earplugs that are worn under the helmet. This combination provides the theoretical maximum attenuation (50 db).

Earplugs and combinations. Properly designed earplugs provide the cheapest and sim-

plest way of preventing the hearing loss that accumulates during long exposure to intense noises. To be effective, they must make an airtight seal in the ear canal. Attenuation of any earplug can be improved somewhat by increasing the radial pressure of the plug against the walls of the ear canal; the increased pressure reduces the motion of the plug in response to sound. This arrangement causes such discomfort, however, that tightly fitted plugs cannot be worn very long.

Attenuation provided by typical earplugs is shown in Fig. 10-72. Various earplugs are shown in the upper left, and their real-ear attenuation is plotted below. It can be seen that dry cotton is a very poor attenuator, but paraffin-impregnated cotton (FLENTS), when properly inserted in the ear canal, provides good attenuation. The V51-R is molded of soft rubber or neoprene in three sizes. The

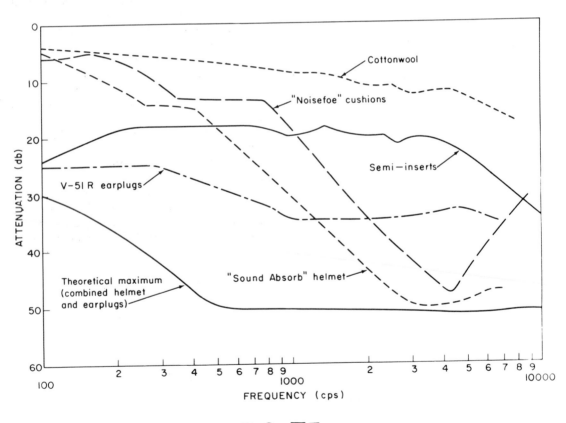

10-71

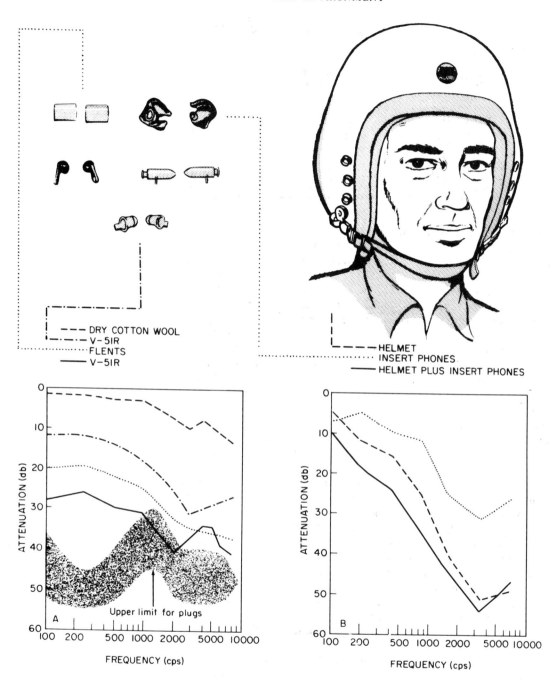

DRY COTTON WOOL
V-5IR
FLENTS
V-5IR

HELMET
INSERT PHONES
HELMET PLUS INSERT PHONES

Upper limit for plugs

ATTENUATION (db)

FREQUENCY (cps)

10-72

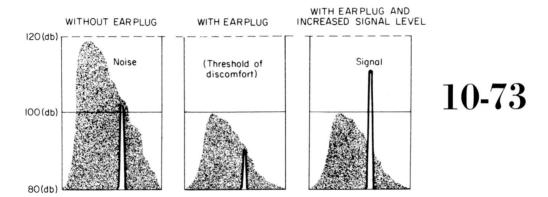

solid curve shows its attenuation with an optimum fit; the dash-dot curve shows an average for a group of 20 unselected persons in which it is expected that some have not obtained a very good fit. The shaded area in Fig. 10-72 represents an estimate of the maximum possible attenuation obtainable by earplugs.

The right-hand graph shows that the attenuation of individually molded insert earphones is no better than that of general-purpose plugs. The helmet shown in the upper right contains cups over the ears and seals to the head by means of an edge bead. Its attenuation is shown by the dashed curve. The solid curve shows the attenuation of insert and helmet worn together.

Earplugs also can be used to increase the detection of signals in very intense noise. When noise levels are very high (110 db or above), the use of an earplug makes a signal more detectable. This is possible because the ear at high intensities acts like a peak clipper or compressor and fails to respond linearly to the signal. By reducing the overall level of the noise and the signal with earplugs, the sound-pressure level is brought within the range at which the ear responds more linearly, and signals are more easily detected.

As previously noted, very-high-noise levels approach the threshold of discomfort and narrow the dynamic range of the ear. At such levels, an operator is unwilling to increase the gain (where it is possible to adjust the gain) because an increased signal becomes uncomfortable. Earplugs, however, reduce the level of both the noise and the signal, thereby

enlarging the ear's usable dynamic range. By increasing the gain now, the signal-to-noise ratio (S/N) is increased, and the signal is more easily detected. Of course, this procedure does not work if the background noise is electrically amplified and comes through the same gain control as the signal.

When adequate signal power is available and earphones have good power-handling capacity, another method of improving the S/N ratio is feasible: earplugs worn under earphones equipped with ear muffs. The plugs attenuate both signal and noise by 20 db or so, but the signal is then restored by additional gain to the same level it would have been in the absence of the earplug. The net advantage in S/N ratio is then 20 db (see Fig. 10-73).

Ear muffs and combinations. The ears can be protected against environmental noise by covering them with ear muffs. Here too, a completely airtight seal is essential to provide maximum attenuation of noise. To make such a seal, the muff must be a suitably shaped cushion with soft, flexible surfaces held tightly to the head by adequate pressure.

An ear muff of the highest attenuation is made of dense material. It encloses a large volume with a minimum opening at the ear or head. A properly designed muff has an attenuation as large or larger than an earplug at frequencies above 1,000 cps and approaches the attenuation of an earplug at lower frequencies. Attenuation of typical ear muffs and phone sockets is shown in Fig. 10-74.

By combining ear muffs and plugs, attenuations somewhat larger than that of either

§ 10.3.3

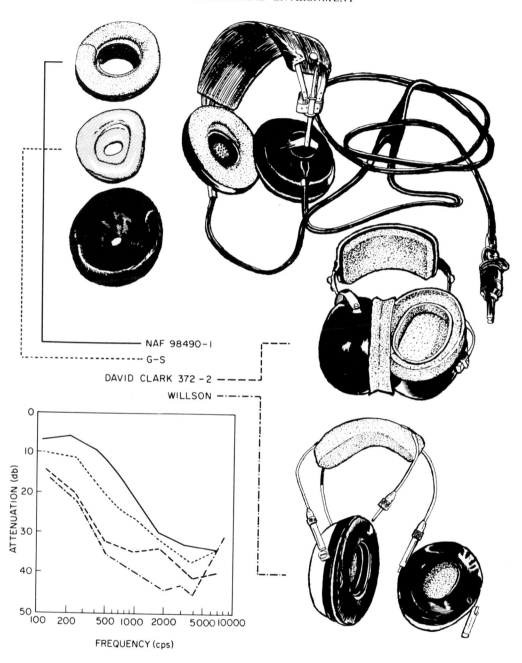

10-74 Acoustic attenuation of ear muffs and earphone sockets. Standard Navy headset with NAF 48490-1 sockets is shown at top right. At top left, reading down, are NAF 48490-1 (Kapok-filled chamois), Grason-Stadler (Mastic-filled plastic), and RCA (glass-fiber-filled rubber) ear muffs. Earphones in center and lower right are fitted with NAF 48490-1 and Grason-Stadler sockets. Willson ear muff has fluid-filled sac. David Clarke ear muff has foam rubber seal.

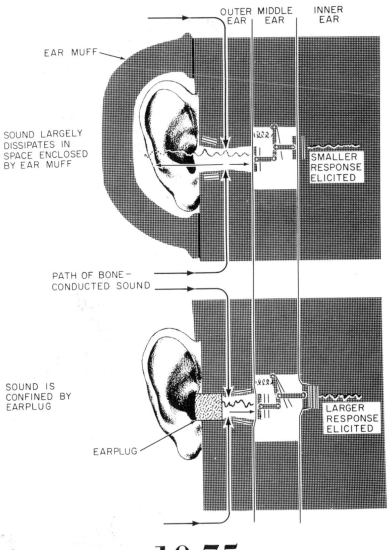

10-75

alone can be achieved. The attenuation of the combination, however, is not as great as the sum of the two separately because sound might be conducted through the bone of the head and around the protective devices to the inner ear. This phenomenon was illustrated by the curve of the combination of insert phone and helmet in Fig. 10-72.

The failure of the separate attenuations to add at the higher frequencies is presumably due to reaching the bone-conduction limit. An earplug actually lowers the bone-conduction threshold (enhances hearing by bone conduction) by confining sound pressure that enters the ear canal by bone conduction (see Fig. 10-75). To attenuate airborne sound without enhancing bone-conducted sound, an ear muff enclosing a volume of about 1,500 cm³ or more is required. This volume permits bone-conducted sound pressure to dissipate and reduces the intensity of such sounds at the eardrum.

Helmets and combinations. The head must be completely enclosed in a suitable helmet to obtain protection that appreciably exceeds the bone-conduction threshold. Even when the head is completely enclosed, attenuation is increased only about 10 db over the bone-conduction limit because sound is then transmitted to the head through the body (see Fig. 10-76).

Helmets can provide some additional protection when they enclose a major portion of the head, include ear muffs, and have an edge bead to seal tightly to the head around the face and neck. If this seal is poor, however, the protection provided by the helmet is little better than that afforded by the ear muffs it contains. In fact, many flying helmets do not satisfactorily hold the ear muffs tightly to the ears. In some cases, the helmet has acted as an amplifier, increasing the sound-pressure level at the ears for certain frequencies. Figure 10-72 shows attenuation of a helmet designed for noise exclusion.

The Acceptability of Ear Protectors

Any device used for protecting the ear from noise must not only attenuate sound, it must also be acceptable to the wearer and not interfere with other tasks he must perform. The ear protector must be comfortable, stay in its proper position, and not irritate the skin. In addition, the protector usually should allow the head to move freely, and it sometimes must permit the person to hear face-to-face speech and warning signals.

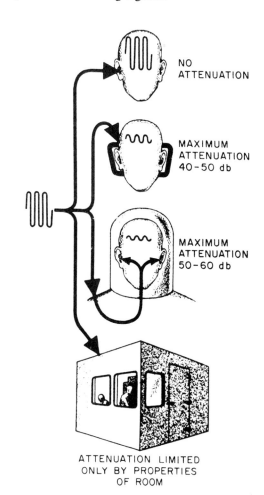

ATTENUATION LIMITED ONLY BY PROPERTIES OF ROOM

10-76 Maximum ear protection afforded by various devices. Protection that closes or covers ears only is limited to about 40 or 50 db before it becomes bypassed by bone conduction. Covering entire head allows another 10 db of attenuation before body-conducted sound bypasses helmet. Complete enclosure of entire body is required to get protection greater than about 60 db

A good ear protector equalizes pressure over the perimeter of the ear canal or skull area because localized pressure becomes extremely uncomfortable when a protector is worn for more than 5–10 min. Ear muffs tend to be more comfortable than earplugs because they distribute pressure over a larger area of the skull, which is relatively less sensitive than the walls of the ear canal. Fluid-filled muffs are more comfortable than rubber- or kapok-filled muffs, because they fit evenly the irregular contours of the head. For the same reason they provide an excellent acoustic seal and, hence, maximum attenuation of external noise.

§ 10.3.3

11

anthropometry

THIS CHAPTER will be somewhat different from the preceding ones. It will have no design recommendations as such; it is a compilation of the available and relevant data on human-body measurements. Yet, in a sense, all of the data included in this chapter are design recommendations—by their mere presence in the Guide, they beg to be used by the engineer in the design of man-machine systems. In addition to this, they form the basis of a great many of the design recommendations made in the preceding chapters, especially Chapters 6, 7, 8, and 9.

11.1 *Physical Anthropology and Equipment Design*

This chapter was written by Albert Damon, Howard W. Stoudt, and Ross A. McFarland of Harvard University.

Anthropology, which means "the science of man," is concerned with man in his biological and social aspects. Physical anthropology is the study of the body characteristics of individual persons or groups of them. Some of these body traits are quantitative, like height and weight, and others are qualitative, like skin color, hair form, and blood group. Anthropometry is concerned with human-body measurement. Such measurement includes body dimensions (see section 11.2), range of motion of body members (see section 11.3), and muscle strength (see section 11.4).

11.1.1 *Goals for the design engineer*

The human body, its structure and mechanical function, occupies a central place in man-machine design. Failure to provide a few inches, which might be critical for the operator, can jeopardize the performance, "health," and "life" of both man and machine. With proper forethought, these critical inches usually can be provided without compromising the design. Reliable anthropometric data and procedures provide the necessary tools for the optimal sizing of many mass-produced items from oxygen masks to airplane cockpits and truck cabs.

The goals that the design engineer should aspire to in accommodating for human dimensions can be listed as follows:

1. All men should be able to operate all machines. This being an ideal goal, compromises on 98% or 95% or even 90%—but no less—might be necessary. Universal operability is desirable for the following reasons:

a. Military combat conditions often require complete human interchangeability.

b. The supply of qualified operators for complex machines is limited enough without limiting this supply still further by design that does not permit universal operability.

c. Equipment that imposes human size limitations unduly complicates the selection and training of operators.

In addition, universal, or virtually universal, operability of equipment is generally feasible for the following reasons:

a. Relatively few limitations on human size are imposed by the gross dimensions of a machine; the fault usually lies with design details (see Fig. 11-1).

b. The range of human variation (see article 11.1.2) is small relative to machine dimensions—even in such close quarters as in aircraft or small automobiles.

c. The human size range, or at least 90–98% of it, in general is readily accommodated by adjustable devices.

2. The machine's performance should not be limited by human failure. Any equipment, however cleverly engineered, can be destroyed or abused by an uncomfortable or inefficient operator. If this results from some oversight of the designer, the failure might better be termed "design error" than "operator error."

11.1.2 *Factors affecting human-body measurements*

The most important factors affecting human-body measurements are those coming under the general headings of "human variation" and "clothing and personal equipment." These factors are discussed in the following paragraphs.

HUMAN VARIATION

One way in which the man differs from the other elements in man-machine-system design is in his innate variation. Chemical compounds have one melting point and one coefficient of conductivity. Metals, plastics, and textiles likewise can be described in terms of relatively fixed properties, with behavior precisely specified under given external conditions of heat, cold, vibration, and the like. Man, however, is not so uniform; unlike inert material, human responses to identical external conditions will vary from person to person (see Chapter 10). For example, fat people are more comfortable than thin people in the

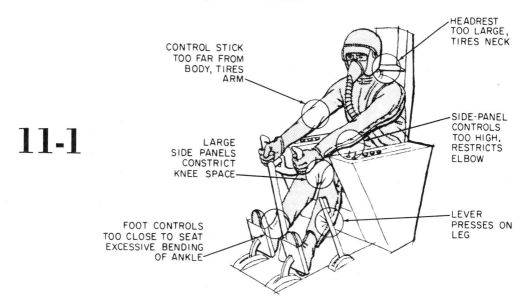

11-1

CONTROL STICK TOO FAR FROM BODY, TIRES ARM

HEADREST TOO LARGE, TIRES NECK

SIDE-PANEL CONTROLS TOO HIGH, RESTRICTS ELBOW

LARGE SIDE PANELS CONSTRICT KNEE SPACE

LEVER PRESSES ON LEG

FOOT CONTROLS TOO CLOSE TO SEAT EXCESSIVE BENDING OF ANKLE

cold, and the reverse holds true for hot conditions.

Also unlike inert material, man's innate variation greatly exceeds that due to external conditions. Men vary, through heredity, from group to group. For instance, Caucasians, Negroes, and Orientals differ significantly in average physique, despite some overlapping (see Fig. 11-2).

Differences in age and sex are obvious causes for physical variation. Less obvious, but sometimes critical, causes are occupation and long-term changes in physique. Even among white men age 18–40, for example, truck drivers differ from research workers, and fighter pilots differ from bomber pilots (see Fig. 11-3). Bomber and fighter pilots also differ from one another in some aspects of body form, as do navigators, bombardiers, and tank crews. In addition, human-body dimensions can change over a period of time. For instance, American soldiers of World War II averaged 0.7 in. taller and 13 lb heavier than those of World War I just 25 yr earlier (see Fig. 11-4).

Thus, human variation is such that the group that will use the equipment must be specified and, if possible, measured directly. It cannot be assumed that one group will resemble, closely enough for design purposes,

other groups for whom anthropometric data are available.

Men also vary within groups. Within any sizable group, such as white aircraft pilots age 20–30, body dimensions are distributed along a bell-shaped "normal" curve (see Fig. 11-5). Most men are included in the middle of the distribution, with fewer and fewer occurring toward the extremes. Anthropometric data, therefore, consist of ranges rather than definite points. Thus, there is no one standard man with given dimensions but only approximations to ranges. Hence, adjustability becomes a keynote of design for human use (see Fig. 11-6).

CLOTHING AND EQUIPMENT

Machines should be designed to suit the operator as he will use the machine under actual operating conditions. These include such extreme environments as heat, cold, altitude, and pressure (see Chapter 10), all of which involve special protective equipment worn by the operator. Thus, clothing and personal equipment affect human-body dimensions. The bulkiest cold-weather or high-altitude outfit, the parachute and life-raft, body armor and ammunition—all of these are

§ 11.1.2

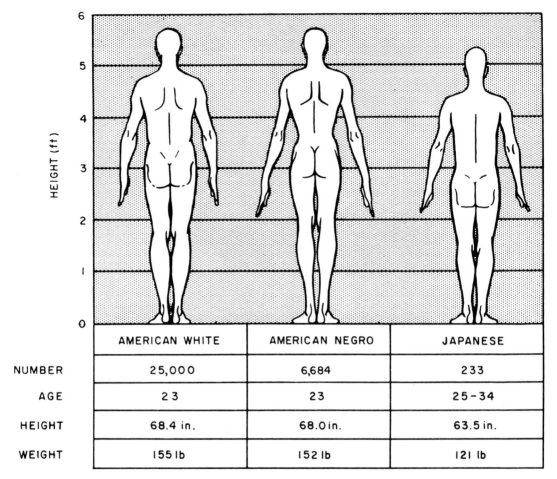

	AMERICAN WHITE	AMERICAN NEGRO	JAPANESE
NUMBER	25,000	6,684	233
AGE	23	23	25-34
HEIGHT	68.4 in.	68.0 in.	63.5 in.
WEIGHT	155 lb	152 lb	121 lb

DATA FROM NEWMAN AND WHITE, 1951 AND ISHII, 1957

11-2

	FIGHTER	BOMBER
NUMBER	210	1184
AGE	27	29
HEIGHT	68.8 in.	69.4 in.
WEIGHT	159 lb	166 lb

DATA FROM HERTZBERG, ET AL., 1954

11-3

	WORLD WAR I 1919	WORLD WAR II 1946
NUMBER	97,000	25,000
AGE	23	25
HEIGHT	67.7in	68.4in
WEIGHT	142 lb	155 lb

DATA FROM DAVENPORT AND LOVE, 1921 AND NEWMAN AND WHITE, 1951

11-4

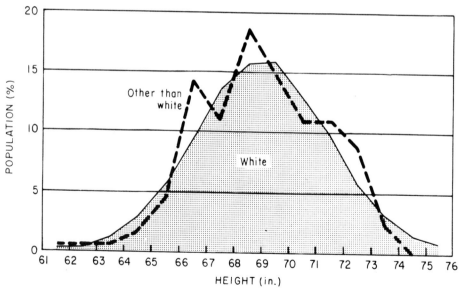

11-5

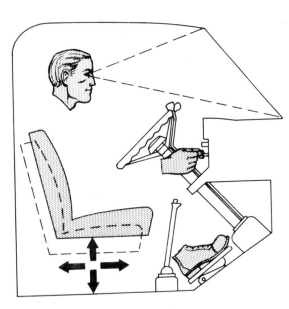

11-6

11-7

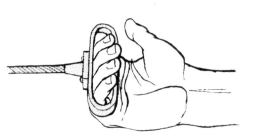

THE BARE HAND FITS

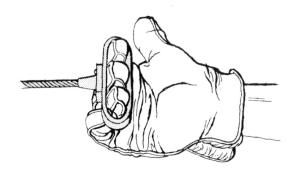

THE GLOVED HAND DOESN'T

11-8

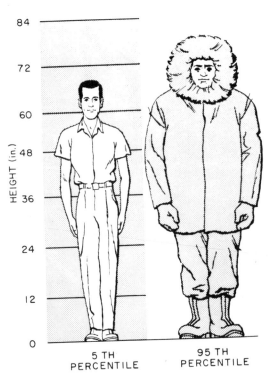

5 TH
PERCENTILE

95 TH
PERCENTILE

11-9

added to the nude body to constitute the functional operator.

Failure to heed this fact has led to such design errors as escape hatches that do not permit the passage of a flyer wearing a parachute (see Fig. 11-7), gun-charging handles in aircraft that cannot be operated by a gloved hand (see Fig. 11-8), and turrets that provide insufficient space for gunners wearing helmets and oxygen masks. Thus, the designer should acquaint himself with the environmental conditions and personal equipment with which the operators of the machines will have to cope. These machines should be designed to fit the extremes of human size, whether lightly clad or encumbered with complete special-purpose outfits (see Fig. 11-9).

11.1.3 *The reliability and limitations of the data*

To be useful in equipment design, anthropometric data should satisfy the following three criteria (see also Chapter 1):

1. The groups measured should be representative of the equipment user. Because one cannot measure every pilot or driver, for example, samples are selected for measurement. In addition to age, sex, race, and occupation, other possible sources of unrepresentative samples are geography (Pacific Northwest men average 0.6 in. taller and 3 lb heavier than New Englanders) and socio-economic factors (college men are larger than non-college men). Also, because one cannot assume, without verification, that anthropometric data from one group apply to another, military personnel, highly selected in respect to age, health, height, and weight standards, cannot represent the general population. Even within a single military service, different specialists are physically distinct, as has been noted.

2. Samples should be large enough to yield reliable results that are reproducible from one sample to another. For most anthropometric purposes, 50–100 persons is a minimum

sample size, but the larger the sample the better. In general, larger samples are more vital for dimensions with a wide range, such as weight, than for relatively range-restricted or small dimensions such as those of the head, hand, and foot.

3. Measuring techniques should be specified and standard. This criterion provides the only valid basis for comparing groups and for locating test subjects as percentiles of the user group. It makes a great deal of difference whether measurements are made with or without clothing, in the erect or in the normal, slumped position, or with chests in expiration or inspiration.

SOURCES OF DATA

The anthropometric data presented in this chapter are heavily weighted toward military populations, particularly those of the Air Force. Unfortunately, there are no comprehensive anthropometric studies of the civilian population, a fact which hampers human-engineering work for this numerically most important of all groups.

Some data applicable to the civilian population are available from a classic study of railway travelers (Hooton, 1945), but the eight measurements taken were chosen for their relevance to the design of railway-coach seats. Furthermore, because of the special measuring chair used, these measurements are not always directly comparable to those taken with standard techniques. A detailed anthropometric study of women (O'Brien and Shelton, 1941) is excellent for its intended purpose, garment and pattern construction, but it consists mostly of body heights, circumferences, and skin-surface measurements, only a few of which are useful in solving engineering problems.

The life-insurance industry has a good deal of data on heights and weights, but these are for economically selected groups of people. In addition, the lack of standardization in measuring techniques and the difficulty of compensating accurately for wide variations in shoes and clothing make it advisable to omit those data here.

§ 11.1.3

When the designer needs more help, either to find specialized data or to solve problems beyond the scope of this chapter or the references cited (especially Hansen and Cornog, 1958), it probably will be more efficient for him to consult with an anthropometrist rather than to attempt to become one himself. The anthropometrist will be acquainted with the relevant literature and, much more important, with its interpretation and application.

There are several laboratories and centers to which the engineer can turn. All of the armed forces have active anthropometric programs and will gladly cooperate with designers, whether civilian or military. These service laboratories and centers include Behavioral Sciences Laboratory, Wright-Patterson Air Force Base, Ohio; U. S. Army Quartermaster Research and Engineering Center, Natick, Massachusetts; and U. S. Naval Training Devices Center, Port Washington, N. Y. Other military sources of information include U. S. Naval Research Laboratory, Washington, D. C., and Human Engineering Laboratory, Aberdeen Proving Ground, Maryland.

In addition, some universities are sources of anthropometric information. Among these are Harvard's Guggenheim Center for Aviation Health and Safety and Tufts' Institute for Psychological Research.

PERCENTILES

Percentiles permit a more realistic concept of the range of dimensions to be accommodated than does the spread from least to greatest value encountered in the normal distribution (see Fig. 11-5). The extreme values represent chance occurrences, which, for practical purposes, should be disregarded in designing equipment. Removing 1% at both ends of the range will eliminate most of these "freak" values and leave a range covering 98% of the population. For some dimensions and equipment, the range from 1st to 99th percentile can be accommodated easily. For others, the 5th to 95th percentile, or 90% of the group, should be provided for. In general, the designer should attempt to accommodate at least 90% of the population as a minimum

and strive for 98% or more, if possible.

Percentiles can serve the design engineer in the following several ways:

a. Percentiles afford a basis for estimating the proportion of a group accommodated or inconvenienced by any specific design. For example, a door 73 in. high corresponds, approximately, to the 95th percentile of height for the military and civilian populations (72 in. plus 1 in. for shoes) and so we know that about 5% of the population will be inconvenienced by that door (see Fig. 11-10).

b. Percentiles permit the selection and accurate use of test subjects. Any body dimension or physical ability of a test subject can be readily located as a percentile of any user population.

c. Percentiles aid in the selection of operators. If the equipment imposes any limitation on the size of operators, misfits can be avoided by eliminating those whose critical dimension exceeds or falls short of the established cutoff point. Of course, the cutoff point could be established in measurement units (in., lb, etc.) without using percentiles, but percentiles indicate the proportion of potential operators re-

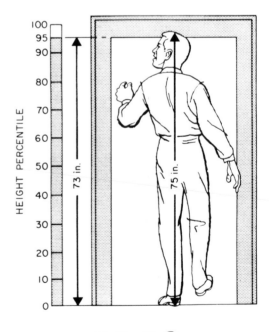

11-10

jected. If this proportion is too large, redesign is in order. For example, during World War II, the Air Force considered raising gunners' height and weight limits to 73 in. and 180 lb, but it was found that, even at the existing limits of 70 in. and 170 lb, a significant percentage of gunners (30% for one turret, 40% for another) had trouble operating the turrets, and larger men could not even enter the turrets. This information made it obvious that a redesign of the turrets was needed.

How to Find Percentiles

Graphically from normal-probability paper. Anthropometric data often are not presented in percentile form. Even when they are, the engineer might need to find percentiles other than those given. Percentiles can be located on normal-probability paper for normally distributed groups, i.e., those following the bell-shaped curve (see Fig. 11-5). On normal-probability paper, a normal distribution is a straight line that is defined by two points (see Fig. 11-11). Thus, any desired percentile can be read from the paper if any two percentiles or any two of the following values are known:

a. A single percentile.

b. An average, whether mean or median (50th percentile).

c. The standard deviation (see below).

Arithmetically from the standard deviation. The standard deviation (S.D.) is a measure of dispersion, variation, or scatter about an average (see Chapter 1). Thus, the average (or 50th percentile) ± 1 S.D. includes 68% of the measured group, ± 2 S.D. includes 95% of the group, and ± 3 S.D. in-

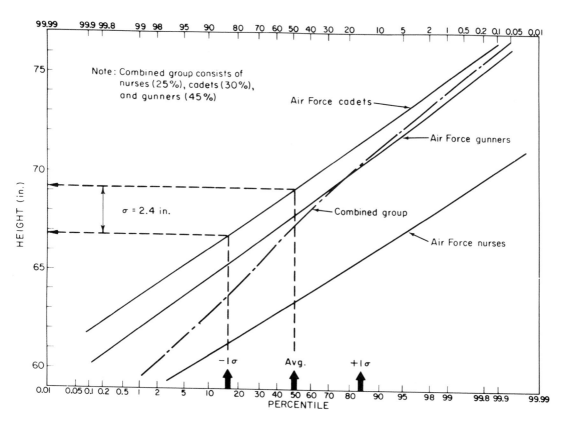

11-11

cludes 99.7% of the group (see Fig. 11-12). The S.D. can be determined from a normal distribution plotted on probability paper. Merely subtract the value corresponding to the 16th from that corresponding to the 50th percentile.

Computing percentiles from the known standard deviation provides an alternative to the graphic technique. To do this, however, the factors given in Table 11-1 must be used. Knowing these factors, the S.D., and the value of either the mean or median, an unknown percentile can be computed as in the following examples:

1. To find the 95th percentile when the mean is 35.1 in. and the S.D. = 1.5 in., find the factor corresponding to the 95th percentile in Table 11-1, multiply the S.D. by it ($1.5 \times 1.645 = 2.5$ in.), and add the result to the mean ($35.1 + 2.5 = 37.6$ in.). This is the 95th percentile.

2. To find the 5th percentile given the same starting information, proceed in exactly the same way, with the same numbers, but subtract instead of add ($35.1 - 2.5 = 32.6$ in.). This is the 5th percentile.

Fallacy of the Average Man

Designing to fit the "average man" is a serious error. By definition, 50% of any group might suffer from a design that accommodates the 50th percentile; and this could have seri-

Table 11-1   Factors for Computing Percentiles from the Standard Deviation *

Percentiles		Factor	Percentiles		Factor
0.5	99.5	2.576	15	85	1.036
1	99	2.326	20	80	0.842
2.5	97.5	1.960	25	75	0.674
5	95	1.645	30	70	0.524
10	90	1.282			

* Roebuck, 1957.

ous consequences. For example, the shorter 50% will be unable to reach the control just suited to the "average," or 50th percentile, operator (see Fig. 11-13).

A further fallacy of the "average man" concept is that it ignores the fact that few people are average in all respects or even in several. If one takes the middle third of a group in any dimension, then the middle third of that third with respect to an independent or uncorrelated dimension, and then repeats the process for a third independent dimension, one reaches $\frac{1}{3} \times \frac{1}{3} \times \frac{1}{3} = \frac{1}{27}$, or less than 4% of the initial population, who are

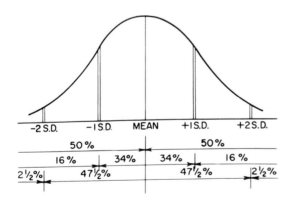

11-12

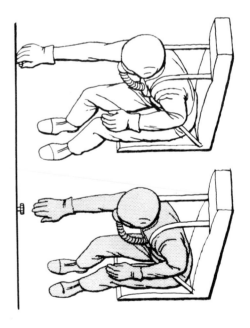

11-13

"average" in only three traits. (Even fewer, about 1%, will be average in four traits.) This has been found true for height, weight, and chest circumference, in spite of the fact that these dimensions are not independent but are correlated (Daniels and Churchill, 1952).

CORRELATION TABLES

Frequently, the engineer is faced with a problem involving the relationship between body dimensions. For instance, he might want to know the range of arm reach for men of the middle 90% in standing height or in sitting height, or, given a severely restricted space for the knees, what will be the range of eye level (seated) for those short-legged men who alone can operate the equipment. Also, without data for a specialized dimension (for example, the height of the back concavity above the buttocks) in a certain group, the designer will need to know how such values can be approximated from the commonly available height and weight data.

Fortunately, the relationships between height and body lengths and between weight and body breadths and also depths are close

enough to allow rough predictions for groups of men (but not for individual men). A "correlation table" (see Tables 11-2 through 11-5) presents the number or percentage of subjects, arranged with respect to dimension A, who fall at each value of dimension B. A glance shows whether and to what extent dimension B varies with dimension A.

The designer can find correlations for any group for which such tables are available. Correlation tables of the more important dimensions in the major military and civilian populations are included in Hooton, 1945; Randall, et al., 1946; and Newman and White, 1951.

An example of the need for specialized dimensions arose during World War II. The specialized dimensions needed were the height of the calf muscles above the floor and the height of the shoulder blades above the seat. Both dimensions were body lengths and hence correlated with height. Rough approximations were obtained by measuring the specialized dimension on several subjects from each end of the using population's height range between the 5th and 95th percentiles, as well as several subjects scattered throughout this range.

Table 11-2   Correlation for Body Weight vs. Hip Breadth (Sitting)[1] of Male Air Force Personnel[2]

Weight (lb)	11.8–12.5	12.6–13.3	13.4–14.1	14.2–14.9	15.0–15.6	15.7–16.4	16.5–17.2	17.3–18.0	18.1–18.8
110–115	4	6							
116–121	3	20	3						
122–127	5	64	20	1	1				
128–133	3	82	68	4					
134–139	1	79	186	22	4				
140–145		44	276	68	4				
146–151		15	257	129	3		1		
152–157		3	182	192	25				
158–163		5	81	211	42	1			
164–169			41	160	68	5			
170–175			7	121	75	8	1		
176–181			4	65	82	10			
182–187				16	60	9	1		
188–193				6	36	14	2		
194–199				2	21	7	1		
200–205					4	6	1		1
206–211					1	2			

[1] In inches (see Fig. 11-43).   [2] Randall, et al., 1946; 2,972 subjects

Table 11-3 Correlation for Standing Height [1] vs. Sitting Height [2] of Male Army Separatees (White) [3]

Standing height (in.)	30.7–31.4	31.5–32.2	32.3–33.0	33.1–33.8	33.9–34.6	34.7–35.4	35.5–36.2	36.3–37.0	37.0–37.7	37.8–38.5	38.6–39.3	39.4–40.1
59.5–60.2	0.008	0.004	0.012		0.004							
60.2–60.9		0.008	0.012	0.016	0.004							
61.0–61.8	0.004	0.041	0.057	0.041	0.012	0.012	0.004					
61.9–62.6	0.008	0.033	0.160	0.213	0.061	0.037	0.008					
62.7–63.4	0.004	0.066	0.213	0.373	0.254	0.111	0.004	0.016	0.004	0.004		
63.5–64.2	0.008	0.053	0.262	0.779	0.856	0.348	0.053	0.016	0.016	0.012		
64.3–65.0	0.004	0.045	0.320	1.049	1.365	0.836	0.262	0.049	0.016	0.012		
65.0–65.7	0.004	0.045	0.229	0.869	1.955	1.742	0.660	0.070	0.016	0.004	0.008	
65.8–66.5	0.020	0.025	0.127	0.783	2.323	2.836	1.746	0.418	0.012	0.020	0.008	
66.6–67.3	0.004	0.016	0.102	0.516	2.135	3.704	2.901	1.029	0.123	0.004	0.004	
67.4–68.1	0.008	0.020	0.033	0.291	1.598	3.708	4.143	2.037	0.422	0.070	0.020	
68.1–68.8	0.004	0.016	0.025	0.197	0.824	2.836	4.553	3.028	0.971	0.115	0.004	
68.9–69.6	0.004	0.008	0.029	0.066	0.389	1.914	4.003	3.819	1.496	0.201	0.045	
69.7–70.4		0.012	0.020	0.049	0.193	1.004	2.643	3.692	1.869	0.504	0.049	
70.5–71.2			0.008	0.045	0.078	0.414	1.537	2.795	2.020	0.717	0.127	0.008
71.3–72.0		0.004	0.008	0.020	0.061	0.176	0.758	1.655	1.754	0.824	0.291	0.016
72.1–72.8				0.004	0.025	0.066	0.311	0.844	1.192	0.779	0.275	0.020
72.9–73.6				0.008	0.012	0.008	0.107	0.283	0.524	0.512	0.238	0.037
73.7–74.4					0.012	0.016	0.029	0.131	0.234	0.299	0.127	0.033
74.5–75.2					0.004		0.008	0.029	0.164	0.217	0.094	0.053
75.3–76.0						0.004			0.037	0.057	0.082	0.033
76.1–76.8						0.004		0.004	0.012	0.008	0.033	0.016
76.9–77.6							0.004		0.012	0.025	0.033	

[1] See Fig. 11-21. [2] See Fig. 11-22. [3] Entries represent percentages of 24,404 subjects (Newman and White, 1951)

The distribution with respect to the specialized measurement was noted, and it was assumed that, just as the test subjects bracketed the height range, so they would bracket the range of the specialized dimensions. Had special body breadths or thicknesses been required, weight would have been the basic variable used. Fortunately, height and weight measurements for various populations are relatively easy to obtain.

A much closer approximation could have been obtained in the above example by setting up a correlation table between the specialized dimension and the closest standard dimension already obtained from the ultimate operators. Thus, the designer might use knee height for correlating with calf height, and shoulder height for shoulder-blade height, measuring both dimensions on subjects selected (by the use of percentiles) to represent the range in height, weight, and the standard knee and shoulder heights. The relationship between the standard and the specialized dimension probably would be closer than the relationship between the specialized dimension and height.

As a third possibility, instead of correlations, the difference between the pair of dimensions on each test subject could be used to derive an average difference, which then could be added to or subtracted from the standard dimension to give the specialized dimension. The nature of the problem, the accuracy required, and the measuring facilities available will indicate, for any specific situation, whether correlations with height and weight are close enough, or whether additional measurements must be taken.

11.1.4 *What the designer should do*

The design engineer needs data on the

Table 11-4   Correlation for Standing Height [1] vs. Knee Height [2] of Male Army Separatees (White) [3]

Standing height (in.)	16.5–17.2	17.3–18.0	18.1–18.8	18.9–19.6	19.7–20.4	20.5–21.2	21.3–22.0	22.1–22.8	22.9–23.6	23.6–24.3	24.4–25.1	25.2–25.9
59.5–60.2			0.008	0.020								
60.2–60.9		0.004	0.012	0.049	0.012							
61.0–61.8	0.004	0.012	0.020	0.102	0.041	0.004	0.012					
61.9–62.6			0.066	0.213	0.176	0.020	0.012	0.008	0.004			
62.7–63.4		0.008	0.025	0.397	0.516	0.160	0.033	0.012	0.004	0.004		
63.5–64.2	0.012	0.008	0.086	0.516	1.040	0.442	0.070	0.025	0.008			
64.3–65.0	0.004	0.008	0.066	0.487	1.892	1.241	0.143	0.025	0.029			
65.0–65.7	0.004	0.012	0.020	0.328	2.032	2.593	0.623	0.086	0.029			
65.8–66.5		0.004	0.033	0.217	1.855	4.444	1.515	0.176	0.066			
66.6–67.3	0.012	0.016	0.008	0.152	1.245	4.686	3.596	0.414	0.057	0.008		
67.4–68.1	0.004	0.016	0.008	0.061	0.659	4.227	5.431	1.311	0.127	0.020	0.004	0.004
68.1–68.8	0.004	0.020	0.004	0.029	0.451	3.080	6.471	2.736	0.197	0.016	0.008	
68.9–69.6		0.012	0.004	0.008	0.201	1.384	5.226	4.219	0.532	0.020	0.008	0.012
69.7–70.4		0.008		0.004	0.061	0.688	3.273	4.964	1.040	0.078	0.025	0.008
70.5–71.2			0.004	0.004	0.029	0.274	1.741	4.071	1.651	0.152	0.029	0.012
71.3–72.0		0.004			0.016	0.102	0.614	2.396	1.823	0.381	0.033	0.004
72.1–72.8					0.020	0.029	0.274	1.094	1.556	0.545	0.041	0.004
72.9–73.6			0.004		0.016	0.033	0.049	0.467	0.868	0.455	0.070	0.004
73.7–74.4					0.004	0.016	0.025	0.156	0.438	0.348	0.082	0.016
74.5–75.2					0.004	0.012	0.008	0.045	0.172	0.250	0.123	0.004
75.3–76.0							0.012	0.012	0.037	0.123	0.041	0.025
76.1–76.8							0.004		0.004	0.041	0.037	0.004
76.9–77.6								0.004		0.004	0.041	0.012

[1] See Fig. 11-21.   [2] See Fig. 11-54.   [3] Entries represent percentages of 24,415 subjects (Newman and White, 1951).

human body for the following purposes:

a. For evaluating the adequacy of operational or prototype equipment.

b. For specifying requirements for or actually designing new equipment.

In answering the question, "How well does the equipment fit the intended operators?", the procedure the designer should observe is that outlined in the paragraphs that follow.

IN EVALUATING EQUIPMENT

The following procedure should be observed when evaluating operational or prototype equipment:

1. Obtain data on the physique of the intended operators. Although human beings vary widely in size and shape, their variability follows certain patterns. The engineer's job is simplified by the fact that groups within the population vary less than the population as a whole. For example, the 5th to 95th percentile of sitting height, and hence of seat adjustability, is less for soldiers (4.4 in.) or airmen (4.2 in.) than for the civilian population, men and women combined (over 5 in.). The limits of this 90% range, however, must be determined by actual measurement of samples from the group to be accommodated. Age, sex, race, and occupation have such bearing on physique that assumptions as to the similarity of any group of operators to other groups or to the "general population" must be tested.

This testing is not the engineer's job. It is his responsibility, however, to seek such information. The data presented in this chapter will cover the major military and civilian groups for whom the engineer is designing. If his group of operators is likely to differ markedly from the data presented with respect to age, sex, race, or occupation, or if the desired data are not available for his own or comparable user groups, he should seek advice from any anthropometric laboratory or

§ 11.1.4

Table 11-5 Correlation for Popliteal Height (Sitting) [1] vs. Buttock-to-Popliteal Length [2] of Male Railroad Travelers [3]

Popliteal height (in.)	16.0-16.4	16.5-16.9	17.0-17.4	17.5-17.9	18.0-18.4	18.5-18.9	19.0-19.4	19.5-19.9	20.0-20.4	20.5-20.9	21.0-21.4	21.5-21.9
16.1-16.4		1		2								
16.5-16.8	3	3	1	4	3							
16.9-17.2	1	2	12	2	7	5	2					
17.3-17.6	2	5	10	19	25	13	5	1				
17.7-18.0		5	10	40	37	39	24	6				
18.1-18.4		3	23	55	83	52	45	19	9	1		
18.5-18.8		4	9	35	82	77	73	35	11			
18.9-19.2		3	8	26	54	92	86	55	30	7	1	
19.3-19.6			3	13	36	54	75	44	40	7	4	1
19.7-20.0				3	16	29	47	41	26	11	7	1
20.1-20.4					6	5	24	19	17	19	8	4
20.5-20.8						2	9	9	18	13	6	4
20.9-21.2							2	3	15	8	8	4
21.3-21.6									4	4	6	4
21.7-22.0												1

[1] In inches (see Fig. 11-56).   [2] See Fig. 11-46.   [3] Hooton, 1945; 1,947 subjects

center such as those mentioned in article 11.1.3.

2. Select and measure a small group of representative test subjects. About ten subjects should be selected, with strong representation at both ends (around the 5th and 95th percentiles) of the height and weight distribution of the operators to be accommodated. This gives reasonable assurance that the range of other dimensions will be approximated as well. For the crudest approximations, five well-chosen subjects might suffice. Nude or seminude height and weight are the only dimensions the engineer has to obtain. Experience has shown that he should obtain them himself because surprisingly few people know their own height and weight accurately.

Ideally, all of the test subjects should be measured in the detail desired for the operator groups, as is done by anthropologists in their own laboratories. The designer then can determine more accurately what percentage of operators would or would not be accommodated by a given design feature. If, for example, a control is located too far away for some operators to reach, it would be more exact to estimate the percentage inconvenienced from arm-reach measurements than from height.

3. Dress the test subjects in the widest range of standard clothing and personal equipment that might be worn while operating the equipment. The machine should accommodate —and can, in most cases—the smallest operators (at the 1st or 5th percentile) in light clothing as well as the largest operators wearing the bulkiest personal equipment.

4. Have the test subjects, wearing the full range of clothing and personal equipment, operate the machine. If a mockup is used, all items that will be in the finished machine should be present in their intended location (in wooden facsimile if not otherwise available). The test subjects should perform all motions necessary to operating the machine, and the test should last as long as an actual operation.

Many difficulties will be noted immediately, but others will become apparent only with time. For example, a cramped space about the knee is tolerable for several minutes, but, over the course of hours, the situation can become, not merely uncomfortable, but dangerous or even fatal. The immobility of the lower legs over such periods of time has caused blood clots in the calf veins that break off, lodge in the lungs, and cause death (Homans, 1954 and Nareff, 1959).

§ 11.1.4

5. Note the difficulties with respect to comfort, efficiency, vision, and safety caused by human-body size and capabilities. As regards human dimensions, comfort is divided, for convenience of analysis, into static and dynamic fit (see Fig. 11-14), the latter including, not only the placement of controls to be operated, but also the subject's fit during such operation. Fit is further subdivided into fore-and-aft, vertical, and transverse clearances at different body levels (see Fig. 11-15). Efficiency involves ranges of motion of body members (see section 11.3) and muscle strength (see section 11.4).

Vision, as measured from the operator's eye location (which is a resultant of human-body size and machine design), comprises those portions of the total visual field that can be seen (see Fig. 11-16) and the quality of vision afforded. For example, the location of certain structures might result in "blind spots," or the optical properties of transparent surfaces might change with varying eye positions.) And, finally, safety includes ease of access and exit, either by the operator (see Fig. 11-17) or by a rescuer in case of an accident.

6. Relate the shortcomings in the design to percentiles of the operator population, and recommend redesign accordingly. Few items of design are wholly bad; a wholly bad feature would have been obvious from the outset and would be unlikely to survive the mockup stage. The same is true, with even more force, of an entire machine or workplace; someone must have been accommodated in the course of its development, if only the engineer himself in shirtsleeves.

The usual problem is to isolate those defects that seriously hamper the operator. As has been mentioned, these defects are almost always remediable. By stating the percentage of operators inconvenienced, the designer can estimate which of the problems are serious and, roughly, how serious.

The critical percentile can be estimated more closely by knowing the percentile of the critical test subject in the most pertinent dimension, in addition to his height and weight, and by having several test subjects available around the critical percentile. This is why it is desirable to have test subjects scattered throughout the mid-range as well as at the extremes. With only one or two critical test subjects, and with only height and weight percentiles known, the *severity of inconvenience* will serve as an additional guide to the *percentage inconvenienced*.

Other things being equal, an item that inconveniences 80% of the operators calls more strongly for correction than one that inconveniences 20%. Other things, however, are not always equal, and inconvenience itself is relative, varying from the awkward or annoying to the intolerable. For example, in one civilian truck model, 20% of the drivers could not operate the clutch or the foot brake without hitting their knees against the steering wheel, but, in the same vehicle, 100% of the drivers could not reach the front hand (emergency) brake without twisting their bodies out of the normal driving position. Despite the differing percentages inconvenienced, however, the first defect took priority because of the frequency of use and the critical role of the controls involved.

IN DESIGNING NEW EQUIPMENT

It is hoped that the data in this chapter will guide the engineer in designing new equipment. When such equipment reaches the mockup stage, it can be tested by the procedure just outlined, but, even in the blueprint stage, the designer should have some indication of the operator's size and shape.

In designing new equipment, the engineer should determine the population to be accommodated and seek reliable data on its dimensions and capabilities. If the needed information is not readily available, the designer should consult anthropometrists at a laboratory or center such as those mentioned in article 11.1.3. If he can use the data in this chapter, the designer should attempt to provide the structural strength, clearances, and placement that will fit at least 90% of his intended population.

In addition, the engineer should observe the following procedures among those he

§ 11.1.4

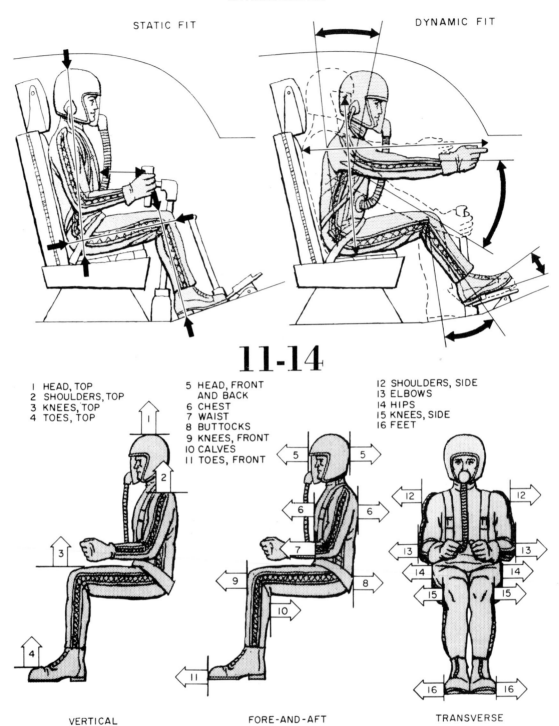

ANTHROPOMETRY

STATIC FIT   DYNAMIC FIT

11-14

1 HEAD, TOP
2 SHOULDERS, TOP
3 KNEES, TOP
4 TOES, TOP

5 HEAD, FRONT
  AND BACK
6 CHEST
7 WAIST
8 BUTTOCKS
9 KNEES, FRONT
10 CALVES
11 TOES, FRONT

12 SHOULDERS, SIDE
13 ELBOWS
14 HIPS
15 KNEES, SIDE
16 FEET

VERTICAL   FORE-AND-AFT   TRANSVERSE

11-15

500

§ 11.1.4

11-16 Visual fields from eye position of three drivers (5th, 50th, and 95th percentile in height) in 1954-model automobile (Sutro and Kydd, 1955)

§ 11.1.4

11-17

regularly uses when designing new equipment:

1. Consider the operator (see Fig. 11-18), and consider him early. Ideally, the man-machine system should take advantage of the most efficient functions of both man and machine. This means that the human body must be kept in mind from the earliest discussion and planning stages of the design. The drawing-board and mockup stages might be too late, and the prototype stage certainly is too late. At the latter stage, even needed and feasible redesign might cost too much in time, money, and lost production to be considered.

2. Obtain dynamic as well as static dimensions. Remember that the operator is functional (see Fig. 11-19), and functional men vary in size and physical capacities. Age, sex, race, and occupation affect body dimensions and capabilities. The group of operators for whom an item is intended might differ significantly from those groups for which measurements are available.

3. Allow ample margins of safety for both men and equipment; both might be subjected to unusual demands. Complex psychomotor

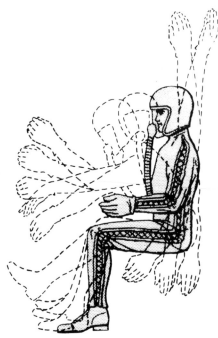

11-19

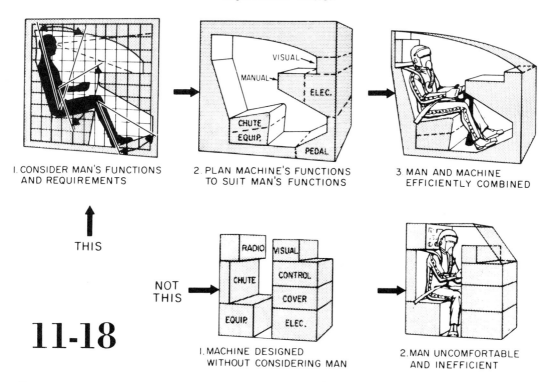

1. CONSIDER MAN'S FUNCTIONS AND REQUIREMENTS

2. PLAN MACHINE'S FUNCTIONS TO SUIT MAN'S FUNCTIONS

3 MAN AND MACHINE EFFICIENTLY COMBINED

THIS

NOT THIS

11-18

1. MACHINE DESIGNED WITHOUT CONSIDERING MAN

2. MAN UNCOMFORTABLE AND INEFFICIENT

adjustments that are possible in normal operation might fail under stress of combat or crisis. Some operators at all times, and most under sufficient stress, will fall short of optimum performance. Therefore, always exceed minimum spatial and mechanical allowances rather than shave tolerances too closely.

4. Evaluate human accommodation and performance in mockups with complete, functional equipment. Men of varying size, especially those toward the extremes of the range, should test machines under conditions simulating actual operation as closely as possible. The operator should wear a complete set of typical equipment, and all machine accessories should be included in mockups in wooden facsimile if not otherwise available (see Fig. 11-20).

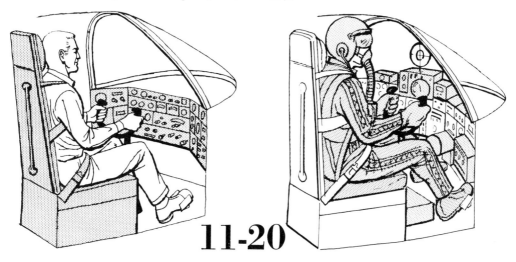

11-20

503

11.2 *Human-Body Dimensions*

Two kinds of anthropometric dimensions, static and dynamic, are related to the practical problems of design engineering. Static dimensions, which are taken with the body of the subjects in rigid standardized positions, are easily obtained and used in equipment design (see article 11.2.3). Dynamic dimensions, which are taken with the body in various working positions, are usually much more complex and difficult to measure (see article 11.2.4).

Functional arm reach, for example, a dynamic dimension, is not a simple derivative of anatomical arm length. Rather, it is a composite function of such factors as shoulder height, shoulder breadth, the length of the various segments of the arm and hand, and the range of motion at the shoulder, elbow, wrist, and fingers. Thus, functional arm reach can change with changes in the placement of the body, of the arm, or of the hand and fingers.

11.2.1 *Factors affecting human-body measurements*

Equipment is designed for use by the general population or by specialized occupational groups that differ significantly in body size from the general population. Group differences in body size result from a variety of factors, both biological and environmental. This article presents the general factors influencing body dimensions.

AGE AND SEX

All body dimensions increase consistently, though sometimes irregularly, from birth to the late teens or early twenties. The precise year at which growth is complete varies with the individual person and the dimension. For height, as for most other body lengths, full growth is attained, for all practical purposes, by the age of 20 in males and 17 in females (see Table 11-6). Sometime around age 60, height decreases, but current evidence is inadequate to establish the time when this begins, its extent, or its bearing on other body lengths. Weight, and its correlated body breadths, thicknesses, and circumferences, continue to increase significantly through middle age and then decrease in old age (see Table 11-6).

Men are larger than women at any given percentile for most body dimensions. The extent of the difference varies considerably from one dimension to another. Women are consistently larger than men only in hip-to-hip breadth, hip circumference, and thigh circumference. Men's arms and legs are not only absolutely longer than women's but, also, are longer relative to standing and sitting height.

RACE AND OCCUPATION

There are wide differences in body dimensions between different races, subraces, and national or ethnic groups. Height extremes are represented by the pygmies of Asia and Africa and by African Negroes and some groups of Northwest-European ancestry. In many cases, racial differences in body dimensions are comparatively small, but they can be of practical significance for equipment design.

Americans, a national group of mixed racial origins, may be considered, comparatively speaking, a "large" group. As a group, they are larger in overall body size than most other Caucasian national groups, most Negroes, and almost all Mongoloids.

Racial differences are sometimes apparent in body build as well as the gross size. Some

Table 11-6 Height and Weight of White Male and Female Americans *

Age (yr)	Male				Female			
	Height (in.)		Weight (lb)		Height (in.)		Weight (lb)	
	Mean	S.D.	Mean	S.D.	Mean	S.D.	Mean	S.D.
1	29.7	1.1	23	3	29.3	1.0	21	3
2	34.5	1.2	28	3	34.1	1.2	27	3
3	37.8	1.3	32	3	37.5	1.4	31	4
4	40.8	1.9	37	5	40.6	1.6	36	5
5	43.7	2.0	42	5	43.8	1.7	41	5
6	46.1	2.1	47	6	45.7	1.9	45	5
7	48.2	2.2	54	7	47.9	2.0	50	7
8	50.4	2.3	60	8	50.3	2.2	58	11
9	52.8	2.4	66	8	52.1	2.3	64	11
10	54.5	2.5	73	10	54.6	2.5	72	14
11	56.8	2.6	82	11	57.1	2.6	82	18
12	58.3	2.9	87	12	59.6	2.7	93	18
13	60.7	3.2	99	13	61.4	2.6	102	18
14	63.6	3.2	113	15	62.8	2.5	112	19
15	66.3	3.1	128	16	63.4	2.4	117	20
16	67.7	2.8	137	16	63.9	2.2	120	21
17	68.3	2.6	143	19	64.1	2.2	122	19
18	68.5	2.6	149	20	64.1	2.3	123	17
19	68.6	2.6	153	21	64.1	2.3	124	17
20–24	68.7	2.6	158	23	64.0	2.4	125	19
25–29	68.7	2.6	163	24	63.7	2.5	127	21
30–34	68.5	2.6	165	25	63.6	2.4	130	24
35–39	68.4	2.6	166	25	63.4	2.4	136	25
40–49	68.0	2.6	167	25	63.2	2.4	142	27
50–59	67.3	2.6	165	25	62.8	2.4	148	28
60–69	66.8	2.4	162	24	62.2	2.4	146	28
70–79	66.5	2.2	157	24	61.8	2.2	144	27
80–89	66.1	2.2	151	24				

* Stoudt, et al., 1960.

groups are characteristically tall and slender (e.g., African Negroes and Scandinavians), others are short and slender (e.g., Mediterraneans), and still others are short and stocky (e.g., Japanese).

Differences in body size and proportions between different occupational groups are common. On the average, steel workers are more muscular than bookkeepers, truck drivers are more muscular than college professors, and athletes are more muscular than artists. In addition, military personnel differ from the general civilian population.

Although there are numerous factors that contribute to such physical differences, e.g., age, diet, health status, and physical activity, there also appear to be selective factors tending to make the members of some occupations more similar in physical type than would be expected on a purely random basis. Some tasks require specific physical abilities, and workers possessing these abilities tend to be similar in physical type. (Weight lifting is a classic, though extreme, case in point.) In addition, there might be an association between physique and temperament—an area of much current research interest.

POSTURE AND BODY POSITION

Some human dimensions vary with posture or body position. For purposes of standardization and comparison, the anthropometrist usually requires rigid, erect positions that are rarely those assumed by people at work or at rest. Few people normally stand or sit completely erect; consequently, "normal" standing height, sitting height, and eye height involve "slump" and, therefore, are significantly less than when measured with the body erect (about 0.75 in. less for standing and 1.75 in. less for sitting heights). Standing height is smaller than prone or supine length. Buttock breadth and waist depth are larger in the seated than in the standing position. Most dynamic dimensions are altered by body movement; thus, maximum arm reach with free movement of the shoulder or trunk is much greater than with the shoulder and trunk restrained.

LONG-TERM CHANGES

Changes in human-body size have been taking place from prehistoric times to the present. There has been a generally worldwide trend toward an increase in height and most other body dimensions. These changes have been large enough in recent years to invalidate anthropometric surveys of the 19th and early 20th centuries for present-day use in design engineering. Comparisons between fathers and sons showed the sons to be significantly taller and heavier than their fathers at the same age (Bowles, 1932). This trend appears to be continuing (see Fig. 11-4).

11.2.2 *Applying human-body dimensions*

To determine the desired equipment dimensions, proceed as follows:

1. Determine which is the most relevant body dimension (e.g., sitting height for seat-to-roof distance).

2. Define the population involved.

3. Select the percentage of the population to be accommodated (e.g., 90% or 98%).

4. Read from the relevant nude-body-dimension table (see article 11.2.3) the appropriate measurement; then check the text.

5. Determine the type of clothing and personal equipment that will be worn (e.g., civilian clothing or winter flying gear).

6. Add the relevant increments (see Tables 11-7 and 11-8) to those indicated in the nude-body-dimension table.

11.2.3 *Static human-body dimensions*

Each of the following paragraphs deals with a single human-body dimension related to some aspect of equipment or workspace design. Discussion is held to a minimum, and only data needed by the designer are presented. The discussion of each human-body dimension includes the following:

a. A definition of the body dimension and how it was measured.

b. The data, in tabular form, for the 1st, 5th, 50th, 95th, and 99th percentiles and the standard deviation (where they are available).

c. Dimensions, with an additional allowance as a safety factor, that will accommodate specified percentages of various populations.

d. Correction factors for females and for clothing and personal equipment, and other relevant variables.

Some features of the tables in this article must be understood for their proper interpretation. These features are as follows:

a. All measurements were made on nude subjects standing or sitting erect unless otherwise indicated.

b. Some groups, notably the military, have upper and lower height-weight limits for acceptance, thus eliminating extremely tall, short, stocky, and thin persons.

c. The column headed "50th percentile" contains, in some cases, the average or arithmetic mean. Ordinarily there is little or no practical difference between these two measures of central tendency. Weight is one exception, however; because of its skewed distribution, the mean exceeds the median, or 50th percentile, by about 2 lb.

§ 11.2.2

Table 11-7 Increments Added to Nude-Body Dimensions by Various Army Clothing [1]

Dimension	Increment (in.[2])		
	Standard uniform [3]	Plus blouse or field jacket	Plus blouse or field jacket and overcoat [4]
Body height, standing	2.65	2.65	2.65
Body height, sitting	1.39	1.43	1.61
Body weight	9.4 lb	11.8 lb	18.6 lb
Head length	3.5	3.5	3.5
Head breadth	2.8	2.8	2.8
Eye height, sitting	0.04	0.08	0.16
Shoulder height, sitting	0.16	0.58	0.92
Shoulder-to-elbow length	0.14	0.50	0.94
Shoulder-to-shoulder breadth	0.24	0.88	1.52
Chest depth	0.41	0.96	1.80
Elbow-to-elbow breadth	0.56	1.04	1.84
Waist depth	0.94	1.18	1.95
Hip-to-hip breadth, standing	0.56	0.76	1.08
Hip-to-hip breadth, sitting	0.56	0.76	1.08
Buttock-to-knee length	0.20	0.30	0.54
Hand length			
Hand breadth			
Knee height, sitting	1.32	1.32	1.44
Knee-to-knee breadth	0.48	0.48	0.72
Foot length	1.6	1.6	1.6
Foot breadth	0.20	0.20	0.20

[1] Roberts, et al., 1945.
[2] Except as noted.
[3] Underwear, shirt and trousers or fatigues, shoes and socks, and steel helmet and liner.
[4] See Roberts, et al., 1945 for additional increments to be added for combat suit, overcoat, wool cap and gloves.

Table 11-8 Increments Added to Nude-Body Dimensions by Various Air Force Clothing

Dimension	Increment (in.[1])		
	Winter flying gear [2]	T-1 partial-pressure suit [3]	T-5 partial-pressure suit [4]
Body height, standing	1.9	2.0	3.3
Body height, sitting	1.6		2.1
Body weight	20.0 lb		
Head length	0.4		
Head breadth	0.4		
Eye height, sitting	0.4		
Shoulder height, sitting	0.6		
Shoulder-to-elbow length	0.3		
Shoulder-to-shoulder breadth	1.3	6.0	0.4
Chest breadth	0.6	2.5	
Chest depth	1.4	4.5	0.8
Elbow-to-elbow breadth	4.4	11.0	
Waist depth	1.4	5.0	
Hip-to-hip breadth, standing	1.3		
Hip-to-hip breadth, sitting	1.7	5.5	2.9
Buttock-to-knee length	0.5	2.0	
Hand length	0.3		
Hand breadth	0.4		
Knee height, sitting	1.8		
Knee-to-knee breadth	2.5	9.5	
Foot length	2.7		
Foot breadth	1.2		

[1] Except as noted.
[2] Underwear, shirt and trousers or fatigues, boots and socks, jacket, helmet, and gloves (Damon, 1943).
[3] Inflated pressure suit, deflated ventilation suit, MD-1 anti-exposure suit, MD-3A liner, and long cotton underwear (no boots).
[4] Uninflated pressure suit, K-1 pressure helmet, and boots (USAF, 1953b).

d. Some of the percentiles presented in the following tables have been computed on normal probability paper (see article 11.1.3). This technique has been used where original frequency distributions were not available, and percentiles could be obtained in no other way. The graphic technique is accurate, however, only to the extent that the measurement is normally distributed. Although most human-body dimensions approximate the normal distribution closely enough to justify using the graphic technique, an occasional group deviates because of the biased or nonrandom selection of subjects or variations in measuring techniques. Weight is the physical trait with a distribution departing farthest from normality.

e. Most of the design recommendations in the following paragraphs are based on the dimensions of Air Force personnel because, anthropometrically, Air Force personnel have been the most thoroughly described for design-engineering purposes. In comparison with the general population, the Air Force groups are taller, larger in some body heights and lengths, somewhat lighter in weight and considerably leaner. They also are smaller in those body breadths, thicknesses, and circumferences to which fatty tissue, which increases with age, contributes substantially. The Air Force populations resemble other military groups of like age but are slightly larger than Army populations.

f. *Minimum* design dimensions, i.e., those that provide clearance and must accommodate the large members of the population, are based on the 95th and 99th percentiles. *Maximum* design dimensions, which must accommodate the small members of the population, are based on the 1st and 5th percentiles. *Adjustable* design dimensions, which must accommodate both large and small persons, are based on the middle 90% (5th to 95th percentiles) and 98% (1st to 99th percentiles) of the populations involved.

g. The numbers of subjects have not been included for reasons of space limitations but are available in the original sources as noted. These numbers range from 100, the smallest for any series, to over 100,000. Most of the military series are based on several thousand subjects.

508

BODY HEIGHT (STANDING)

This is the vertical distance from the floor to the top of the head. The subject stands erect and looks straight ahead (see Fig. 11-21). The data are given in Tables 11-9 through 11-12.

For men, 75.1 in. will accommodate all but the largest 1% of Air Force personnel, and 73.3 in. will accommodate all but the largest 5%. Corresponding values for Army personnel are: 99th percentile, 74.7 in. and 95th percentile, 72.8 in. For civilian men, the 99th percentile is 74.8 in. and the 95th percentile is 73.0 in. These values represent nude height plus 0.2 in.—an arbitrary safety factor.

For women, subtract 4.5 in. from the above values. For clothing increments, add 1.0 in. for men's shoes, 1.3 in. for military boots, up to 3.0 in. for women's shoes, roughly 1.0 in. for civilian caps, 1.4 in. for steel helmets, and up to 2.6 in. for flying helmets.

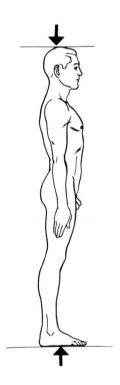

11-21

Table 11-9   Nude-Body Height (Standing) of Male Military Personnel

Population	Percentiles (in.)					S.D.
	1st	5th	50th	95th	99th	
Air Force personnel [1]	63.5	65.2	69.1	73.1	74.9	2.44
Pilots, multi-engine	64.4	65.9	69.4	73.3	74.9	2.31
Pilots, fighter	63.8	65.2	68.8	72.6	74.2	2.24
Cadets	63.6	65.2	69.2	73.1	74.7	2.45
Bombardiers	63.5	65.2	69.1	73.0	74.5	2.32
Navigators	63.5	65.2	69.2	73.3	75.0	2.46
Observers	63.8	65.4	69.1	72.8	74.2	2.44
Flight engineers	63.1	64.8	69.0	73.2	75.0	2.51
Gunners	62.4	64.2	68.3	72.2	73.7	2.43
Radio Operators	63.0	64.6	68.3	71.8	73.2	2.37
Basic trainees [2]	62.5	64.2	68.6	72.7	74.7	2.61
Army personnel						
Inductees less than 20 yr old [3]	62.4	64.3	68.7	73.1	74.9	2.66
Inductees more than 20 yr old [3]	62.7	64.6	69.0	73.4	75.2	2.65
Separatees, white [4]	62.7	64.3	68.5	72.6	74.5	2.52
Separatees, Negro [5]	62.3	64.0	68.0	72.2	74.0	2.58
Marine Corps personnel [6]	64.4	66.1	69.7	73.5	74.5	2.18
Recruits [7]	63.0	64.6	68.6	72.5	74.1	2.40
Navy personnel [8]	64.1	65.7	69.7	73.5	75.1	2.34
Recruits, 18 yr old [7]	62.8	64.5	68.5	72.6	74.2	2.50
Recruits, 17–25 yr old [9]	62.9	64.6	68.6	72.7	74.4	2.48
Enlisted men, general [10]	63.2	64.8	69.5	73.5	75.5	2.48
Enlisted men, submarine [11]	63.3 *	65.0 *	69.9 *	74.1 *	76.1 *	
Officers, submarine [11]	63.7 *	65.6 *	70.8 *	74.7 *	76.4 *	2.80
Pilots, aircraft [12]	64.9	66.3	70.2	74.1	75.9	4.70
Cadets, aviation [10]	65.1	66.6	70.1	73.8	75.2	

[1] Hertzberg, et al., 1954 (except as noted).
[2] Daniels, et al., 1953b.
[3] Damon, 1957.
[4] Newman and White, 1951.
[5] USA, 1946.
[6] USMC, 1949.

[7] USN, 1949b.
[8] King, et al., 1947.
[9] Gibbons, et al., 1953.
[10] USN, 1955.
[11] USN, 1957.
[12] USN, 1959.

* Including shoes (subtract 1 in. for nude height).

Table 11-10   Nude-Body Height (Standing) of Female Military Personnel

Population	Percentiles (in.)					S.D.
	1st	5th	50th	95th	99th	
Air Force personnel						
WAF basic trainees [1]	59.3	60.3	64.0	68.2	69.9	2.34
Pilots [2]	60.8	61.7	64.9	68.3	70.0	
Flight nurses [2]	59.0	60.2	63.5	67.7	69.3	
Army personnel [3]	58.4	59.9	63.9	68.0	69.7	2.42
WAC enlisted women [4]	58.3	60.0	63.9	68.0	69.6	2.40
WAC officers [4]	59.2	61.0	64.5	68.9	70.6	2.40
Nurses [4]	58.7	60.4	64.1	68.3	70.0	2.40

[1] Daniels, et al., 1953a.
[2] Randall, et al., 1946.

[3] Randall and Munro, 1949.
[4] Randall, 1947.

Table 11-11   Nude-Body Height (Standing) of Male Civilian Populations

Population	Percentiles (in.)					
	1st	5th	50th	95th	99th	S.D.
Railroad travelers [1]	62.5 *	64.5 *	69.0 *	73.8 *	75.6 *	
Truck and bus drivers [2]	63.0	64.6	68.4	72.5	74.1	
Airline pilots [3]	64.4	64.6	66.0	73.9	75.6	2.40
Industrial workers [4]	64.4 *	66.1 *	70.3 *	74.4 *	76.2 *	2.46
College students [5]	62.5	64.4	68.7	73.1	74.9	2.68
Eastern, 18 yr old [6]	64.5	66.1	69.9	73.8	75.4	2.38
Eastern, 19 yr old [7]	65.0	66.5	70.2	74.0	75.5	2.30
Midwest, 18 yr old [8]	63.2	65.0	69.1	73.3	75.0	2.60
Midwest, 18–22 yr old [9]	64.2	65.9	70.0	74.1	75.8	2.49
Draft registrants [10]						
18–19 yr old	62.0	63.8	68.0	72.3	74.1	2.61
20–24 yr old	62.1	63.9	68.2	72.4	74.2	2.60
25–29 yr old	61.9	63.7	68.1	72.4	74.2	2.63
30–34 yr old	61.7	63.5	67.8	72.1	73.9	2.66
35–37 yr old	61.3	63.2	67.6	72.0	73.8	2.64
Spanish-American-War veterans	61.1	62.6	66.1	69.7	71.2	2.15
Canadians [11]						
18–19 yr old	62.4	64.1	68.2	72.1	73.7	
20–24 yr old	62.0	63.8	68.3	72.5	74.3	
25–29 yr old	60.6	62.9	68.3	74.0	76.2	
30–34 yr old	61.5	63.4	68.1	72.8	74.8	
35–44 yr old	60.5	62.7	67.6	72.6	74.7	
45–54 yr old	59.7	61.8	66.8	72.0	74.1	
55–64 yr old	58.4	60.6	66.0	71.3	73.6	
More than 64 yr old	58.6	60.6	65.1	69.8	71.8	

[1] Hooton, 1945.
[2] McFarland, et al., 1958.
[3] McCormick, 1947.
[4] Tyroler, 1958.
[5] Diehl, 1933a.
[6] Bowles, 1932.

[7] Heath, 1945.
[8] Damon, 1955.
[9] Elbel, 1954.
[10] Karpinos, 1958.
[11] Pett and Ogilvie, 1957.

* Including shoes (subtract 1 in. for nude height).

BODY HEIGHT (SITTING)

This is the vertical distance from the sitting surface to the top of the head. The subject sits erect, looks straight ahead, and his knees and ankles form right angles (see Fig. 11-22). The data are given in Tables 11-13 and 11-14.

For men, 39.1 in. will accommodate all but the largest 1%, and 38.2 in. will accommodate all but the largest 5%, of Air Force personnel. For Army personnel, the corresponding values are 39.2 in. (99th percentile) and 38.2 in. (95th percentile); for civilians, 39.2 in. (99th percentile) and 38.4 in. (95th percentile). These values refer to the nude dimension and include a safety factor of 0.2 in.

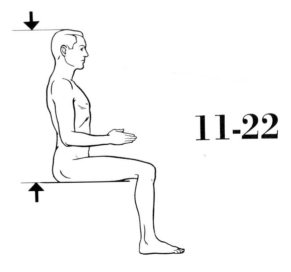

11-22

Table 11-12   Nude-Body Height (Standing) of Female Civilian Populations

Population	Percentiles (in.)					S.D.
	1st	5th	50th	95th	99th	
Railroad travelers [1]	59.1 *	60.8 *	64.9 *	69.1 *	70.8 *	
Working women [2]	58.1	59.7	63.6	67.5	69.2	2.43
City women						
Eastern, white	56.5	58.4	62.8	67.3	69.2	2.69
Eastern, Negro	57.3	59.0	63.1	67.3	69.0	2.53
College students [3]	58.5	60.0	63.8	67.6	69.2	2.33
Eastern [4]	59.8	61.2	64.8	68.3	69.7	2.15
Midwest [5]	58.8	60.5	64.4	68.4	70.0	2.36
Canadians [6]						
18–19 yr old	57.4	59.0	62.7	66.3	67.8	
20–24 yr old	57.2	58.8	62.9	66.8	68.4	
25–29 yr old	56.9	58.5	62.6	66.5	68.2	
30–34 yr old	57.0	58.7	62.6	66.5	68.2	
35–44 yr old	56.6	58.2	62.4	66.4	68.0	
45–54 yr old	56.6	58.1	61.8	65.4	67.0	
55–64 yr old	55.9	57.4	61.0	64.9	66.4	
More than 64 yr old	54.8	56.4	60.6	64.7	66.4	
General [7]	57.4	59.1	63.2	67.2	68.8	2.48

[1] Hooton, 1945.
[2] Bayer and Gray, 1934.
[3] Diehl, 1933b.
[4] Bowles, 1932.
* Including shoes (subtract 2 in. for nude height).

[5] Donelson, et al., 1940.
[6] Pett and Ogilvie, 1957.
[7] O'Brien and Shelton, 1941.

Table 11-13   Nude-Body Height (Sitting) of Male Military and Civilian Populations

Population	Percentiles (in.)					S.D.
	1st	5th	50th	95th	99th	
Air Force personnel [1]	32.9	33.8	36.0	38.0	38.9	1.29
Cadets [2]	33.7	34.5	36.4	38.5	39.4	
Gunners [2]	32.9	33.6	35.9	37.8	38.7	
Army personnel						
Separatees, white [3]	32.5	33.5	35.8	38.0	39.0	1.34
Separatees, Negro [4]	31.2	32.2	34.3	36.5	37.4	1.35
Navy personnel [5]	33.6	34.5	36.7	39.0	39.9	1.35
Enlisted men [6]	33.4	34.3	36.2	38.3	39.1	1.16
Pilots, aircraft [7]	32.4	33.5	36.0	38.3	39.8	
Cadets, aviation [6]	33.8	34.7	36.5	38.5	39.3	
Truck and bus drivers [8]	33.5	34.3	36.3	38.2	39.0	
College students [9]	32.8	33.9	36.5	39.2	40.2	1.57

[1] Hertzberg, et al., 1954.
[2] Randall, et al., 1946.
[3] Newman and White, 1951.
[4] USA, 1946.
[5] King, et al., 1947.

[6] USN, 1955.
[7] USN, 1959.
[8] McFarland, et al., 1958.
[9] Damon, 1955.

§ 11.2.3

Table 11-14   Nude-Body Height (Sitting) of Female Military and Civilian Populations

Population	Percentiles (in.)					
	1st	5th	50th	95th	99th	S.D.
Air Force personnel [1]						
Pilots	31.8	32.4	34.1	35.8	36.3	
Flight nurses	31.1	31.9	33.7	35.7	36.6	
Working women [2]	30.9	31.7	33.7	35.7	36.5	1.15
College students,						
Eastern [3]	31.6	32.4	34.2	36.0	36.7	1.10
Southern [4]	31.0	31.7	33.6	35.4	36.2	1.06

[1] Randall, et al., 1946.
[2] Bayer and Gray, 1934.
[3] Bowles, 1932.
[4] Carter, 1932.

For women, subtract 2.2 in. from the above values. Add 0.2–0.3 in. for heavy clothing under the buttocks, roughly 1.0 in. for civilian caps, 1.4 in. for steel helmets, and up to 2.6 in. for flying helmets.

BODY WEIGHT

The data are given in Tables 11-15 through 11-18. For men, a structure stressed for 216 lb will support all but the heaviest 1% of Air Force personnel, and 201 lb will support all but the heaviest 5%. For Army personnel, the 99th percentile is 215 lb and the 95th percentile is 192 lb. For civilian men, the 99th percentile is 247 lb, and the 95th is 213 lb. These values represent actual percentiles of nude weight without any safety margin.

For women, subtract 25–35 lb from the above values. Add 5 lb for men's light clothing, 3.5 lb for women's light clothing, and up to 23 lb or more for military winter clothing (see also Table 11-7).

Table 11-15   Nude-Body Weight of Female Military Personnel

Population	Percentiles [1] (lb)					
	1st	5th	50th	95th	99th	S.D.
Air Force personnel						
WAF basic trainees [2]	95	102	122	148	162	14.5
Pilots [3]	102	106	129	155	169	
Flight nurses [3]	104	107	122	135	143	
Army personnel [4]	97	105	129	170	192	20.0
WAC enlisted women [5]		(97)	130	(163)		20.6
WAC officers [5]		(105)	132	(158)		16.1
Nurses [5]		(95)	129	(162)		20.2

[1] Percentiles in parentheses were computed from the 50th percentile using the S.D. Because of the skewed distribution of weight, these values might differ somewhat from the true values and should be used with caution.
[2] Daniels, et al., 1953a.
[3] Randall, et al., 1946.
[4] Randall and Munro, 1949.
[5] Randall, 1947.

Table 11-16 Nude-Body Weight of Male Military Personnel

Population	Percentiles [1] (lb)					
	1st	5th	50th	95th	99th	S.D.
Air Force personnel [2]	123	133	162	201	216	20.9
Pilots, multi-engine	123		166		217	20.5
Pilots, fighter	123		159		225	20.7
Cadets	123		159		199	17.4
Bombardiers	126		169		211	20.6
Navigators	125		165		214	20.6
Observers	113		166		217	22.4
Flight engineers	124		166		222	23.3
Gunners	121		158		214	21.3
Radio operators	115		157		199	19.0
Basic trainees [3]	109	118	145	186	208	21.0
Army personnel						
Inductees less than 20 yr old [4]		(111)	159	(206)		29.4
Inductees more than 20 yr old [4]		(122)	162	(202)		23.9
Separatees, white [5]	114	124	153	192	215	20.6
Separatees, Negro [6]		(120)	152	(183)		19.2
Marine Corps personnel [7]	130	139	170	212	228	22.4
Recruits [8]		(112)	143	(174)		18.7
Navy personnel [9]		(126)	162	(197)		21.5
Recruits, 18 yr old [8]		(110)	140	(171)		18.5
Recruits, 17–25 yr old [10]		(119)	152	(185)		20.6
Enlisted men, general [11]		132	160	197		19.9
Enlisted men, submarine [12]		135 *	162 *	195 *		
Officers, submarine [12]		143 *	176 *	209 *		19.7
Pilots, aircraft [13]	127	138	168	198	212	
Cadets, aviation [11]		135	166	196		

[1] Percentiles in parentheses were computed from the 50th percentile using the S.D. Because of the skewed distribution of weight, these values might differ somewhat from the true values and should be used with caution.

[2] Hertzberg, et al., 1954 (except as noted).

[3] Daniels, et al., 1953b.

[4] Damon, 1957.

[5] Newman and White, 1951.

[6] USA, 1946.

[7] USMC, 1949.

[8] USN, 1949a.

[9] King, et al., 1947.

[10] Gibbons, et al., 1953.

[11] USN, 1955.

[12] USN, 1957.

[13] USN, 1959.

* Including shoes and underwear (subtract 3 lb for nude weight).

Table 11-17   Nude-Body Weight of Female Civilian Populations

Population	Percentiles [1] (lb)					
	1st	5th	50th	95th	99th	S.D.
Railroad travelers [2]		104 *	133 *	179 *		
Working women [3]		(110)	136	(163)		16.0
City women						
Eastern, white	95	108	140	200	229	27.2
Eastern, Negro	85	104	143	193	210	34.5
College students [4]		(94)	121	(149)		17.1
Eastern [5]		(101)	125	(149)		15.2
Midwest [6]		(99)	126	(154)		16.9
Canadians [7]						
18–19 yr old			120			
20–24 yr old			122			
25–29 yr old			123			
30–34 yr old			126			
35–44 yr old			132			
45–54 yr old			142			
55–64 yr old			145			
More than 64 yr old			136			
General [8]	91	100	129	184	213	26.0

[1] Percentiles in parentheses were computed from the 50th percentile using the S.D. Because of the skewed distribution of weight, these values might differ somewhat from the true values and should be used with caution.
[2] Hooton, 1945.
[3] Bayer and Gray, 1934.
[4] Diehl, 1933b.
[5] Bowles, 1932.
[6] Donelson, et al., 1940.
[7] Pett and Ogilvie, 1957.
[8] O'Brien and Shelton, 1941.
* Including shoes and indoor clothing (subtract 3 or 4 lb for nude weight).

MAXIMUM BODY DEPTH

For this dimension, measurement is made, on a lateral photograph of the subject, of the maximum horizontal distance between the vertical planes passing through the most anterior and posterior points on the trunk. The anterior points are on the chest or abdomen; the posterior points are in the shoulder or buttock region. The subject stands erect with his arms at his sides (see Fig. 11-23). The data are given in Table 11-19.

MAXIMUM BODY BREADTH

For this dimension, measurement is made of the maximum breadth of the body, including arms, as the subject stands erect with his arms hanging relaxed at his sides (see Fig. 11-24). The data are given in Table 11-19.

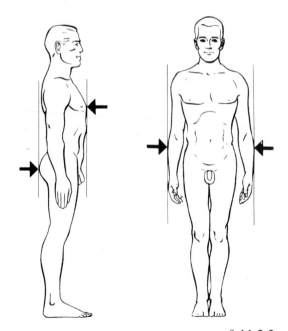

§ 11.2.3

Table 11-18   Nude-Body Weight of Male Civilian Populations

| Population | Percentiles [1] (lb) | | | | | S.D. |
	1st	5th	50th	95th	99th	
Railroad travelers [2]		132 *	167 *	218 *		
Truck and bus drivers [3]		129	164	213	247	
Airline pilots [4]		(134)	168	(201)		20.3
Industrial workers [5]		(130) *	170 *	(210) *		24.5
College students [6]		(112)	142	(172)		18.1
Eastern, 18 yr old [7]		(122)	150	(178)		17.2
Eastern, 19 yr old [8]		(132)	159	(187)		16.2
Midwest, 18 yr old [9]		(115)	148	(180)		19.7
Midwest, 18–22 yr old [10]		(118)	156	(195)		23.5
Draft registrants [11]						
18–19 yr old		(106)	141	(176)		21.1
20–24 yr old		(109)	146	(183)		22.4
25–29 yr old		(110)	151	(192)		24.8
30–34 yr old		(110)	153	(195)		25.8
35–37 yr old		(111)	154	(197)		26.1
Spanish-American-War veterans	110	118	153	190	200	22.1
Canadians [12]						
18–19 yr old			140			
20–24 yr old			151			
25–29 yr old			157			
30–34 yr old			168			
35–44 yr old			165			
45–54 yr old			161			
55–64 yr old			159			
More than 64 yr old			156			

[1] Percentiles in parentheses were computed from the 50th percentile using the S.D. Because of the skewed distribution of weight, these values might differ somewhat from the true values and should be used with caution.

[2] Hooton, 1945.
[3] McFarland, et al., 1958.
[4] McCormick, 1947.
[5] Tyroler, 1958.
[6] Diehl, 1933a.
[7] Bowles, 1932.
[8] Heath, 1945.
[9] Damon, 1955.
[10] Elbel, 1954.
[11] Karpinos, 1958.
[12] Pett and Ogilvie, 1957.

* Including shoes and indoor clothing (subtract 5 or 6 lb for nude weight).

Table 11-19   Maximum Body Depth and Breadth of Male Air Force Personnel and College Students *

| Dimension | Percentiles (in.) | | | S.D. |
	5th	50th	95th	
Body depth	10.1	11.5	13.0	0.88
Body breadth	18.8	20.9	22.8	1.19

* Hertzberg, et al., 1956.

Table 11-20 Head Length of Male Military and Civilian Populations

Population	Percentiles (in.)					S.D.
	1st	5th	50th	95th	99th	
Air Force personnel [1]	7.2	7.3	7.7	8.2	8.3	0.25
Cadets [2]	7.2	7.4	7.8	8.2	8.4	0.26
Basic trainees [3]	7.0	7.2	7.6	8.1	8.3	0.28
Army separatees [4]	7.0	7.2	7.7	8.1	8.3	0.28
College students						
Eastern [5]	7.1	7.3	7.7	8.2	8.4	0.27
Midwest [5]	7.1	7.3	7.7	8.2	8.4	0.27

[1] Hertzberg, et al., 1954.
[2] Randall, et al., 1946.
[3] Daniels, et al., 1953b.
[4] Newman and White, 1951.
[5] Damon, 1955.

HEAD LENGTH

This is the distance between the most anterior point on the head (between the brow ridges) and the most posterior point on the head in the midplane of the body (see Fig. 11-25). The data are given in Tables 11-20 and 11-21.

For men, 8.5 in. will accommodate 99% or more and 8.3 in. 95% or more of all groups. These values represent the corresponding percentile plus 0.1 in. as a safety factor.

For women, subtract 0.5 in. from the above values. Clothing adds varying amounts, depending on the type of headgear; flying helmets add about 3.5 in.

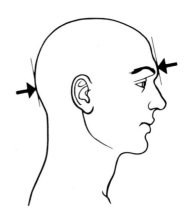

11-25

Table 11-21 Head Length of Female Military and Civilian Populations

Population	Percentiles (in.)					S.D.
	1st	5th	50th	95th	99th	
WAF basic trainees [1]	6.1	6.4	6.9	7.3	7.5	0.30
WAC personnel and Army nurses [2]	6.7	6.8	7.2	7.7	7.8	0.26
Working women [3]	6.8	7.0	7.4	7.7	7.9	0.23
College students						
Eastern [4]	6.8	7.0	7.4	7.7	7.9	0.24
Southern [4]	6.8	7.0	7.4	7.8	7.9	0.23

[1] Daniels, 1953a.
[2] Randall and Munro, 1949.
[3] Bayer and Gray, 1934.
[4] Carter, 1932.

§ 11.2.3

Table 11-22   Head Breadth of Male Military and Civilian Populations

Population	Percentiles (in.)					
	1st	5th	50th	95th	99th	S.D.
Air Force personnel [1]	5.6	5.7	6.1	6.4	6.6	0.20
Cadets [2]	5.6	5.7	6.1	6.4	6.6	0.21
Basic trainees [3]	5.4	5.6	5.9	6.3	6.5	0.23
Army separatees [4]	5.4	5.6	6.0	6.4	6.6	0.23
College students						
Eastern [5]	5.5	5.7	6.0	6.4	6.5	0.22
Midwest [5]	5.6	5.8	6.1	6.5	6.6	0.20

[1] Hertzberg, et al., 1954.
[2] Randall, et al., 1946.
[3] Daniels, et al., 1953b.
[4] Newman and White, 1951.
[5] Bowles, 1932.

HEAD BREADTH

For this dimension, measurement is made of the maximum head breadth above the ears and at right angles to the midplane of the body (see Fig. 11-26). The data are given in Tables 11-22 and 11-23.

For men, 6.7 in. will accommodate at least 99% and 6.5 in. at least 95% of all groups. These values represent the corresponding percentile plus 0.1 in. as a safety factor.

For women, subtract 0.3 in. Clothing increments vary, depending on the type of headgear; add 3.5 in. for steel helmets and 4.3 in. or more for flying helmets.

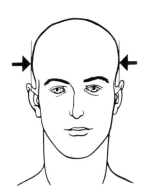

11-26

Table 11-23   Head Breadth of Female Military and Civilian Populations

Population	Percentiles (in.)					
	1st	5th	50th	95th	99th	S.D.
WAF basic trainees [1]	5.3	5.4	5.7	6.1	6.2	0.20
WAC personnel and Army nurses [2]	5.2	5.4	5.7	6.1	6.2	0.22
Working women [3]	5.5	5.6	5.9	6.1	6.3	0.17
College students						
Eastern [4]	5.4	5.5	5.8	6.2	6.3	0.20
Southern [4]	5.4	5.5	5.8	6.1	6.2	0.18

[1] Daniels, et al., 1953a.
[2] Randall and Munro, 1949.
[3] Bayer and Gray, 1934.
[4] Carter, 1932.

INTERPUPILLARY DISTANCE

This is the horizontal distance between the centers of the pupils with the subject looking straight ahead (see Fig. 11-27). The data are given in Table 11-24.

For men, 2.5 in. will accommodate average Air Force personnel, 2.3–2.8 in. will accommodate the 90% between the 5th and 95th percentiles, and 2.2–3.0 in. will accommodate the middle 98%. No other groups have been measured.

EYE HEIGHT (STANDING)

This is the vertical distance from the floor to the inner corner of the eye. The subject stands erect and looks straight ahead (see Fig. 11-28). The data are given in Table 11-24.

For men, 64.7 in. will accommodate average or 50th-percentile Air Force personnel. A range of 60.8 in. (5th percentile) to 68.6 in. (95th percentile) will accommodate the middle 90%, and a range of 59.2 in. (1st percentile) to 70.3 in. (99th percentile) will accommodate the middle 98%. There are no data for any other groups.

For women, subtract 4.5 in. from the above values. For clothing, add 1.0 in. for men's shoes, 1.3 in. for military boots, and up to 3.0 in. for women's shoes.

EYE HEIGHT (SITTING)

This is the vertical distance from the sitting surface to the inner corner of the eye. The subject sits erect and looks straight ahead (see Fig. 11-29). The data are given in Table 11-25.

For men, 31.5 in. will accommodate average or 50th-percentile Air Force personnel. A range of 29.4 in. (5th percentile) to 33.5 in. (95th percentile) will accommodate the middle 90%, and a range of 28.5 in. (1st percentile) to 34.4 in. (99th percentile) will accommodate the middle 98%. For civilians, 31.2 in. will accommodate the 50th percentile, 29.3–33.2 in. the middle 90%, and 28.6–33.9 in. the middle 98%.

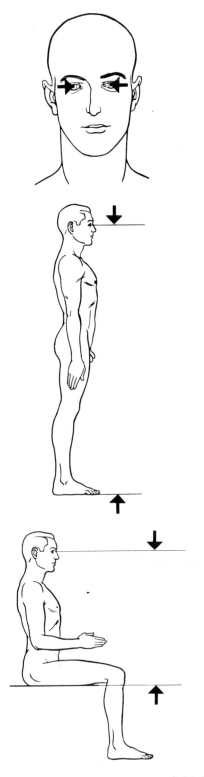

§ 11.2.3

Table 11-24   Interpupillary Distance and Eye Height (Standing) of Male Air Force Personnel *

Dimension	Percentiles (in.)					S.D.
	1st	5th	50th	95th	99th	
Interpupillary distance	2.19	2.27	2.49	2.84	3.04	0.14
Eye height (standing)	59.2	60.8	64.7	68.6	70.3	2.38

* Hertzberg, et al., 1954.

Table 11-25   Eye Height (Sitting) of Male and Female Air Force Personnel

Population	Percentiles (in.)					S.D.
	1st	5th	50th	95th	99th	
Male flight personnel [1]	28.5	29.4	31.5	33.5	34.4	1.27
Female pilots [2]	27.9	28.5	30.0	31.6	32.4	
Female flight nurses [2]	26.3	27.3	29.3	31.1	32.2	

[1] Hertzberg, et al., 1954.   [2] Randall, et al., 1946.

Table 11-26   Shoulder Height (Standing) of Male and Female Air Force Personnel

Population	Percentiles (in.)					S.D.
	1st	5th	50th	95th	99th	
Male flight personnel [1]	51.2	52.8	56.6	60.2	61.9	2.28
Male basic trainees [2]	50.3	52.0	55.9	59.9	61.8	2.41
Female basic trainees [3]	46.9	48.2	51.9	55.4	57.3	2.18

[1] Hertzberg, et al., 1954.   [2] Daniels, et al., 1953a.   [3] Daniels, et al., 1953b.

Table 11-27   Shoulder Height (Sitting) of Male and Female Air Force Personnel

Population	Percentiles (in.)					S.D.
	1st	5th	50th	95th	99th	
Male flight personnel [1]	20.6	21.3	23.3	25.1	25.8	1.14
Female pilots [2]	21.8	22.4	23.8	25.2	25.9	
Female flight nurses [2]	20.4	21.1	23.1	24.8	25.9	

[1] Hertzberg, et al., 1954.   [2] Randall, et al., 1946.

For women, subtract 2.0 in. from the above values. Add 0.2–0.3 in. for heavy clothing under the buttocks.

For women, subtract 2.0 in. from the above values. For light clothing, add 0.2 in. and, for heavy clothing, about 1.0 in.

SHOULDER HEIGHT (STANDING)

This is the vertical distance from the floor to the uppermost point on the lateral edge of the shoulder with the subject standing erect (see Fig. 11-30). The data are given in Table 11-26.

For men, 62.1 in. will accommodate all but the largest 1% of Air Force personnel and 60.4 in. all but the largest 5%. There are no data for any other groups. These values represent the nude percentile plus 0.2 in. as a safety factor. (Another 1.5 in. should be added for vertical distance from the point of measurement to the highest point between the shoulder and neck—the more functional dimension.)

For women, subtract 4.0 in. from the above values. For clothing, add 1.0 in. for men's shoes, 1.3 in. for military boots, up to 3.0 in. for women's shoes, 0.2 in. for light clothing, and 0.9 in. or more for heavy clothing.

11-30

SHOULDER HEIGHT (SITTING)

This is the vertical distance from the sitting surface to the uppermost point on the lateral edge of the shoulder with the subject sitting erect (see Fig. 11-31). The data are given in Table 11-27.

For men, 26.0 in. will accommodate all but the largest 1%, and 25.3 in. will accommodate all but the largest 5%, of Air Force personnel. For Army personnel, the corresponding values are 26.0 in. (99th percentile) and 25.2 in. (95th percentile). For civilians, these values are 26.1 and 25.4 in. These values represent the nude percentiles plus 0.2 in. as a safety factor. (Another 1.5 in. should be added for vertical distance from the point of measurement to the highest point between the shoulder and neck—the more functional dimension.)

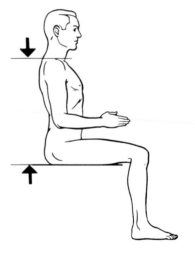

11-31

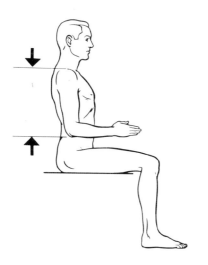

11-32

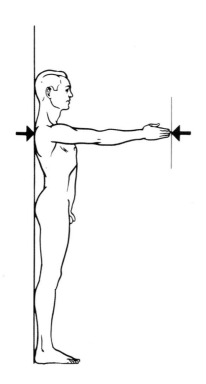

11-33

SHOULDER-TO-ELBOW LENGTH

This is the vertical distance from the uppermost point on the lateral edge of the shoulder to the bottom of the elbow. The subject sits erect with his upper arm vertical at his side and the forearm making a right angle with it (see Fig. 11-32). The data are given in Tables 11-28 and 11-29.

For men, 16.1 in. will accommodate all but the largest 1%, and 15.6 in. will accommodate all but the largest 5%, of Air Force personnel. Corresponding values for Army personnel are 16.5 and 15.8 in. and, for civilians, 16.5 and 16.1 in. These dimensions refer to the nude body and include an added 0.2 in. as a safety factor. (Another 1.5 in. should be added for vertical distance from the point of measurement to the highest point between the shoulder and neck—the more functional dimension.)

For women, subtract 1.0 in. from the above values. Add 0.2 in. for light clothing and 1.0 in. or more for heavy clothing.

ARM REACH

This is the horizontal distance from the posterior surface of the right shoulder to the tip of the extended middle finger. The subject stands erect with heels, buttocks, and shoulders against the wall and the right arm and hand extended forward horizontally to their maximum length (see Fig. 11-33). The data are given in Tables 11-30 and 11-31.

For men, the smallest 1% of Air Force personnel can reach 30.9 in. comfortably, and the smallest 5% can reach 31.9 in. comfortably. For civilians, the corresponding values are 31.9 in. for the smallest 1% and 33.0 in. for the smallest 5%.

For women, subtract 3.5 in. from the above values. Add 0.3 in. for light clothing, 0.2 in. for light gloves, and 0.3 in. for heavy clothing and gloves. For fingertip manipulation of controls, subtract 0.5 in. for flip and 1.0 in. for push. For manipulation by the thumb and forefinger, subtract 3.0 in. For grasping by the whole hand, subtract 5.0 in.

Table 11-28 Shoulder-Elbow Length of Male Military and Civilian Populations

Population	Percentiles (in.)					S.D.
	1st	5th	50th	95th	99th	
Air Force personnel [1]	12.8	13.2	14.3	15.4	15.9	0.69
Cadets [2]	13.2	13.6	14.7	15.8	16.3	
Gunners [2]	12.9	13.3	14.5	15.6	16.1	
Army personnel						
Separatees, white [3]	12.3	12.9	14.3	15.6	16.3	0.81
Separatees, Negro [4]	12.4	13.0	14.3	15.6	16.1	0.80
Truck and bus drivers [5]	13.3	13.8	14.8	15.9	16.3	0.81
College students [6]	12.8	13.3	14.5	15.7	16.1	0.66

[1] Hertzberg, et al., 1954.
[2] Randall, et al., 1946.
[3] Newman and White, 1951.
[4] USA, 1946.
[5] McFarland, et al., 1958.
[6] Bowles, 1932.

Table 11-29 Shoulder-Elbow Length of Female Military Personnel

Population	Percentiles (in.)					S.D.
	1st	5th	50th	95th	99th	
Air Force personnel [1]						
Pilots	12.3	12.7	13.7	14.7	15.2	
Flight nurses	12.3	12.7	13.6	14.8	15.3	
Army personnel [2]	11.3	11.9	13.1	14.3	14.9	0.74

[1] Randall, et al., 1946.
[2] Randall and Munro, 1949.

Table 11-30 Arm Reach of Male Military and Civilian Populations

Population	Percentiles (in.)					S.D.
	1st	5th	50th	95th	99th	
Air Force personnel [1]	30.9	31.9	34.6	37.3	38.6	1.70
Cadets [2]	31.6	32.7	35.2	37.8	38.8	
Gunners [2]	30.9	31.9	34.8	37.4	38.6	
Navy personnel [3]	30.0	31.1	33.7	36.3	37.4	1.57
Enlisted men [4]	31.6	32.7	35.7	38.2	39.5	1.70
Cadets, aviation [4]	31.7	32.8	35.4	38.1	39.2	
Truck and bus drivers [5]	31.9	32.9	35.7	38.4	39.5	

[1] Hertzberg, et al., 1954.
[2] Randall, et al., 1946.
[3] King, et al., 1947.
[4] USN, 1955.
[5] McFarland, et al., 1958.

§ 11.2.3

Table 11-31 Arm Reach of Female Air Force Personnel *

Population	Percentiles (in.)				
	1st	5th	50th	95th	99th
Pilots	29.2	29.7	31.8	34.1	34.9
Flight nurses	27.9	28.7	31.0	33.5	34.4

* Randall, et al., 1946.

Table 11-32 Shoulder Breadth of Male Military and Civilian Populations

Population	Percentiles (in.)					S.D.
	1st	5th	50th	95th	99th	
Air Force personnel [1]	15.9	16.5	17.9	19.4	20.1	0.91
Cadets [2]	16.1	16.7	18.0	19.3	19.9	
Gunners [2]	16.0	16.5	17.7	19.0	19.5	
Army personnel						
Separatees, white [3]	15.8	16.4	17.9	19.6	20.6	0.99
Separatees, Negro [4]	15.8	16.4	17.9	19.4	20.0	0.89
Navy personnel [5]	15.1	15.8	17.6	19.4	20.2	1.09
Railroad travelers [6]	15.7 *	16.4 *	17.6 *	19.2 *	19.8 *	
Truck and bus drivers [7]	16.2	16.9	18.3	19.9	20.5	
College students [8]	15.1	15.7	17.2	18.7	19.3	0.86

[1] Hertzberg, et al., 1954.
[2] Randall, et al., 1946.
[3] Newman and White, 1951.
[4] USA, 1946.
[5] King, et al., 1947.
[6] Hooton, 1945.
[7] McFarland, et al., 1958.
[8] Bowles, 1932.

* Including light clothing (subtract 0.3 in. for nude dimension).

Table 11-33 Shoulder Breadth of Female Military and Civilian Populations

Population	Percentiles (in.)				
	1st	5th	50th	95th	99th
Air Force personnel [1]					
Pilots	14.3	14.9	16.1	17.6	18.0
Flight nurses	14.1	14.5	15.7	16.8	17.2
Railroad travelers [2]	13.7 *	14.4 *	15.7 *	17.6 *	18.2 *

[1] Randall, et al., 1946.
[2] Hooton, 1945.

* Including light clothing (subtract 0.3 in. for nude dimension).

§ 11.2.3

SHOULDER BREADTH

For this dimension, measurement is made of the maximum horizontal distance across the deltoid muscles. The subject sits erect with his upper arms touching his sides and his forearms extended horizontally (see Fig. 11-34). The data are given in Tables 11-32 and 11-33.

For men, 20.3 in. will accommodate all but the largest 1% and 19.6 in. all but the largest 5% of Air Force personnel. Corresponding values for Army personnel are 20.8 and 19.8 in. and, for civilians, 19.7 and 19.1 in. These values are nude percentiles plus 0.2 in. as a safety factor.

For women, subtract 2.0 in. from the above values. Add 0.3 in. for light clothing, 1.5 in. for heavy clothing, 0.4 in. for the partial-pressure suit uninflated, and 6.0 in. for the inflated suit.

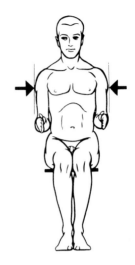

CHEST DEPTH

This is the horizontal distance from the front to the back of the chest at nipple level (on women, at the level where the 4th rib meets the breastbone). The subject stands erect and breathes normally (see Fig. 11-35). The data are given in Tables 11-34 and 11-35.

For men, 11.3 in. will accommodate 99% of Air Force personnel and almost 100% of Army personnel. Values for civilians in their mid-thirties are about 11.3 in. for 99% and 10.7 in. for 95%. These values refer to the nude dimension plus 0.2 in. as a safety factor. Add 0.5 in. for light clothing, 2 in. for heavy clothing, and 4.5 in. for inflated partial-pressure suits.

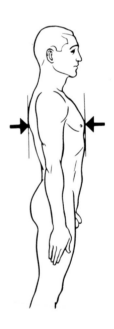

CHEST BREADTH

This is the horizontal distance across the chest at nipple level. The subject stands erect, breathes normally, and has his arms hanging naturally at his sides (see Fig. 11-36). The data are given in Tables 11-36 and 11-37.

For men, 14.3 in. will accommodate 99%, and 13.6 in. will accommodate 95%, of Air Force personnel and the same or larger percentages of Army personnel and civilians. These values refer to nude chest breadth plus 0.2 in. as a safety margin.

For women, subtract 1.5 in. from the above values. Add 0.3 in. for light clothing, 0.6 in. for heavy clothing, and 2.5 in. for inflated partial-pressure suits.

§ 11.2.3

WAIST DEPTH (STANDING)

This is the horizontal distance between the back and abdomen at the level of the greatest lateral indentation of the waist (if this is not apparent, at the level at which the belt is worn). The subject stands erect with his abdomen relaxed (see Fig. 11-37). The data are given in Table 11-38.

For men, 13.3 in. will accommodate 99% of civilians averaging 36 yr of age and almost 100% of all military groups. These values refer to the nude dimension plus 0.2 in. as a safety factor. Add 1.0 in. for light clothing, 2.5 in. for heavy clothing, and 5.0 in. for inflated partial-pressure suits. Add 0.1 in. for the sitting dimension.

ELBOW HEIGHT (STANDING)

This is the vertical distance from the floor to the depression at the elbow between the bones of the upper arm and forearm. The subject stands erect with his arms hanging naturally at his sides (see Fig. 11-38). The data are given in Table 11-39.

For men, 40.5 in. will accommodate average or 50th-percentile Air Force personnel. A range of 37.6 in. (5th percentile) to 43.4 in.

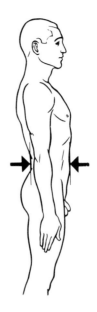

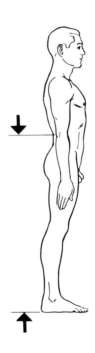

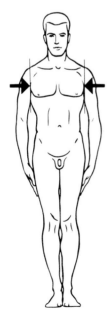

(95th percentile) will accommodate the middle 90%, and a range of 36.5 in. (1st percentile) to 44.7 in. (99th percentile) will accommodate the middle 98%. These values are based on nude percentiles minus 3.0 in. for comfort.

§ 11.2.3

Table 11-34 Chest Depth of Male Military and Civilian Populations

Population	Percentiles (in.)					S.D.
	1st	5th	50th	95th	99th	
Air Force personnel [1]	7.6	8.0	9.0	10.4	11.1	0.75
Cadets [2]	6.8	7.2	8.2	9.3	9.7	
Gunners [2]	6.7	7.1	8.2	9.2	9.6	
Army separatees [3]	6.7	7.2	8.3	9.6	10.5	0.75
Truck and bus drivers [4]	7.1	7.6	8.9	10.5	11.1	
College students						
Eastern [5]	6.5	6.9	7.9	8.9	9.3	0.55
Midwest [6]	6.4	6.9	8.0	9.2	9.7	0.71

[1] Hertzberg, et al., 1954.   [4] McFarland, et al., 1958.
[2] Randall, et al., 1946.   [5] Heath, 1945.
[3] Newman and White, 1951.   [6] Damon, 1955.

Table 11-35 Chest Depth of Female College Students

Population	Percentiles (in.)					S.D.
	1st	5th	50th	95th	99th	
Eastern [1]	5.8	6.3	7.4	8.6	9.0	0.68
Midwest [2]	6.0	6.4	7.3	8.2	8.6	0.56

[1] Carter, 1932.   [2] Donelson, et al., 1940.

Table 11-36 Chest Breadth of Male Military and Civilian Populations

Population	Percentiles (in.)					S.D.
	1st	5th	50th	95th	99th	
Air Force personnel [1]	10.4	10.8	12.0	13.4	14.1	0.80
Cadets [2]	9.8	10.3	11.3	12.4	12.8	
Gunners [2]	9.7	10.1	11.1	12.1	12.5	
Basic trainees [3]	9.7	10.2	11.4	13.0	14.3	0.91
Army separatees [4]	9.3	10.0	11.1	12.4	13.2	0.77
Truck and bus drivers [5]	9.6	10.2	11.8	13.5	13.9	
College students						
Eastern [6]	9.9	10.4	11.5	12.7	13.1	0.67
Midwest [7]	9.3	9.9	11.1	12.4	12.9	0.79

[1] Hertzberg, et al., 1954.   [5] McFarland, et al., 1958.
[2] Randall, et al., 1946.   [6] Heath, 1945.
[3] Daniels, et al., 1953b.   [7] Damon, 1955.
[4] Newman and White, 1951.

     § 11.2.3

Table 11-37   Chest Breadth of Female Air Force Personnel and College Students

Population	Percentiles (in.)					S.D.
	1st	5th	50th	95th	99th	
WAF basic trainees [1]	8.9	9.1	9.9	10.9	11.3	0.55
College students						
Eastern [2]	8.3	8.7	9.7	10.7	11.1	0.59
Midwest [3]	8.6	9.0	10.1	11.1	11.5	0.64

[1] Daniels, et al., 1953a.
[2] Carter, 1932.
[3] Donelson, et al., 1940.

Table 11-38   Waist Depth (Standing) of Male Military and Civilian Populations

Population	Percentiles (in.)					S.D.
	1st	5th	50th	95th	99th	
Air Force personnel [1]	6.3	6.7	7.9	9.5	10.3	0.88
Cadets [2]	6.7	7.2	8.2	9.3	9.8	
Gunners [2]	6.7	7.2	8.2	9.3	9.8	
Army separatees [3]	7.5	7.9	9.0	10.5	11.5	0.81
Truck and bus drivers [4]	7.3	7.9	9.5	12.1	13.1	

[1] Hertzberg, et al., 1954.
[2] Randall, et al., 1946.
[3] Newman and White, 1951.
[4] McFarland, et al., 1958.

Table 11-39   Elbow Height of Male Air Force Personnel *

Posture	Percentiles (in.)					S.D.
	1st	5th	50th	95th	99th	
Standing	39.5	40.6	43.5	46.4	47.7	1.77
Sitting	6.6	7.4	9.1	10.8	11.5	1.04

* Hertzberg, et al., 1954.

Table 11-40   Elbow Height (Sitting) of Railroad Travelers *

Sex	Percentiles (in.)				
	1st	5th	50th	95th	99th
Male	7.5	8.1	9.6	11.1	11.7
Female	7.8	8.4	9.7	11.1	11.7

* Subjects are clothed and, in addition, the dimension is measured to a vertically adjustable elbow rest, the fixed lateral distance from the body of which sometimes results in increased values (Hooton, 1945).

§ 11.2.3

ELBOW HEIGHT (SITTING)

This is the vertical distance from the sitting surface to the bottom of the right elbow. The subject sits erect with his upper right arm vertical at his side and his forearm at a right angle to the upper arm (see Fig. 11-39). The data are given in Tables 11-39 and 11-40.

For men, 8.0 in. will accommodate many around the average or 50th percentile, and a range of 6.5–10.5 in. will accommodate almost everyone. These values are based on the nude percentiles minus 1.0–1.5 in. for slump.

For women, use the same values as given above. Clothing makes no difference because that under the buttocks is balanced by that under the elbow.

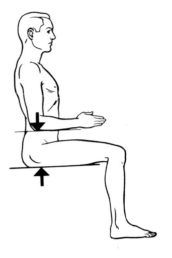

FOREARM-HAND LENGTH

This is the horizontal distance from the tip of the right elbow to the tip of the longest finger. The subject sits erect with his upper right arm vertical at his side and his forearm, hand, and fingers extended horizontally (see Fig. 11-40). The data are in Table 11-41.

For men, 17.0 in. will accommodate all but the smallest 1% and 17.6 in. all but the smallest 5% of Air Force personnel. Corresponding values for Army personnel are 16.6 and 17.3 in. and, for civilians, 16.7 and 17.3. Add 0.2 in. for light clothing without gloves, 0.2 in. for light gloves, and 0.8–1.0 in. for heavy clothing and gloves.

For fingertip manipulation of controls, subtract 0.5 in. for flip and 1.0 in. for push. For manipulation by the thumb and forefinger, subtract 3.0 in. For grasp by the whole hand, subtract 5.0 in.

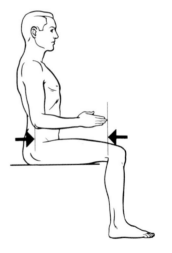

ELBOW-TO-ELBOW BREADTH

For this dimension, measurement is made of the maximum horizontal distance across the lateral surface of the elbows. The subject sits erect with his upper arms vertical and touching his sides and his forearms extended horizontally (see Fig. 11-41). The data are given in Tables 11-42 and 11-43.

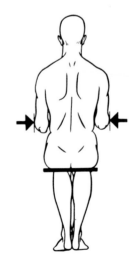

§ 11.2.3

For men, 21.1 in. will accommodate all but the largest 1%, and 20.0 in. will accommodate all but the largest 5%, of Air Force personnel. Corresponding figures for Army personnel are 22.0 and 20.5 in. and, for civilians, 22.4 and 20.9 in. These values refer to the nude dimension plus 0.2 in. as a safety factor.

For women, subtract 2 in. from the above values. Add 0.5 in. for light clothing and 4.5 in. for heavy clothing.

Table 11-41   Forearm-Hand Length of Male Military and Civilian Populations

Population	Percentiles (in.)					
	1st	5th	50th	95th	99th	S.D.
Air Force personnel [1]	17.0	17.6	18.9	20.2	20.7	0.81
Army personnel						
Separatees, white [2]	16.6	17.3	18.7	20.1	20.8	0.88
Separatees, Negro [3]	17.3	18.0	19.6	21.4	22.1	0.94
Truck and bus drivers [4]	16.7	17.3	18.8	20.2	20.8	
College students [5]	17.0	17.6	18.9	20.2	20.7	0.75

[1] Hertzberg, et al., 1954.
[2] Newman and White, 1951.
[3] USA, 1946.
[4] McFarland, et al., 1958.
[5] Bowles, 1932.

Table 11-42   Elbow-to-Elbow Breadth of Male Military and Civilian Populations

Population	Percentiles (in.)					
	1st	5th	50th	95th	99th	S.D.
Air Force personnel [1]	14.5	15.2	17.2	19.8	20.9	1.42
Cadets [2]	14.4	15.1	16.7	18.4	19.1	
Gunners [2]	13.9	14.6	16.4	18.2	18.9	
Army personnel						
Separatees, white [3]	14.4	15.3	17.4	20.3	21.8	1.54
Separatees, Negro [4]	14.4	15.1	16.9	19.3	20.4	1.28
Truck and bus drivers [5]	13.8	14.9	17.5	20.7	22.2	

[1] Hertzberg, et al., 1954.
[2] Randall, et al., 1946.
[3] Newman and White, 1951.
[4] USA, 1946.
[5] McFarland, et al., 1958.

Table 11-43   Elbow-to-Elbow Breadth of Female Air Force Personnel *

Population	Percentiles (in.)				
	1st	5th	50th	95th	99th
Pilots	12.8	13.3	15.1	17.1	18.5
Flight nurses	13.0	13.5	14.9	16.7	17.3

* Randall, et al., 1946.

Table 11-44   Hip Breadth (Standing) of Male and Female Air Force Personnel and College Students

Population	Percentiles (in.)					S.D.
	1st	5th	50th	95th	99th	
Male flight personnel [1]	11.3	12.1	13.2	14.4	15.2	0.73
Male basic trainees [2]	11.5	12.1	13.3	15.0	16.3	0.94
Male college students [3]	11.4	11.8	13.0	14.2	14.7	0.67
Female basic trainees [4]	12.2	12.5	13.5	15.4	16.9	0.95

[1] Hertzberg, et al., 1954.   [3] Bowles, 1932.
[2] Daniels, et al., 1953b.   [4] Daniels, et al., 1953a.

Table 11-45   Hip-to-Hip Breadth (Sitting) of Male Military and Civilian Populations

Population	Percentiles (in.)					S.D.
	1st	5th	50th	95th	99th	
Air Force personnel [1]	12.2	12.7	13.9	15.4	16.2	0.87
Cadets [2]	12.6	13.1	14.2	15.5	15.9	
Gunners [2]	12.1	12.7	13.8	15.1	15.5	
Army personnel						
Separatees, white [3]	12.2	12.7	13.9	15.5	16.7	0.90
Separatees, Negro [4]	11.6	12.1	13.4	15.0	15.8	0.84
Navy personnel [5]						
Enlisted men	12.4	13.0	14.8	16.4	17.2	1.05
Cadets, aviation	13.4	14.0	15.4	16.8	17.3	
Railroad travelers [6]	12.9 *	13.7 *	15.3 *	17.4 *	18.1 *	
Truck and bus drivers [7]	12.4	13.2	14.5	16.3	16.8	

[1] Hertzberg, et al., 1954.   [5] USN, 1955.
[2] Randall, et al., 1946.   [6] Hooton, 1945.
[3] Newman and White, 1951.   [7] McFarland, et al., 1958.
[4] USA, 1946.
* Including light clothing (subtract 0.5 in. for nude dimension).

Table 11-46   Hip Breadth (Sitting) of Female Military and Civilian Populations

Population	Percentiles (in.)				
	1st	5th	50th	95th	99th
Air Force personnel [1]					
Pilots	13.0	13.5	15.0	16.9	18.1
Flight nurses	13.1	13.5	15.1	16.6	17.1
Railroad travelers [2]	12.2 *	13.1 *	14.6 *	17.2 *	17.8 *

[1] Randall, et al., 1946.   [2] Hooton, 1945.
* Including light clothing (subtract 0.5 in. for nude dimension).

§ 11.2.3

HIP BREADTH (STANDING)

For this dimension, measurement is made of the maximum horizontal distance across the hips. The subject stands erect with his heels together (see Fig. 11-42). The data are given in Table 11-44.

For men, 15.4 in. will accommodate all but the largest 1% and 14.6 in. all but the largest 5% of Air Force personnel. For Army personnel, the corresponding values are 16.5 and 15.2 in. These values refer to the nude dimension plus 0.2 in. as a safety factor.

For women, add 0.5 in. to the above values. Add 0.5 in. for light clothing and 1.5 in. or more for heavy clothing.

HIP BREADTH (SITTING)

For this dimension, measurement is made of the maximum horizontal distance across the hips. The subject sits erect with his knees and ankles at right angles and his knees and heels together (see Fig. 11-43). The data are given in Tables 11-45 and 11-46.

For men, 16.4 in. will accommodate all but the largest 1% and 15.6 in. all but the largest 5% of Air Force personnel. Corresponding values for Army personnel are 16.9 and 15.7 in. and, for civilians, 17.0 and 16.5 in. These values refer to the nude dimension plus 0.2 in. as a safety factor.

For women, add 1.0 in. to the values given above. Add 0.5 in. for light clothing, 2.0 in. for heavy clothing, and, for partial-pressure suits, 3.0 in. when uninflated and 5.5 in. when inflated.

BUTTOCK-LEG LENGTH

This is the horizontal distance from the most posterior point on the buttocks to the base of the heel. The subject sits erect with his legs as far forward as possible on a horizontal surface (see Fig. 11-44). The data are given in Table 11-47. This dimension is involved in two considerations: leg *reach* (the maximum forward distance reachable by the leg

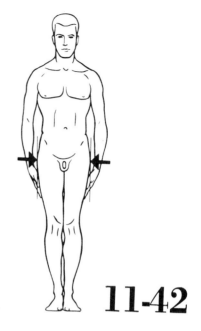

11-42

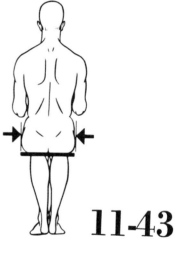

11-43

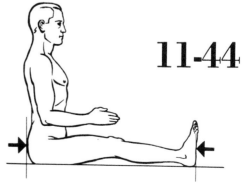

11-44

§ 11.2.3

from a seated position) and *clearance* for the outstretched leg (the distance between the seat back, or objects located behind the buttocks, and objects in front of the feet).

For men, 38.2 in. can be reached by all but the *smallest* 1%, and 39.4 inches can be reached by all but the smallest 5%, of Air Force personnel. Corresponding values for Navy personnel are 37.0 and 38.4 in. For clothing, add 1.0 in. for men's shoes, 1.3 in.

for military boots, 0.3 in. for heavy clothing behind the buttocks, and 2.5 in. for partial-pressure suits.

For men, 47.9 in. will accommodate all but the *largest* 1%, and 46.3 in. will accommodate all but the largest 5%, of Air Force personnel. Corresponding values for Navy personnel are 48.6 and 46.6 in. Add 1.1 in. for shoes and light clothing and 1.7 in. or more for boots and heavy clothing.

BUTTOCK-KNEE LENGTH

This is the horizontal distance from the most posterior point on the buttocks to the most anterior point on the knee. The subject sits erect with his knees and ankles at right angles (see Fig. 11-45). The data are given in Tables 11-48 and 11-49.

For men, 26.4 in. will accommodate all but the largest 1%, and 25.6 in. will accommodate all but the largest 5%, of Air Force personnel. Corresponding values for Army personnel are 26.2 and 25.4 in. and, for civilians, 26.7 and 26.0 in. These values represent nude percentiles plus a safety factor of 0.2 in.

For women, subtract 1.0 in. from the above values. Add 0.2 in. for light clothing, 0.7 in. or more for heavy clothing, and 2.9 in. for partial-pressure suits.

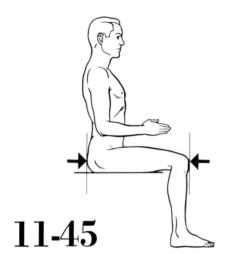

11-45

BUTTOCK-POPLITEAL LENGTH

This is the horizontal distance from the plane of the most posterior point on the buttocks to the back of the lower leg at the knee. The subject sits erect with his knees and ankles at right angles (see Fig. 11-46). The data are given in Table 11-50.

For men, 16.4 in. will accommodate all but the smallest 1%, and 17.2 in. will accommodate all but the smallest 5%, of civilians. There are no data for military groups. These values represent the clothed 1st and 5th percentiles minus an arbitrary 0.2 in. For women, subtract 0.7 in. from these values.

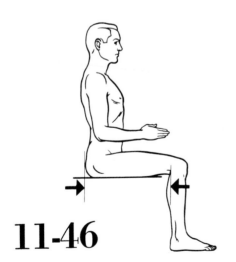

11-46

§ 11.2.3

Table 11-47 Buttock-Leg Length of Male Military Personnel

Population	Percentiles (in.)					S.D.
	1st	5th	50th	95th	99th	
Air Force personnel [1]	38.2	39.4	42.7	46.1	47.7	2.04
Navy personnel						
General [2]	36.5	38.0	41.5	44.9	46.4	2.07
Pilots, aircraft [3]	36.8	38.3	42.3	46.3	48.8	

[1] Hertzberg, et al., 1954.   [2] King, et al., 1947.   [3] USN, 1959.

Table 11-48 Buttock-Knee Length of Male Military and Civilian Populations

Population	Percentiles (in.)					S.D.
	1st	5th	50th	95th	99th	
Air Force personnel [1]	21.2	21.9	23.6	25.4	26.2	1.06
Cadets [2]	21.2	22.0	23.6	25.6	26.2	
Gunners [2]	20.5	21.1	23.1	24.7	25.6	
Army personnel						
Separatees, white [3]	20.7	21.5	23.4	25.2	26.0	1.12
Separatees, Negro [4]	21.1	21.9	23.8	25.8	26.6	1.17
Navy personnel [5]	20.6	21.4	23.4	25.0	25.8	1.18
Enlisted men [6]	21.7	22.5	24.5	26.5	27.3	1.23
Cadets, aviation [6]	21.8	22.6	24.3	26.2	26.9	
Truck and bus drivers [7]	21.3	22.1	23.8	25.8	26.5	

[1] Hertzberg, et al., 1954.
[2] Randall, et al., 1946.
[3] Newman and White, 1951.
[4] USA, 1946.
[5] King, et al., 1947.
[6] USN, 1955.
[7] McFarland, et al., 1958.

Table 11-49 Buttock-Knee Length of Female Air Force Personnel *

Population	Percentiles (in.)				
	1st	5th	50th	95th	99th
Pilots	20.4	21.1	22.6	24.2	25.0
Flight nurses	20.2	20.9	22.4	24.0	24.8

* Randall, et al., 1946.

§ 11.2.3

533

BUTTOCK DEPTH

This is the horizontal distance between the buttocks and the abdomen at the level of the maximum protrusion of the buttocks. The subject stands erect (see Fig. 11-47). The data are given in Table 11-51.

For men, 11.1 in. will accommodate 99%, and 10.4 in. will accommodate 95%, of Air Force personnel. No other groups have been measured. These values refer to the nude percentiles plus 0.2 in. as a safety factor.

THIGH HEIGHT (SITTING)

This is the vertical distance from the sitting surface to the top of the thigh at its intersection with the abdomen. The subject sits erect with his knees and ankles at right angles (see Fig. 11-48). The data are given in Table 11-51.

For men, 7.0 in. will accommodate all but the largest 1%, and 6.7 in. will accommodate all but the largest 5%, of Air Force personnel. These values represent the nude percentiles plus the arbitrary 0.2-in. safety factor. Only Air Force personnel have been measured for thigh height.

For women, use the same values given above. Add 0.1–0.2 in. for light clothing and 1.4 in. or more for heavy clothing.

KNUCKLE HEIGHT (STANDING)

This is the vertical distance from the floor to the point where the middle finger of the right hand meets the palm. The subject stands erect with his palm flat against the side of his thigh (see Fig. 11-49). The data are given in Table 11-51.

For men, 24.7 in. will accommodate all but the smallest 1%, and 25.7 in. will accommodate all but the smallest 5%, of Air Force personnel. No other groups have been measured. These values represent the nude dimension minus 2 in. as a safety factor. For clothing, add 1.0 in. for shoes and 1.3 in. for military boots.

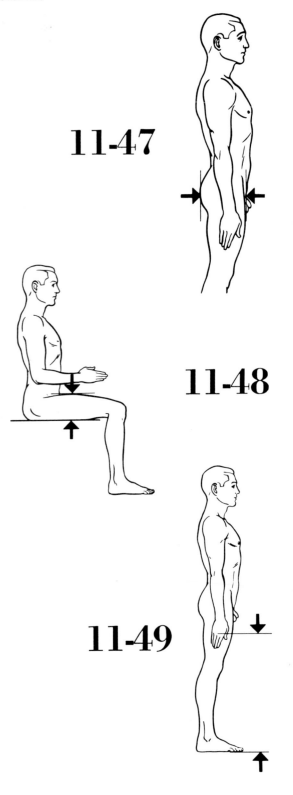

Table 11-50 Buttock-Popliteal Length of Railroad Travelers *

Sex	Percentiles (in.)				
	1st	5th	50th	95th	99th
Male	16.6	17.4	18.9	20.8	21.5
Female	16.0	16.8	18.2	20.0	20.6

* Hooton, 1945.

Table 11-51 Buttock Depth, Thigh Height (Sitting), and Knuckle Height (Standing) of Male Air Force Personnel *

Dimension	Percentiles (in.)					S.D.
	1st	5th	50th	95th	99th	
Buttock thickness	7.2	7.6	8.8	10.2	10.9	0.82
Thigh height (sitting)	4.5	4.8	5.6	6.5	6.8	0.52
Knuckle height (standing)	26.7	27.7	30.0	32.4	33.5	1.45

* Hertzberg, et al., 1954.

Table 11-52 Hand Thickness of Male and Female Air Force Personnel

Population	Percentiles (in.)					S.D.
	1st	5th	50th	95th	99th	
Male flight personnel [1]	1.0	1.1	1.2	1.3	1.4	0.07
Male basic trainees [2]	1.0	1.1	1.2	1.4	1.4	0.09
Female basic trainees [3]	0.8	0.8	1.0	1.1	1.2	0.09

[1] Hertzberg, et al., 1954.　　[2] Daniels, et al., 1953b.　　[3] Daniels, et al., 1953a.

Table 11-53 Hand Length of Male Military and Civilian Populations

Population	Percentiles (in.)					S.D.
	1st	5th	50th	95th	99th	
Air Force personnel [1]	6.7	6.9	7.5	8.0	8.3	0.34
Cadets [2]	6.8	7.1	7.6	8.2	8.4	
Gunners [2]	6.6	6.9	7.5	8.1	8.4	
Basic trainees [3]	6.7	6.9	7.5	8.2	8.5	0.38
Army personnel						
Separatees, white [4]	6.7	7.0	7.6	8.2	8.5	0.36
Separatees, Negro [5]	7.0	7.3	8.0	8.7	9.0	0.42
Truck and bus drivers [6]	6.9	7.1	7.6	8.1	8.3	

[1] Hertzberg, et al., 1954.　　　　　　　　[4] Newman and White, 1951.
[2] Randall, et al., 1946.　　　　　　　　　[5] USA, 1946.
[3] Daniels, et al., 1953b.　　　　　　　　　[6] McFarland, et al., 1958.

§ 11.2.3

HAND THICKNESS

For this dimension, measurement is made of the maximum distance between the dorsal and palmar surfaces of the knuckle of the middle finger where it joins the palm of the right hand when the fingers are extended (see Fig. 11-50). The data are given in Table 11-52.

For men, 1.5 in. will accommodate 99% and 1.4 in. about 95% of Air Force personnel. No other groups have been measured. These values include a safety factor of plus 0.1 in.

For women, subtract 0.2 in. from the above values. Add 0.2 in. for wool or leather gloves and about 1.5 in. for arctic mittens.

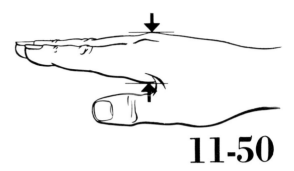

11-50

HAND LENGTH

This is the distance from the base of the thumb to the middle fingertip of the right hand held straight and stiff (see Fig. 11-51). The data are given in Tables 11-53 and 11-54.

For men, 6.6 in. can be reached by all but the smallest 1% or fewer and 6.9 in. by all but the smallest 5% of all military groups. For women, subtract 0.7 in. from these values.

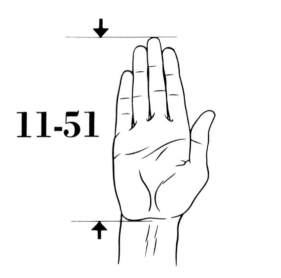

11-51

HAND BREADTH AT THUMB

For this dimension, measurement is made of the maximum breadth across the palm (at right angles to the long axis of the hand) at the knuckle of the thumb of the right hand with the fingers extended and the thumb lying alongside and in the plane of the hand (see Fig. 11-52). The data are given in Table 11-55.

For men, 4.7 in. will accommodate all but the largest 1% and 4.5 in. all but the largest 5% of Air Force personnel. No other groups have been measured. These values include a safety factor of plus 0.1 in.

For women, subtract 0.5 in. from the above values. Add 0.3 in. for wool or leather gloves and about 1.0 in. for arctic mittens.

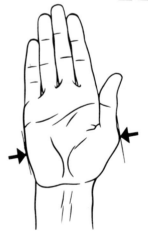

11-52

§ 11.2.3

Table 11-54 Hand Length of Female Military and Civilian Populations

Population	Percentiles (in.)					S.D.
	1st	5th	50th	95th	99th	
Air Force personnel						
Pilots [1]	6.2	6.4	6.9	7.5	7.7	
Flight nurses [1]	6.3	6.5	6.9	7.4	7.6	
Basic trainees [2]	6.0	6.2	6.8	7.3	7.6	0.34
Army personnel [3]	6.1	6.4	6.9	7.4	7.7	0.33
College students [4]	6.0	6.2	6.7	7.2	7.4	0.31

[1] Randall, et al., 1946.   [3] Randall and Munro, 1949.
[2] Daniels, et al., 1953a.   [4] Carter, 1932.

Table 11-55 Hand Breadth at Thumb of Male and Female Air Force Personnel

Population	Percentiles (in.)					S.D.
	1st	5th	50th	95th	99th	
Male flight personnel [1]	3.6	3.7	4.1	4.4	4.6	0.21
Male basic trainees [2]	3.5	3.7	4.1	4.5	4.7	0.25
Female basic trainees [3]	3.1	3.2	3.6	4.0	4.1	0.23

[1] Hertzberg, et al., 1954.   [2] Daniels, et al., 1953b.   [3] Daniels, et al., 1953a.

Table 11-56 Hand Breadth at Metacarpale of Male Military and Civilian Populations

Population	Percentiles (in.)					S.D.
	1st	5th	50th	95th	99th	
Air Force personnel [1]	3.1	3.2	3.5	3.7	3.9	0.16
Cadets [2]	3.0	3.1	3.4	3.7	3.8	
Gunners [2]	3.0	3.1	3.4	3.6	3.7	
Basic trainees [3]	3.0	3.2	3.5	3.7	3.9	0.18
Army personnel						
Separatees, white [4]	2.9	3.1	3.4	3.8	3.9	0.19
Separatees, Negro [5]	3.0	3.2	3.5	3.8	4.0	0.20
Truck and bus drivers [6]	3.1	3.2	3.5	3.8	4.0	

[1] Hertzberg, et al., 1954.   [4] Newman and White, 1951.
[2] Randall, et al., 1946.   [5] USA, 1946.
[3] Daniels, et al., 1953b.   [6] McFarland, et al., 1958.

HAND BREADTH AT METACARPALE

For this dimension, measurement is made of the maximum breadth across the ends of the metacarpale bones (where the fingers join the palm) of the index and little fingers of the right hand held straight and stiff with the fingers together (see Fig. 11-53). The data are given in Tables 11-56 and 11-57.

For men, 4.1 in. will accommodate all but the largest 1% or fewer, and 3.9 in. will accommodate all but the largest 5% or fewer, of all groups, military and civilian. These values include a safety factor of plus 0.2 in.

For women, subtract 0.3 in. from the above values. Add 0.3 in. for woolen or leather gloves and about 1.0 in. for arctic mittens.

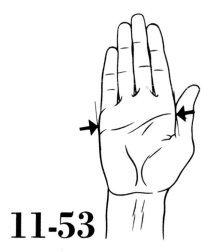

11-53

Table 11-57   Hand Breadth at Metacarpale of Female Military Personnel

Population	Percentiles (in.)					
	1st	5th	50th	95th	99th	S.D.
Air Force personnel						
Pilots [1]	2.8	2.8	3.0	3.3	3.4	
Flight nurses [1]	2.7	2.8	3.0	3.2	3.3	
Basic trainees [2]	2.6	2.7	3.0	3.4	3.6	0.19
Army personnel [3]	2.6	2.7	3.0	3.4	3.6	0.20

[1] Randall, et al., 1946.   [2] Daniels, et al., 1953a.   [3] Randall and Munro, 1949.

Table 11-58   Knee Height (Sitting) of Male Military and Civilian Populations

Population	Percentiles (in.)					
	1st	5th	50th	95th	99th	S.D.
Air Force personnel [1]	19.5	20.1	21.7	23.3	24.0	0.99
Cadets [2]	19.7	20.4	22.0	23.6	24.3	
Gunners [2]	19.2	19.8	21.5	23.0	23.7	
Army personnel						
Separatees, white [3]	19.0	19.8	21.6	23.5	24.3	1.09
Separatees, Negro [4]	19.6	20.3	22.2	24.0	24.7	1.14
Navy personnel [5]	18.8	19.7	21.8	23.8	24.7	1.25
Truck and bus drivers [6]	19.3	20.1	21.7	23.5	24.2	

[1] Hertzberg, et al., 1954.   [4] USA, 1946.
[2] Randall, et al., 1946.   [5] King, et al., 1947.
[3] Newman and White, 1951.   [6] McFarland, et al., 1958.

§ 11.2.3

KNEE HEIGHT (SITTING)

This is the vertical distance from the floor to the uppermost point on the knee. The subject sits erect with his knees and ankles at right angles (see Fig. 11-54). The data are given in Tables 11-58 and 11-59.

For men, 24.2 in. will accommodate all but the largest 1%, and 23.5 in. will accommodate all but the largest 5%, of Air Force personnel. Corresponding values for Army personnel are 24.5 in. (99th percentile) and 23.7 in. (95th percentile). For civilians, the corresponding values are 24.4 and 23.7 in. These values represent nude percentiles plus the arbitrary 0.2-in. safety factor.

For women, subtract 2.0 in. from the above values. Add 1.0 in. for men's shoes and light clothing, 1.5 in. or more for military boots and heavy clothing, and up to 3.0 in. for women's shoes and light clothing.

KNEE-TO-KNEE BREADTH

For this dimension, measurement is made of the maximum horizontal distance across the lateral surfaces of the knees. The subject sits erect with his knees at right angles and pressed together (see Fig. 11-55). The data are given in Tables 11-60 and 11-61.

For men, 9.6 in. will accommodate all but the largest 1% and 9.0 in. all but the largest 5% of all groups. These values represent nude percentiles plus the arbitrary 0.2-in. safety factor.

For women, the same values hold. Add 0.5 in. for light clothing, 2.0 in. for heavy clothing, and 9.5 in. for partial-pressure suits.

POPLITEAL HEIGHT (SITTING)

This is the vertical distance from the floor to the underside of the thigh immediately behind the knee. The subject sits erect with his knees and ankles at right angles and the bottom of his thighs and the back of his knees barely touching the sitting surface (see Fig. 11-56). The data are given in Table 11-62.

For men, 15.1 in. will accommodate all but

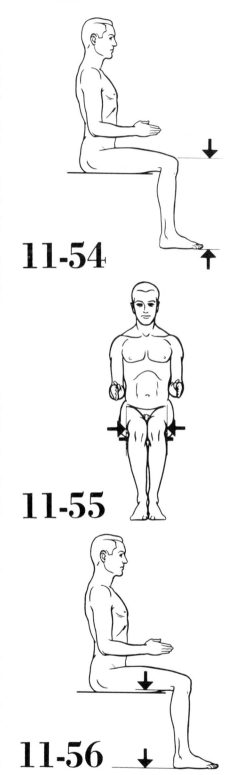

11-54

11-55

11-56

§ 11.2.3

Table 11-59   Knee Height (Sitting) of Female Military Personnel

Population	Percentiles (in.)					S.D.
	1st	5th	50th	95th	99th	
Air Force personnel [1]						
Pilots	18.3	18.7	20.1	21.5	22.2	
Flight nurses	17.7	18.1	19.5	20.8	21.5	
Army personnel [2]	16.6	17.2	18.8	20.3	21.1	0.95

[1] Randall, et al., 1946.   [2] Randall and Munro, 1949.

Table 11-60   Knee-to-Knee Breadth of Male Military and Civilian Populations

Population	Percentiles (in.)					S.D.
	1st	5th	50th	95th	99th	
Air Force personnel [1]	7.0	7.2	7.9	8.8	9.4	0.52
Cadets [2]	6.8	7.1	7.7	8.4	8.7	
Gunners [2]	6.7	6.9	7.6	8.2	8.5	
Truck and bus drivers [3]	6.8	7.3	8.1	9.2	9.5	

[1] Hertzberg, et al., 1954.   [2] Randall, et al., 1946.   [3] McFarland, et al., 1958.

Table 11-61   Knee-to-Knee Breadth of Female Air Force Personnel *

Population	Percentiles (in.)				
	1st	5th	50th	95th	99th
Pilots	6.5	6.7	7.6	8.6	9.6
Flight nurses	6.6	6.8	7.5	8.4	9.6

* Randall, et al., 1946.

Table 11-62   Popliteal Height (Sitting) of Male and Female Military and Civilian Populations

Population	Percentiles (in.)					S.D.
	1st	5th	50th	95th	99th	
Male Air Force personnel [1]	15.3	15.7	17.0	18.2	18.8	0.77
Male railroad travelers [2]	16.9 *	17.6 *	19.0 *	20.6 *	21.1 *	
Female railroad travelers [2]	16.2 *	16.7 *	18.1 *	19.5 *	20.1 *	

[1] Hertzberg, et al., 1954.   [2] Hooton, 1945.

* Including shoes and light clothing (subtract 2 in. for nude dimension).

§ 11.2.3

Table 11-63 Foot Length of Male Military and Civilian Personnel

Population	Percentiles (in.)					
	1st	5th	50th	95th	99th	S.D.
Air Force personnel [1]	9.5	9.8	10.5	11.3	11.6	0.45
Cadets [2]	9.5	9.8	10.5	11.3	11.6	
Gunners [2]	9.3	9.6	10.4	11.1	11.4	
Basic trainees [3]	9.2	9.5	10.3	11.2	11.5	0.50
Army personnel [4]	9.3	9.6	10.4	11.1	11.5	0.47
Separatees, white [5]	9.3	9.7	10.4	11.2	11.5	0.48
Separatees, Negro [6]	9.6	9.9	10.8	11.6	12.0	0.50
Truck and bus drivers [7]	9.2	9.6	10.4	11.3	11.6	
College students [8]	9.2	9.4	10.3	11.1	11.4	0.48

[1] Hertzberg, et al., 1954.
[2] Randall, et al., 1946.
[3] Daniels, et al., 1953b.
[4] Randall, et al., 1951.
[5] Newman and White, 1951.
[6] USA, 1946.
[7] McFarland, et al., 1958.
[8] Bowles, 1932.

Table 11-64 Foot Length of Female Military and Civilian Populations

Population	Percentiles (in.)					
	1st	5th	50th	95th	99th	S.D.
Air Force personnel						
Pilots [1]	8.6	8.9	9.6	10.2	10.5	
Flight nurses [1]	8.7	8.9	9.6	10.3	10.5	
Basic trainees [2]	8.4	8.7	9.4	10.2	10.5	0.46
Army personnel [3]	8.4	8.7	9.4	10.2	10.5	0.44
College students [4]	8.3	8.7	9.5	10.3	10.7	0.45

[1] Randall, et al., 1946.
[2] Daniels, et al., 1953a.
[3] Randall and Munro, 1949.
[4] Carter, 1932.

Table 11-65 Foot Breadth of Male Military and Civilian Populations

Population	Percentiles (in.)					
	1st	5th	50th	95th	99th	S.D.
Air Force personnel [1]	3.4	3.5	3.8	4.1	4.4	0.19
Cadets [2]	3.5	3.6	3.9	4.2	4.3	
Gunners [2]	3.3	3.5	3.8	4.2	4.3	
Basic trainees [3]	3.5	3.6	4.0	4.4	4.7	0.25
Army personnel [4]	3.4	3.5	3.9	4.2	4.3	0.20
Separatees, white [5]	3.3	3.5	3.9	4.3	4.4	0.25
Separatees, Negro [6]	3.4	3.6	4.0	4.4	4.6	0.25
Truck and bus drivers [7]	3.6	3.7	4.0	4.3	4.4	

[1] Hertzberg, et al., 1954.
[2] Randall, et al., 1946.
[3] Daniels, et al., 1953b.
[4] Randall, et al., 1951.
[5] Newman and White, 1951.
[6] USA, 1946.
[7] McFarland, et al., 1958.

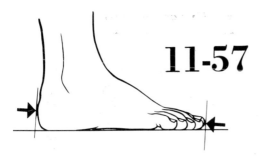

FOOT LENGTH

This is the horizontal distance from the back of the heel to the tip of the longest toe (see Fig. 11-57). The subject stands with his weight equally distributed on both feet. The data are given in Tables 11-63 and 11-64.

For men, 11.8 in. will accommodate all but the largest 1% and 11.5 in. all but the largest 5% of Air Force personnel and all other white groups. For Negroes, corresponding values are 12.2 and 11.8 in. These values refer to nude percentiles plus 0.2 in. as a safety factor.

For women, subtract 1.0 in. from the above values. For clothing, add 1.2 in. for men's shoes, 1.6 in. for military boots, and 2.7 in. for heavy flying boots.

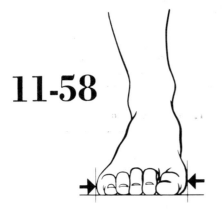

FOOT BREADTH

For this dimension, measurement is made of the maximum horizontal distance across the foot (wherever it is found) at right angles to the long axis (see Fig. 11-58). The subject stands with his weight equally distributed on both feet. The data are given in Tables 11-65 and 11-66.

For men, 4.6 in. will accommodate 99% or more, and 4.3 in. will accommodate 95% or more, of all groups. These values include a safety factor of plus 0.2 in.

For women, subtract 0.4 in. from the above values. For clothing, add 0.3 in. for men's shoes and military boots and 1.2 in. or more for heavy flying boots.

the smallest 1%, and 15.5 in. will accommodate all but the smallest 5%, of Air Force personnel. These values represent nude percentiles minus the arbitrary safety factor of 0.2 in.

For women, subtract 2.0 in. from the above values. For clothing, add 1.0 in. for men's shoes, 1.3 in. for military boots, and up to 3.0 in. for women's shoes.

Table 11-66   Foot Breadth of Female Military Personnel

Population	Percentiles (in.)					S.D.
	1st	5th	50th	95th	99th	
Air Force personnel						
Pilots [1]	3.2	3.3	3.6	3.9	4.1	
Flight nurses [1]	3.2	3.3	3.6	3.9	4.1	
Basic trainees [2]	3.1	3.2	3.6	3.9	4.0	0.20
Army personnel [3]	3.1	3.2	3.6	4.0	4.1	0.22

[1] Randall, et al., 1946. [2] Daniels, et al., 1953a. [3] Randall and Munro, 1949.

§ 11.2.3

11.2.4 *Dynamic human-body dimensions*

Unlike static body dimensions, which are measured with the subject in rigid standardized positions, dynamic body measurements usually vary with body movements. Dynamic measurements include those made with the subjects in various working positions and functional arm and leg reaches. Static dimensions corresponding to functional reaches would be anatomical arm and leg lengths. Dynamic dimensions in equipment design relate more to human performance than to human "fit."

WORKING POSITIONS

The following six body measurements are related to the design of spatially restricted areas where workers, such as mechanics, repairmen for heavy equipment, plumbers, or pipe fitters, often perform their jobs. All data are from a small group of college students and young Air Force personnel—the only group measured to date in working positions.

Kneeling

For this position, measurements are made while the subject kneels with his knees and feet together and his fists clenched and on the floor in front of his knees. His arms are roughly vertical and his head is in line with the long axis of his body (see Fig. 11-59). Length (A) is measured from the most rearward point on the foot to the most forward point on the head. Height (B) is measured vertically from the floor to the highest point on the head. The data are given in Table 11-67.

Crawling

For this position, measurements are made while the subject rests on his knees and flattened palms with his arms and thighs perpendicular to the floor and his feet comfort-

§ 11.2.4

Table 11-67   Working-Position Dimensions of Male Air Force Personnel *

Dimension	Percentiles (in.)			S.D.
	5th	50th	95th	
Kneeling				
Height	29.7	32.0	34.5	1.57
Length	37.6	43.0	48.1	3.26
Crawling				
Height	26.2	28.4	30.5	1.30
Length	49.3	53.2	58.2	2.61
Prone				
Height	12.3	14.5	16.4	1.28
Length	84.7	90.1	95.8	3.41

* Hertzberg, et al., 1956.

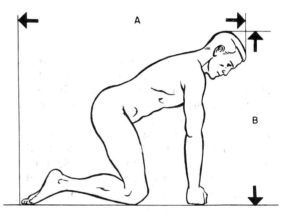

11-59

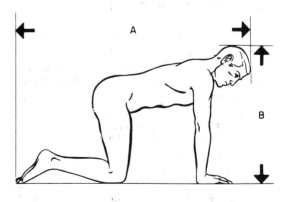

11-60

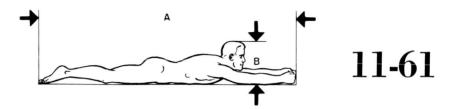

11-61

ably extended and spaced. His body is straight with his head in line with the long axis of the body (see Fig. 11-60). Length (A) is measured from the most rearward point on the foot to the most forward point on the head. Height (B) is measured from the floor to the highest point on the head. The data are given in Table 11-67.

Prone

For this position, measurements are made while the subject lies prone with his feet together and comfortably extended, his arms extended forward as far as possible without strain, and his fists clenched (see Fig. 11-61). Length (A) is measured horizontally from the most rearward point on the foot to the most forward point on the fists. Height (B) is measured vertically from the floor to the highest point on the head when the head is raised as high as possible while the chest is on the floor. The data are given in Table 11-67.

FUNCTIONAL ARM REACH

Functional arm-reach data are used to determine the outer limits of the workplace or "space envelope" for the placement of controls, tools, or materials to be handled. Reach measurements to any point on the edge of the space envelope vary with body size and position, clothing and personal equipment, the nature of the task, and the design of the control, tool, or material to be handled. Variations in any one of these factors will alter functional reach. Thus, it is difficult to derive generally applicable functional-reach data. It is possible, however, to present functional-reach data for a given task at any specified

position in elevation and azimuth. Such data can be used as guides in the design and placement of items within the workplace.

Standing

Forward reach. This is the horizontal distance from the wall to the most forward point on the fists. The subject stands erect with his heels, buttocks, and shoulders against a wall, his right arm extended horizontally to its maximum length, and the tips of his thumb and forefinger pressed together (see Fig. 11-62). The data are given in Table 11-68.

Overhead reach. For this dimension, measurement is made while the subject stands erect, grasps a horizontal bar above his right side with his right hand (at the bend formed

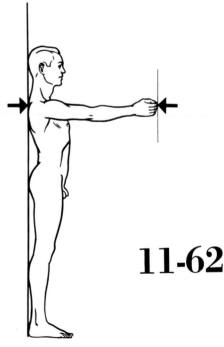

11-62

§ 11.2.4

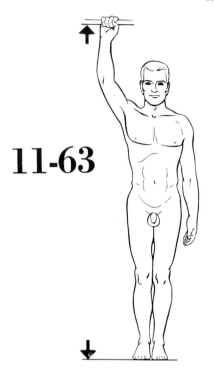

11-63

by palm and fingers), and raises the bar to the highest position attainable without strain (see Fig. 11-63). The data are given in Table 11-68.

Sitting

For purposes of standardization, body-reach dimensions are measured with reference to some fixed location within the workplace. The most commonly used such location for functional arm reach in the sitting position is the seat reference point (SRP), defined as the intersection of the plane of the seat surface

with the plane of the backrest surface in the midplane of the subject's body. Functional arm reach is measured horizontally from a vertical line projected through this point.

The data. Functional-arm-reach data for the sitting position are presently available only for two male military populations (Air Force and Navy personnel). The arm-reach data in Tables 11-69 through 11-78 are from the Air Force study. Each subject sat in a standard Air Force aircraft seat with the backrest inclined 13 deg to the rear.

Maximum normal reach was measured horizontally from a vertical line through the SRP to the farthest point at which the vertical handgrip of a control stick could be grasped with both shoulders against the backrest and the right arm extended as far forward as possible without noticeable discomfort. The data are given for ten vertical locations at each of ten angles to the right of the midplane of the body (see Figs. 11-64 through 11-73). For practical purposes, the reach area of the left arm may be considered as a mirror image of that of the right arm.

Using the data. In applying these data, it should be borne in mind that all reach measurements are to controls grasped by the entire hand. Knobs operated by the thumb and forefinger could be located 2 in. farther away from the SRP, and pushbuttons or switches operated by the fingertips could be 4 in. farther away. In addition, the Air Force population on which these measurements were taken have somewhat longer arms than the civilian male population, most other selected or occupationally specialized groups, and all female groups. A final and most important caution: the data hold only for the workplace and personal equipment described above.

Table 11-68   Functional Arm Reach (Standing) of Male Air Force Personnel

	Percentiles (in.)					
Reach	1st	5th	50th	95th	99th	S.D.
Forward [1]	28.8	29.7	32.3	35.0	36.4	1.60
Overhead [2]		76.8	82.5	88.5		3.33

[1] Hertzberg, et al., 1954.   [2] Hertzberg, et al., 1956.

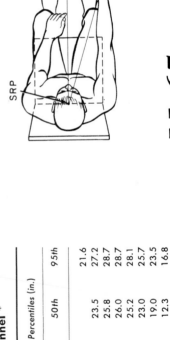

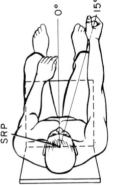

11-64

11-65

Table 11-69 Functional Arm Reach (Sitting) 0 deg from the Midplane of the Body of Male Air Force Personnel *

Height above SRP (in.)	Percentiles (in.)		
	5th	50th	95th
6	17.0	19.5	22.7
12	19.4	22.5	25.1
18	21.3	24.0	26.6
24	21.6	24.5	26.3
30	20.1	23.6	25.9
36	17.4	21.0	24.5
42	12.7	17.0	20.8
48		11.0	15.4

* See Fig. 11-64.

Table 11-70 Functional Arm Reach (Sitting) 15 deg from the Midplane of the Body of Male Air Force Personnel *

Height above SRP (in.)	Percentiles (in.)		
	5th	50th	95th
6			21.6
12	21.5	23.5	27.2
18	22.9	25.8	28.7
24	23.4	26.0	28.7
30	22.0	25.2	28.1
36	18.7	23.0	25.7
42	13.2	19.0	23.5
48		12.3	16.8

* See Fig. 11-65.

§ 11.2.4

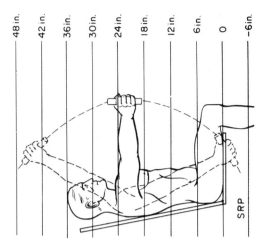

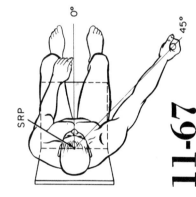

11-66

11-67

Table 11-71 Functional Arm Reach (Sitting) 30 deg from the Midplane of the Body *

Height above SRP (in.)	Percentiles (in.)		
	5th	50th	95th
0		17.5	21.2
6		23.0	25.5
12	23.5	26.0	28.7
18	25.4	27.0	29.8
24	24.9	27.5	30.1
30	23.7	26.9	29.4
36	20.2	24.5	28.1
42	13.6	19.5	24.6
48		13.5	18.3

* See Fig. 11-66.

Table 11-72 Functional Arm Reach (Sitting) 45 deg from the Midplane of the Body *

Height above SRP (in.)	Percentiles (in.)		
	5th	50th	95th
0	16.0	19.0	22.4
6	22.4	24.5	27.3
12	24.9	27.5	29.7
18	26.9	29.0	31.2
24	26.4	29.5	31.1
30	26.4	28.4	30.6
36	22.4	25.5	28.1
42	16.0	22.0	24.5
48		15.0	18.2

* See Fig. 11-67.

§ 11.2.4

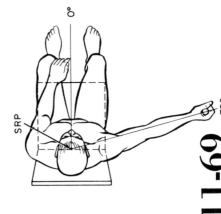

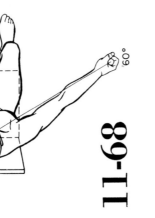

11-68

11-69

Table 11-73 Functional Arm Reach (Sitting) 60 deg from the Midplane of the Body *

Height above SRP (in.)	Percentiles (in.)		
	5th	50th	95th
0	17.9	20.0	23.5
6	23.8	26.0	28.6
12	27.0	28.5	31.1
18	28.1	30.1	32.5
24	28.0	30.5	33.0
30	27.4	29.5	31.9
36	23.9	27.0	29.6
42	19.2	23.0	26.5
48		16.0	20.1

* See Fig. 11-68.

Table 11-74 Functional Arm Reach (Sitting) 75 deg from the Midplane *

Height above SRP (in.)	Percentiles (in.)		
	5th	50th	95th
−6		12.0	
0	17.4	21.0	24.5
6	23.9	26.5	29.6
12	27.6	29.5	32.1
18	29.3	31.1	34.1
24	28.9	31.5	34.0
30	28.3	30.6	33.5
36	25.1	28.0	31.1
42	20.3	24.5	27.3
48		16.8	21.7

* See Fig. 11-69.

§ 11.2.4

11-70

11-71

Table 11-75 Functional Arm Reach (Sitting) 90 deg from the Midplane *

Height above SRP (in.)	Percentiles (in.)		
	5th	50th	95th
−6			11.9
0	18.5	21.0	24.8
6	25.6	27.0	30.3
12	28.0	30.0	33.2
18	30.0	32.0	34.6
24	30.0	32.5	35.0
30	29.3	31.6	34.4
36	25.9	29.0	32.0
42	25.9	29.0	29.0
48	21.1	18.0	21.9

* See Fig. 11-70.

Table 11-76 Functional Arm Reach (Sitting) 105 deg from the Midplane *

Height above SRP (in.)	Percentiles (in.)		
	5th	50th	95th
−6			15.0
0	19.2	22.0	25.5
6	25.8	28.0	30.5
12	28.8	31.0	33.1
18	30.8	32.7	35.0
24	31.1	33.0	35.1
30	30.0	32.2	34.6
36	26.9	30.0	32.7
42	22.2	26.5	29.7
48		19.5	24.6

* See Fig. 11-71.

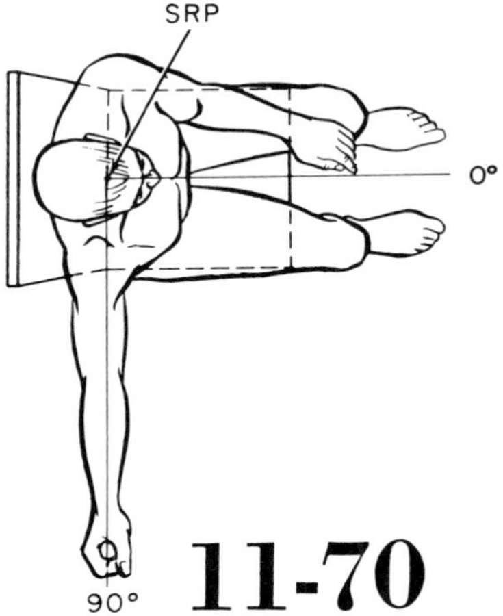

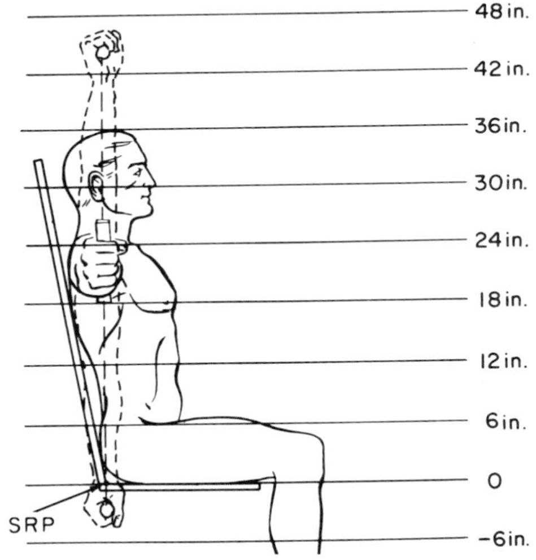

§ 11.2.4

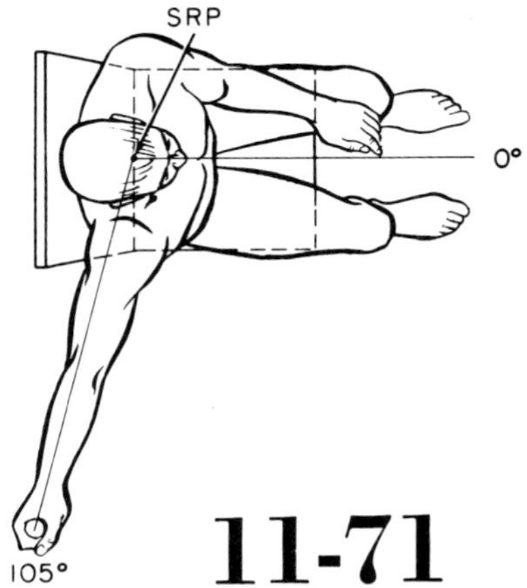

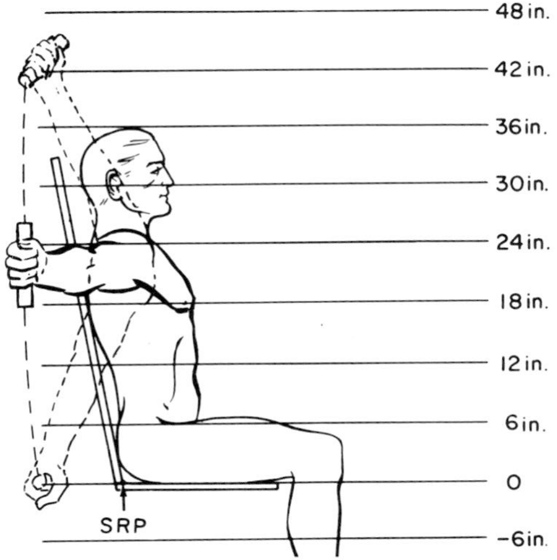

549

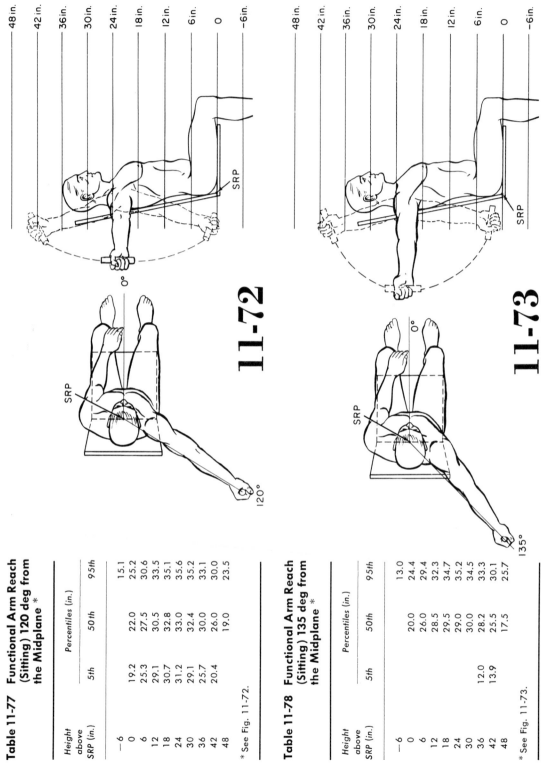

11-72

0°

120°

SRP

48 in. 42 in. 36 in. 30 in. 24 in. 18 in. 12 in. 6 in. 0 −6 in.

11-73

0°

135°

SRP

48 in. 42 in. 36 in. 30 in. 24 in. 18 in. 12 in. 6 in. 0 −6 in.

Table 11-77 Functional Arm Reach (Sitting) 120 deg from the Midplane *

Height above SRP (in.)	Percentiles (in.)		
	5th	50th	95th
−6			15.1
0	19.2	22.0	25.2
6	25.3	27.5	30.6
12	29.1	30.5	33.5
18	30.7	32.8	35.1
24	31.2	33.0	35.6
30	29.1	32.4	35.2
36	25.7	30.0	33.1
42	20.4	26.0	30.0
48		19.0	23.5

* See Fig. 11-72.

Table 11-78 Functional Arm Reach (Sitting) 135 deg from the Midplane *

Height above SRP (in.)	Percentiles (in.)		
	5th	50th	95th
−6			13.0
0		20.0	24.4
6		26.0	29.4
12		28.5	32.3
18		29.5	34.7
24		29.0	35.2
30		30.0	34.5
36	12.0	28.2	33.3
42	13.9	25.5	30.1
48		17.5	25.7

* See Fig. 11-73.

§ 11.2.4

11.3 *Range of Movement of Body Members*

Data on the range of movement of body members help the designer plan the proper placement and excursion of controls. Required body movements should be kept well within the comfortable limits because efficiency falls off at or beyond such limits.

11.3.1 *Joints and "links"*

The movable joints of the body, articulated by means of ligaments (tough, fibrous bands), are of several different types, of which the three most important are: hinge joints (finger), pivot joints (elbow), and ball and socket joints (shoulder and hip). The range of motion is determined by the joint's bony configuration; by the attached muscles, tendons, and ligaments; and by the amount of surrounding fatty tissue, all of which vary to some extent from person to person and in the same person from time to time, i.e., as the person grows older (see below).

Bones articulated at movable joints may be regarded as the rigid levers of the body's mechanical system. Each of these levers or movable body segments may be likened to the links of mechanical engineering, i.e., an intermediate rod or piece that transmits force or motion. Body links, however, are not identical to mechanical links; they are functional rather than structural and may be defined as the distances between centers of rotation of adjacent joints (see Fig. 11-74). Thus, the human body is basically an open-chain system of "links" rotating around joint centers. The end members of these open-chain links, the hands and feet, can occupy a limitless number of positions in space as a result of the cumulative ranges of these joints (Dempster, 1955a).

11.3.2 *Factors affecting the range of joint movement*

The range of joint motion varies from person to person for the purely structural reasons described above and for numerous other reasons, the more important of which are discussed below. The designer will need to con-

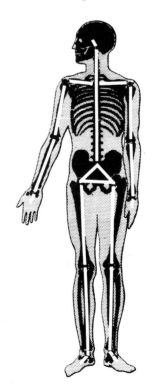

11-74 Simplified kinematic system of body links and joints. Detailed individual links of vertebrae, fingers, toes, etc. are not shown (Dempster, 1955a)

§ 11.3.1

551

sider certain of these factors when dealing with specialized populations.

AGE AND SEX

Joint mobility decreases only slightly in healthy people between 20 and 60 yr of age. The incidence of arthritis increases so markedly beyond age 45, however, that any older population will have a considerably decreased average joint mobility (Smyth, et al., 1959). Women exceed men in the range of movement at all joints but the knee (see Table 11-79).

BODY BUILD AND OCCUPATION

Slender men and women have the widest range of joint movements, fat ones the smallest. Average and muscular body builds, in descending order, have intermediate ranges (Barter, et al., 1957). These differences are often significant, especially those between the thin and the fat groups, where variations of more than 10 deg in a given movement are not uncommon (Sinelnikoff and Grigorowitsch, 1931).

Physical exercise can increase the range of motion of a joint, but excessive exercise can result in the so-called "muscle-bound" condition in which the range of motion is actually reduced. Some specialized tasks involve the repetition of certain body movements, and, as a result, the range of movement at the affected joints increases.

POSTURE AND BODY POSITION

The range of movement of one part of the body is affected by the position or movement of neighboring parts, e.g., hand rotation can be considerably increased if shoulder movements are added to those at the elbow, and wrist flexion is greater with the hand pronated than it is with the hand supinated. In addition, prone-position movements are not necessarily exactly the same as those made from the standing position.

Table 11-79 Average Increase in Range of Joint Movement of Women over Men *

Movement	Difference (deg)
Wrist flexion and extension	14
Wrist adduction and abduction	11
Elbow flexion and extension	8
Shoulder abduction (rearward)	2
Ankle flexion and extension	4
Knee flexion and extension	0
Hip flexion	3

* Sinelnikoff and Grigorowitsch, 1931.

11.3.3 Static range-of-movement measurements

Joint movement is measured at the angle formed by the long axes of two adjoining body segments (link lines) or, in some cases, at the angle formed by one body segment and a vertical or horizontal plane. The total range of movement is measured between the two extreme positions of the joint. The ranges, in angular degrees, of each of the types of voluntary movement possible at the joints of the body are presented in Tables 11-80 through 11-82. The types of movement measured are as follows (see Figs. 11-75 through 11-77):

a. Flexion. Bending, or *decreasing* the angle between the parts of the body.

b. Extension. Straightening, or *increasing* the angle between the parts of the body.

c. Adduction. Moving *toward* the midline of the body.

d. Abduction. Moving *away* from the midline of the body.

e. Medial rotation. Turning *toward* the midplane of the body.

f. Lateral rotation. Turning *away* from the midplane of the body.

g. Pronation. Rotating the palm of the hand *downward*.

Table 11-80 Range of Movement at the Joint of the Neck of Male Civilians [1]

	Range (deg)	
Movement [2]	Avg.	S.D.
Ventral flexion	60	12
Dorsal flexion	61	27
Right or left flexion	41	7
Right or left rotation	79	14

[1] Glanville and Kreezer, 1937.
[2] See Fig. 11-75.

Table 11-81 Range of Movement at the Joints of the Hand and Arm of Male Air Force Personnel [1]

	Range (deg)	
Movement [2]	Avg.	S.D.
Wrist flexion	90	12
Wrist extension	99	13
Wrist adduction	27	9
Wrist abduction	47	7
Forearm supination	113	22
Forearm pronation	77	24
Elbow flexion	142	10
Shoulder flexion	188	12
Shoulder extension	61	14
Shoulder adduction	48	9
Shoulder abduction	134	17
Shoulder rotation		
Medial	97	22
Lateral	34	13

[1] Barter, et al., 1957.
[2] See Fig. 11-76.

Table 11-82 Range of Movement at the Joints of the Foot and Leg of Male Air Force Personnel [1]

	Range (deg)	
Movement [2]	Avg.	S.D.
Ankle flexion	35	7
Ankle extension	38	12
Ankle adduction	24	9
Ankle abduction	23	7
Knee flexion		
Standing	113	13
Kneeling	159	9
Prone	125	10
Knee rotation		
Medial	35	12
Lateral	43	12
Hip flexion	113	13
Hip adduction	31	12
Hip abduction	53	12
Hip rotation (sitting)		
Medial	31	9
Lateral	30	9
Hip rotation (prone)		
Medial	39	10
Lateral	34	10

[1] Barter, et al., 1957.
[2] See Fig. 11-77.

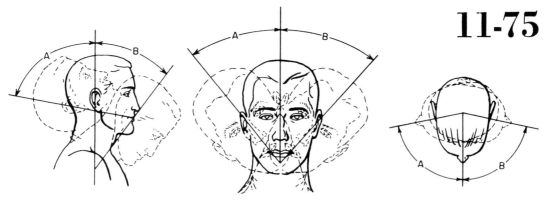

NECK FLEXION, DORSAL (A),
VENTRAL (B)

NECK FLEXION, RIGHT (A),
LEFT (B)

NECK ROTATION, RIGHT (A),
LEFT (B)

11-75

§ 11.3.3

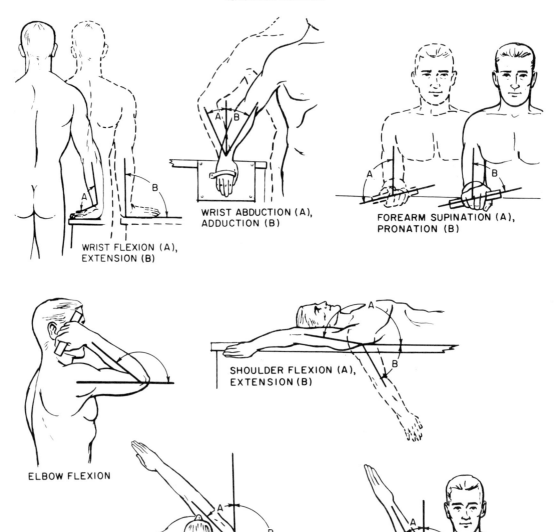

WRIST FLEXION (A),
EXTENSION (B)

WRIST ABDUCTION (A),
ADDUCTION (B)

FOREARM SUPINATION (A),
PRONATION (B)

ELBOW FLEXION

SHOULDER FLEXION (A),
EXTENSION (B)

SHOULDER ADDUCTION (A),
ABDUCTION (B)

SHOULDER ROTATION, LATERAL (A),
MEDIAL (B)

11-76

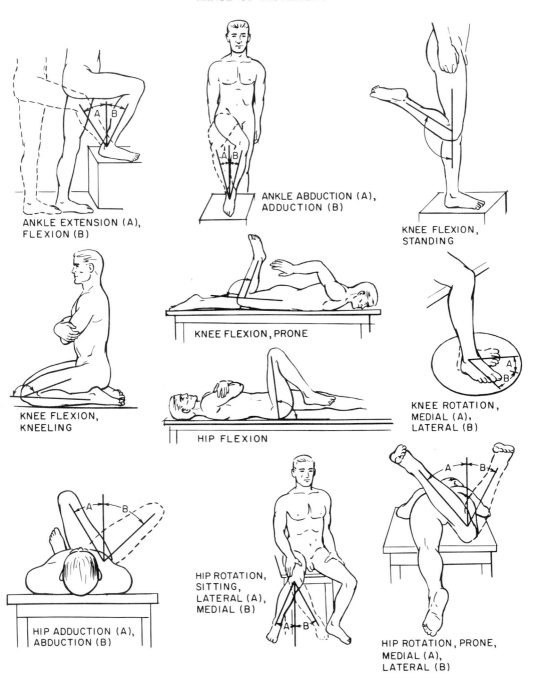

ANKLE EXTENSION (A),
FLEXION (B)

ANKLE ABDUCTION (A),
ADDUCTION (B)

KNEE FLEXION,
STANDING

KNEE FLEXION, PRONE

KNEE FLEXION,
KNEELING

HIP FLEXION

KNEE ROTATION,
MEDIAL (A),
LATERAL (B)

HIP ADDUCTION (A),
ABDUCTION (B)

HIP ROTATION,
SITTING,
LATERAL (A),
MEDIAL (B)

HIP ROTATION, PRONE,
MEDIAL (A),
LATERAL (B)

11-77

h. Supination. Rotating the palm of the hand *upward*.

11.3.4 *Dynamic range-of-movement measurements*

An example of dynamic anthropometry involving body movements is a study of head and eye movements undertaken in connection with gunsight and sighting-panel design (Brues, 1946). Figure 11-78, which shows the location of the head and eyes at various angles of gaze, is based on data taken from measuring the movements of 21 Air Force men. As can be seen, eye movement is a somewhat circular arc from 90 deg above to 45 deg below the horizontal. The ear, on the other hand, does not move in a circular arc, as was commonly supposed, but follows a paraboloid curve. Finally, the pivot point or center of the arc described by the eye is not at the ear but roughly 2 in. below and ½ in. behind it.

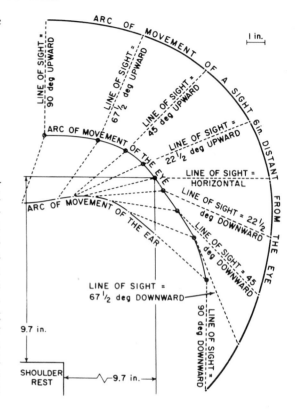

11.4 *Muscle Strength*

The voluntary muscles of the body stabilize the joints, maintain desired body positions, rotate the body segments around the joints, and transmit force to objects outside the body such as controls or tools. Data on voluntary muscle strength are used by the design engineer to determine maximum and optimum control resistances (see Chapter 6), forces required in other manual tasks, and the arrangement of weight for safe, efficient lifting or carrying (see Chapter 9).

Maximum control resistances should be based on the strength of the weakest potential operators and should never be exceeded, particularly for critical controls. Optimum or "operational" resistance levels, however, should not require the application of maximum strength by any operator. Operational resistance levels affect comfort and efficiency and, therefore, should be low enough to prevent fatigue or discomfort but high enough to prevent inadvertent operation of the control and to provide kinesthetic cues to control movement.

As with control resistance, schedules for other physical tasks or for lifting or carrying must be set with regard to the strength of the weakest operator. Performance at or near the limits of physical abilities should not be required because fatigue will develop rapidly, and actual injury (muscle sprain or rupture, strained or torn ligaments) might occur.

11.4.1 *How the muscles do their job*

The force developed by a muscle depends, primarily, on the following two factors:

a. Muscle tension, which "reaches a maximum when the length is greatest, and there is, momentarily, no change in length" (Elftman, 1941). The tension, or contractile force, decreases as the muscle shortens and as its rate of shortening increases (Arkin, 1941; Darcus, 1951; and Elftman, 1941).

b. The mechanical advantage of the body's lever system. The long bones are the lever arms, the joints the fulcra. Power is applied at the points of muscle attachment.

Both of the above factors vary with changes at the joints. At the elbow, for example, the force of extension is greatest when the elbow is flexed. This position permits the triceps to attain its greatest length but does not provide the optimum mechanical advantage. In elbow flexion, however, the force is greatest toward the midpoint of the full range of movement (Darcus, 1954). Here the increasing mechanical advantage of the forearm relative to the upper arm more than compensates for the reduction in strength caused by the shortening of the biceps (Haggard, 1946). Although human muscles in maximum contraction can exert large forces—often exceeding 1,000 lb in the line of the tendon—such forces cannot be utilized directly because all muscles work at a mechanical disadvantage (high ratio of resistance to power) to permit rapid movement (Hugh-Jones, 1947).

11.4.2 *Factors affecting muscle strength*

Many factors—biological, environmental, and occupational—affect muscle strength.

The designer should be aware of these factors if he is to evaluate accurately the physical capabilities of the potential users of his equipment. Tasks requiring strength easily exerted by young soldiers, for example, might exceed the capacity of other groups or the general male population. All of the factors in the following paragraphs are relevant to equipment design.

BIOLOGICAL FACTORS

Strength increases rapidly in the teens, more slowly in the early 20's, reaches a maximum by the middle to late 20's, remains at this level for 5–10 yr, and thereafter declines slowly but continuously (Hunsicker, 1955 and Hunsicker and Greey, 1957). From a summary of the various studies relating strength to age (Fisher and Birren, 1945), the following rough estimates can be made: by the age of 40, muscle strength is approximately 90–95% of the earlier maximum in the late 20's; by age 50, it is about 85%, and by 60, about 80% of this maximum.

Not all muscle strengths, however, decline with age at the same rate. Hand grip, for example, which forms a large part of age-strength data, seems to be relatively stronger in later years than other types of muscular performance, and the strength of the back muscles drops faster with age than that of either the hands or the arms (Simonson, 1947).

Body build is markedly related to strength. In a group of young, healthy college men of various body builds, strength varied 10-fold, with the 95th percentile being four to five times greater than the 5th percentile (Hunsicker, 1955). And strength correlated significantly with height and weight (Fisher and Birren, 1945) but at low levels (r = 0.2–0.5).

Body position is an important factor affecting strength. For example, in an upward movement of the arm, strength in the weakest position of elbow flexion is only 44% of that at the strongest position (Hunsicker, 1955). Similarly, higher torques can be applied by the hand when the elbow is at 90 deg of flexion than when it is at 150 deg (next best) or

30 deg (Salter and Darcus, 1952). Fortunately, when large forces must be overcome, people instinctively tend to assume the position from which maximum strength can be exerted even though this position is not necessarily the one in which lesser forces can be maintained most easily (Darcus, 1954).

In right-handed persons (roughly 90% of the entire population), the left hand is about 10% weaker than the right (Hunsicker, 1955). One study (Schochrin, 1934) found the left leg to be 10% weaker, although a smaller study (Elbel, 1949) found no difference. In general, the preferred side is the stronger.

ENVIRONMENTAL FACTORS

Strength decreases with altitude because the reduced oxygen supply results in decreased physiological efficiency of muscle tissue (Dill, 1938). Individual variability and acclimatization determine the amount of strength decrement. Full acclimatization can take from weeks to months, depending on the altitude. Persons who are fully acclimatized can maintain their sea-level static strength (as measured by hand grip) up to about 13,000 ft. Above this altitude, strength decreases slowly but consistently until about 16,500 ft, then remains fairly constant until about 23,000 ft, where a much more rapid decline sets in (Ruff and Strughold, 1942).

Brief muscular exertions are less affected by altitude than is muscular endurance. Endurance time for moderate to heavy muscular activity begins to decline at altitudes as low as 6,500 ft (Ruff and Strughold, 1942). At around 20,000 ft, muscular endurance, even for the fully acclimatized, is only about one half that at sea level (Pugh and Ward, 1953). Above 23,000 ft, heavy exertions of only the briefest duration (seconds to minutes) have been deemed possible (Ruff and Strughold, 1942), but the strenuous physical activity of mountain climbing has been continued without supplementary oxygen up to 28,000 ft or higher (Pugh and Ward, 1953).

Muscular forces acting against the direction of acceleration forces are decreased, those exerted with acceleration forces are increased, and those exerted perpendicular to acceleration forces are least affected. Acceleration forces up to 5g do not markedly influence strength (Brown and Lechner, 1956) unless large forces, or more moderate forces over long periods, are required. Acceleration forces above 5g impair strength progressively. "It is generally recognized that highly effective arm movements cannot be executed above 6g, although wrist and finger movements can be executed up to at least 12g" (Bondurant, et al., 1958).

The force of push and pull movements on a control stick during positive (headward) acceleration increases slightly from 1g to 2–3g and decreases slightly thereafter up to and including 5g. Push-right and push-left movements, on the other hand, generally increase from 1 to 5g (Lombard, et al., 1948 and Canfield, et al., 1948).

OCCUPATIONAL FACTORS

White-collar workers are significantly weaker in muscle strength as measured by hand grip and lumbar pull, by some 10–20%, than manual workers, whether skilled, semiskilled, or unskilled (Nemethi, 1952; Schochrin, 1934; and Cathcart, et al., 1935). Items of clothing and personal equipment decrease maximum push and 1-min push endurance by 12–14% for one harness simulating restrictive clothing (Fox, 1957). In general, heavy items increase body weight and require additional muscular energy for any movement, and tight or bulky items restrict the range of body movement and, possibly, preclude getting into the positions for exerting maximum force.

Backrests on seats increase pushing strength; footrests increase pulling strength. Restraining harnesses or seat belts generally increase pulling strength, but, by restricting body movements, they also might eliminate the most efficient positions for other types of muscular effort such as lifting with the leg and back muscles.

11.4.3 *The data*

The 5th, 50th, and 95th percentiles and the standard deviation are given for each strength measurement, wherever available, in Tables 11-83 through 11-108. Unfortunately, many muscle strength studies include few subjects, and those are not always representative of the larger populations from which they were drawn. Adequate studies should contain at least 50 subjects.

Table 11-83 Maximum Force that Can Be Exerted in Lifting [1] by Male Air Force Personnel [2]

| Type of lift | Percentiles (lb) | | | |
	5th	50th	95th	S.D.
Backlift [3]	375	520	665	90
Leglift [4]	1010	1480	1950	290

[1] Two-handed vertical pull on a horizontal bar about 28 in. above floor level.
[2] Clarke, 1945.
[3] Legs are straight and the back is bent and then straightened for the lift.
[4] Back is straight and the legs are bent and then straightened for the lift.

Table 11-84 Maximum Weight that can be Lifted [1] to Various Heights by Male Air Force Personnel [2]

| Height lifted (ft) | Percentiles (lb) | | | |
	5th	50th	95th	S.D.
One	142	231	301	47
Two	139	193	259	40
Three	77	119	172	31
Four	55	81	112	19
Five	36	58	83	16

[1] Subjects lifted a maximally weighted ammunition case ($25\frac{1}{2} \times 10\frac{3}{4} \times 6$ in.) from the floor and placed it on platforms of various heights.
[2] Emanuel, Chaffee, and Wing, 1956.

Table 11-85 Maximum Force that Can Be Exerted in Backlift [1] by Male British Civilian Populations [2]

| Population | Percentiles (lb) | | | |
	5th	50th	95th	S.D.
Students	271	367	643	58.9
Employed	251	363	474	67.7
Unemployed	214	315	415	60.8

[1] Two-handed vertical pull on a horizontal bar about 28 in. above floor level.
[2] Cathcart, et al., 1935.

Table 11-86 Maximum Force that Can be Exerted in Backlift [1] by Female British Civilian Populations [2]

| Population | Percentiles (lb) | | | |
	5th	50th	95th	S.D.
College students	160	216	272	34.4
Factory workers				
employed	119	183	247	38.8
unemployed	101	165	229	39.2

[1] Two-handed vertical pull on a horizontal bar about 28 in. above floor level.
[2] Cathcart, et al., 1927.

Table 11-87 Maximum Force Exerted in the Sitting Position on a Vertical Handgrip at Various Elbow Angles by the Right Arm of Male College Students [1]

Table 11-88 Maximum Force Exerted in the Sitting Position on a Vertical Handgrip at Various Elbow Angles by the Left Arm of Male College Students [1]

Direction of force	Elbow angle [2] (deg)	Percentiles (lb)			S.D.
		5th	50th	95th	
Push	60	34	92	150	38
	90	36	86	154	33
	120	36	103	172	43
	150	42	123	194	45
	180	50	138	210	49
Pull	60	24	63	74	23
	90	37	88	135	30
	120	42	104	154	31
	150	56	122	189	36
	180	52	120	171	37
Left	60	20	52	87	19
	90	18	50	97	23
	120	22	53	100	26
	150	20	54	104	25
	180	20	50	104	26
Right	60	17	42	82	20
	90	16	37	68	18
	120	15	34	62	17
	150	15	33	64	18
	180	14	34	62	24
Up	60	20	49	82	18
	90	20	56	106	22
	120	24	60	124	24
	150	18	56	118	28
	180	14	43	88	22
Down	60	20	51	89	21
	90	26	53	88	20
	120	26	58	98	23
	150	20	47	80	18
	180	17	41	82	18

[1] Hunsicker, 1955.　　　[2] See Fig. 11-79.

Direction of force	Elbow angle [2] (deg)	Percentiles (lb)			S.D.
		5th	50th	95th	
Push	60	22	79	164	31
	90	22	83	172	35
	120	26	99	180	42
	150	30	111	192	48
	180	42	126	196	47
Pull	60	26	64	110	23
	90	32	80	122	28
	120	34	94	152	34
	150	42	112	168	37
	180	50	116	172	37
Left	60	12	32	62	17
	90	10	33	72	19
	120	10	30	68	18
	150	8	29	66	20
	180	8	30	64	20
Right	60	17	50	83	21
	90	16	48	87	22
	120	20	45	89	21
	150	15	47	113	27
	180	13	43	92	22
Up	60	15	44	82	18
	90	17	52	100	22
	120	17	54	102	25
	150	15	52	110	27
	180	9	41	83	23
Down	60	18	46	76	18
	90	21	49	92	20
	120	21	51	102	23
	150	18	41	74	16
	180	13	35	72	15

[1] Hunsicker, 1955.　　　[2] See Fig. 11-79.

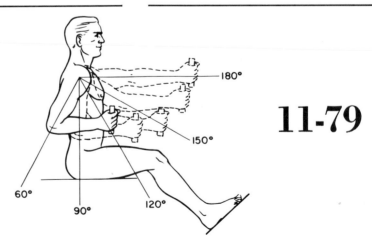

11-79

Table 11-89 Maximum Force Exerted in the Prone Position on a Vertical Handgrip at Various Elbow Angles by the Right Arm of Male College Students [1]

Direction of force	Elbow angle [2] (deg)	Percentiles (lb)			S.D.
		5th	50th	95th	
Push	60	24	66	119	26
	90	26	63	103	23
	120	29	73	128	28
	150	29	73	127	30
	180	31	69	123	26
Pull	60	21	61	113	26
	90	24	73	121	30
	120	31	86	147	34
	150	29	81	133	33
	180	31	69	118	26
Left	60	16	48	91	22
	90	16	46	87	21
	120	15	48	97	25
	150	15	45	93	26
	180	12	37	71	17
Right	60	12	29	57	12
	90	13	28	51	11
	120	11	28	58	12
	150	12	28	60	14
	180	9	24	61	14
Up	60	13	44	85	21
	90	15	52	94	22
	120	13	50	91	21
	150	13	41	83	23
	180	8	23		12
Down	60	13	34	61	13
	90	16	36	60	13
	120	15	35	61	15
	150	15	34	60	13
	180	13	25	47	10

[1] Hunsicker, 1955.   [2] See Fig. 11-80.

Table 11-90 Maximum Force Exerted in the Prone Position on a Vertical Handgrip at Various Elbow Angles by the Left Arm of Male College Students [1]

Direction of force	Elbow angle [2] (deg)	Percentiles (lb)			S.D.
		5th	50th	95th	
Push	60	17	52	87	21
	90	18	54	91	22
	120	21	63	108	27
	150	24	65	111	26
	180	26	67	116	28
Pull	60	17	57	97	24
	90	23	66	118	26
	120	22	74	126	30
	150	21	70	122	28
	180	18	61	111	26
Left	60	8	24	49	12
	90	6	22	45	10
	120	6	20	38	9
	150	5	20	56	15
	180	4	22	57	19
Right	60	11	44	99	24
	90	13	40	92	22
	120	9	38	91	23
	150	8	34	79	23
	180	10	31	67	19
Up	60	13	35	71	17
	90	15	40	78	18
	120	11	40	81	21
	150	7	31	62	17
	180	5	18	44	12
Down	60	10	30	51	12
	90	12	31	57	12
	120	11	31	57	14
	150	10	28	48	11
	180	7	25	41	10

[1] Hunsicker, 1955.   [2] See Fig. 11-80.

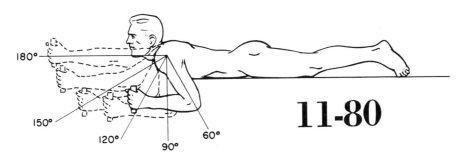

180°
150°
120°
90°
60°

11-80

§ 11.4.3

Table 11-91 Maximum Force Exerted in the Sitting Position with the Wrist Pronated [1] on a Horizontal Handgrip at Various Elbow Angles by the Right Arm of Male College Students [2]

Direction of force	Elbow angle [3] (deg)	Percentiles (lb) 5th	50th	95th	S.D.
Push	60	40	94	156	36
	90	25	65	100	24
	120	23	46	70	15
	150	18	40	66	18
	180	17	32	59	12
Pull	60	13	37	50	16
	90	14	32	54	13
	120	13	26	43	10
	150	12	29	48	10
	180	11	28	48	12
Right	60	19	41	72	19
	90	12	31	64	15
	120	9	26	53	13
	150	9	21	39	11
	180	10	19	34	7
Left	60	16	48	73	18
	90	16	39	59	15
	120	15	34	47	11
	150	18	32	45	7
	180	16	31	57	13
Up	60	23	49	79	20
	90	28	69	112	29
	120	41	91	138	30
	150	43	99	165	38
	180	35	95	156	35
Down	60	23	81	158	35
	90	22	83	142	35
	120	37	92	161	35
	150	40	90	154	34
	180	41	87	143	31

[1] See Fig. 11-76.
[2] Hunsicker and Greey, 1957.   [3] See Fig. 11-81.

Table 11-92 Maximum Force Exerted in the Sitting Position with the Wrist Pronated [1] on a Horizontal Handgrip at Various Elbow Angles by the Left Arm of Male College Students [2]

Direction of force	Elbow angle [3] (deg)	Percentiles (lb) 5th	50th	95th	S.D.
Push	60	33	86	138	35
	90	27	60	93	28
	120	17	43	71	17
	150	15	37	69	18
	180	12	32	59	13
Pull	60	20	39	64	18
	90	17	37	65	18
	120	12	30	56	14
	150	15	32	52	13
	180	16	34	61	15
Right	60	20	42	66	15
	90	17	38	60	12
	120	17	34	53	8
	150	17	31	54	11
	180	15	28	41	8
Left	60	18	36	51	15
	90	11	27	54	11
	120	10	22	39	10
	150	9	23	53	16
	180	10	20	49	13
Up	60	22	57	100	22
	90	37	77	123	24
	120	45	91	145	30
	150	58	100	159	32
	180	47	101	171	11
Down	60	18	74	139	35
	90	23	75	136	34
	120	29	75	148	40
	150	39	79	136	29
	180	34	76	138	31

[1] See Fig. 11-76.
[2] Hunsicker and Greey, 1957.   [3] See Fig. 11-81.

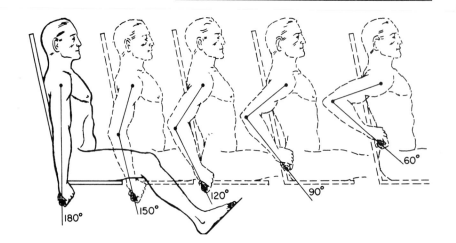

Table 11-93 Maximum Force Exerted in the Sitting Position with the Wrist Supinated [1] on a Horizontal Handgrip at Various Elbow Angles by the Right Arm of Male College Students [2]

Direction of force	Elbow angle [3] (deg)	Percentiles (lb)			S.D.
		5th	50th	95th	
Push	60	34	96	172	39
	90	25	65	117	24
	120	20	43	71	17
	150	17	36	59	14
	180	12	32	58	15
Pull	60	16	51	93	25
	90	13	43	74	19
	120	11	40	63	17
	150	11	37	66	17
	180	15	39	73	19
Right	60	18	44	73	19
	90	18	39	72	24
	120	17	34	64	15
	150	15	32	60	14
	180	14	29	48	12
•Left	60	13	36	70	17
	90	13	31	48	12
	120	12	30	46	11
	150	12	31	52	14
	180	10	28	44	10
Up	60	17	45	78	22
	90	21	63	107	27
	120	41	88	143	33
	150	37	103	161	40
	180	51	113	165	34
Down	60	20	59	132	35
	90	17	80	143	37
	120	29	92	148	13
	150	37	93	150	35
	180	44	87	135	32

[1] See Fig. 11-76.
[2] Hunsicker and Greey, 1957.　　　[3] See Fig. 11-81.

Table 11-94 Maximum Force Exerted in the Sitting Position with the Wrist Supinated [1] on a Horizontal Handgrip at Various Elbow Angles by the Left Arm of Male College Students [2]

Direction of force	Elbow angle [3] (deg)	Percentiles (lb)			S.D.
		5th	50th	95th	
Push	60	35	89	176	42
	90	25	59	104	27
	120	15	40	80	18
	150	13	38	69	30
	180	14	30	47	10
Pull	60	23	54	87	23
	90	13	42	68	21
	120	14	40	66	18
	150	16	40	62	15
	180	17	40	70	18
Right	60	16	38	64	12
	90	12	32	46	12
	120	14	31	55	13
	150	12	32	62	15
	180	12	29	43	9
Left	60	17	42	81	20
	90	16	33	52	12
	120	14	28	45	8
	150	12	26	43	10
	180	8	27	44	10
Up	60	20	49	89	22
	90	24	75	131	29
	120	38	94	152	33
	150	44	104	164	36
	180	45	111	173	40
Down	60	20	58	138	41
	90	23	80	160	43
	120	35	84	136	33
	150	43	84	136	29
	180	36	78	124	28

[1] See Fig. 11-76.
[2] Hunsicker and Greey, 1957.　　　[3] See Fig. 11-81.

11-81

Table 11-95 Maximum Force Exerted in Pushing on an Aircraft Control Stick by the Right Arm of Male Air Force Personnel in the Sitting Position [1]

Control distance from SRP [2] (in.)	Control distance from mid-plane of body [2] (in.)	Percentiles (lb) [3]		
		5th	50th	95th
9	0	26	46	67
	4½ (left)	18	33	54
	8 (left)	12	29	44
	4½ (right)	34	58	82
	8 (right)	37	65	95
12½	8 (left)	18	36	68
	8 (right)	43	74	102
15½	0	43	86	160
	8 (left)	23	60	118
	8 (right)	53	100	164
18¾	0	64	124	177
	8 (left)	36	72	114
	8 (right)	70	125	198
23¾	0	54	106	141
	8 (left)	29	64	104
	8 (right)	56	100	147

[1] Stick is grasped 13½ in. above the SRP.
[2] See Fig. 11-82.
[3] Unpublished data, Anthropology Section, Aerospace Medical Laboratory.

Table 11-96 Maximum Force Exerted in Pulling on an Aircraft Control Stick by the Right Arm of Male Air Force Personnel in the Sitting Position [1]

Control distance from SRP [2] (in.)	Control distance from mid-plane of body [2] (in.)	Percentiles (lb) [3]		
		5th	50th	95th
9	0	34	57	86
	4½ (left)	28	45	66
	8 (left)	26	40	67
	4½ (right)	39	62	88
	8 (right)	39	58	86
12½	8 (left)	33	53	77
	8 (right)	49	80	108
15½	0	54	83	113
	8 (left)	39	64	98
	8 (right)	55	89	119
18¾	0	56	86	127
	8 (left)	45	74	108
	8 (right)	58	99	126
23¾	0	62	102	138
	8 (left)	51	90	129
	8 (right)	58	103	133

[1] Stick is grasped 13½ in. above the SRP.
[2] See Fig. 11-82.
[3] Unpublished data, Anthropology Section, Aerospace Medical Laboratory.

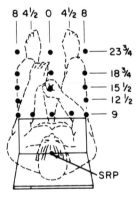

11-82

Table 11-97   **Maximum Force Exerted to the Left on an Aircraft Control Stick by the Right Arm of Male Air Force Personnel in the Sitting Position** [1]

Control distance from SRP [2] (in.)	Control distance from mid-plane of body [2] (in.)	Percentiles (lb) [3]		
		5th	50th	95th
9	0	30	47	66
	4½ (left)	31	49	67
	8 (left)	24	44	65
	4½ (right)	26	46	78
	8 (right)	26	44	72
12½	8 (left)	23	44	70
	8 (right)	22	39	59
15½	0	24	38	52
	8 (left)	20	35	58
	8 (right)	24	40	70
18¾	0	8	32	53
	8 (left)	16	30	56
	8 (right)	22	39	70
23¾	0	14	29	46
	8 (left)	11	21	49
	8 (right)	20	37	66

[1] Stick is grasped 13½ in. above the SRP.
[2] See Fig. 11-82.
[3] Unpublished data, Anthropology Section, Aerospace Medical Laboratory.

Table 11-98   **Maximum Force Exerted to the Right on an Aircraft Control Stick by the Right Arm of Male Air Force Personnel in the Sitting Position** [1]

Control distance from SRP [2] (in.)	Control distance from mid-plane of body [2] (in.)	Percentiles (lb) [3]		
		5th	50th	95th
9	0	23	38	49
	4½ (left)	31	48	64
	8 (left)	34	55	74
	4½ (right)	15	27	51
	8 (right)	12	22	43
12½	8 (left)	31	48	70
	8 (right)	16	24	46
15½	0	20	28	39
	8 (left)	25	43	63
	8 (right)	13	22	49
18¾	0	15	25	35
	8 (left)	22	36	61
	8 (right)	14	24	50
23¾	0	13	20	30
	8 (left)	19	31	48
	8 (right)	12	22	51

[1] Stick is grasped 13½ in. above the SRP.
[2] See Fig. 11-82.
[3] Unpublished data, Anthropology Section, Aerospace Medical Laboratory.

Table 11-99 Maximum Force Exerted in Pushing on an Aircraft Control Wheel by the Right Arm of Male Air Force Personnel in the Sitting Position [1]

Control distance from SRP [2] (in.)	Control position (deg)	Percentiles (lb) [3]		
		5th	50th	95th
10¾	0	52	86	135
	45 (left)	48	84	149
	90 (left)	32	67	125
	45 (right)	40	67	128
	90 (right)	19	52	112
13¼	90 (left)	32	54	93
	90 (right)	25	51	83
15¾	0	61	90	155
	90 (left)	32	59	139
	90 (right)	32	53	102
19	0	64	121	235
	90 (left)	37	88	171
	90 (right)	33	67	140
23¼	0	105	171	242
	90 (left)	82	131	211
	90 (right)	49	117	197

[1] Wheel grips are 18 in. above the SRP and 15 in. apart.
[2] See Fig. 11-83.
[3] Unpublished data, Anthropology Section, Aerospace Medical Laboratory.

Table 11-100 Maximum Force Exerted in Pulling on an Aircraft Control Wheel by the Right Arm of Male Air Force Personnel in the Sitting Position [1]

Control distance from SRP [2] (in.)	Control position (deg)	Percentiles (lb) [3]		
		5th	50th	95th
10¾	0	44	66	102
	45 (left)	40	67	111
	90 (left)	23	55	109
	45 (right)	39	67	97
	90 (right)	18	43	87
13¼	90 (left)	33	67	120
	90 (right)	31	60	102
15¾	0	66	94	145
	90 (left)	42	71	144
	90 (right)	49	80	130
19	0	73	106	169
	90 (left)	60	88	127
	90 (right)	61	94	149
23¼	0	77	125	182
	90 (left)	73	117	162
	90 (right)	74	110	186

[1] Wheel grips are 18 in. above the SRP and 15 in. apart.
[2] See Fig. 11-83.
[3] Unpublished data, Anthropology Section, Aerospace Medical Laboratory.

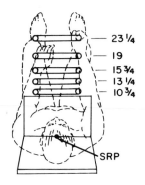

23¼
19
15¾
13¼
10¾

SRP

11-83

Table 11-101 Maximum Force Exerted to the Left on an Aircraft Control Wheel by the Right Arm of Male Air Force Personnel in the Sitting Position [1]

Control distance from SRP [2] (in.)	Control position (deg)	Percentiles (lb) [3]		
		5th	50th	95th
10¾	0	26	46	88
	45 (left)	21	54	123
	90 (left)	23	47	91
	45 (right)	31	54	120
	90 (right)	21	42	104
13¼	90 (left)	26	44	86
	90 (right)	25	45	99
15¾	0	27	46	112
	90 (left)	27	43	82
	90 (right)	29	50	86
19	0	25	44	95
	90 (left)	22	43	76
	90 (right)	33	52	104
23¼	0	20	39	86
	90 (left)	21	38	73
	90 (right)	26	55	109

[1] Wheel grips are 18 in. above the SRP and 15 in. apart.
[2] See Fig. 11-83.
[3] Unpublished data, Anthropology Section, Aerospace Medical Laboratory.

Table 11-102 Maximum Force Exerted to the Right on an Aircraft Control Wheel by the Right Arm of Male Air Force Personnel in the Sitting Position [1]

Control distance from SRP [2] (in.)	Control position (deg)	Percentiles (lb) [3]		
		5th	50th	95th
10¾	0	20	48	96
	45 (left)	24	69	121
	90 (left)	27	59	101
	45 (right)	24	51	118
	90 (right)	15	54	112
13¼	90 (left)	21	52	98
	90 (right)	19	51	111
15¾	0	27	59	97
	90 (left)	19	53	96
	90 (right)	20	46	91
19	0	30	63	104
	90 (left)	27	46	94
	90 (right)	22	41	87
23¼	0	35	60	98
	90 (left)	26	42	82
	90 (right)	22	40	68

[1] Wheel grips are 18 in. above the SRP and 15 in. apart.
[2] See Fig. 11-83.
[2] Unpublished data, Anthropology Section, Aerospace Medical Laboratory.

Table 11-103 Maximum Force Exerted in the Sitting Position on a Vertical Handgrip by Pronation and Supination of the Wrist of Male College Students [1]

Body member	Movement [2]	Percentiles (lb)			S.D.
		5th	50th	95th	
Right wrist	Pronation	29	71	119	28
	Supination	35	64	93	18
Left wrist	Pronation	31	71	132	31
	Supination	30	62	88	16

[1] Hunsicker and Greey, 1957.　　　[2] See Fig. 11-76.

Table 11-104 Maximum Force Exerted in Squeezing the Hand by Male Military and Civilian Populations

	Percentiles [1] (lb)			
Population	5th	50th	95th	S.D.
Air Force personnel, general [2]				
Right hand	(59)	104	(148)	27.3
Left hand	(56)	94	(134)	23.7
Air Force personnel, aircrewmen [3]				
Right hand	105	134	164	18.0
Left hand	96	124	154	16.0
Navy personnel [4]				
Mean of both hands	95	119	143	14.4
Truck and bus drivers [5]				
Right hand	91	121	151	18.1
Left hand	86	113	140	16.4
Industrial workers [4]				
Preferred hand	92	117	143	15.4
College students [6]				
Right hand	(74)	108	(142)	21.0
Left hand	(65)	95	(124)	18.0

[1] Percentiles in parentheses were computed from the 50th percentile using the S.D.
[2] Barter, et al., 1956.   [5] Damon and McFarland, 1955.
[3] Clarke, 1945.   [6] Tuttle, et al., 1950.
[4] Fisher and Birren, 1946.

TYPES OF HAND PREHENSION

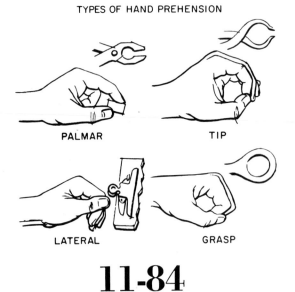

PALMAR   TIP

LATERAL   GRASP

Table 11-106 Maximum Force Exerted through Hand Prehension by Male Civilians [1]

Type of prehension [2]	Force (lb)	
	Avg.	S.D.
Palmar	21.5	5.4
Tip	21.0	4.8
Lateral	23.2	4.8
Grasp	90	16.0

[1] Taylor, 1954.   [2] See Fig. 11-84.

11-84

Table 11-105 Maximum Force Exerted in Squeez- ing the Hand by Female Military and Civilian Populations *

Population	Percentiles (lb)			
	5th	50th	95th	S.D.
Navy personnel				
Mean of both hands	58	73	87	8.8
Industrial workers				
Preferred hand	57	74	91	10.3

* Fisher and Birren, 1946.

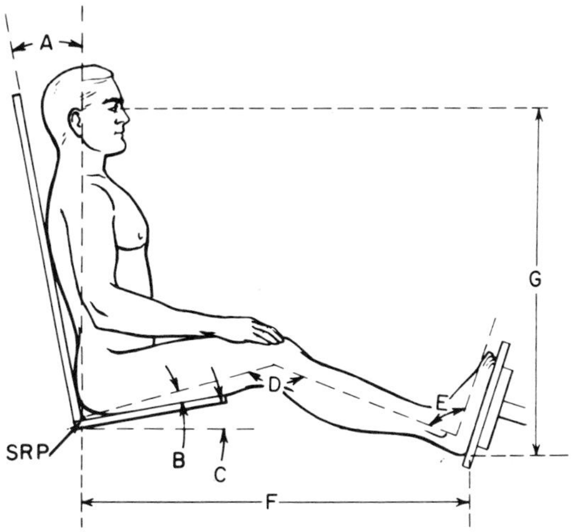

Table 11-107 Maximum Force that Can Be Exerted in Extension of the Leg at the Hip and Knee by British Male Ci- vilians in the Sitting Position [1]

Test conditions [2]				Avg. force (lb)
A	B	C	D	
0	0	0	90	63
0	0	0	113	89
0	0	0	135	156
0	5	0	164	559
0	6	0	94	73
0	8	0	93	87
0	10	0	80	77
0	10	0	90	59
0	10	0	135	270
0	10	0	165	346
0	15	0	149	227
0	15	0	160	845
0	15	0	169	530
0	16	0	129	319
0	17	0	117	212
0	17	0	151	684
0	33	0	106	184

[1] Clark and Weddell, 1944 and Hugh-Jones, 1947.
[2] See Fig. 11-85.

11-85

569

Table 11-108 Maximum Force that Can Be Exerted in Extension of the Ankle by Male Air Force Personnel Under Various Test Conditions [1]

Test conditions [2]				Percentiles (lb)			
A	E	F	G	5th *	50th	95th *	S.D.
13	10	35¼	37	14	120	227	64.8
13	10	38½	37	54	149	244	57.7
13	30	35¼	37	25	137	249	68.3
13	30	38½	37	64	184	303	72.7
13	50	35¼	37	24	88	152	38.9
13	50	38½	37	48	133	218	51.7
13	10	35¼	39	15	111	207	58.6
13	10	38½	39	37	135	232	59.4
13	30	35¼	39	26	137	249	67.8
13	30	38½	39	60	178	297	72.0
13	50	35¼	39	22	91	161	42.4
13	50	38½	39	50	132	213	49.4
13	10	35¼	41	18	118	218	60.8
13	10	38½	41	35	122	209	53.1
13	30	35¼	41	32	143	254	67.5
13	30	38½	41	50	175	300	76.1
13	50	35¼	41	23	98	174	46.0
13	50	38½	41	50	138	226	53.5

[1] Hertzberg, et al., 1954.   [2] See Fig. 11-85.
* Computed from the 50th percentile using the S.D.

BIBLIOGRAPHY
AND AUTHOR INDEX

The numbers in brackets at the end of each entry refer to the pages on which references to the entries can be found.

ADAMS, J. A. (1956) Vigilance in the detection of low-intensity visual stimuli, *J. Exp. Psychol.*, 52, 204 [235]

AERO MEDICAL ASSOC. (1953) "Aviation Toxicology: An Introduction to the Subject and a Handbook of Data" (McGraw-Hill Book Co., Inc., New York) [436]

ÅKERBLOM, B. (1954) Chairs and sitting, in "Symposium on Human Factors in Equipment Design" (W. E. Floyd and A. T. Welford, eds., H. K. Lewis & Co., Ltd., London) [314, 315]

AMERICAN COLLEGE OF CHEST PHYSICIANS (1960) Air travel in cardio-respiratory disease, *Diseases of Chest,* 37, 579 [427]

ASHRAE (1960) "Heating Ventilating Air Conditioning Guide," Vol. 38 (American Society of Heating, Refrigerating and Air-Conditioning Engineers, New York) [431–433]

AMERICAN STANDARDS ASSOC. (1954) The relations of hearing loss to noise exposure, American Standards Association, New York, N. Y. [142]

ARKIN, A. M. (1941) Absolute muscle power, *Arch. Surg.,* 42, 395 [557]

ATKINSON, W. H., et al. (1952) A study of the requirements for letters, numbers, and markings to be used on trans-illuminated aircraft control panels: V. The comparative legibility of three fonts for numerals, Rept. TED-NAMEL-609-5, Naval Air Material Center, Philadelphia, Pa. [102]

BAILEY, A. W. and J. S. SWEENEY (1955) Preliminary study of helicopter attitude display systems, Rept. No. 451, Naval Research Lab., Washington, D. C. [241, 242]

571

BAINES, R. M. and E. S. KING (1950) A study in the relationship between maximum cranking speed and cranking radius, *Motor Skills Research Exchange*, 2, 24 [264, 274]

BAKAN, P. (1955) Discrimination decrement as a function of time in a prolonged vigil, *J. Exp. Psychol.*, 50, 387 [235]

BAKER, C. A. and W. F. GRETHER (1954) Visual presentation of information, WADC-TR-54-160, Aero Medical Lab., Wright Air Development Center, Wright-Patterson AFB, Ohio [86, 303]

BAKER, C. A. and J. M. VANDERPLAS (1956) Speed and accuracy of scale reading as a function of the number of reference markers, *J. Appl. Psychol.*, 40, 307 [117]

BAKER, C. A., et al. (1960) Target recognition on complex displays, *Human Factors*, Vol. 2, No. 2, p. 51 [51, 68]

BALLARD, J. W. and R. W. HESSINGER (1954) Human-engineered electro-mechanical tactual sensory control system, *Elec. Mfg.*, Vol. 54, No. 4, p. 118 [27]

BALLINGER, E. R. and C. A. DEMPSEY (1952) The effects of prolonged acceleration on the human body in the prone and supine positions, WADC-TR-52-250, Aero Medical Lab., Wright Air Development Center, Wright-Patterson AFB, Ohio [453]

BARBER, J. L. and W. R. GARNER (1951) The effect of scale numbering on scale-reading accuracy and speed, *J. Exp. Psychol.*, 41, 298 [116]

BARNES, R. M. (1936) An investigation of some hand motions used in factory work, *Studies in Engineering*, Bull. No. 6, Univ. of Iowa, Iowa City, Iowa [251, 263]

BARNES, R. M. (1950) "Motion and Time Study" (John Wiley & Sons, Inc., New York [297]

BARNES, R. M. and M. E. MUNDELL (1939) A study of simultaneous symmetrical hand motions, *Studies in Engineering*, Bull. No. 17, Univ. of Iowa, Iowa City, Iowa [264]

BARNES, R. M., et al. (1942) Which pedal is best?, *Factory Management and Maintenance*, 100, 98 [267, 308]

BARTER, J. T., et al. (1956) Unpublished data [568]

BARTER, J. T., et al. (1957) A statistical evaluation of joint range data, WADC-TN-57-311, Aero Medical Lab., Wright Air Development Center, Wright-Patterson AFB, Ohio [552, 553]

BARTLETT, N. R. and S. B. WILLIAMS (1947) Signal mark size and visibility of radar signals on a plan position indicator, Rept. No. 166-I-30, Psychological Lab., The Johns Hopkins Univ., Baltimore, Md. [114]

BATTIG, W. F., et al. (1955) Effect of frequency of target intermittence upon tracking, *J. Exp. Psychol.,* 49, 244 [222]

BAYER, L. M. and H. GRAY (1934) Anthropometric standards for working women, *Human Biol.,* 6, 472 [511–514, 516, 517]

BEDALE, E. M. (1924) Comparison of the energy expenditure of a woman carrying loads in eight different positions, in The effects of posture and rest in muscular work, Rept. No. 29, Industrial Fatigue Research Board, Medical Research Council, London, England [374]

BEDFORD, T. and C. G. WARNER (1937) Strength tests: Observations on the effects of posture on strength of pull, *Lancet,* 2, 1328 [373]

BELDING, H. S. (1949) Protection against dry cold, in "Physiology of Heat Regulation and the Science of Clothing" (L. H. Newburgh, ed., W. B. Saunders Co., Philadelphia) [433]

BERANEK, L. L. (1947) The design of speech communication systems, *Proc. Inst. Radio Engrs.* 35, 880 [174, 181, 182]

BERANEK, L. L. (1949) "Acoustic Measurements" (John Wiley & Sons, Inc., New York) [202, 204]

BERANEK, L. L. (1957) Revised criteria for noise in buildings, *Noise Control,* Vol. 3, No. 1, p. 19 [156, 174, 186–188]

BERRY, R. N., et al. (1950) The relation of vernier and depth discriminations to field brightness, *J. Exp. Psychol.,* 40, 349 [61]

BERTSCH, W. F., et al. (1956) Effects of two message-storage schemes upon communications within a small problem-solving group, *J. Acoust. Soc. Am.,* 28, 550 [159]

BEXTON, W. H., et al. (1954) Effects of decreased variation in the sensory environment, *Can. J. Psychol.,* 8, 70 [236]

BILINSKI, C. R. (1959) Utilization of hand tools in U. S. Navy electronic equipment maintenance, Rept. No. 888, U. S. Navy Electronics Lab., San Diego, Calif. [410]

BIRMINGHAM, H. P. and F. V. TAYLOR (1954) A human engineering approach to the design of man-operated continuous control systems, Rept. No. 4333, Naval Research Lab., Washington, D. C. [242–244]

BIRMINGHAM, H. P., et al. (1954) A demonstration of the effects of quickening in multiple-coordinate control tasks, Rept. No. 4380, Naval Research Lab., Washington, D. C. [243]

573

BLACKWELL, H. R. (1946) Contrast thresholds of the human eye, *J. Opt. Soc. Am.,* 36, 624 [110]

BLOCKLEY, W. V., et al. (1954) Prediction of human tolerance for heat in aircraft: A design guide, WADC-TR-53-346, Aero Medical Lab., Wright Air Development Center, Wright-Patterson AFB, Ohio [432]

BLODGETT, H. C., et al. (1956) Effect of large interaural time differences upon the judgment of sidedness, *J. Acoust. Soc. Am.,* 28, 639 [140]

BLONDEL, A. and J. REY (1911) Sur la perception des lumières brèves à la limite de leur portée, *J. Phys. (Paris),* 1, 530 [111]

BONDURANT, S., et al. (1958) Human tolerance to some of the accelerations anticipated in space flight, WADC-TR-58-156, Aero Medical Lab., Wright Air Development Center, Wright-Patterson AFB, Ohio [453, 558]

BOWEN, H. M. (1956) On the appreciation of visual displays, Unpublished Ph.D. thesis, Univ. of Cambridge, Cambridge, England [235–237]

BOWLES, G. T. (1932) "New Types of Old Americans at Harvard and at Eastern Women's Colleges" (Harvard Univ. Press, Cambridge, Mass.) [506, 510–517, 522, 523, 530, 541]

BOYNTON, R. M., et al. (1958) Laboratory studies pertaining to visual air reconnaissance, WADC-TR-55-304, Aero Medical Lab., Wright Air Development Center, Wright-Patterson AFB, Ohio [67]

BRADLEY, J. V. (1954a) Control-display association preferences for ganged controls, WADC-TR-54-379, Aero Medical Lab., Wright Air Development Center, Wright-Patterson AFB, Ohio [312]

BRADLEY, J. V. (1954b) Desirable control-display relationships for moving-scale instruments, WADC-TR-54-423, Aero Medical Lab., Wright Air Development Center, Wright-Patterson AFB, Ohio [106, 254]

BRADLEY, J. V. (1957) Glove characteristics influencing control manipulability, WADC-TR-57-389, Aero Medical Lab., Wright Air Development Center, Wright-Patterson AFB, Ohio [272]

BRADLEY, J. V. and J. ARGINTEANU (1956) Optimum knob diameter, WADC-TR-56-96, Aero Medical Lab., Wright Air Development Center, Wright-Patterson AFB, Ohio [272]

BRADLEY, J. V. and N. E. STUMP (1955) Minimum allowable dimensions for controls mounted on concentric shafts, WADC-TR-55-355, Aero Medical Lab., Wright Air Development Center, Wright-Patterson AFB, Ohio [272]

BRADLEY, J. V. and R. A. WALLIS (1959) Spacing of on-off controls: II. Toggle switches, WADC-TR-59-475, Aero Medical Lab., Wright Air Development Center, Wright-Patterson AFB, Ohio [263]

BRENNAN, T. N. N. and G. M. MORANT (1950) Selection of knob shapes for radio and other controls, Rept. FPRC-702, Flying Personnel Research Committee, RAF Institute of Aviation Medicine, Farnborough, England [259]

BRIGGS, S. J. (1955) A study in the design of work areas, Unpublished Ph.D. thesis, Purdue Univ., Lafayette, Ind. [309, 310]

BRISSENDEN, R. F. (1957) Some ground measurements of the forces applied by pilots to a side-located aircraft controller, NACA-TN-4171, National Aeronautics and Space Admin., Washington, D. C. [310]

BROADBENT, D. E. (1951a) The twenty dials and twenty lights test under noise conditions, Rept. APU-160, Applied Psychology Research Unit, Medical Research Council, Cambridge, England [236]

BROADBENT, D. E. (1951b) Failures of attention in selective listening, Rept. APU-168, Applied Psychology Research Unit, Medical Research Council, Cambridge, England [222]

BROADBENT, D. E. (1953) Noise, paced performance and vigilance tasks, *Brit. J. Psychol.,* 44, 295 [234, 235]

BROADBENT, D. E. (1954) Some effects of noise on visual performance, *Quart. J. Exp. Psychol.,* 6, 1 [229]

BROADBENT, D. E. (1955) Successive responses to simultaneous stimuli, Rept. FPRC-934, Flying Personnel Research Committee, RAF Institute of Aviation Medicine, Farnborough, England [222]

BROWN, C. W., et al. (1949a) Magnitude of forces which may be applied by the prone pilot to aircraft control devices: I. Three-dimensional hand controls, Rept. MCREXD-694-4J, Aero Medical Lab., Wright Air Development Center, Wright-Patterson AFB, Ohio [307, 310]

BROWN, C. W., et al. (1949b) Magnitude of forces which may be applied by the prone pilot to aircraft control devices: III. Foot controls, AF-TR-5955, Aero Medical Lab., Wright Air Development Center, Wright-Patterson AFB, Ohio [315]

BROWN, F. R. (1953) A study of the requirements for letters, numbers, and markings to be used on trans-illuminated aircraft control panels: IV. Legibility of uniform stroke capital letters as determined by size and height to width ratio and as compared to Garamond Bold, Rept. TED-NAMEL-609-4, Naval Air Material Center, Philadelphia, Pa. [102]

BROWN, J. L. and R. E. BURKE (1957) The effect of positive acceleration on visual reaction time, NADC-MA-5712, Aviation Medical Acceleration Lab., U. S. Naval Air Development Center, Johnsville, Pa. [459]

BROWN, J. L. and M. LECHNER (1956) Acceleration and human performance, *J. Aviation Med.,* 27, 32 [558]

BROWN, J. S. and A. T. SLATER-HAMMEL (1949) Discrete movements in the horizontal plane as a function of their length and direction, *J. Exp. Psychol.,* 39, 84 [251, 264]

BROWN, J. S., et al. (1948) Discrete movements toward and away from the body in the horizontal plane, Rept. No. 6, Proj. No. 2, Contr. N5ori-57, U. S. Naval Training Devices Center, Port Washington, N. Y. [251]

BROWNE, R. C. (1953) Fatigue, fact or fiction?, in "Symposium on Fatigue" (W. F. Floyd and A. T. Welford, eds., H. K. Lewis & Co., Ltd., London) [235]

BRUES, A. (1946) Movement of the head and eye in sighting, in Human body size in military aircraft and personal equipment, AF-TR-5501, Aero Medical Lab., Wright Air Development Center, Wright-Patterson AFB, Ohio [556]

BUSKIRK, E. R. and D. E. BASS (1957) Climate and exercise, Rept. EP-61, Environmental Protection Branch, U. S. Army Quartermaster Research and Development Center, Natick, Mass. [430, 432]

BYRNES, V. A. (1951) Visual problems of supersonic speeds, *Am. J. Ophthalmol.,* 34, 169 [222, 227]

CALDWELL, L. S. (1959a) The effect of elbow angle and back support height on the strength of horizontal push by the hand, Rept. No. 378, U. S. Army Medical Research Lab., Fort Knox, Ky. [309]

CALDWELL, L. S. (1959b) The effect of the spatial position of a control on the strength of six linear hand movements, Rept. No. 411, U. S. Army Medical Research Lab., Fort Knox, Ky. [309, 310]

CANFIELD, A. A., et al. (1948) An investigation of the maximum forces which can be exerted on aircraft elevator and aileron controls, Contr. N6ori-77, U. S. Naval Training Devices Center, Port Washington, N. Y. [558]

CARPENTER, T. M. (1948) Tables, factors, and formulas for computing respiratory exchange and biological transformations of energy, Pub. No. 303C, Carnegie Institution of Washington, Washington, D. C. [422]

CARTER, I. G. (1932) Physical measurements of "old American" college women, *Am. J. Phys. Anthropol.,* 16, 497 [511, 516, 517, 526, 527, 537, 541]

CARTER, L. F. (1946) A study of the best design of tables and graphs used for presenting numerical data, Rept. TSEAA-694-1C, Aero Medical Lab., Wright Air Development Center, Wright-Patterson AFB, Ohio [122]

CATHCART, E. P., et al. (1927) The physique of women in industry, Rept. No. 44, Industrial Health Research Board, Medical Research Council, London, England [559]

CATHCART, E. P., et al. (1935) The physique of man in industry, Rept. No. 71, Industrial Health Research Board, Medical Research Council, London, England [558, 559]

CHALMERS, E. L., et al. (1950) The effect of illumination on dial reading, AF-TR-6021, Aero Medical Lab., Wright Air Development Center, Wright-Patterson AFB, Ohio [78]

CHAMBERS, R. M. and J. L. BROWN (1959) Acceleration, a paper presented at the symposium on environmental stress and human performance at the meeting of the American Psychological Association in Cincinnati [460, 463]

CHAPANIS, A. (1949) Some aspects of operator performance on the VJ remote radar indicator, Rept. No. 166-I-91, Psychological Lab., The Johns Hopkins Univ., Baltimore, Md. [118, 233]

CHAPANIS, A. (1951a) Theory and methods for analyzing errors in man-machine systems, *Ann. N. Y. Acad. Sci.,* 51, 1179 [39]

CHAPANIS, A. (1951b) Studies of manual rotary positioning movements: I. The precision of setting an indicator knob to various angular positions, *J. Psychol.,* 31, 51 [263, 268]

CHAPANIS, A. (1951c) Studies of manual rotary positioning movements: II. The accuracy of estimating the position of an indicator knob, *J. Psychol.,* 31, 65 [268]

CHAPANIS, A. (1959) "Research Techniques in Human Engineering" (The Johns Hopkins Press, Baltimore) [39, 49]

CHAPANIS, A. (1960) Human engineering, in "Operations Research and Systems Engineering" (C. D. Flagle, et al., eds., The Johns Hopkins Press, Baltimore) [238]

CHAPANIS, A. and M. LEYZOREK (1950) Accuracy of visual interpolation between scale markers as a function of the number assigned to the scale interval, *J. Exp. Psychol.,* 40, 655 [116]

CHAPANIS, A., et al. (1949) "Applied Experimental Psychology" (John Wiley & Sons, Inc., New York) [18, 22, 23, 236, 260]

CHAPMAN, S. (1950) Upper atmospheric nomenclature, *Bull. Am. Meteorol. Soc.,* 31, 288 [414]

CHERNIKOFF, R., et al. (1956) A comparison of pursuit and compensatory tracking in a simulated aircraft control loop, *J. Appl. Psychol.,* 40, 47 [219]

CHERNIKOFF, R. and F. V. TAYLOR (1957) Effects of course frequency and aided time constant on pursuit and compensatory tracking, *J. Exp. Psychol.,* 53, 285 [226, 240, 245]

CHERNIKOFF, R., et al. (1955) A comparison of pursuit and compensatory tracking under conditions of aiding and no aiding, *J. Exp. Psychol.*, 49, 55 [219, 240]

CHRISTENSEN, J. M. (1949) Arctic aerial navigation: A method for the analysis of complex activities and its applications to the job of the arctic aerial navigator, *Mech. Eng.*, 71, 11 [8]

CLARK, W. E. le G. and G. WEDDELL (1944) The pressure which can be exerted by the foot of a seated operator with the leg in various positions, Rept. No. 44/153, Royal Naval Personnel Research Committee, Medical Research Council, London, England [280, 308, 569]

CLARKE, H. (1945) Analysis of physical fitness index test scores of air crew students at the close of a physical conditioning program, *Research Quart.*, 16, 192 [373, 559, 568]

COAKLEY, J. D. and J. T. FUCIGNA (1955) Human engineering recommendations for the instrumentation of radar AN/FPS-16 (Xn-2), Radio Corp. of America, Moorestown, N. J. [6]

COBB, P. W. and F. K. MOSS (1928) The four variables of the visual threshold, *J. Franklin Inst.*, 205, 831 [59]

COERMANN, R. R. (1959) The response of the human to low frequency vibration, a paper presented to a meeting of the Society of Experimental Stress Analysis in Detroit [467]

COLLINS, C. A. and L. H. HOFMANN (1957) Switching control at television operating centers, *Bell Lab. Rec.*, 35, 10 [37]

COMFORT, E. and J. W. WILSON (1950) Some factors affecting time consciousness at high altitudes, AF-TR-5970, Aero Medical Lab., Wright Air Development Center, Wright-Patterson AFB, Ohio [420]

CONNELL, S. C. (1947) The relative effectiveness of presenting numerical data by the use of scales and graphs, Rept. TSEAA-694-1M, Aero Medical Lab., Wright Air Development Center, Wright-Patterson AFB, Ohio [122]

CONRAD, R. (1951) Speed and load stress in a sensorimotor skill, *Brit. J. Ind. Med.*, 8, 1 [232]

CONRAD, R. (1955a) Adaptation to time in a sensorimotor skill, *J. Exp. Psychol.*, 49, 115 [232, 234]

CONRAD, R. (1955b) Some effects on performance of changes in perceptual load, *J. Exp. Psychol.*, 49, 313 [232]

CORNELL AERONAUTICAL LAB. (1948) The binaural presentation of guidance data, Rept. OM-568-P-2, Cornell Univ., Buffalo, N. Y. [135]

CORNELL AERONAUTICAL LAB. (1958) Pocket data for human factor engineering, Rept. UB-1227-V-3, Cornell Univ., Buffalo, N. Y. [426]

CRAIG, D. R. (1949) Effect of amplitude range on duration of responses to step function displacements, AF-TR-5913, Aero Medical Lab., Wright Air Development Center, Wright-Patterson AFB, Ohio [224]

CRAIK, K. J. W. (1948) Theory of the human operator in control systems: II. Man as an element in a control system, *Brit. J. Psychol.*, 38, 142 [224]

CRAIK, K. J. W. and S. J. MacPHERSON (1945) The effect of certain operating conditions on the visibility of PPI radar echoes, Rept. APU-16, Applied Psychology Research Unit, Medical Research Council, Cambridge, England [114]

CRAIK, K. J. W. and M. A. VINCE (1945) A note on the design and manipulation of instrument knobs, Rept. APU-14, Applied Psychology Research Unit, Medical Research Council, Cambridge, England [272]

CRITCHLOW, E. F. (1944) Measurement and prediction of aircraft vibration, *Soc. Automotive Engrs. J.*, 52, 368 [466]

CROSSMAN, E. R. F. W. (1953) Entropy and choice time: The effect of frequency unbalance on choice-response, *Quart. J. Exp. Psychol.*, 5, 41 [231]

CROSSMAN, E. R. F. W. (1955) The measurement of discriminability, *Quart. J. Exp. Psychol.*, 7, 176 [230]

DAMON, A. (1943) Effect of flying clothing on body measurements of Army Air Force flyers, Rept. ENG-49-695-32, Aero Medical Lab., Wright Air Development Center, Wright-Patterson AFB, Ohio [507]

DAMON, A. (1955) Physique and success in military flying, *Am. J. Phys. Anthropol.*, 13, 217 [510, 511, 515, 516, 526]

DAMON, A. (1957) Constitutional factors in acne vulgaris: Prevalence in white soldiers and lack of association with ancestry, complexion, body hair, blood group, handedness, plasma pepsinogen, and physique, *A.M.A. Arch. Dermatol.*, 76, 172 [509, 513]

DAMON, A. and R. A. McFARLAND (1955) The physique of bus and truck drivers: With a review of occupational anthropology, *Am. J. Phys. Anthropol.*, 13, 711 [568]

DANIELS, G. S. and E. CHURCHILL (1952) The "average man"?, WCRD-TN-53-7, Aero Medical Lab., Wright Air Development Center, Wright-Patterson AFB, Ohio [495]

DANIELS, G. S., et al. (1953a) Anthropometry of WAF basic trainees, WADC-TR-53-12, Aero Medical Lab., Wright Air Development Center, Wright-Patterson AFB, Ohio [512, 513, 516–519, 527, 530, 535–538, 541, 542]

DANIELS, G. S., et al. (1953b) Anthropometry of male basic trainees, WADC-TR-53-49, Aero Medical Lab., Wright Air Development Center, Wright-Patterson AFB, Ohio [509, 519, 526, 530, 535–537, 541]

DARCUS, H. D. (1951) The maximum torques developed in pronation and supination of the right hand, *J. Anat.*, 85, 55 [557]

DARCUS, H. D. (1954) The range and strength of joint movement, in "Symposium on Human Factors in Equipment Design" (W. F. Floyd and A. T. Welford, eds., H. K. Lewis & Co., Ltd., London) [557, 558]

DARCUS, H. D. and A. G. M. WEDDELL (1947) Some anatomical and physiological principles concerned in the design of seats for naval war weapons, *Brit. J. Ind. Med.*, 4, 77 [315]

DAVENPORT, C. B. and A. G. LOVE (1921) Army anthropology, in "Medical Department of the U. S. Army in the World War," Vol. 15 (Office of the Surgeon General, Dept. of the Army, Washington, D. C.) [489]

DAVIS, D. R. (1948) Pilot error: Some laboratory experiments, Applied Psychology Research Unit, Medical Research Council, Cambridge, England [231, 235, 236]

DEESE, J. (1955) Some problems in the theory of vigilance, *Psychol. Rev.*, 62, 359 [235]

DEESE, J. and E. ORMOND (1953) Studies of detectability during continuous visual search, WADC-TR-53-8, Aero Medical Lab., Wright Air Development Center, Wright-Patterson AFB, Ohio [235]

DE HAVEN, H. (1942) Mechanical analysis of survival in falls from heights of 50 to 150 feet, *War Med.*, 2, 586 [449]

DEMPSTER, W. T. (1955) The anthropometry of body action, *Ann. N. Y. Acad. Sci.*, 63, 559 [264, 551]

DIECKMANN, D. (1957) Einfluss vertikaler mechanischer Schwingungen auf den Menschen, *Int. Z. angew. Physiol.*, 16, 519 [468, 469]

DIECKMANN, D. (1958) Einfluss horizontaler mechanischer Schwingungen auf den Menschen, *Int. Z. angew. Physiol.*, 17, 83 [470]

DIEHL, H. S. (1933a) Height and weight of American college men, *Human Biol.*, 5, 445 [510]

DIEHL, H. S. (1933b) The heights and weights of American college women, *Human Biol.*, 5, 600 [511, 514, 515]

DILL, D. B. (1938) "Life, Heat and Altitude" (Harvard Univ. Press, Cambridge, Mass.) [558]

DI TARANTO, R. A. and J. J. LAMB (1958) The space environment—A preliminary study, *Elec. Mfg.,* Vol. 62, No. 4, p. 54 [416]

DIXON, W. J. and F. J. MASSEY (1951) "Introduction to Statistical Analysis" (McGraw-Hill Book Co., Inc., New York) [49]

DONELSON, E. G., et al. (1940) Anthropometric data on college women of the Middle States, *Am. J. Phys. Anthropol.,* 27, 319 [511, 514, 526, 527]

DOUGHTY, J. M. and W. R. GARNER (1947) Pitch characteristics of short tones: I. Two kinds of pitch threshold, *J. Exp. Psychol.,* 37, 351 [158]

DUNN, H. K. and S. D. WHITE (1940) Statistical measurements on conversational speech, *J. Acoust. Soc. Am.,* 11, 278 [165]

DU BOIS, E. F. (1941) The temperature of the human body in health and disease, in "Temperature: Its Measurement and Control in Science and Industry" (Reinhold Publishing Corp., New York) [428]

DUPUIS, H. (1958) Some standards for the design of the tractor driver's workplace, a paper presented at the annual meeting of the American Society of Agricultural Engineers in Chicago [280]

DUPUIS, H., et al. (1955) Zweckmässige Gestaltung des schlepperführerstandes, *Schriftenreihe Landarbeit und Technik,* 20 [264, 280, 311]

EDELBERG, R., et al. (1956) Comparison of human tolerance to accelerations of slow and rapid onset, *J. Aviation Med.,* 27, 482 [466]

EDWARDS, E. A. and S. Q. DUNTLEY (1939) The pigments and color of living human skin, *Am. J. Anat.,* 65, 1 [315]

EGAN, J. P. (1948) Articulation testing methods, *Laryngoscope,* 58, 955 [173]

EGAN, J. P. and H. W. HAKE (1950) On the masking pattern of a simple auditory stimulus, *J. Acoust. Soc. Am.,* 22, 622 [145]

EGAN, J. P. and F. M. WEINER (1946) On the intelligibility of bands of speech in noise, *J. Acoust. Soc. Am.,* 18, 435 [181]

EGAN, J. P., et al. (1943) The effects of Army gas masks on speech communication, OSRD Rept. No. 1816, Harvard Psycho-Acoustic Lab., Harvard Univ., Cambridge, Mass. [210]

EIBAND, A. M. (1959) Human tolerance to rapidly applied accelerations: A summary of the literature, NACA Memo. No. 5-19-59-E, National Aeronautics and Space Administration, Washington, D. C. [448, 449, 451]

ELBEL, E. R. (1949) Relationship between leg strength, leg endurance and other body measurements, *J. Appl. Physiol.,* 2, 197 [280, 558]

ELBEL, E. R. (1954) Body measurements of male students entering the University of Kansas, *Kansas Studies in Education,* Vol. 4, No. 2, p. 1 [510, 515]

ELDRED, K. M., et al. (1955) Criteria for short time exposure of personnel to high intensity jet aircraft noise, WADC-TN-55-355, Aero Medical Lab., Wright Air Development Center, Wright-Patterson AFB, Ohio [152]

ELFTMAN, H. (1941) The action of muscles in the body, *Biol. Symposia,* 3, 191 [557]

ELKIND, J. I. (1953) Tracking response characteristics of the human operator, Memo. No. 40, Human Factors Operations Research Lab., Air Research and Development Command, Bolling AFB, Washington, D. C. [226]

ELKIND, J. I. (1956) Characteristics of simple manual control systems, Rept. No. 111, Lincoln Lab., Massachusetts Institute of Technology, Cambridge, Mass. [226]

ELLIS, W. A. B., et al. (1953) Presentation of air speed while deck landing: Comparison of visual and auditory methods, Rept. FPRC-841, Flying Personnel Research Committee, U. K. Air Ministry, London, England [134]

ELLSON, D. G. and D. GILBARG (1948) The application of operational analysis to human motor behavior, Rept. MCREXD-694-2J, Aero Medical Lab., Wright Air Development Center, Wright-Patterson AFB, Ohio [223]

ELLSON, D. G. and F. E. GRAY (1948) Frequency responses of human operators following a sine wave input, Rept. MCREXD-694-2N, Aero Medical Lab., Wright Air Development Center, Wright-Patterson AFB, Ohio [226]

ELLSON, D. G. and H. HILL (1947) Wave length and amplitude characteristics of tracking error curves: II. Individual differences and learning effects, Rept. TSEAA-694-2H, Aero Medical Lab., Wright Air Development Center, Wright-Patterson AFB, Ohio [226]

ELLSON, D. G. and H. HILL (1948) The interaction or responses to step function stimuli: I. Opposed steps of constant amplitude, Rept. MCREXD-694-2P, Aero Medical Lab., Wright Air Development Center, Wright-Patterson AFB, Ohio [224]

ELLSON, D. G. and L. WHEELER (1949) The range effect, AF-TR-5813, Aero Medical Lab., Wright Air Development Center, Wright-Patterson AFB, Ohio [224]

ELY, J. H., et al. (1956) Layout of workplaces, WADC-TR-56-171, Aero Medical Lab., Wright Air Development Center, Wright-Patterson AFB, Ohio [280, 288, 294, 315]

ELY, J. H. (1957) Tracking training: I. An approach, Rept. No. 1908-00-1, U. S. Naval Training Devices Center, Port Washington, N. Y. [240, 245]

EMANUEL, I., J. W. CHAFFEE, and J. WING (1956) A study of human weight-lifting capabilities for loading ammunition into the F-86H aircraft, WADC-TR-56-367, Aero Medical Lab., Wright Air Development Center, Wright-Patterson AFB, Ohio [373, 559]

ERIKSEN, C. W. (1954) Multidimensional stimulus differences and accuracy of discrimination, WADC-TR-54-165, Aero Medical Lab., Wright Air Development Center, Wright-Patterson AFB, Ohio [259]

FALKOWSKI, S. J. and A. D. HASTINGS (1958) Windchill in the Northern Hemisphere, Rept. EP-82, Environmental Protection Branch, U. S. Army Quartermaster Research and Development Center, Natick, Mass. [435]

FARRELL, W. R. (1958) Reverberation time criteria, Bolt Beranek & Newman, Inc., Cambridge, Mass. [200]

FINAN, J. L., et al. (1949) A review of representative tests used for the quantitative measurements of behavior decrement under conditions related to aircraft flight, AF-TR-5830, Aero Medical Lab., Wright Air Development Center, Wright-Patterson AFB, Ohio [422]

FISHER, M. B. and J. E. BIRREN (1946) Standardization of a test of hand strength, *J. Appl. Psychol.,* 30, 380 [557]

FISHER, M. B. and J. E. BIRREN (1947) Age and hand strength, *J. Appl. Psychol.,* 31, 490 [568, 569]

FITTS, P. M. (1947) A study of location discrimination ability, in Psychological research on equipment design, Rept. No. 19 of the Army Air Force Aviation Psychology Program, Aero Medical Lab., Wright Air Development Center, Wright-Patterson AFB, Ohio [312]

FITTS, P. M., ed. (1951) "Human Engineering for an Effective Air-Navigation and Traffic-Control System" (National Research Council, Washington, D. C.) [8]

FITTS, P. M. and C. CRANNELL (1950) Location discrimination: II. Accuracy of reaching movements to twenty-four different areas, AF-TR-5833, Aero Medical Lab., Wright Air Development Center, Wright-Patterson AFB, Ohio [312]

FITTS, P. M. and R. H. JONES (1961) Analysis of factors contributing to 460 "pilot-error" experiences in operating aircraft controls, in "Selected Papers on Human Factors in the Design and Use of Control Systems" (H. W. Sinaiko, ed., Dover Publications, Inc., New York) [28]

FITTS, P. M., et al. (1953) The interrelations of task variables in continuous pursuit tasks: I. Visual-display scale, arm-control scale, and target frequency in pursuit tracking, HRRC-TR-53-34, Human Resources Research Center, Air Research and Development Command, Lackland AFB, Texas [226]

FLETCHER, H. (1938) Loudness, masking, and their relation to the hearing process and the problem of noise measurement, *J. Acoust. Soc. Am.,* 9, 275 [147]

FLETCHER, H. (1940) Auditory patterns, *Revs. Modern Phys.,* 12, 47 [147]

FLETCHER, H. (1953) "Speech and Hearing in Communication" (D. Van Nostrand Co., Inc., New York) [141, 146–148, 166–168, 200, 201, 213]

FLETCHER, H. and W. A. MUNSON (1933) Loudness, its definition, measurement and calculation, *J. Acoust. Soc. Am.,* 5, 82 [143]

FLETCHER, H. and W. A. MUNSON (1937) Relation between loudness and masking, *J. Acoust. Soc. Am.,* 9, 1 [143, 148]

FLETCHER, H. and J. C. STEINBERG (1929) Articulation testing methods, *Bell Syst. Tech. J.,* 8, 806 [173]

FLOYD, W. F. and D. F. ROBERTS (1958) Anatomical and physiological principles in chair and table design, *Ergonomics,* 2, 1 [315]

FORBES, W. H., et al. (1945) The rate of carbon monoxide uptake by normal men, *Am. J. Physiol.,* 143, 594 [439]

FORD, A., et al. (1949) Pantograph radar tracking: Point centering experiments, AF-TR-5969, Aero Medical Lab., Wright Air Development Center, Wright-Patterson AFB, Ohio [118]

FOX, K. (1957) The effect of clothing on certain measures of strength of upper extremities, Rept. EP-47, Environmental Protection Branch, U. S. Army Quartermaster Research and Development Center, Natick, Mass. [558]

FOXBORO COMPANY (1943) Handwheel speed and accuracy of tracking, Rept. No. 3453, National Defense Research Committee, Office of Scientific Research and Development, Washington, D. C. [274]

FRASER, D. C. (1953) Relationship of an environmental variable to performance in a prolonged visual task, *Quart. J. Exp. Psychol.,* 5, 31 [236]

FRENCH, N. R. and J. C. STEINBERG (1947) Factors governing the intelligibility of speech sounds, *J. Acoust. Soc. Am.,* 19, 90 [147, 164, 173]

FRENCH, R. S. (1954) Pattern recognition in the presence of visual noise, *J. Exp. Psychol.,* 47, 27 [34]

FRICK, F. C. and W. H. SUMBY (1952) Control tower language, *J. Acoust. Soc. Am.,* 24, 595 [212]

GAGGE, A. P. (1946) Human requirements for the design of supersonic aircraft, a paper presented to the meeting of the American Association for the Advancement of Science at Boston [464]

GAMBLE, J. L. and R. S. SHAW (1947) Pathology in dogs exposed to negative acceleration, Rept. TSEAA-695-74B, Aero Medical Lab., Wright Air Development Center, Wright-Patterson AFB, Ohio [450]

GAMBLE, J. L. and R. S. SHAW (1948) Animal studies on impact negative acceleration, Rept. MCREXD-695-74G, Aero Medical Lab., Wright Air Development Center, Wright-Patterson AFB, Ohio [450]

GARNER, W. R. and G. A. MILLER (1947) The masked threshold of pure tones as a function of duration, *J. Exp. Psychol.,* 37, 293 [158]

GARNER, W. R., et al. (1949) Some design factors affecting the speed of identification of range rings on polar coordinate displays, Rept. No. 166-I-95, Psychological Lab., The Johns Hopkins Univ., Baltimore, Md. [117]

GARRY, R. C. (1930) The factors determining the most effective push or pull which can be exerted by a human being on a straight lever moving in a vertical plane, *Arbeitsphysiologie,* 3, 330 [310]

GAUER, O. H. and G. D. ZUIDEMA, eds. (1961) "Gravitational Stress in Aerospace Medicine" (Little, Brown and Co., Boston) [447]

GEBHARD, J. W. (1948) Accuracy of aligning the movable range marker with blips on the PPI, Rept. No. 166-I-46, Systems Research Field Lab., The Johns Hopkins Univ., Jamestown, R. I. [118]

GEBHARD, J. W. and E. A. BILODEAU (1947) Appraisal of an experimental PPI presenting simulated bearing, range, and height information, Rept. No. 166-I-37, Systems Research Field Lab., The Johns Hopkins Univ., Jamestown, R. I. [118–120]

GELDARD, F. A. (1957) Adventures in tactile literacy, *Am. Psychologist,* 12, 115 [27]

GELDARD, F. A. (1960) Some neglected possibilities of communication, *Science,* 131, 1583 [26]

GERATHEWOHL, S. J. (1954) Conspicuity of flashing light signals: Effects of variation among frequency, duration, and contrast of the signals, Rept. No. 1, Proj. No. 21-1205-0012, School of Aviation Medicine, Randolph AFB, Texas [229]

GERSON, N. C. and J. KAPLAN (1951) Nomenclature of the upper atmosphere, *J. Atmospheric and Terrest. Phys.,* 1, 200 [414]

GIBBONS, T. B., et al. (1953) Age, height and weight of 2173 men entering recruit training during 1952, Naval Medical Research Unit No. 4, U. S. Naval Training Center, Great Lakes, Ill. [509, 513]

GIBBS, C. B. (1954) Servo principles in sensory organization and the transfer of skill, Rept. APU-218/54, Applied Psychology Research Unit, Medical Research Council, Cambridge, England [226]

GIBBS, C. B., et al. (1955) Reaction times to the flashing light signals of cars: The effects of varying the frequency and duration of the flash, Rept. APU-245, Applied Psychology Research Unit, Medical Research Council, Cambridge, England [229]

GLANVILLE, A. D. and G. KREEZER (1937) The maximum amplitude and velocity of joint movements in normal male human adults, *Human Biol.,* 9, 197 [553]

GOLDMAN, D. E. (1948) A review of subjective responses to vibratory motion of the human body in the frequency range 1 to 70 cycles per second, Rept. No. 1, Project NM-004-001, U. S. Naval Medical Research Institute, Bethesda, Md. [471]

GOLDMAN, D. E. and H. E. VON GIERKE (1960) The effects of shock and vibration on man, Lecture and Review Series No. 60-3, U. S. Naval Medical Research Institute, Bethesda, Md. [447, 467, 471, 472]

GOODRICH, J. W. (1956) Escape from high performance aircraft, WADC-TN-56-7, Aero Medical Lab., Wright Air Development Center, Wright-Patterson AFB, Ohio [457]

GOODY, R. M. (1954) "The Physics of the Stratosphere" (Univ. of Cambridge Press, Cambridge, England) [414]

GOODYEAR AIRCRAFT CORP. (1952) Final report: Human dynamics study, Rept. GER-4750, Goodyear Aircraft Corp., Akron, Ohio [222]

GREEN, B. F., et al. (1953) The time required to search for numbers on large visual displays, Rept. No. 36, Lincoln Lab., Massachusetts Institute of Technology, Cambridge, Mass. [85]

GRETHER, W. F. (1947) The effect of variations in indicator design upon speed and accuracy of altitude readings, Rept. TSEAA-694-14, Aero Medical Lab., Wright Air Development Center, Wright-Patterson AFB, Ohio [51, 97]

HAGGARD, H. W. (1946) The mechanics of human muscles, *Mech. Eng.,* 68, 321 [547]

HAIG, C. (1941) The course of rod adaptation as influenced by the intensity and duration of preadaptation to light, *J. Gen. Physiol.,* 24, 735 [77]

HALLENBECK, G. A., et al. (1945) Magnitude and duration of opening parachute shock, *Air Surgeon's Bull.,* 2, 35 [452]

HAMILTON, P. M. (1957) Underwater hearing thresholds, *J. Acoust. Soc. Am.,* 29, 792 [140]

HANES, R. M. and S. B. WILLIAMS (1948) Visibility on cathode-ray tube screens: The effects of light adaptation, *J. Opt. Soc. Am.,* 38, 363 [111, 112]

HANSEN, R. and D. Y. CORNOG (1958) Annotated bibliography of applied physical anthropology in human engineering WADC-TR-56-30, Aero Medical Lab., Wright Air Development Center, Wright-Patterson AFB, Ohio [492]

HATHAWAY, J. L. (1950) Automatic audio gain controls, *Audio Engineering,* Vol. 34, No. 9, p. 16 [154]

HAWKINS, J. E. and S. S. STEVENS (1950) The masking of pure tones and of speech by white noise, *J. Acoust. Soc. Am.,* 22, 6 [146, 147]

HAWLEY, M. E. and K. D. KRYTER (1957) Effects of noise on speech, in "Handbook of Noise Control" (C. M. Harris, ed., McGraw-Hill Book Co., Inc., New York) [190, 191]

HEATH, C. W. (1945) "What People Are" (Harvard Univ. Press, Cambridge, Mass.) [510, 515, 526]

HECHT, S., et al. (1946) Anoxia and brightness discrimination, *J. Gen. Physiol.,* 29, 335 [421]

HECHT, S., et al. (1947) The visibility of lines and squares at high brightnesses, *J. Opt. Soc. Am.,* 37, 500 [60]

HELSON, H. (1945) Studies in aided tracking, Memo. No. 25, Anthropology and Psychology Div., National Research Council, Washington, D. C. [240]

HELSON, H. (1949) Design of equipment and optimal human operation, *Am. J. Psychol.,* 62, 473 [264, 274]

HERBERT, M. J. (1957) Speed and accuracy with which six linear arm movements can be visually positioned from two different control locations, Rept. No. 260, U. S. Army Medical Research Lab., Fort Knox, Ky. [264]

HERTZBERG, H. T. E. (1954) Unpublished data [280]

HERTZBERG, H. T. E. (1955) Some contributions of applied physical anthropology to human engineering, *Ann. N. Y. Acad. Sci.,* 63, 616 [264, 315]

HERTZBERG, H. T. E., et al. (1954) Anthropometry of flying personnel—1950, WADC-TR-52-321, Aero Medical Lab., Wright Air Development Center, Wright-Patterson AFB, Ohio [489, 509–519, 522, 523, 526–530, 533–541, 545, 570]

HERTZBERG, H. T. E., et al. (1956) The anthropometry of working positions: I. A preliminary study, WADC-TR-54-520, Aero Medical Lab., Wright Air Development Center, Wright-Patterson AFB, Ohio [515, 543, 545]

HICK, W. E. (1945) Friction in manual controls with special reference to its effect on accuracy of corrective movements in conditions simulating jolting, Rept. APU-18, Applied Psychology Research Unit, Medical Research Council, Cambridge, England [276]

HICK, W. E. (1952) On the rate of gain of information, *Quart. J. Exp. Psychol.*, 4, 11 [230, 231]

HICK, W. E. and J. A. V. BATES (1950) The human operator of control mechanisms, Rept. No. 17-204, Permanent Records of Research and Development, U. K. Ministry of Supply, London, England [225]

HILL, N. E. G. (1947) The recognition of coloured light signals which are near the limit of visibility, *Proc. Phys. Soc. (London)*, 59, 560 [66]

HIRSH, I. J. (1948) The influence of interaural phase on interaural summation and inhibition, *J. Acoust. Soc. Am.*, 20, 536 [140]

HIRSCH, M. J. and F. W. WEYMOUTH (1947) Distance discrimination: V. Effect of motion and distance of targets on monocular and binocular distance discrimination, *J. Aviation Med.*, 18, 594 [61]

HOLLAND, J. G. and J. B. HENSON (1956) Transfer of training between quickened and unquickened tracking systems, Rept. No. 4703, Naval Research Lab., Washington, D. C. [243]

HOMANS, J. (1954) Thrombosis of the deep leg veins due to prolonged sitting, *New Engl. J. Med.*, 250, 148 [498]

HOOTON, E. A. (1945) "A Survey in Seating" (Heywood-Wakefield Co., Gardner, Mass.) [491, 495, 498, 510, 511, 514, 515, 523, 527, 530, 535, 540]

HORTON, J. W. (1957) "Fundamentals of Sonar" (U. S. Naval Institute, Annapolis, Md.) [128]

HOUSTON, R. C. and R. Y. WALKER (1949) The evaluation of auditory warning signals for aircraft, AF-TR-5762, Aero Medical Lab., Wright Air Development Center, Wright-Patterson AFB, Ohio [130]

HOWES, D. H. (1957) On the relation between the intelligibility and frequency of occurrence of English words, *J. Acoust. Soc. Am.*, 29, 296 [211]

HOWES, D. H. and R. L. SOLOMON (1951) Visual duration threshold as a function of word-probability, *J. Exp. Psychol.*, 41, 401 [121]

HUGH-JONES, P. (1947) The effect of limb position in seated subjects on their ability to utilize the maximum contractile force of the limb muscles, *J. Physiol.*, 105, 332 [280, 309, 310, 557, 569]

HUMPHREY, C. E. (1952) Auditory displays: I. Spatial orientation by means of auditory signals—an exploratory study, APL/JHU-TG-122, Applied Physics Lab., The Johns Hopkins Univ., Silver Spring, Md. [135]

HUMPHREY, C. E. and J. E. THOMPSON (1952) Auditory displays: II. Comparison of auditory and visual tracking in one dimension: A. Discontinuous signals, simple course, APL/JHU-TG-146, Applied Physics Lab., The Johns Hopkins Univ., Silver Spring, Md. [137]

HUMPHREY, C. E. and J. E. THOMPSON (1952) Auditory displays: II. Comparison of auditory and visual tracking in one dimension: B. Discontinuous signals, complex course, APL/JHU-TG-147, Applied Physics Lab., The Johns Hopkins Univ., Silver Spring, Md. [137]

HUMPHREY, C. E. and J. E. THOMPSON (1953) Auditory displays: II. Comparison of auditory tracking with visual tracking in one dimension: C. Continuous signals, simple, intermediate and complex courses, APL/JHU-TG-194, Applied Physics Lab., The Johns Hopkins Univ., Silver Spring, Md. [137]

HUMPHREY, C. E., et al. (1953) Time-sharing and the tracking task, APL/JHU-TG-201, Applied Physics Lab., The Johns Hopkins Univ., Silver Spring, Md. [222]

HUNSICKER, P. A. (1955) Arm strength at selected degrees of elbow flexion, WADC-TR-54-548, Aero Medical Lab., Wright Air Development Center, Wright-Patterson AFB, Ohio [307–309, 557, 558–563]

HUNSICKER, P. A. and G. GREEY (1957) Studies in human strength, *Research Quart.*, 28, 109 [557, 562, 563, 567]

HUNT, D. P. (1953) The coding of aircraft controls, WADC-TR-53-221, Aero Medical Lab., Wright Air Development Center, Wright-Patterson AFB, Ohio [259, 265]

HUNT, D. P. and D. R. CRAIG (1954) The relative discriminability of thirty-one differently shaped knobs, WADC-TR-54-108, Aero Medical Lab., Wright Air Development Center, Wright-Patterson AFB, Ohio [271]

HUTCHINSON, F. W. (1942) The paradox of acclimatization, *Heating and Ventilating*, Vol. 39, No. 2, p. 25 [430]

HYMAN, R. (1953) Stimulus information as a determinant of reaction time, *J. Exp. Psychol.*, 45, 188 [230]

ISHII, Y. (1957) Studies on the physique and physical strength of workers, *J. Sci. Labour (Japan)*, 33, 259 [488]

JANEWAY, R. N. (1948) Vehicle vibration limits to fit the passenger, a paper presented to the passenger car and production meeting of the Society of Automotive Engineers at Detroit [466]

JENKINS, W. L. (1953) Design factors in knobs and levers for making settings on scales and scopes, WADC-TR-53-2, Aero Medical Lab., Wright Air Development Center, Wright-Patterson AFB, Ohio [249]

JENKINS, W. L. and M. B. CONNOR (1949) Some design factors in making settings on a linear scale, *J. Appl. Psychol.*, 33, 395 [250, 251, 272]

JENKINS, W. L. and A. C. KARR (1954) The use of a joy-stick in making settings on a simulated scope face, *J. Appl. Psychol.*, 38, 457 [250]

JENKINS, W. L. and M. W. OLSON (1952) The use of levers in making settings on a linear scale, *J. Appl. Psychol.*, 36, 269 [250]

JENKINS, W. L., et al. (1950) Influence of friction in making settings on a linear scale, *J. Appl. Psychol.*, 34, 434 [250]

JENKINS, W. L., et al. (1951) Influence of inertia in making settings on a linear scale, *J. Appl. Psychol.*, 35, 208 [250]

JERISON, H. J. and R. A. WALLIS (1957a) Experiments on vigilance: II. One-clock and three-clock monitoring, WADC-TR-57-206, Aero Medical Lab., Wright Air Development Center, Wright-Patterson AFB, Ohio [235]

JERISON, H. J. and R. A. WALLIS (1957b) Experiments on vigilance: III. Performance on a simple vigilance task in noise and in quiet, WADC-TR-57-318, Aero Medical Lab., Wright Air Development Center, Wright-Patterson AFB, Ohio [236]

JERISON, H. J. and S. WING (1957) Effects of noise and fatigue on a complex vigilance task, WADC-TR-57-14, Aero Medical Lab., Wright Air Development Center, Wright-Patterson AFB, Ohio [236]

KAPPAUF, W. E. (1951) Design of instrument dials for maximum legibility: V. Origin location, scale break, number location, and contrast direction, AF-TR-6366, Aero Medical Lab., Wright Air Development Center, Wright-Patterson AFB, Ohio [103]

KARPINOS, B. D. (1958) Height and weight of selective service registrants processed for military service during World War II, *Human Biol.*, 30, 292 [515]

KENNEDY, J., et al. (1952) Handbook of human engineering data, Institute for Applied Experimental Psychology, Tufts Univ., Medford, Mass. [228, 282, 421, 422]

KING, B. G., et al. (1947) Cockpit studies—The boundaries of the maximum area for the operation of manual controls, Rept. No. 3, Project X-651, U. S. Naval Medical Research Institute, Bethesda, Md. [509–513, 522, 523, 533, 538]

KLEITMAN, N. (1939) "Sleep and Wakefulness" (Univ. of Chicago Press, Chicago) [236]

KLEMMER, E. T. (1956) Time uncertainty in simple reaction time, *J. Exp. Psychol.*, 51, 179 [232]

KLUMPP, R. G. and H. R. EADY (1956) Some measurements of interaural time difference thresholds, *J. Acoust. Soc. Am.*, 28, 859 [140]

KOCH, H. (1941) Fussbediente Arbeitsmaschinen und Ermüdung, *Arbeitsschutz*, 3, 52 [308–312]

KRAFT, C. L. and P. M. FITTS (1954) A broad-band blue lighting system for radar air traffic control center, WADC-TR-53-416, Aero Medical Lab., Wright Air Development Center, Wright-Patterson AFB, Ohio [75]

KRULEE, G. K. and A. WEISZ (1954) Studies in the visual discrimination of multiple unit displays, Rept. No. 1954-494-03-23, Tufts Univ., Medford, Mass. [231]

KRYTER, K. D. (1944) Articulation test comparisons of six Signal Corps aircraft interphones at low and high altitudes, OSRD Rept. No. 1974, Harvard Psycho-Acoustic Lab., Harvard Univ., Cambridge, Mass. [208]

KRYTER, K. D. (1946) Effects of ear protective devices on the intelligibility of speech in noise, *J. Acoust. Soc. Am.,* 18, 413 [189]

KRYTER, K. D. (1958) Human engineering principles for the design of speech communication systems, AFCRC-TR-58-62, Air Force Cambridge Research Center, Cambridge, Mass. [181]

KRYTER, K. D. (1962) Standard procedures for the calculation of the articulation index, ESD-TDR-62-1, Electronic Systems Div., Air Force Systems Command, L. G. Hanscom Field, Bedford, Mass. [185]

LAURU, L. and L. BROUHA (1957) Physiological study of motions, *Advanced Management,* Vol. 22, No. 3, p. 17 [308]

LE BLANC, J. S. (1956) Impairment of manual dexterity in the cold, *J. Appl. Physiol.,* 9, 62 [435]

LEHMANN, G. (1927) Arbeitsphysiologische Studien IV, *Pflüger's Arch. ges. Physiol.,* 215, 329 [310]

LEHMANN, G. (1958) Physiological basis of tractor design, *Ergonomics,* 1, 197 [280]

LENARD, D. E. and W. E. NORTH (1952) Senior control tower operator: A job description, HRRC-TR-52-10, Human Resources Research Center, Air Training Command, Chanute AFB, Ill. [12]

LEONARD, J. A. (1952) Some experiments on the temporal relation between information and action, Unpublished Ph.D. thesis, Univ. of Cambridge, Cambridge, England [232]

LEONARD, J. A. (1954) The effect of partial advance information, Rept. APU-217/54, Applied Psychology Research Unit, Medical Research Council, Cambridge, England [232]

LICKLIDER, J. C. R. (1946) Effects of amplitude distortion upon the intelligibility of speech, *J. Acoust. Soc. Am.,* 18, 429 [198]

591

LICKLIDER, J. C. R. (1951) Basic correlates of the auditory stimulus, in "Handbook of Experimental Psychology" (S. S. Stevens, ed., John Wiley & Sons, Inc., New York) [139]

LICKLIDER, J. C. R., et al. (1948) The intelligibility of rectangular speechwaves, *Am. J. Psychol.*, 61, 1 [195]

LINCOLN, R. S. and K. U. SMITH (1952) Systematic analysis of factors determining accuracy in visual tracking, *Science*, 116, 183 [240]

LINDSLEY, D. B. (1944) Radar operator fatigue: The effects of length and repetition of operating periods on efficiency of performance, Rept. No. 3334, Office of Scientific Research and Development, Washington, D. C. [235]

LOMBARD, C. F., et al. (1948a) The effects of negative radial acceleration on large experimental animals (goats), Proj. NR-161-014, U. S. Naval Training Devices Center, Port Washington, N. Y. [450, 558]

LOMBARD, C. F., et al. (1948b) The influence of positive (head to foot) centrifugal force upon a subject's (pilot's) ability to exert maximum pull on an aircraft control stick, Contr. N6ori-77, U. S. Naval Training Devices Center, Port Washington, N. Y. [558]

LOVELACE, W. R. and H. C. HINSHAW (1942) Dangers of aerial transportation to persons with pneumothorax, *J. Am. Med. Assoc.*, 118, 1275 [424]

LYTHGOE, R. J. (1932) The measurement of visual acuity, Rept. No. 173, Medical Research Council, London, England [62]

MACKWORTH, J. F. and N. H. MACKWORTH (1956) The overlapping of signals for decisions, *Am. J. Psychol.*, 69, 26 [232]

MACKWORTH, N. H. (1947) High incentives versus hot and humid atmospheres in a physical effort task, *Brit. J. Psychol.*, 38, 90 [236]

MACKWORTH, N. H. (1950) Researches on the measurement of human performance, Rept. APU-268, Applied Psychology Research Unit, Medical Research Council, Cambridge, England [235, 236, 432]

MACKWORTH, N. H. (1953) Finger numbness in very cold winds, *J. Appl. Physiol.*, 5, 533 [435]

MANDELBAUM, J. and L. L. SLOAN (1947) Peripheral visual acuity with special reference to scotopic illumination, *Amer. J. Opthalmol.*, 30, 581 [64]

MARTIN, W. B. and E. E. JOHNSON (1952) An optimum range of seat positions as determined by exertion of pressure upon foot control, Rept. No. 86, U. S. Army Medical Research Lab., Fort Knox, Ky. [310]

MATHENY, B. J. (1955) Human performance in radar vectoring (the study of the effects of varying loads of aircraft pips and pip speed upon vectoring performance in air traffic control), Rept. No. 71-16-14, U. S. Naval Training Devices Center, Port Washington, N. Y. [351]

MAYNE, J. W. (1957) Role of statistics in scientific research, *Sci. Monthly*, 84, 26 [49]

MAYO, A. M. (1957) Some survival aspects of space travel, *J. Aviation Med.*, 28, 498 [462]

McCORMICK, M. Y. (1947) Physical characteristics of the 1946 airline transport pilot population, Civil Aeronautics Admin., Washington, D. C. [510, 515]

McFADDEN, E. B., et al. (1959) The magnitude and direction of forces that man can exert in operating aircraft emergency exits, *Human Factors*, Vol. 1, No. 4, p. 16 [307]

McFARLAND, R. A. (1932) The psychological effects of oxygen deprivation (anoxemia) on human behavior, *Arch. Psychol. N. Y.*, No. 145 [422]

McFARLAND, R. A. (1946) "Human Factors in Air Transport Design" (McGraw-Hill Book Co., Inc., New York) [438]

McFARLAND, R. A. (1953) "Human Factors in Air Transportation: Occupational Health and Safety" (McGraw-Hill Book Co., Inc., New York) [425, 441]

McFARLAND, R. A., et al. (1942) "Studies of Visual Fatigue" (Graduate School of Business Administration, Harvard Univ., Boston, Mass.) [114]

McFARLAND, R. A., et al. (1944) The effects of carbon monoxide and altitude on visual thresholds, *J. Aviation Med.*, 15, 381 [439, 440]

McFARLAND, R. A., et al. (1958) Anthropometry in the design of the driver's workspace, *Am. J. Phys. Anthropol.*, 16, 1 [510, 511, 515, 522, 523, 526–530, 533–541]

McNEMAR, Q. (1955) "Psychological Statistics" (John Wiley & Sons, Inc., New York) [49]

MECHLER, E. A., et al. (1949) The basis for the optimum aided-tracking time constant, *J. Franklin Inst.*, 248, 327 [240]

MILLER, G. A. (1947a) Sensitivity to changes in the intensity of white noise and its relation to masking and loudness, *J. Acoust. Soc. Am.*, 19, 609 [156]

MILLER, G. A. (1947b) The masking of speech, *Psychol. Bull.*, 44, 105 [184]

MILLER, G. A. and J. C. R. LICKLIDER (1950) The intelligibility of interrupted speech, *J. Acoust. Soc. Am.*, 22, 167 [185]

MILLER, G. A. and P. E. NICELY (1955) An analysis of perceptual confusions among some English consonants, *J. Acoust. Soc. Am.*, 27, 338 [213–215]

MILLER, G. A., et al. (1946) Combat instrumentation, in "Transmission and Reception of Sounds under Combat Conditions," Vol. 3 of "Summary Technical Report of Division 17" (C. E. Waring, ed., National Defense Research Committee, Office of Scientific Research and Development, Washington, D. C.) [134]

MILLER, R. B., et al. (1953) Systematic trouble shooting and the half-split technique, HRRC-TR-53-21, Human Resources Research Center, San Antonio, Texas [407]

MILTON, J. L., et al. (1947) Pilot reaction time: The time required to comprehend and react to contact and instrument recovery problems, Rept. TSEAA-694-13a, Aero Medical Lab., Wright Air Development Center, Wright-Patterson AFB, Ohio [227]

MINZNER, R. A., et al. (1959) The ARDC model atmosphere, AFCRC-TR-59-267, Geophysics Research Directorate, Air Force Cambridge Research Center, Bedford, Mass. [416]

MOON, P. and D. E. SPENCER (1944) Visual data applied to lighting design, *J. Opt. Soc. Am.*, 34, 605 [58]

MOSER, H. M. and G. E. BELL (1955) Joint United States–United Kingdom report, AFCRC-TN-55-56, Air Force Cambridge Research Center, Cambridge, Mass. [216]

MOTE, F. A. and A. J. RIOPELLE (1953) The effect of varying the intensity and the duration of pre-exposure upon subsequent dark adaptation in the human eye, *J. Comp. Physiol. Psychol.*, 46, 49 [113]

MOWBRAY, G. H. and J. W. GEBHARD (1961) Man's senses as informational channels, in "Selected Papers on Human Factors in the Design and Use of Control Systems" (H. W. Sinaiko, ed., Dover Publications, Inc., New York) [24–26]

MÜLLER, E. A. (1935) Der beste Handgriff und Stiel, *Arbeitsphysiologie*, 8, 28 [264]

MÜLLER, E. A. (1937) Die günstigste Anordnung im Sitzen betätigter Fusshebel, *Arbeitsphysiologie*, 9, 125 [308–311]

MUNSELL, A. H. (1942) "Book of Color" (Munsell Color Book Co., Inc., Baltimore, Md.) [84]

MUNSON, W. A. (1947) The growth of auditory sensation, *J. Acoust. Soc. Am.*, 19, 584 [157]

NAREFF, M. J. (1959) Passenger phlebitis: A complication of long distance aerial travel, *Aerospace Med.,* 30, 197 [498]

NEMETHI, C. E. (1952) An evaluation of hand grip in industry, *Ind. Med. Surg.,* 21, 65 [558]

NEWMAN, R. W. and R. M. WHITE (1951) Reference anthropometry of Army men, Rept. No. 180, Environmental Protection Branch, U. S. Army Quartermaster Research and Development Center, Natick, Mass. [488, 489, 495–497, 509–517, 522, 523, 526–530, 533–538, 541]

NOBLE, M. E., et al. (1953) The interrelations of task variables in continuous pursuit tasks: II. Visual-display scale, arm-control scale, and target frequency in compensatory tracking, HRRO-TR-53-55, Human Resources Research Office, Air Research and Development Command, Lackland AFB, Texas [226]

NOBLE, M. E., et al. (1955) The frequency response of skilled subjects in a pursuit tracking task, *J. Exp. Psychol.,* 49, 249 [226]

NYSTROM, C. O. and D. A. GRANT (1954) Performance on a key pressing task as a function of the angular correspondence between stimulus and response elements, WADC-TR-54-71, Aero Medical Lab., Wright Air Development Center, Wright-Patterson AFB, Ohio [301]

O'BRIEN, R. and W. C. SHELTON (1941) Women's measurements for garment and pattern construction, Pub. No. 454, Dept. of Agriculture, Washington, D. C. [491, 511, 514]

ODELGARD, B. and P. O. WEMAN (1957) Safety belts for motorcars, Blue-White Series No. 18, Swedish State Power Board, Stockholm, Sweden [448]

ORLANSKY, J. (1948) The human factor in the design of stick and rudder controls for aircraft, Rept. SPECDEVCEN-151-1-8, U. S. Naval Training Devices Center, Port Washington, N. Y. [263, 264, 280, 308]

ORLANSKY, J. (1949) Psychological aspects of stick and rudder controls in aircraft, *Aeronaut. Eng. Rev.,* 8, 22 [265]

OWINGS, J. L. (1956) Human engineering the bizmac system, *RCA Eng.,* 2, 16 [38]

PEPLER, R. D. (1950) The effect of climatic factors on the performance of skilled tasks by young European men living in the tropics; IV. A task of prolonged visual vigilance, Rept. APU-156, Applied Psychology Research Unit, Medical Research Council, Cambridge, England [236]

PEPLER, R. D. (1958) Warmth and performance: An investigation in the tropics, *Ergonomics,* 2, 63 [432]

PESKIN, J. C. and J. BJORNSTAD (1948) The effect of different wavelengths of light on visual sensitivity, Rept. MCREXD-694-93A, Aero Medical Lab., Wright Air Development Center, Wright-Patterson AFB, Ohio [77]

PETERS, W. and A. A. WENBORNE (1936) The time pattern of voluntary movements, *Brit. J. Psychol.,* 26, 388 [251]

PETT, L. B. and G. F. OGILIVE (1957) The report on Canadian average weights, heights and skinfolds, *Canadian Bulletin on Nutrition,* Vol. 5, No. 1, p. 1 [510, 511, 514, 515]

POLLACK, I. (1952) Comfortable listening levels for pure tones in quiet and noise, *J. Acoust. Soc. Am.,* 24, 158 [152, 153]

POLLACK, I. (1953) The information of elementary auditory displays, *J. Acoust. Soc. Am.,* 25, 745 [160]

POLLACK, I. and L. FICKS (1954) Information of elementary multidimensional auditory displays, *J. Acoust. Soc. Am.,* 26, 155 [160]

POULTON, E. C. (1952) Perceptual anticipation in tracking with two-pointer and one-pointer displays, *Brit. J. Psychol.,* 43, 222 [219]

PROVINS, K. A. (1953) A study of some factors affecting speed of cranking, Rept. No. 53/755, Royal Naval Personnel Research Committee, Medical Research Council, London, England [264, 310]

PROVINS, K. A. (1955) Maximum forces exerted about the elbow and shoulder joints on each side separately and simultaneously, *J. Appl. Physiol.,* 7, 390 [263]

PROVINS, K. A. and N. SALTER (1955) Maximum torque exerted about the elbow joint, *J. Appl. Physiol.,* 7, 393 [308]

PUGH, L. G. C. E. and M. WARD (1953) Physiology and medicine, in "The Ascent of Everest" (J. Hunt, Hodder & Stoughton, London) [558]

RAMSEY, C. G. and H. R. SLEEPER (1956) "Architectural Graphic Standards for Architects, Engineers, Decorators, Builders, and Draftsmen" (John Wiley & Sons, Inc., New York) [355]

RANDALL, F. E. (1947) Survey of body size of Army personnel, male and female: IV. Body dimension of Army females—methodology and general considerations, Rept. No. 123, Environmental Protection Branch, U. S. Army Quartermaster Research and Development Center, Natick, Mass. [509, 512]

RANDALL, F. E. and E. H. MUNRO (1949) Reference anthropometry of Army women, Rept. No. 159, Environmental Protection Branch, U. S. Army Quartermaster Research and Development Center, Natick, Mass. [509, 512, 516, 517, 522, 537–542]

RANDALL, F. E., et al. (1946) Human body size in military aircraft and personal equipment, AF-TR-5501, Aero Medical Lab., Wright Air Development Center, Wright-Patterson AFB, Ohio [315, 495, 509–512, 516–519, 522, 523, 526–530, 533–542]

RANDALL, F. E., et al. (1951) Anthropometry of the foot, Rept. No. 172, Environmental Protection Branch, U. S. Army Quartermaster Research and Development Center, Natick, Mass. [541]

REED, J. D. (1949) Factors influencing rotary performance, J. Psychol., 28, 65 [264, 274]

REID, L. S. and J. G. HOLLAND (1954) The influence of stimulus similarity and stimulus rate: The third of a series of reports on experimental analysis of complex task performance, WADC-TR-54-146, Aero Medical Lab., Wright Air Development Center, Wright-Patterson AFB, Ohio [230]

RIESZ, R. R. (1928) Differential intensity sensitivity of the ear for pure tones, Phys. Rev., 31, 867 [151, 156]

ROBERTS, L. B., et al. (1945) Size increase of men wearing various clothing combinations, Project No. 9, File No. 741-3, U. S. Army Medical Research Lab., Fort Knox, Ky. [507]

ROBINSON, D. W. and R. S. DADSON (1957) Threshold of hearing and equal-loudness relations for pure tones and the loudness function, J. Acoust. Soc. Am., 29, 1284 [143]

ROCKWAY, M. R. (1954) The effect of variations in control-display ratio and exponential time delay on tracking performance, WADC-TR-54-618, Aero Medical Lab., Wright Air Development Center, Wright-Patterson AFB, Ohio [240, 245, 251]

ROEBUCK, J. A. (1957) Anthropometry in aircraft engineering design, J. Aviation Med., 28, 41 [494]

ROSENBLITH, W. A. and K. N. STEVENS (1953) Noise and man, Vol. II of Handbook of acoustic noise control, WADC-TR-52-204, Aero Medical Lab., Wright Air Development Center, Wright-Patterson AFB, Ohio [151, 474, 477]

ROSS, D. M. (1956) The use of mechanical principles in the evaluation of a human functional dimension, Unpublished Ph.D. thesis, School of Public Health, Univ. of Pittsburgh, Pittsburgh, Pa. [310]

ROSSEN, R., et al. (1943) Acute arrest of cerebral circulation in man, *Arch. Neurol. Psychiat.*, 50, 510 [452]

RUFF, S. and H. STRUGHOLD (1942) "Compendium of Aviation Medicine" (National Research Council, Washington, D. C.) [558]

SABEH, R., et al. (1958) Shape coding of aircraft instrument zone markings, WADC-TN-57-260, Aero Medical Lab., Wright Air Development Center, Wright-Patterson AFB, Ohio [104]

SALTER, N. and H. D. DARCUS (1952) The effect of the degree of elbow flexion on the maximum torques developed in pronation and supination of the right hand, *J. Anat.*, 86, 197 [558]

SCARPELLI, E. M. (1958) Physiological training, Gunter Branch, School of Aviation Medicine, Brooks AFB, Texas [418]

SCHAEFER, K. E., et al. (1960) Respiratory adaptation to chronic CO_2 exposure, *Federation Proc.*, 19, 381 [437]

SCHAEFER, K. E. (1961) A concept of triple tolerance limits based on chronic carbon dioxide toxicity studies, *Aerospace Med.*, 32, 197 [437]

SCHAFER, T. H., et al. (1950) The frequency selectivity of the ear as determined by masking experiments, *J. Acoust. Soc. Am.*, 22, 490 [149]

SCHOCHRIN, W. A. (1935) Die Muskelkraft der Beuger und Strecker des Unterschenkels, *Arbeitsphysiologie*, 8, 251 [558]

SEAMANS, R. C. and H. W. PICKFORD (1956) Development of the airborne systems, *RCA Eng.*, 2, 37 [39]

SEARLE, L. V. (1948) Psychological studies of tracking behavior: I. Rate and time characteristics of simple corrective movements, Rept. R-3248, Naval Research Lab., Washington, D. C. [225]

SEARLE, L. V. (1951) Psychological studies of tracking behavior: IV. The intermittency hypothesis as a basis for predicting optimum aided-tracking time constants, Rept. No. 3872, Naval Research Lab., Washington, D. C. [241]

SEARLE, L. V. and F. V. TAYLOR (1948) Studies of tracking behavior: I. Rate and time characteristics of simple corrective movements, *J. Exp. Psychol.*, 38, 615 [272]

SENDERS, J. W. (1953) The influence of surround on tracking performance: I. Tracking on combined pursuit and compensatory one-dimensional tasks with and without a structured surround, WADC-TR-52-229, Aero Medical Lab., Wright Air Development Center, Wright-Patterson AFB, Ohio [220]

SENDERS, J. W. (1955) Tracking with intermittently illuminated displays, WADC-TR-55-378, Aero Medical Lab., Wright Air Development Center, Wright-Patterson AFB, Ohio [222]

SENDERS, J. W. and J. V. BRADLEY (1956) Effect of backlash on manual control of pitch on a simulated aircraft, WADC-TR-56-107, Aero Medical Lab., Wright Air Development Center, Wright-Patterson AFB, Ohio [240, 245]

SENDERS, J. W. and M. CRUZEN (1952) Tracking performance on combined compensatory and pursuit tasks, WADC-TR-52-39, Aero Medical Lab., Wright Air Development Center, Wright-Patterson AFB, Ohio [219]

SHOWER, E. G. and R. BIDDULPH (1931) Differential pitch sensitivity of the ear, *J. Acoust. Soc. Am.,* 3, 275 [153–155]

SIEKER, H. O. (1952) Devices for protection against negative acceleration: I. Centrifuge studies, WADC-TR-52-87, Aero Medical Lab., Wright Air Development Center, Wright-Patterson AFB, Ohio [465]

SIMONSON, E. (1947) Physical fitness and work capacity of older men, *Geriatrics,* 2, 110 [557]

SINELNIKOFF, E. and M. GRIGOROWITSCH (1931) Die Beweglikeit der Gelenke als sekundäres geschlechtliches und konstitutionelles Merkmal, *Z. Konstitutionslehre,* 15, 679 [552]

SLATER-HAMMEL, A. T. and J. S. BROWN (1947) Discrete movements in the horizontal plane as a function of their length and direction, Rept. No. 57-2-2, U. S. Naval Training Devices Center, Port Washington, N. Y. [225]

SLECHTA, R. F., et al. (1957) Comparative evaluation of aircraft seating accommodation, WADC-TR-57-136, Aero Medical Lab., Wright Air Development Center, Wright-Patterson AFB, Ohio [315]

SLEIGHT, R. B. (1952) The relative discriminability of several geometric forms, *J. Exp. Psychol.,* 43, 324 [85]

SLIVINSKE, A. J. (1959) Vibratory communication: Feasibility and application, Final Rept. on Contr. Nonr-656(17), Penn. State Univ., State College, Pa. [27]

SLOAN, L. L. (1947) Rate of dark adaptation and regional threshold gradient of the dark-adapted eye: Physiologic and clinical studies, *Am. J. Ophthalmol.,* 30, 705 [65]

SMITH, G. M. (1946) The effect of prolonged mild anoxia on speech intelligibility, *J. Appl. Psychol.,* 30, 255 [421]

SMITH, G. M. and C. P. SEITZ (1946) Speech intelligibility under various degrees of anoxia, *J. Appl. Psychol.*, 30, 182 [421]

SMYTH, C. J., et al. (1959) Rheumatism and arthritis, *Ann. Internal Med.*, 50, 366 [552]

SNOW, W. B. (1953) Basic principles of stereophonic sound, *J. Soc. Motion Picture and Television Engrs.*, 61, 567 [140]

SAE (1950) Ride and vibration data, Special Pub. No. 6, Society of Automotive Engineers, New York, N. Y. [466]

SPECTOR, W. S., ed. (1956) Handbook of biological data, WADC-TR-56-273, Aero Medical Lab., Wright Air Development Center, Wright-Patterson AFB, Ohio [434]

SPIETH, W. (1956) Annoyance threshold judgments of bands of noise, *J. Acoust. Soc. Am.*, 28, 872 [475]

SPIETH, W., et al. (1954) Cues that aid listening to one of two simultaneous voice messages, Rept. No. 446, U. S. Navy Electronics Lab., San Diego, Calif. [207]

STAPP, J. P. (1949) Human exposures to linear deceleration: I. Preliminary survey of aft-facing seated position, AF-TR-5915, Aero Medical Lab., Wright Air Development Center, Wright-Patterson AFB, Ohio [449]

STAPP, J. P. (1951) Human exposures to linear deceleration: II. The forward-facing position and the development of a crash harness, AF-TR-5915, Aero Medical Lab., Wright Air Development Center, Wright-Patterson AFB, Ohio [449]

STAPP, J. P. (1955a) Effects of mechanical force on living tissues: I. Abrupt deceleration and windblast, *J. Aviation Med.*, 26, 268 [449, 450]

STAPP, J. P. (1955b) Tolerance to abrupt deceleration, in "Collected Papers on Aviation Medicine," AGARDograph No. 6 (Butterworths Scientific Publications, London) [449, 450]

STAPP, J. P. (1957) Human tolerance to deceleration, *Am. J. Surgery*, 93, 734 [452]

STAUFFER, F. R. (1951) Further evidence of fluid translocation during varied acceleration stresses: Gross pathological findings and weight changes in specific tissues, Dept. of Aviation Medicine, Univ. of Southern Calif., Los Angeles, Calif. [450]

STAUFFER, F. R. (1953) Acceleration problems of naval air training: I. Normal variations in tolerance to positive radial acceleration, *J. Aviation Med.*, 24, 167 [461]

STEEDMAN, W. C. and C. A. BAKER (1960) Target size and visual recognition, *Human Factors,* Vol. 2, No. 3, p. 120 [67, 115]

STEVENS, S. S. (1955) The measurement of loudness, *J. Acoust. Soc. Am.,* 27, 815 [142]

STEVENS, S. S. and H. DAVIS (1938) "Hearing, Its Psychology and Physiology" (John Wiley & Sons, Inc., New York) [157]

STEVENS, S. S. and J. VOLKMANN (1940) The relation of pitch to frequency: A revised scale, *Am. J. Psychol.,* 53, 329 [143]

STEVENS, S. S., et al. (1947) Methods of measuring speech spectra, *J. Acoust. Soc. Am.,* 19, 771 [164]

STOLL, A. M. (1956) Human tolerance to positive g as determined by the physiological end points, *J. Aviation Med.,* 27, 356 [462]

STOUDT, H. W., et al. (1960) Heights and weights of white Americans, *Human Biol.,* 32, 331 [505]

STRUGHOLD, H. (1949) The human time factor in flight, *J. Aviation Med.,* 20, 300 [227]

STUMP, N. E. (1953) Manipulability of rotary controls as a function of knob diameter and control orientation, WCRD-TN-53-12, Aero Medical Lab., Wright Air Development Center, Wright-Patterson AFB, Ohio [272]

SUTRO, P. J. and G. H. KYDD (1955) Human visual capacities as a basis for the safer design of vehicles, in annual report to the Armed Forces Epidemiological Board from the Commission on Accidental Trauma, Office of the Surgeon General, Dept. of the Army, Washington, D. C. [501]

SYSTEMS RESEARCH LAB. (1945) Time and motion analysis of combat information centers: CL-106 class light cruiser, Rept. No. 2, Contr. OEMsr-658, Harvard Univ., Cambridge, Mass. [8]

TAYLOR, C. L. (1951) Environmental biotechnology, Dept. of Engineering, Univ. of Calif., Los Angeles, Calif. [419, 423, 425, 427, 438]

TAYLOR, C. L. (1954) The biomechanics of the normal and of the amputated upper extremity, in "Human Limbs and Their Substitute" (P. E. Klopsteg and P. D. Wilson, eds., McGraw-Hill Book Co., Inc., New York) [568]

TAYLOR, F. V. and H. P. BIRMINGHAM (1948) Psychological studies of tracking behavior: II. A study of the acceleration pattern of quick manual corrective responses, Rept. R-3249, Naval Research Lab., Washington, D. C. [225]

TEICHNER, W. H. (1954) Recent studies of simple reaction time, *Psychol. Bull.,* 51, 128 [228, 229, 233]

TEICHNER, W. H. (1957) Manual dexterity in the cold, *J. Appl. Physiol.,* 11, 333 [435]

TEICHNER, W. H. (1958) Reaction time in the cold, *J. Appl. Psychol.,* 42, 54 [435]

TEICHNER, W. H. (1959) Environmental factors affecting human performance, in "Human Engineering Concepts and Theory" (P. M. Fitts, ed., Univ. of Mich. Press, Ann Arbor) [432, 435]

THORNDIKE, E. L. and I. LORGE (1944) "Teacher's Word Book of 30,000 Words" (Teachers College, Columbia Univ., New York) [216]

THORNDIKE, R. L. (1949) "Personnel Selection" (John Wiley & Sons, Inc., New York) [49, 121]

TONNDORF, J. (1953) Combined effect of noise and hypoxia upon the auditory threshold, Rept. No. 1, Proj. 21-1203-0001, U. S. Air Force School of Aviation Medicine, Randolph AFB, Texas [421]

TURNBULL, W. W. (1944) Pitch discrimination as a function of tonal duration, *J. Exp. Psychol.,* 34, 302 [158]

TUTTLE, W. W., et al. (1950) Relation of maximum grip strength to grip strength endurance, *J. Appl. Physiol.,* 2, 663 [568]

TYROLER, H. A. (1958) Preliminary cross-sectional documentation of physical measurements of male population at risk by geographic location and age, Health Research Foundation, Asheville, N. C. [510, 515]

U. S. AIR FORCE (1953a) Physiology of flight, AFM-160-30, Dept. of the Air Force, Washington, D. C. [420]

U. S. AIR FORCE (1953b) B-52 airplane mock-up human factors study, WCRD-TN-53-130, Aero Medical Lab., Wright Air Development Center, Wright-Patterson AFB, Ohio [507]

U. S. ARMY (1946) Unpublished data, Environmental Protection Branch, U. S. Army Quartermaster Research and Development Center, Natick, Mass. [509, 511, 513, 522, 523, 529, 530, 533, 535, 537, 538, 541]

U. S. ARMY (1954) Cartridge actuated device for aircraft use, Frankford Arsenal, Philadelphia, Pa. [450]

U. S. MARINE CORPS (1949) Unpublished data, U. S. Marine Corps Research Lab., Marine Clothing Depot, Philadelphia, Pa. [509, 513]

U. S. NAVY (1949a) Weight distribution of recruits, *Statistics of Navy Medicine,* Vol. 5, No. 6, p. 2 [513]

U. S. NAVY (1949b) Height distribution of recruits, *Statistics of Navy Medicine,* Vol. 5, No. 7, p. 2 [509]

U. S. NAVY (1955) Unpublished data, U. S. Naval School of Aviation Medicine, NAS, Pensacola, Fla. [509, 511, 513, 522, 530, 533]

U. S. NAVY (1957) Unpublished data, U. S. Naval Medical Research Lab., U. S. Navy Submarine Base, New London, Conn. [509, 513]

U. S. NAVY (1959) Anthropometric data, *U. S. Navy Med. News Letter,* Vol. 33, No. 4, p. 33 [509, 511, 513, 533]

VINCE, M. A. (1948) The intermittency of control movements and the psychological refractory period, *Brit. J. Psychol.,* 38, 149 [272]

VOSS, J. F. (1955) Effect of target brightness and target speed upon tracking proficiency, *J. Exp. Psychol.,* 49, 237 [222]

WARES, G. W. (1957) Atmospheric shells, in "Handbook of Geophysics for Air Force Designers" (Geophysics Research Directorate, Air Force Cambridge Research Center, Bedford, Mass.) [414]

WARRICK, M. J. (1947) Direction of movement in the use of control knobs to position visual indicators, in "Psychological Research on Equipment Design" (P. M. Fitts, ed., U. S. Government Printing Office, Washington, D. C.) [255]

WARRICK, M. J. (1949) Effect of transmission-type control lags on tracking accuracy, AF-TR-5916, Aero Medical Lab., Wright Air Development Center, Wright-Patterson AFB, Ohio [245]

WATHEN-DUNN, W. and D. W. LIPKE (1958) On the power gained by clipping speech in the audio band, *J. Acoust. Soc. Am.,* 30, 36 [199]

WATTS, D. T., et al. (1947) Human tolerance to accelerations applied from seat to head during ejection seat tests, Rept. TED-NAM-2560-5, Naval Materiel Center, Philadelphia, Pa. [450]

WEBSTER, A. P. (1953) High-altitude, high-velocity flying with reference to the human factors: IV. Opening shock of parachute descents, *J. Aviation Med.,* 24, 189 [452]

WEGEL, R. L. and C. E. LANE (1924) The auditory masking of one pure tone by another and its probable relation to the dynamics of the inner ear, *Phys. Rev.,* 23, 266 [146]

WEINER, F. W. and A. S. FILLER (1945) The response of certain earphones on the ear and on closed couplers, Rept. PNR-2, Harvard Psycho-Acoustic Lab., Harvard Univ., Cambridge, Mass. [202]

WEISS, H. S., et al. (1954) The physiology of simple tumbling: II. Human studies, WADC-TR-53-139, Aero Medical Lab., Wright Air Development Center, Wright-Patterson AFB, Ohio [457]

WELFORD, A. T. (1952) The "psychological refractory period" and the timing of high-speed performance—a review and a theory, Brit. J. Psychol., 43, 2 [231]

WHITE, C. B., et al. (1952) Review of escape hatch sizes for bailout and ditching, WCRD-TN-52-81, Aero Medical Lab., Wright Air Development Center, Wright-Patterson AFB, Ohio [336]

WHITE, W. J. (1958) Acceleration and vision, WADC-TR-58-333, Aero Medical Lab., Wright Air Development Center, Wright-Patterson AFB, Ohio [459]

WHITE, W. J. and W. R. JORVE (1956) The effects of gravitational stress upon visual acuity, WADC-TR-56-247, Aero Medical Lab., Wright Air Development Center, Wright-Patterson AFB, Ohio [460]

WHITE, W. J. and M. B. RILEY (1956) The effect of positive acceleration on the relation between illumination and dial reading, in "Symposium on Air Force Human Engineering, Personnel, and Training Research" (G. Finch and F. Cameron, eds., National Research Council, Washington, D. C.) [460]

WHITNEY, R. J. (1958) The strength of the lifting action in man, Ergonomics, 1, 101 [373]

WILLIAMS, A. C., et al. (1960) Operator performance in strike reconnaissance, WADD-TN-60-521, Aero Medical Lab., Wright Air Development Center, Wright-Patterson AFB, Ohio [68]

WILLIAMS, S. B. (1949) Visibility on radar scopes, in "Human Factors in Undersea Warfare" (D. B. Lindsley, ed., National Research Council, Washington, D. C.) [114]

WOODSON, W. E. (1954) "Human Engineering Guide for Equipment Designers" (Univ. of Calif. Press, Berkeley, Calif.) [71, 73, 74, 264, 299]

WOODWORTH, R. S. and H. SCHLOSBERG (1954) "Experimental Psychology" (Henry Holt & Co., Inc., New York) [228–230, 233]

YAGLOU, C. P., et al. (1936) How much outside air is necessary for ventilation?, Heating and Ventilating, Vol. 33, No. 3, p. 31 [444]

YOUNG, M. L. (1951) Psychological studies of tracking behavior: III. The characteristics of quick manual corrective movements made in response to step-function velocity inputs, Rept. No. 3850, Naval Research Lab., Washington, D. C. [225, 226]

ZIEGENRUECKER, G. H. and E. B. MAGID (1959) Short time human tolerance to sinusoidal vibrations, WADC-TR-59-391, Aero Medical Lab., Wright Air Development Center, Wright-Patterson AFB, Ohio [471]

ZWISLOCKI, J. (1957) Ear protectors, in "Handbook of Noise Control" (C. M. Harris, ed., McGraw-Hill Book Co., Inc., New York) [478]

SUBJECT INDEX

Acceleration, effects of, 445–465
  workplace dimensions, 291
Access, for maintainability, 385–388
Accessibility, designing for, 396
Accident, control activation, 260, 261
Accounting, RCA Bizmac Electronic, 37
Accuracy, decoding, 89, 90
Activity analysis, of system, 8
Acuity, visual, factors affecting, 57–62
Adaptation, and cathode-ray tube visibility, 111–113
  to heat, 432
  physiological, 412
Age, and body dimension, 504
  and joint movement, 552
Aided tracking, machine transfer functions, 239–241
  value of, 220
Aiding, constant in tracking, 240
  vs. quickening, 245
Air conditioning, comfort charts, 432
Air route traffic control system, flow analysis of, 8, 9
Airspeed, auditory representation of, 134
Aircraft, cabin pressure, 427
Aisle, in auditorium, 356

Aisle, design of, 330
  space and compartment layout, 327
  space for maintenance, 345
Alarm, characteristics of, 131
  and warning devices, 129–132
Alcohol, effects of, 441
Aldehydes, as toxins, 441
Alphabet, word spelling, 215, 216
Altitude, auditory representation of, 134
  effects of, 419–427
  protection against, 424
  speech communication at, 208, 209
Amplifiers, selection and use, 193–199
Angle, of viewing displays, 52
Angular acceleration, 458
Annoyance from noise, 474
Antenna search pattern check, 404
Anthropology, and equipment design, 485–503
Anthropometry, 485–569
Anti-aircraft Defense System, functional analysis of, 5
Anticipation, and human time lag, 232
Anxiety in system design, 31
Arm reach, dimensions, 544–550
Army-Navy Aeronautical Specification AN-C, 56, 84

Armrest, design, 315
Arrangement, of groups of men, 358–366
Articulation index, for clipped speech, 199
  computation of, 174–177
Association, value of codes, 88
Atmosphere, as environment, 414
  and human performance, 414–445
  physical characteristics of, 414
  U. S. Standard, 418
Attention, and fatigue in system design, 31
  selective, to signals, 35
  signals to get, 91, 92
Audibility, Normal Threshold of, 141
Audition, information presentation, 123–160
Auditorium, design of, 353–358
Auditory presentation, use of, 125–138
  visual presentation compared, 125
Automatic Annunciator, altitude indicator, 134
Automatic gain control, in speech communication, 193, 194
Average man, fallacy of, 494

Backrest, design, 315
Balcony, design of, 358

607

Barometric pressure, pain, 424

Bearing, indication on radar displays, 119, 120

information in sonar, 128, 129

Bells, as warning devices, 130

Binaural presentation, of auditory signals, 139, 140

Biophysical systems, considerations of, 412–414

Bit, human channel capacity, 23

Body, build and joint movement, 552

dimensions, 504–550

functions, altitude effects, 419

height standing, 508

position and dimension, 505

position and joint movement, 552

restraint for acceleration, 463

support against acceleration, 451

temperature and humidity, 428–431

Bolts, mounting, maintenance, 377

Bone conduction, as auditory presentation, 140

Boredom, in system design, 31

Breadth, head, 517

Brightness, cathode-ray tube, 110, 111

coding of information, 86, 87

contrast and visual acuity, 59

units, conversion factors for, 59

of warning devices, 92

Broad-band-blue lighting system, 75

Buttock, to foot length, 531

Buttock, to knee length, 532

to popliteal length, 532

depth, 534

Cable, for maintainability, 382

Carbon dioxide, effects of, 436

Carbon monoxide, effects of, 437, 439

Carbon tetrachloride, as toxin, 442

Case, unit for maintenance, 380

Cathode-ray tube, 109–120

visibility, design factors in, 113, 114

Catwalks, design of, 330

Caution signals, 93

Ceilings, height of, 344

Cellosolves, 442

Channel capacities, human, 23–25

Chart, lighting, recommendations for, 79

Check list, decals and labels, 121, 122

Check reading, display, 52, 53

Chest, depth and breadth, 524

Clearance, around seat, 316

Clothing, and human body measurements, 487

Code (See also Coding)

compatibility of, 88

compound, 90

scaling quantitative, 88

selection, 87–90

Coding, of auditory displays, 160

of controls, 257–260

of indicators, 108, 109

mode of operation, 259

visual, 81–90

Cold, biological response to, 429

Cold stress, 433–436

Color, blindness and color coding, 84

(See also Color coding)

Color, for coding, 83

coding of indicators, 104

of lighting and visual acuity, 62, 63

surface and lights, detecting, 66

Color coding, 81–84

of controls, 260

of indicators, 109

for maintenance, 379

Combat Information Center, aircraft, arrangement, 362

flow analysis of, 8–11

Comfort, headsets, 204, 205

Communication, and compartment layout, 329

component selection and application, 191–206

face to face, 177–179

factors affecting, 210–216

in noise, criteria, 186–188

speech, 161–216

systems, intelligibility of, 174–177

touch used in, 26, 27

Compartment layout, 324–358

Compatibility, displays and controls, 52

Compensatory tracking and pursuit tracking, 218, 219

Compression, acoustic and dynamic range, 154

Computer, simulation of system, 41

Connector, for maintainability, 383

Consciousness, time at altitude, 426

Contaminants, effects of, 436–445

Contour, of panel, 317

Control, characteristics of, 17

design of, 247–280

-display associations, 300–303

grouped with display, 299

important factors in design, 250–261

Control, layout, 307–313
location of, 298–303,
308–312
for maintenance, 393, 394
man as controller, 36
resistance, 256, 257
selection of, 247–250
spacing between, 312
Control Tower Operator, job
analysis of, 12
Coordination, altitude effect,
421
Correlation, tables for anthropometric data, 495
Corridors, design of, 330
Course, LF/MF radio range,
133, 134
Cover, unit for maintenance,
380
Crank, design of, 274–276
Crawling, body dimensions
while, 543
Crew, size and compartment
layout, 325
Critical design requirements,
of system, 12, 13
Cross-polarization, lighting
system, 75
Cursor, range, radar display,
117

Damage-risk criteria, for
sound exposure, 151,
152
speech communication,
186
Dark adaptation, 77, 78
Data processing, human vs.
machine, 35, 36
room, arrangement of, 360
Dead man switch, as moni-
tor, 37
Decal, check lists and labels,
121, 122
Decision analysis, of system,
6, 7
Decision time, and choices,
227, 228
Depth, body, 514
Derivative, in aided tracking,
241

Derivative, first, combining
displays of, 54
Design, anthropometry, 486
counterbalanced in system
evaluation, 42
schedule for maintainability, 369–371
Design recommendations
(See specific topics)
Detectability (See also Detection)
increasing binaural, 140
and tonal duration, 157,
158
Detection, of colored targets,
65, 66
of frequency changes, 155,
156
sonar signal, 127–129
target on nonuniform
backgrounds, 66
target, CRT, and bright-
ness, 112, 113
visual, identification and
estimation, 56–70
Development, scheduling of,
3
Dial, layout, 302–305
long-scale indicators, 97
Discomfort, from noise, 474
Discrimination, human ability, 23–26
human capabilities, 34, 35
Display, compensatory, 218
complex, identifying tar-
gets, 67, 68
conditions of use, 52
control associations, 300–
303
control-display relation-
ships, 250–256
grouped with controls, 299
grouping, 305, 306
integration of, 54–56
layout, 303–307
location of, 298–303
location and shared dis-
play, 318
for maintenance, 391–393
method of use, 52, 53
new auditory, 134–137

Display, in pictogram, 4
principles of, 51–56
purpose of, 53
pursuit or compensatory,
219–221
quickened, 242
simultaneous auditory and
visual, 27
size, CRT, 115
symbolic vs. pictorial, 53
three-coordinate displays,
120
view of, and compartment
layout, 329
Distortion, in peak clipping,
196
Distribution, cumulative, nature of, 21, 22
Gaussian, of error, 20–23
Doorways, design of, 334–
338
Doppler, effect in sonar, 129
Dot, coding of information,
86
Duplication, verification by,
37
Duration, tonal, and detectability, 157, 158
Dynamic range, and volume
control, 153, 154

Ear, anatomy of, 124
muffs for protection, 480
protection, face-to-face
communication, 177
protective devices, 477
speech communication,
188–190
Earphone sockets, comfort
and performance, 203–
206
Earplugs, for protection, 478
Echo, -ranging sonar, 128–
129
Effective Temperature Index,
432
Elbow, to elbow breadth, 528
to hand length, 528
height, 525–528
Electronics laboratory, arrangement of, 359

Elevators, design of, 343, 344

Emotional effects, of altitude, 422

Environment, 445–484
and human time lag, 236
of man-machine system, 5
and muscle strength, 558
in system evaluation, 48

Equipment characteristics, 13–20
design for body size, 499–503
evaluation for body size, 497–499
maintenance space, 346–348
and human body measurement, 487
size and compartment layout, 326, 327

Error, human, 20
measurement of, 22, 23

Escalators, design of, 343, 344

Estimation, size, distance and speed, 69, 70
visual, detection and identification, 56–70

Evaluation, of system, 39–50
system, 3

Exit, in auditorium, 356

Eye height, standing and sitting, 518

Fasteners, mounting, maintenance, 377

Fatigue, in system design, 31

Fault, human location of, 39

Federal Specification TT-C-595, 84

Feedback, and learning rate, 29
prevention in loudspeakers, 201
to talker, 216

Filtering, and audibility in noise, 148–150

Flag, signals, 93

Flash-rate, coding of information, 87

Flight deck operations, tactile communications in, 27

Flow analysis, of system, 8–11

Flow diagram, grouping, 305
for maintenance, 406

Flybar, auditory display, 135

Foot (See also Foot control)
length and breadth, 542
pushbutton controls, 268

Foot control, design recommendations, 262–265
layout, 308
location of, 310–312

Footrest, design, 315

Force, and control design, 249

Frequency, detection of changes, 155, 156
intelligibility contribution, 174
representation of speech, 162–164
response of headsets, 202
in sonar use, 128

Friction, resistance of control, 257

Functional analysis, of system, 5

Gas, evolved, syndrome, 424
masks, filtering materials, 444

Glare, reduction of, 71, 72

Glycols, as toxins, 442

Graduation, of scales, 98–100

Graph, tables and scales, 122

Group, arrangement of, 358–366
men and machines, 321–366

Habituation, environmental effects, 412
to heat, 432

Hand, one vs. two in control design, 263
measurements, 536–538

Hand control, design recommendation, 262–265
layout, 307, 308
location of, 309, 310

Hand grip, design of, 264

Handle, for maintainability, 381

Handwheel, design of, 276–280

Hardness, seat, 315

Hatch, design of, 334–338

Headset, selection and use, 202–206

Hearing (See Auditory presentation)

Hearing damage risk, prediction, 475

Hearing loss, from noise, 473

Heat, biological response to, 430
Stress Index, 431

Height, sitting, 510
and buttock popliteal, 498
standing, 508
and knee, 496, 497
and weight, 505
in workplace design, 18

Helmet, for noise protection, 483

Heterodyne clipping, in speech communication, 196–198

Hip breadth, 531

Human-body size, and compartment layout, 325

Human dynamics, 223–237

Human time lag, 226–235

Humidity, effects of, 428–436

Hydrocarbons, as toxins, 442

Hydrophone, sonar use, 127

Hypoxia, effects of, 420–423

Identification, of indicators, 108, 109
layout for, 305
range mark, radar display, 117

Identification, visual, detection and estimation, 56–70
Illumination, ambient, in radar operation, 15
  of displays, 52
  in scale design, 101, 102
  and visual acuity, 58
  workplace, 70–81
Indicator, identification, 108, 109
  lighting of, 76–81
  mechanical, 95–109
Information, and anxiety, 31
  partial, ability to interpret, 35
  visual presentation of, 51–126
Inputs, ramp, human responses to, 225, 226
  sine-wave, human responses to, 225, 226
  step, human responses to, 224, 225
Installation, and maintainability, 395–397
Intellectual functions, altitude effects, 422
Intelligibility, criteria for speech communication, 186
  predicting, 173–180
  in speech communication, 168–180
  testing, 169–180
Intensity, level of speech, 163
  of speech sounds, 166
  stimulus, for human senses, 25
Intermittency, of display information, 222, 223
Interpolation, range mark, radar display, 116, 117
  of scales, 100, 101
Interval, signal, and reaction time, 231

Job analysis and description in system, 11, 12

Joints, range of movement, 551
Just noticeable difference, of frequency, 155, 156

Ketones, as toxins, 44
Knee, height and breadth, 539
Kneeling, body dimensions while, 543
Knobs, design and use, 271–274
Knuckle height, 534

Label (See also Labeling) decals and check lists, 121
Labeling, controls, of indicators, 108, 109
  for maintenance, 379
  test points for maintainability, 389
Ladders, design of, 339–341
Lag, effects of, 245
  human time, 226–235
Language, factor in communication system, 211, 212
Layout, of workplaces, 281–320
Learning, human, in system design, 28, 29
Length, head, 516
Letter, coding of information, 84, 85
  style in scale design, 102, 103
Lever, design of, 274–276
Light (See also Lighting) colored, for coding, 83
  distribution on workplace, 70–73
Lighting, edge, of indicators, 80
  flood, of indicators, 80
  indirect, of indicators, 80
  rear, of indicators, 80, 81
Line, coding of information, 86

Linear acceleration, 447–454
Link analysis, description of, 321–324
Listening (See also Auditory presentation; Hearing) multichannel, 207
  sonar, 127, 128
Loading, of human senses, 23
Location, shared controls and displays, 318
Loudness, reduction and filtering, 149, 150
  of sounds, 139–144
Loudspeakers, selection and use, 200, 201

Machine, dynamics, 237–245
  vs. human capabilities, 32–37
Magnification aids, design and use, 68, 69
Maintenance, design for, 367–410
  space, layout of, 345–348
Man, height of, 18
  vs. machine capabilities, 32–37
  as monitor of automatic system, 38, 39
  as system component, 32, 33
  in system design, 20–38
  variations in, 20–23
Man-Machine dynamics, 217–248
Manual (See also Manual area) maintenance, 409
Manual area, standing workplace dimension, 296
  workplace dimensions, 287–291
Mark, range, separation, 116, 117
Masking, and noise filtering, 148, 149
  of sound by noise, 144–148
Masks, communication through, 209, 210

Mean, of distribution, 21
Measurement, human body, 486–569
of performance, in system evaluation, 48–50
Mechanical environment, 445–484
Mercury-minus-red, lighting system, 76
Message, size in communication, 211
Methyl bromide, 443
Microphones, selection and use, 191–193
Minimum Audible Field, pure-tone threshold, 141
Minimum Audible Pressure, pure-tone threshold, 141
Mission, system, and requirements, 4
Mock up, bench, for maintenance, 401
simulation of system, 41
Monitor, of man, dead man switch and television distribution network, 37
Morse code, rate of receiving, 27
Motion, of moving element indicators, 105–107
Motivation, and human time lag, 233
and system design, 29–32
in system evaluation, 48
Motor performance, in acceleration, 460
Movement, range of, 552–556
range of body members, 551
speed and control design, 263
Multichannel listening, design recommendation, 207
Muscle, strength, 556–570

Navigator, activities of, on mission, 8
Navy, communications and control center, 324

Nitrogen dioxide, as toxin, 443
Noise, attenuation, headsets, 202–204
bands of, and detection, 156, 157
criteria for speech communication, 186–188
general effects, 473–484
intermittent, and speech communication, 185
as masker of sound, 144–148
narrow-band, AI for, 184, 185
shields, microphone, 190
and signal relationships, 144
in speech communication, 179–190
Nonsense syllable, lists for intelligibility tests, 170
Number, coding of information, 84
Numbness Index, 435
Numeral, style in scale design, 102, 103

Occupation, and body dimension, 504
and joint movement, 552
and muscle strength, 558
Octave-band, method for articulation index, 176, 177
spectrum and speech representation, 163
Odors, sensitivity to, 34
Office, noise criteria for, 188
On-off control, 255, 256
Operator, arrangement of, 362–366
controls in man-machine system, 17
performance, and machine dynamics, 244
radar search, and illumination, 15
seated, foot control location, 310

Operator, seated and workplace dimensions, 284–294
sharing displays and controls, 318
Optimization, environmental conditions, 413
Output, complexity and pursuit or compensatory tracking, 219, 220
Overloading, man-machine system, 11
Oxygen deficiency, effects of, 420–423
Ozone, in atmosphere, 416

Pacing, and human reaction time, 234
Pain, barometric pressure, 424
Panel, design, 316–318
of integrated displays, 56
lighting of, 76–81
Pattern, discrimination, human, 34, 35
Peak clipping, of auditory signals, 154
in speech communication, 195–200
Pedal (See also Pedal areas) design of, 276–280
Pedal areas, standing workplace dimensions, 297
workplace dimensions, 291–294
Percentile, definition, 21, 22
human body measurements, 493–495
Perception, of sound signals, 138–144
Performance, in acceleration, 459–461
environmental effects on, 411–484
measurement in system evaluation, 48–50
in noise, 474
system, limiting factors, 3
Personnel, maintenance capability, 373

Personnel, transient in compartment, 325
Personal Protective Equipment, 444
Phonetic, symbols, 212
    word list, for intelligibility testing, 171
Pictogram, system, 4
Pictorial, display, use of, 53
    indicators, design of, 108
Pitch, and loudness, 142–144
Plan Position Indicator, in sonar use, 129
Platforms, design of, plotting spaces, 348–350
Plotting, layout of spaces, 348–351
Pointer, fixed, indicators, 107
    long-scale indicators, 96, 97
Popliteal height, 539
Position coding, of indicators, 109
Posture, and human dimensions, 505
    and joint movement, 552
Practice, and human time lag, 233
Preflight check, 404
Pressure, suits and helmets against acceleration, 464
Printed material, 121, 122
Protection, against G forces, 462–465
    against noise, 475
    against vibration, 473
Pupil, interpupillary distance, 518
Pure tone, masking by, 145
Pushbuttons, design of, 265–268

Qualitative reading, of displays, 52
Quantitative reading, displays, 52
Quickening, value of, 241–245

Race, and body dimension, 504
Radar, illumination in search, 15
    room lighting, 75–77
    screen brightness, 34
    tracking system, 6, 7
Radar Target Detection System, critical design requirements, 14
Radial acceleration, 455
Radio magnetic indicator, as display, 54
Radio range, four course system, 133, 134
Ramp inputs, human responses to, 225, 226
Ramps, design of, 342
Range, effect, step and ramp inputs, 224, 225
    indication on radar displays, 116–119
    markers, radar displays, 116, 117
Rate, movable element, 220
Reach, in plotting spaces, 348
Reaction time, characteristics of, 227–234
Readout-on-Demand Message Expeditor, 159
Realism, in system evaluation, 45–48
Receivers, selection and use, 193–199
Reflectance, of workplace, 72, 73
Reflection, hazards of, 78
Refractory period, "psychological," and reaction time, 231
Reliability, and maintainability, 368
    in system evaluation, 49
Resistance, control, 256, 257, 264
Resolution, display and detection, 68
Retina, location on and visual acuity, 65

Requirements, general system, 4
Reverberation, effects of loudspeakers, 201
Rotary controls, 252–255
Rotary switches, design of, 270

Safety, compressed air, altitude, 425
Scale, design of, 101, 102
    graph and table, 121
    layout of, 103
    long, indicators, 96, 97
    selection of, 98–103
Searching, for targets, 63–65
Seat, adjustment and workplace dimensions, 290
    design, 314–316
    operator and workplace dimension, 284–294
    operators and foot controls, 310–312
    type and arrangement in auditoriums, 353–356
Sense, used and reaction time, 228
Sensitivity, human sensory, 34, 35
    of senses, 24
Sensors, in pictogram, 4
Sensory, abilities, of man, 23–28
    effects, of altitude, 421
    interaction, 27, 28
Sentence, test for intelligibility testing, 171, 172
Sex, and joint movement, 552
Shadows, and surface colors, 73–75
Shape (See also Shape coding)
    of panel, 316
    seat, 315
Shape coding, 84, 85
    of controls, 259
    of indicators, 104, 109
Shop, noise criteria for, 188
Shoulder, to elbow and hand length, 521

Shoulder, height, standing and sitting, 520
to shoulder breadth, 524
Signal, auditory presentation, 125
characteristics, and reaction time, 229
cathode-ray tube, 111
detection by man, 26
devices, visual, 90–94
frequency, and time lag, 235
level control, sound, 151–153
level in sonar, 128
magnitude and duration, 235
and noise relationships, 144
processing and control, 144–154
selection of auditory, 155–160
sound, perception of, 137–144
strength, cathode-ray tube, 112
type of, and reaction time, 230–232
Simulation, of system, 41
Sine-wave inputs, human responses to, 226
Sitting, arm reach while, 545
and standing alternated, 297
Size, cathode-ray tube, 114, 115
coding of controls, 259
coding of information, 85, 86
target, and identification, 67
Skill, maintenance, 374
Sonar, as auditory presentation, 127–129
Sound, sensitivity, 34
shadows cast by obstacles, 133
Space, equipment, for maintenance, 395

Spacing, between controls, 312
Spatial orientation, and auditory presentation, 132–137
Spectrum level, of speech, 163
speech intelligibility, 182, 183
Speech (See also Speech communication)
as auditory presentation, 126
characteristics of, 162–168
-interference level, computation, 178, 179
level, estimation of, 167, 168
representation of, 162–165
sounds, interaction, 213, 214
system requirements, 206–210
Speech communication, 161–216
designing for, 161
Standing, arm reach while, 544
workplace dimensions, 294–297
Stairs, design of, 340–342
Standard deviation, definition, 21
human body measurements, 493
Status, signals, 93
Step inputs, human responses to, 224, 225
Stereo-depth, coding of information, 87
Stereoscopic acuity, 60
Subjects, training, in system evaluation, 45, 46
use in system evaluation, 43–46
Sulfur dioxide as toxin, 443
Surround, brightness and visual acuity, 62
brightness of workplace, 72

Switches, design of, 268–271
Symbolic indicators, design of, 97–107
selection of, 94–97
use of, 53
System, analysis, 1–19
concept, 1, 2
considerations, 1, 2
design, 1
man in, 20–38
displays, 13–17
evaluation, and testing, 39–50
use of, 3
man-machine, 1–50
methods of analysis, 1–12
pictogram, 4
requirements, 4
special requirements, speech, 206–210

Table, graph and scale, 122
Tactical Range Recorder, in sonar use, 129
Talker, speech intensity of, 167
Target, cathode-ray tube, 110, 111
colored, detection of, 65, 66
detection, and exposure brightness, CRT, 112
on nonuniform backgrounds, 66
searching for, 63–65
tracking by auditory means, 137, 138
Task, choice of, in system evaluation, 42, 43
conflicting inputs in, 27
description of operators, 12
nature of, and time lag, 236
realism of, in system evaluation, 46, 47
Television, human and machine fault location, 39
Temperature, effects of, 428–436

Test, equipment and bench mockup, 397
intelligibility, material, 170–172
points for maintainability, 389
of system, 39–50
Thigh, height, 534
Threshold, of hearing, 141, 142
masked, predicting, 146
Time, characteristics of speech, 165, 166
location, for codes, 88, 89
Toggle-switch controls, design of, 269
Tolerance, for acceleration, 461
for vibration, 471
Tools, maintenance, 409
Touch, use in communication, 26, 27
Toxicity, effects, 436–445
protection against, 443–445
Tracking, aided, 239–241
closed loop manual, 217–223
compensatory and pursuit, 218, 219
target, by auditory signals, 137, 138
visual display for, 53
Traffic, spaces, layout of, 330–344
Training, of subjects in system evaluation, 45, 46
transfer of, in system design, 28, 29
Transfer (See also Transfer function)
of training, in system design, 28, 29
Transfer function, human, 223, 224
machine, 237–239
Transmitters, selection and use, 193–199
Trouble-shooting procedures, 403

Truck, and compartment layout, 333
Tumbling, effects of, 457
Tunnels, design of, 330

Under water communication, 209

Validity, in system evaluation, 49, 50
Variability, human vs. machine, 20–23
Variation, human body, 486
in tolerance limits, 413
Ventilation, requirements, 443
Verification, by duplication, 37
Vernier acuity, 61
Vibration, effects of, 466–473
Viewing angle, displays, 304
Viewing distance, 304
of displays, 52
workplace dimensions, 285–287
Visibility, cathode-ray tube, 110–114
layout for good, 304
Vision (See also Visual acuity; Visual angle; Visual area; Visual coding)
and audition compared, 125
and compartment layout, 327
and cathode-ray tube, 110–113
of drivers, body size, 501
information presentation, 51–126
performance in acceleration, 459
sensitivity, 34
Visual acuity, and angle of view, 65
factors affecting, 57–62
measurement of, 58–62
minimum separable, 58–60
stereoscopic, 60
vernier, 61

Visual angle, and visual acuity, 65
Visual area, standing workplace dimension, 296
workplace dimensions, 285–287
Visual coding (See also Coding; Color coding; Shape coding; Size coding), 81–90
Volume control, and dynamic range, 153, 154

Waist, depth, 525
Warning, auditory devices, 129–132
visual devices, 90–94
Watchkeeping, and human time lags, 235–237
Weight (See also Weightlessness)
body, 512
and height, 505
human lifting capacity, 373
Weightlessness, as prolonged acceleration, 453
Windchill Index, 433
Wire, connections for maintainability, 378
Word-spelling alphabet, 215, 216
Work (See also Working; Workplace)
space for maintenance, 345
Working, body dimensions when, 543
Workplace, dimensions, 284–298
illumination, 70–81
layout of, 281–320
in system analysis, 18

Yellow-minus-yellow, lighting system, 76

Zero Reader, as combination display, 55
Zone, marking of scales, 104